Property of

Gene B. Welsh

INTRODUCTION TO STATISTICAL ANALYSIS

INTRODUCTION TO STATISTICAL ANALYSIS

WILFRID J. DIXON

Professor of Biostatistics
University of California, Los Angeles

FRANK J. MASSEY, Jr.

Associate Professor of Biostatistics
University of California, Los Angeles

SECOND EDITION

McGRAW-HILL BOOK COMPANY, INC.

New York Toronto London

1957

INTRODUCTION TO STATISTICAL ANALYSIS

Library of Congress Catalog Card Number 56-9805

III

THE MAPLE PRESS COMPANY, YORK, PA.

PREFACE

This textbook is written for a basic course in statistics to be taken by students from all fields in which statistics finds application. We have attempted to present the fundamental concepts of the subject in a manner which will show the student how general is the application of the statistical method. It is intended that interested students continue this type of training in courses giving special applications in their own fields after one, two, or three quarters of this course.

We have found that the contents of this revised text can easily be covered in a one-year course having either three lectures per week or two lectures with one laboratory per week. For shorter courses the following topics are suggested: For a one-semester course, Chapters 1 to 9 plus selections from any of Chapters 10, 11, 13, 17, and 20. For a one-quarter course, Chapters 1 to 7 plus selections from any of Chapters 9, 13, 17, and 20. Except for parts of Chapter 20 the only mathematical ability assumed of the student is a knowledge of algebraic addition, subtraction, and multiplication. We feel that the topic of probability is more meaningful for students having a minimum of mathematical background if it is presented late in the year course. With students who have the equivalent of two years of high school algebra some teachers may wish to present Chapter 20 quite early, and it has been arranged to make this convenient. It may be noted that in Chapter 20 we have avoided conventional gambling games, dice problems, etc., and have stressed the statistical applications of the theory.

The principal changes from the first edition are as follows: Chapters 6 and 7 are largely rewritten. Chapter 10 is completely rewritten and now covers several additional topics. Chapter 20 is a new chapter, dealing with probability. Many sections in other chapters are revised and new topics included. New tables are added to the Appendix and several of the original tables are expanded.

The order and emphasis of topics are based largely on the recommendations for a basic course in statistics stated by the committee on teaching of statistics of the National Research Council.

The concepts of distribution, sample, and population are introduced early. The elementary descriptive procedures of statistics are introduced as they are needed in the development of the ideas of sampling, tests of hypotheses, and design of experiments. The analysis of variance is introduced sufficiently early for its inclusion in a one-semester or two-term course. Modern developments (e.g., sequential analysis, nonparametric statistics) have been included because of their wide applicability and because of their validity under general conditions. The sampling distributions of the various statistics are introduced by means of experimental sampling. Experimental verifications of tabled distributions have been carried out by comparing percentiles of observed sampling distributions with the mathematical results. The sampling experiments indicated at the end of the chapters are integrated so that computations on the samples drawn are used in several following class exercises. Samples may be drawn from the random-number tables or from populations of tags, disks, or beads. Our experience has indicated that the performance of sampling experiments by the students is one of the most effective aids to the understanding of statistical concepts. This is true for students with or without mathematical preparation.

Chapter 19 is an abridgment of an article by A. M. Mood and W. J. Dixon in the *Journal of the American Statistical Association*, March, 1948, p. 109. The material on the sign test in Chapter 17 is an abridgment of an article by the same authors in the December, 1946, issue of that journal. A portion of the material in Chapters 16 and 17 was developed by the authors under a contract with the Office of Naval Research at the Statistical Laboratory, Department of Mathematics, University of Oregon.

The authors wish to express their appreciation to Professor E. S. Pearson for permission to reprint from *Biometrika* parts of Tables A-7, A-8, A-9, A-13, A-18, and A-30; to S. K. Banerjee for permission to reprint from *Sankhyā* Table A-25; to the RAND Corporation for permission to print the random-number tables; to A. Hald and John Wiley & Sons for permission to copy certain percentiles forming part of Table A-7*c*. We are indebted to Sir Ronald A. Fisher, Frank Yates, and to Messrs. Oliver & Boyd, Ltd., Edinburgh, for permission to reprint, in part, Table III from their book *Statistical Tables for Biological, Agricultural and Medical Research*. For other tables in the Appendix we are indebted to C. Colcord, L. S. Deming, C. Eisenhart, M. W. Hastay, L. A. Knowler, R. F. Link, F. Mosteller, E. G. Olds, F. Swed, W. A. Wallis, J. E. Walsh, and E. K. Yost.

We wish to take this opportunity to express our appreciation to the many friends and colleagues who have made helpful criticisms and suggestions on the first edition and on preliminary revised forms of Chapters

10 and 20. The authors are indebted to Eva M. Dixon for her careful reading of the manuscript and for making a number of valuable suggestions and to Mildred G. Massey for the preparation of many of the original figures and for assistance in reading proof.

WILFRID J. DIXON
FRANK J. MASSEY, JR.

CONTENTS

LIST OF TABLES

CHAPTER 1

INTRODUCTION

This book will look upon statistics as the science of experimentation. The laws of physical and social science have their proof in statistical facts. The study of statistics here will not stop with the mere description of an existing situation but will continue on to the study of procedures of scientific inference and proof.

1-1. Types of Proof

You, no doubt, have heard the statement "You can prove anything with statistics." We shall determine just what sort of things can be proved by statistics and, furthermore, just what we mean by proof. Natural and physical *laws* are *hypotheses* which have been subjected to various tests and have become accepted or, as some say, proved. The proof of a hypothesis is the *testing* of a hypothesis. If the tests find the hypothesis satisfactory, it is accepted. If the tests find the hypothesis unsatisfactory, it is rejected. When have we sufficiently tested a hypothesis to reject it? The standard procedure will be to collect information in the form of numerical observations and to base our decision on these observations. For example, if someone tosses a coin 100 times and obtains heads every time, he may feel that the hypothesis that he has an unbiased coin is no longer acceptable, and reject that hypothesis. It is well known that it is possible for the above result to occur with a true coin, but if we demand that we be completely positive before we make a decision, one could never decide that he had a biased coin even if it had two heads, unless he were allowed to examine the coin. We would not be able to accept the hypothesis of gravity as a law until all the apples of all time have fallen. The procedures of *statistical inference* will make it possible for us to state just what proportion of the time we will accept false hypotheses and what proportion of the time we will reject true hypotheses. We, of course, will never know for sure in any particular case whether the hypothesis is true or not. This *statistical proof* is the basic form of proof used in the investigations of all sciences. The student should make a distinction between the methods of statistical proof and the methods of mathematical proof. *Mathematical proof* is available only in the framework of mathematics itself but cannot be applied outside that field. A hypothesis in mathematics may be declared false by the presentation of a single example which violates the hypothesis. A single example which does not agree with the hypothesis cannot usually by itself cause us to reject a hypothesis outside of mathematics.

The methods of proof used to develop the statistical procedures presented in this book will in a few cases be *mathematical proof* in the adaptation of various formulas. For the most part, however, the development will be that of statistical proof, or *experimentation*. These statistical procedures can all be developed by mathematical means. It will not be possible in most cases to present these mathematical developments because of the limited mathematical background assumed of the reader of this text. The development by experimentation will serve a double purpose, for here we are interested not only in the results of the experiments but also in a study of the process of proof by experiment.

1-2. Generality of Applications of Statistics

There does not exist a theory of statistics applicable only to economics or only to education. There is a *general* theory of statistics which is applicable to any field of study in which observations are made. Statistical procedures form an important part, now, of all the fields of science and are rapidly developing in psychology, economics, and sociology. Procedures which have been developed for use in one field have almost invariably found important application in a number of other fields. There are, however, statistical procedures which are more frequently used in one field than another. We shall concentrate on those procedures which are most widely used. Some of these procedures were introduced by Karl Gauss, but the main impetus to the general use of statistics was given by Karl Pearson and R. A. Fisher in the early part of this century.

1-3. Examples of Statistical Problems

We need not look far to find problems using statistical ideas. The concept of average is used by everyone in referring to a man of average height, to a ballplayer's batting average, or to the average speed during a trip between two towns. We use the single figure of an average to represent the whole group of men, or the ballplayer's performance in all his games, or the many different speeds on the trip between towns. We use the single quantity, the average, to describe one characteristic of the group. For example, the average height of a group of men is 69 inches. We do not mean to indicate that all men in the group are 69 inches tall. We use the average as a number which describes the whole *group* of men, so that if we were to pick a man at random from this group and were asked what height we would *expect* him to be, we would give, as our estimate, 69 inches.

Another concept with which we are all familiar is that of *dispersion*, or variability. A teacher may say one class is more uniform in ability than another class. An engineer may say that one batch of electric-light bulbs is more variable in quality than another batch. A textile worker may say that one type of yarn is more variable in breaking strength than it should be. A manufacturer who wishes to use mass production must reduce the variability in the dimensions of parts, if any shaft is to fit into any sleeve. The manufacturer of powder for bazooka shells must produce powder of sufficiently uniform burning time so that he can adjust the shell to the burning time. If the powder burns too rapidly, the shell explodes before it leaves the bazooka tube. If the powder burns too slowly, the backward stream of gases will still be issuing after the shell has left the bazooka tube.

Another commonly used statistical description of data is that of *correlation*, or association. The teacher may say of his class that the faster readers are also better at arithmetic, the slower readers poorer at arithmetic. As an example of an negative relationship, a teacher may say of a particular class that the older children read more slowly, the younger children more rapidly.

These concepts of proof and concepts of average, dispersion, and correlation will be developed more fully and their combined use in various types of statistical investigations will be illustrated in the ensuing chapters.

A major area of statistical theory is concerned with the design of experiments and the efficient collection of information to aid in the design of experiments. Many experimental materials are so expensive that it is essential that the desired information be obtained with a minimum number of observations. Statistics is also concerned with problems which arise from the necessity of designing experiments to investigate several factors at the same time, either because of the great length of time required for the experiment or because of the difficulty in reproducing the experimental treatments or conditions. Here, statistical methods must be used to separate the effects of the separate treatments.

Whenever anything is measured numerically, even though the attempt to make an assessment results in numbers no more refined than simple counting, there arises the desire for judging the significance of the data and for making the maximum use of the information gathered. These are the principal problems with which statistical methods are concerned.

CHAPTER 2

DISTRIBUTIONS

It is necessary in the investigation of any phenomenon, whether it be the study of forces of attraction by the physicist, the study of the effects of anxiety by the psychologist, the study of radiation effects on animals by the biologist, or any other research, to observe and record some characteristic of the objects under consideration.

2-1. Observations

We must have observations of some form even if they are of a very rudimentary sort. It is perhaps easiest to think of *measurements* of such simple properties as length, weight, volume. For such properties it is generally easy to establish a measuring stick to compare objects or individuals. For example, we may mark off a pole in units of equal length and use it to show that an object 60 inches long is twice as long as another 30 inches long.

It perhaps seems nonsense to point out something so obvious, but let us consider, for example, such a characteristic as intelligence. It is possible to construct an examination which will indicate whether one individual has *more* than another of something which might be called intelligence, but this scale does not enable one to say that a particular individual is twice as intelligent as some other individual. The physical sciences also deal with quantities for which only a *scale* is established, for example, the common property, temperature. We may say that today is hotter than yesterday, but we cannot decide that today is twice as hot as yesterday.

Scores are often applied to indicate quality such as the scores applied to butter or to meat. Here there is not even the comparability between individuals that is available when a scale is established. Scores are compiled from an arbitrary assignment of a certain number of points for various characteristics such as flavor, appearance, consistency. The term score is correctly used with reference to a football score. Here various points have been assigned for a touchdown, a conversion after touchdown, a field goal, and a safety. The team obtaining the highest score wins the game. There is not always general agreement, however, that the team with the highest score played the best football, nor is it possible to say that a team making 14 points played twice as well as the team making 7 points.

A *rank* is used merely to indicate where a particular individual stands with respect to the others which have been observed at the same time. For example, we may decide that this painting is the best, this is next best, etc.

Many statistical procedures can be applied alike to numbers which are true measurements, readings from a scale, scores, or ranks. In some cases the procedure must be different. We shall avoid the use of the term measurement when referring to scores or ranks. The term *observation* will be used to represent any sort of numerical recording of information.

It will be necessary to distinguish between *continuous* and *discrete* observations. A continuous observation is one for which successive refinements of our measuring stick or scale will give more precise observations. Discrete observations always result in one of a particular set of values. In a five-man committee the number of aye votes recorded must always be exactly 0, 1, 2, 3, 4, or 5. Other examples of discrete observations would be the number of bolts in a box, the number of people entering a department store in a day, the number of β rays counted in 1 second, the number of petals on a flower, etc. Examples of observations which are usually continuous are lengths, weights, amount of current, velocity, etc.

In the following section the observations used as an illustration are the heights of boys. The student should keep in mind that the procedures developed are equally applicable to observations in general. Height is chosen for illustration since it is a measurement familiar to all. Height is a continuous variable which is recorded in discrete units.

2-2. Histogram

A histogram is a picture of a number of observations. Suppose we have measured the heights of 5 boys in a certain school and have recorded

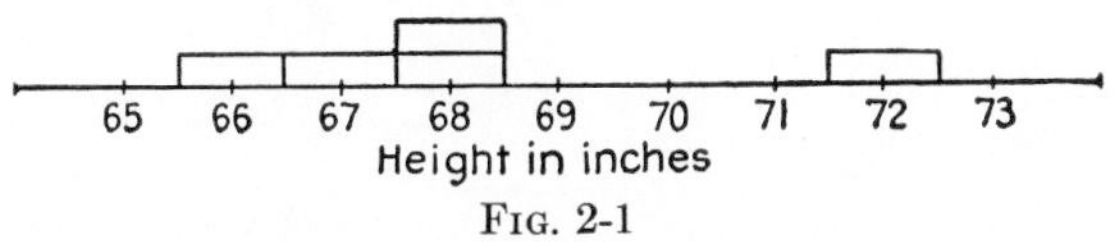

FIG. 2-1

them to the nearest inch as follows: 68, 72, 66, 67, 68. We then represent them by *equal units of area* above a scale marked with those heights (Fig. 2-1). If we measure another 75 boys, we would get a picture from which we can form at sight an idea of how the heights are distributed at various values along a line marked off in inches (Fig. 2-2).

It is not difficult to see from this histogram that the average height is around 69 or 70 inches and that a small proportion of the boys are less than 66 inches or more than 73 inches in height.

This picture, or histogram, is particularly useful when a large number of measurements have been made. The histogram of the first five measurements was not very informative.

The histogram is usually presented without the lines showing the individual observations, and the *frequencies* are not indicated in every case

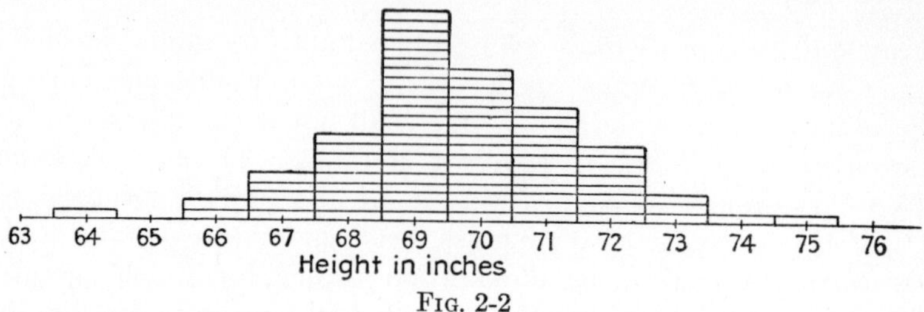

FIG. 2-2

but are indicated along a scale to the left. Note that each observation is represented by an equal amount of area.

As more and more measurements are made, the histogram approaches more and more closely the distribution of the heights of all the boys in this school. Although a histogram of only five measurements does not suggest the form which the distribution will take, some indication of the final form of the distribution is present before a very large number of observations have been added to the distribution.

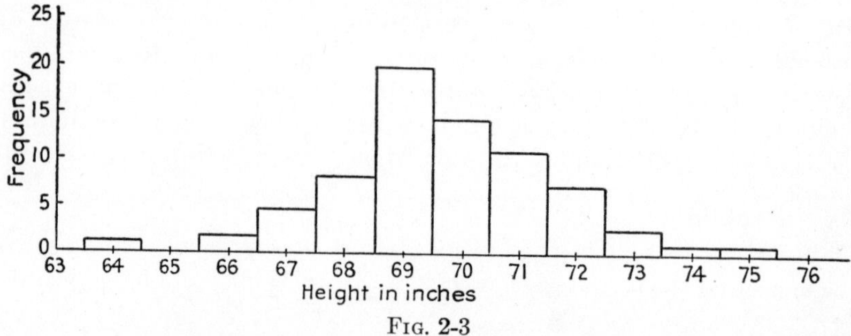

FIG. 2-3

We have drawn here a histogram assuming that height is a discrete variable, i.e., could only be 64, 65, 66, etc., inches. The above description of how to draw a histogram will thus apply to discrete measurements as they occur and will apply to continuous measurements if they are grouped into a number of categories (e.g., to the nearest inch). Even if the measurements had been made to a much greater precision, they could be represented by the above histogram, by combining all measurements between 68.5 and 69.5 inches into the group at 69 inches, all measurements between 69.5 and 70.5 into the group at 70, etc. The measurements can of course be grouped into any length interval. If we had assumed that the measurements had been made to the nearest half inch, or had grouped, for example, all measurements between 68.25 and 68.75 at 68.5, those between 68.75 and 69.25 at 69, etc., we would obtain a histogram similar in appearance to that above but the data would be grouped into about twice as many groups. We have made each rectangle half as wide to indicate that we are now reading to the nearest half inch and have

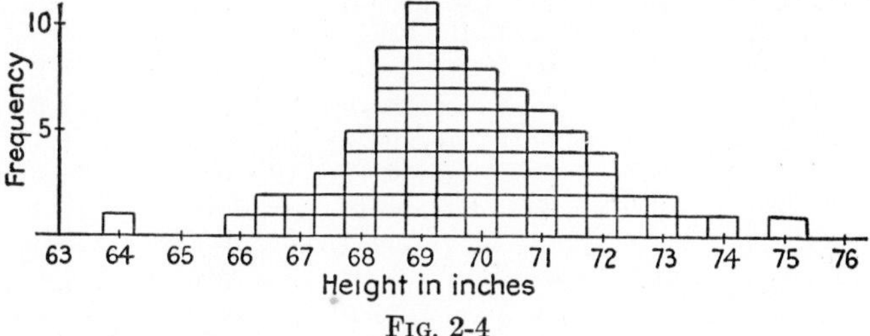

FIG. 2-4

increased the height of each rectangle to hold the area the same for each observation. Also notice that the total area will be 80 units of area to represent 80 observations.

It is important to record observations to the proper degree of precision for the study which is being attempted. For the purpose of giving a picture of the data in general, it is important to leave enough groups of data to discern the shape of the distribution, but it is also important not to have so many groups that too much detail is present and we have lost the advantage of constructing such a picture.

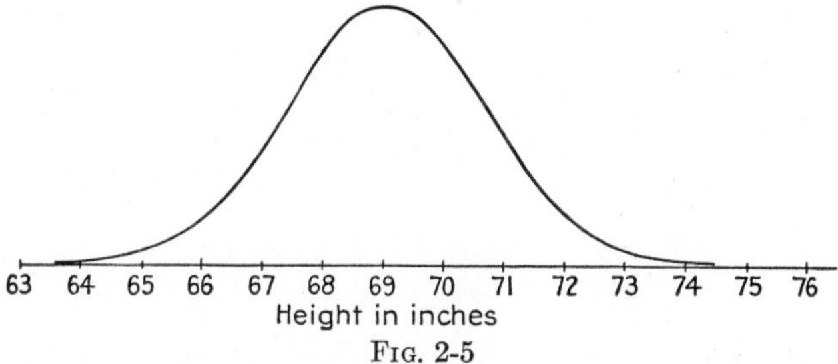

FIG. 2-5

Either of the histograms above would usually be considered to be satisfactory. For most studies 8 to 20 groups would meet the usual requirements.

If more and more observations were taken and the histograms were constructed by grouping the measurements into intervals of less and less width, it is possible to imagine that the histograms would approach a smooth curve which would represent more truly the distribution of continuous measurements. Figure 2-5 illustrates such a smooth curve. Here again the total area is equal to the number of observations. Often, in order to have comparable pictures for different numbers of observations, the proportion is indicated in place of the frequencies. This change would leave the shapes of the distributions the same and would change only the scale at the left. If the above figures were changed in this manner, the scale in Fig. 2-3 would be marked $\frac{5}{80}$ in place of 5 and $\frac{10}{80}$ in place of 10, etc. The same change would be necessary for Fig. 2-4. Below is a list of the 80 measurements of height (to the nearest tenth of an inch) from which the histograms in Figs. 2-1 to 2-4 were drawn. The measurements have been arranged in order of size.

64.2	67.9	68.6	69.1	69.5+	70.2	71.0	72.0
65.8	67.9	68.7	69.1	69.6	70.3	71.0	72.1
66.3	68.2	68.7	69.1	69.7	70.4	71.1	72.2
66.6	68.2	68.8	69.2	69.8	70.4	71.2	72.4
66.9	68.3	68.9	69.3	69.9	70.5−	71.4	72.5−
67.0	68.4	68.9	69.3	69.9	70.5+	71.4	72.8
67.4	68.5−	68.9	69.4	70.0	70.6	71.4	73.0
67.5−	68.5+	69.0	69.5−	70.0	70.6	71.6	73.4
67.6	68.6	69.0	69.5−	70.1	70.9	71.7	74.2
67.8	68.6	69.0	69.5+	70.1	70.9	71.8	74.9

Although it is difficult to make measurements to greater precision than tenths of an inch, the observer was requested when a boy's measurement was near a half inch to indicate whether it was above or below and indicate that decision with a plus sign or a minus sign. Thus we can decide in which group to place these measurements. For example, 68.5− will go in the lower group and 68.5+ in the upper group.

2-3. Frequency Polygon

Another graphical description of the *frequency* with which each measurement occurs is given by a *frequency polygon*. This is constructed by drawing line segments joining mid-points at the top of each column in the histogram. For histograms in Figs. 2-2 and 2-3 the frequency polygon would be as in Fig. 2-6.

When the proportion scale is used, it is seen that the total area is one square unit. The frequency polygon for the histogram in Fig. 2-4, given

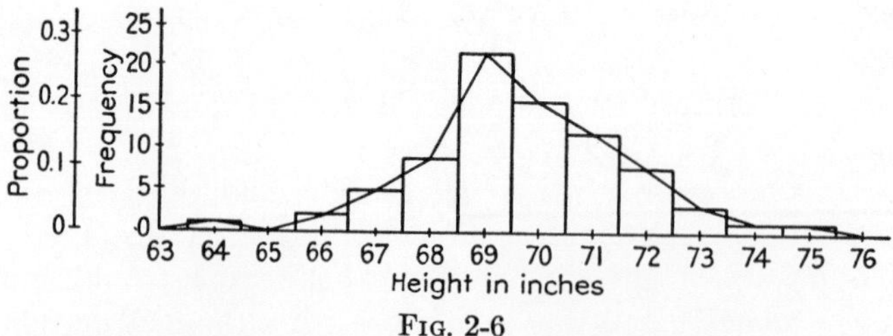

FIG. 2-6

in Fig. 2-7, is, of course, very similar in appearance to Fig. 2-6, since it represents the same data tabulated in different intervals. When these histograms, or frequency polygons, are drawn with proportion in place of actual frequencies, we call them *frequency distributions* of the measurements they represent. In this case we have a frequency distribution of the heights of boys.

For the frequency distribution in Fig. 2-7 it is necessary to plot the points twice as high as the computed proportion since the measurements are grouped in half-inch intervals. This same effect was noted when we discussed the histograms on page 7. The proportion of cases in a single interval can no longer be read from the proportion scale, but we maintain an equal area for each observation and a total area of 1. Thus the amount of area above a particular portion of the scale of measurements can be interpreted as the proportion of cases having measurements in that range. We shall follow the practice of drawing our histograms and frequency distributions so that the total area will be one square unit.

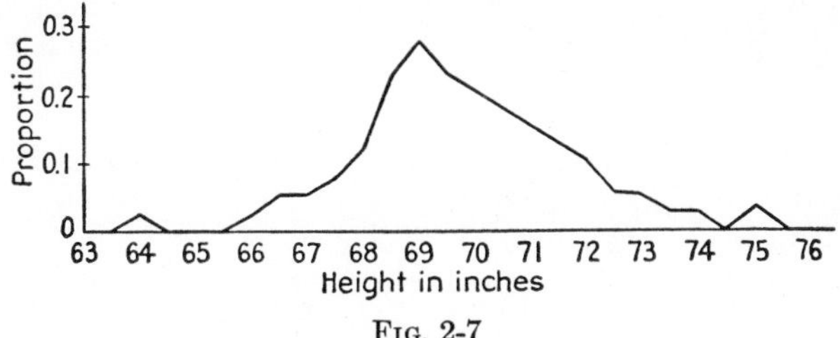

FIG. 2-7

Suppose that, instead of indicating the number or proportion of boys at each height as in the histogram of Fig. 2-2 or the frequency histogram of Fig. 2-3, we wished to draw a corresponding polygon which would indicate the percentage of boys shorter than a given height. If we look at the histogram (Fig. 2-2), we can see that, starting from the left and progressing toward the right, when we have reached the point 63.5 inches, zero boys, or zero per cent, is below that value; by the time we have reached 64.5, we know 1 boy, or $\frac{1}{80}$ (1.25 per cent) of the boys, is shorter than 64.5 inches. If we continue in this manner, we obtain the following values,

Height, in.	No.	Per cent	Proportion
75.5	80	100	1.0
74.5	79	98.75	.9875
73.5	78	97.50	.9750
72.5	75	93.75	.9375
71.5	67	83.75	.8375
70.5	55	68.75	.6875
69.5	39	48.75	.4875
68.5	17	21.25	.2125
67.5	8	10.00	.1000
66.5	3	3.75	.0375
65.5	1	1.25	.0125
64.5	1	1.25	.0125
63.5	0	0	0

where the first column represents height in inches, the second column the *number* of individuals whose heights are less than that height, i.e., 8 boys have height less than 67.5 inches, the third column indicates the percentage of boys who have a height less than that height, and the fourth column indicates the proportion of boys with a height less than that height. A graph of the percentage values we call a *cumulative-percentage polygon*, or curve. If proportions are used in drawing the graph, the polygon is called a *cumulative-distribution polygon.*

The student should note that the cumulative distribution indicates by its height above a particular point on the scale the proportion of the area in the corresponding histogram to the left of that point.

It is sometimes desirable to perform the cumulation across the distribution, stopping halfway through each group of values in place of recording the cumulations as above. To illustrate this procedure, refer again to Fig. 2-2, and note that we could consider that $\frac{1}{2}$ an observation is below 64, 1 observation below 65, 2 observations below 66, etc. We merely assume that half the measurements recorded for each value are above that value and half below. If we do this, we obtain

Height, in.	No.	Per cent	Proportion
76.0	80.0	100.0	1.0
75.0	79.5	99.4	.994
74.0	78.5	98.1	.981
73.0	76.5	95.6	.956
72.0	71.0	88.8	.888
71.0	61.0	76.2	.762
70.0	47.0	58.8	.588
69.0	28.0	35.0	.350
68.0	12.5	15.6	.156
67.0	5.5	6.9	.069
66.0	2.0	2.5	.025
65.0	1.0	1.2	.012
64.0	.5	.6	.006
63.0	0	0	0

where the first column gives the height in inches, the second column the number of observations less than that value and the third and fourth columns the percentage and proportion of values below that point. We shall assume here that we have only the information in Fig. 2-2, and draw Fig. 2-8. If more information is available such as that in Fig. 2-5, it would be more appropriate to use the actual values instead of assuming that half the values in each group are above the mid-point and half below the mid-point. The cumulative-distribution polygon constructed from these values will differ little from Fig. 2-8.

Percentiles. The term percentile will be used in reference to a distribution of observations. For example, the 10th percentile, P_{10}, is defined as the value below which 10 per cent of the distribution of values will fall.

In our example above we would obtain $P_{10} = 67.5$ inches since 10 per cent of the boys were shorter than 67.5 inches. Notice that this value or the value for any other percentile can be obtained by reference to the cumulative-distribution polygon. Notice that in Fig. 2-8, if we find 10 per cent

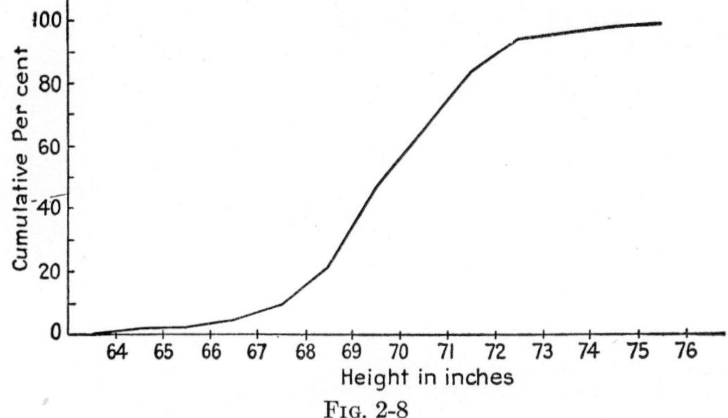

FIG. 2-8

on the left-hand scale, draw a line horizontally to the polygon, and then draw a line down to the lower scale from the point of intersection with the polygon, we can read the value 67.5 inches. In this manner we find, for example, $P_{10} = 69.6$. Rarely is it necessary to report percentiles to more accuracy than can be obtained easily from a graph such as Fig. 2-8.

TABLE 2-1. HEIGHTS OF 80 BOYS
(Measurements to nearest inch)

Height, in. (mid-point)	Freq.	Per cent	Freq. cum. through interval	Per cent	Freq. cum. to mid-point	Per cent
76	...	......	...	......	80.0	100
75	1	1.25	80	100.00	79.5	99.4
74	1	1.25	79	98.75	78.5	98.1
73	3	3.75	78	97.50	76.5	95.6
72	8	10.00	75	93.75	71.0	88.8
71	12	15.00	67	83.75	61.0	76.2
70	16	20.00	55	68.75	47.0	58.8
69	22	27.50	39	48.75	28.0	35.0
68	9	11.25	17	21.25	12.5	15.6
67	5	6.25	8	10.00	5.5	6.9
66	2	2.50	3	3.75	2.0	2.5
65	...	......	1	1.25	1.0	1.2
64	1	1.25	1	1.25	.5	.6
63	...	......	0	0	0	0
Total.........	80	100	...	......	....	.....

If we wish to know the *percentile rank* for any particular height, i.e., the per cent of individuals who are shorter than some particular height, we need only to refer to the polygon in Fig. 2-8. For example, suppose we wish to find the percentile rank of 67.5 inches. The answer is, of course, 10, as we computed above and observed from this same polygon. The percentile rank of 70 inches is obtained by drawing a line vertically from the point marked 70 on the lower scale, extending this line up to the polygon, and then drawing a line horizontally to the left-hand scale. Here, we read 59 per cent.

Frequency Table. The most widely used method for the numerical reporting of data is the *frequency table.* The first two columns of Table 2-1 show a frequency table. The third column has been added to indicate the per cent at each height. The fourth and fifth columns have been added to indicate a cumulation of the frequency table and the computation for a cumulative-distribution polygon with the cumulation to the mid-point of each group of values.

GLOSSARY

In the development of any phase of science the student will find that certain words are used with specific meanings. The words introduced thus far which have special import in statistics are:

average
continuous
correlation
cumulative distribution
discrete
dispersion
experiment
frequency polygon
frequency table
histogram
hypothesis
induction
inference
law
measurement
percentile
percentile rank
proof
rank
scale
score

DISCUSSION QUESTIONS

1. What information can be obtained from a frequency distribution?

2. Distinguish between percentile and percentile rank.

3. What is the interpretation of the area under a histogram? Is there an interpretation of the area under the cumulative-percentage curve?

4. What distinction has been made between a frequency polygon and a frequency-distribution polygon?

5. What assumption is made in drawing a cumulative-distribution curve by cumulation halfway through each interval?

6. What is an advantage in having a large number of intervals? What is a disadvantage?

7. Give two examples each of scores, ranks, and measurements other than those examples mentioned in the text.

8. Define each of the terms in the glossary. Give for each the statistical meaning, and compare your definition with that in a dictionary.

PROBLEMS

1. Construct the frequency polygons for the data in Figs. 2-2 and 2-4 on the same graph. Use a different scale for each as was done in Figs. 2-2 and 2-4 so the polygons will approximately coincide.

2. Construct on the same graph two cumulative-distribution polygons for the data in Fig. 2-4 (*a*) by cumulation completely through each group, (*b*) by cumulation halfway through each group. Note that the points for constructing these polygons must be plotted (*a*) at the dividing points for the groups and (*b*) at the mid-point of each group in order to obtain agreement between the two polygons.

3. Read, from each of the two polygons constructed in Prob. 2, P_{10}, P_{25}, P_{40}, P_{50}, P_{60}, P_{75}, P_{90}. The values obtained from the two polygons should agree fairly closely.

4. Read, from the polygon constructed in Prob. 2 from cumulations to the midpoint of each group, the percentile rank of 66 inches, 68.5 inches, 72 inches.

5. Read from Fig. 2-8 the percentage of boys who have heights between 67.5 and 71.5 inches. Verify your answer by reference to the distribution as given on page 11.

6. Classify the following observations as continuous or discrete; and, if continuous, classify as to measurement, scale, score, rank:

(*a*) Bearing diameter of 3.25 millimeters.
(*b*) 9,750 pounds breaking strength of a cable.
(*c*) 23 students attending class.
(*d*) 75 on a history examination.
(*e*) A toss of 10 coins resulting in 6 heads.
(*f*) 7 petals on a flower.
(*g*) Relative humidity reading of 55 per cent.
(*h*) Jerry was 13th in his class.
(*i*) A man swam 100 yards in 73 seconds.
(*j*) Receipts for the day were $416.75.
(*k*) The guinea pig was 10 months old.
(*l*) A man's yearly income was $3,600.
(*m*) A man's blood pressure (systaltic) was 120.
(*n*) The half-life of a sample of an element was 6.8 minutes.
(*o*) A river was 3 feet above flood stage.

CHAPTER 3

INTRODUCTION TO MEASURES OF CENTRAL VALUE AND DISPERSION

In order to investigate the character of a distribution it is useful to have various words and measurements which will serve to describe the distribution. In Chap. 2 we drew pictures (histograms, polygons, etc.) of distributions, but it is not always possible or convenient to do so (sometimes not even desirable). In this chapter we shall define certain measurements which are most commonly used to describe a distribution. In Chaps. 4 and 5 we shall see how these particular measurements are used, and later in Chap. 6 we shall examine certain alternative measurements and explain how a choice is made among them.

3-1. Measures of Central Value. The Arithmetic Mean

Central value refers to the location of the *center* of the distribution. One of the intuitive notions of the center of a distribution is the *arithmetic mean*, or average. It is defined as the sum of all the observations divided by the number of observations. If you think of each observation as having a unit mass and being distributed along an axis (as in a histogram), then the arithmetic mean is located at the centroid, or center of gravity, of the distribution. The equal amount of area allotted to each observation would have equal mass so that if the histogram were a sheet of metal it would balance on a pivot under the arithmetic mean. Throughout this book we shall use $\bar{X}$ for the value of the observed arithmetic mean.

If there is a small number of observations, we shall add them directly and divide the total by the number of observations. Suppose we let X_1 be the value of the first observation, X_2 be the value of the second observation, X_3 the value of the third, etc. If there are four observations X_1, X_2, X_3, X_4, then we shall have

$$\bar{X} = \frac{X_1 + X_2 + X_3 + X_4}{4}$$

If there are 100 observations, then

$$\bar{X} = \frac{X_1 + X_2 + X_3 + \cdots + X_{100}}{100}$$

Many occasions will arise when we need to add several numbers. Whenever we use the symbol Σ (Greek letter capital sigma), we shall understand that it is read "the sum of" and that it tells us to add certain expressions. For example, if there are four observations X_1, X_2, X_3, X_4, then

$$\sum_{i=1}^{4} X_i = X_1 + X_2 + X_3 + X_4$$

and

$$\bar{X} = \frac{\sum_{i=1}^{4} X_i}{4}$$

For the sum of the numbers $X_1, \ldots, X_{20}$ we write $\sum_{i=1}^{20} X_i$. This is read as "the sum of the 20 observations X_1 up to X_{20}." The subscript i attached to the X refers to the ith observation, while X_i is the value of the ith observation. The symbol $\sum_{i=1}^{20}$ tells us to substitute $i = 1$, then $i = 2$, $i = 3, \ldots, i = 20$ into the expression immediately following the Σ sign and then to add the 20 numbers obtained. Frequently, if there is no chance of ambiguity, the symbol is abbreviated to ΣX_i or ΣX, and it is understood in either case that you are to add the 20 observations $X_1, \ldots, X_{20}$.

Following are several examples of situations where it is convenient to use the Σ symbol. It might be noticed that these are not only examples of the notation but are also typical of the uses we shall make of this notation. Verbal statements for the summation precede each example.

1. The sum of squares of the four observations X_1, X_2, X_3, X_4:

$$\sum_{i=1}^{4} X_i^2 = X_1^2 + X_2^2 + X_3^2 + X_4^2$$

2. The sum of the products of pairs of values a_i, X_i:

$$\sum_{i=1}^{6} a_iX_i = a_1X_1 + a_2X_2 + a_3X_3 + a_4X_4 + a_5X_5 + a_6X_6$$

3. The sum of products of a constant times each of 6 numbers is equal to the constant times the sum of the 6 numbers:

$$\sum_{i=1}^{6} aX_i = aX_1 + aX_2 + aX_3 + aX_4 + aX_5 + aX_6$$

$$= a(X_1 + X_2 + X_3 + X_4 + X_5 + X_6) = a \sum_{i=1}^{6} X_i$$

Similarly, if a is a constant, then $\sum_{i=1}^{N} aX_i = a \sum_{i=1}^{N} X_i$

4. The sum of six numbers, each of which is the number 2:

$$\sum_{i=1}^{6} 2 = 2 + 2 + 2 + 2 + 2 + 2 = 6 \times 2 = 12$$

5. The sum of N numbers, each number having the value a:

$$\sum_{i=1}^{N} a = a + a + \cdots + a = Na$$

6. The arithmetic mean is equal to the sum of the N observations divided by the number of observations:

$$\bar{X} = \frac{X_1 + X_2 + \cdots + X_N}{N} = \frac{\sum_{i=1}^{N} X_i}{N}$$

7. The sum of products of pairs of observations. We shall use this particular example where the f_i refers to the frequency of observations of value X:

$$\sum_{i=1}^{4} f_i X_i = f_1 X_1 + f_2 X_2 + f_3 X_3 + f_4 X_4$$

8. The sum of products, each product being $\frac{1}{3}$ times the square of the observation:

$$\sum_{i=1}^{12} \tfrac{1}{3} X_i^2 = \tfrac{1}{3} X_1^2 + \tfrac{1}{3} X_2^2 + \cdots + \tfrac{1}{3} X_{12}^2$$

9. The sum of four numbers, each number being the deviation of the observation from 3. This is equal to the sum of the four observations minus 4 times 3:

$$\sum_{i=1}^{4} (X_i - 3) = (X_1 - 3) + (X_2 - 3) + (X_3 - 3) + (X_4 - 3)$$

$$= X_1 + X_2 + X_3 + X_4 - 4 \times 3 = \sum_{i=1}^{4} X_i - 12$$

10. The sum of deviations of N observations from the number a is equal to the sum of the N observations minus N times a:

$$\sum_{i=1}^{N} (X_i - a) = \sum_{i=1}^{N} X_i - Na$$

Computation Procedure. If the data are arranged in a frequency table, the computation of the value of $\bar{X}$ can be shortened as follows:

Let X_1 be the value of the mid-point of the first interval, and let f_1 be the number of observations that fall in this interval. Now instead of adding X_1 to itself f_1 times, the sum can be obtained by multiplying f_1 by X_1. In the same way the sum of all observations in the second interval is

f_2X_2, in the third interval f_3X_3, and so on. If there are k intervals, the sum of all the observations can be written as

$$f_1X_1 + f_2X_2 + \cdots + f_kX_k = \sum_{i=1}^{k} f_iX_i$$

The total number of observations is

$$f_1 + f_2 + f_3 + \cdots + f_k = \sum_{i=1}^{k} f_i = N$$

Thus we have

$$\bar{X} = \frac{\sum_{i=1}^{k} f_iX_i}{\Sigma f_i}$$

Referring to the observations on boys' heights in Chap. 2, there was one boy whose height was in the interval 63.5 to 64.5. The mid-point of this interval is 64.0. Here, then, $X_1 = 64.0$, and $f_1 = 1$; $X_2 = 65$, $f_2 = 0$; $X_3 = 66$, $f_3 = 2$; $X_4 = 67$, $f_4 = 5$, etc. Further

$$\Sigma f_iX_i = 64(1) + 65(0) + 66(2) + 67(5) + \cdots$$
$$= 64 + 0 + 132 + 335 + \cdots$$

and $$\Sigma f_i = 1 + 0 + 2 + 5 + \cdots$$

In Table 3-1 is an example of the computation for finding $\bar{X}$ from the frequency table of the heights of boys given in Chap. 2.

TABLE 3-1

Mid-point of interval X_i	Frequency f_i	f_iX_i
75	1	75
74	1	74
73	3	219
72	8	576
71	12	852
70	16	1,120
69	22	1,518
68	9	612
67	5	335
66	2	132
65	0	0
64	1	64
Total......	80	5,577

$N = \Sigma f_i = 80 \qquad \Sigma f_iX_i = 5{,}577$

$$\bar{X} = \frac{\Sigma f_iX_i}{\Sigma f_i} = \frac{5{,}577}{80} = 69.7 \text{ inches}$$

Other Measures of Central Value. Two other commonly used measures of the "center" of a distribution are the *mode* and the *median.* The mode is the value which occurs most frequently. In a histogram it is the mid-point of the interval with the greatest frequency. The median is the point on the scale of observations which has an equal area under the histogram on either side. This point is also the 50th percentile, P_{50}. Thus the median is the middle observation if there are an odd number of cases and is the mean of the two central observations if there are an even number of cases. Further discussion of the median is in Chap. 6.

3-2. Measures of Dispersion. The Variance

An important concept in statistics is that an average does not in itself give a clear picture of a distribution. The graphs of Fig. 3-1 show a group of distributions all having the same arithmetic mean yet obviously differing in general appearance.

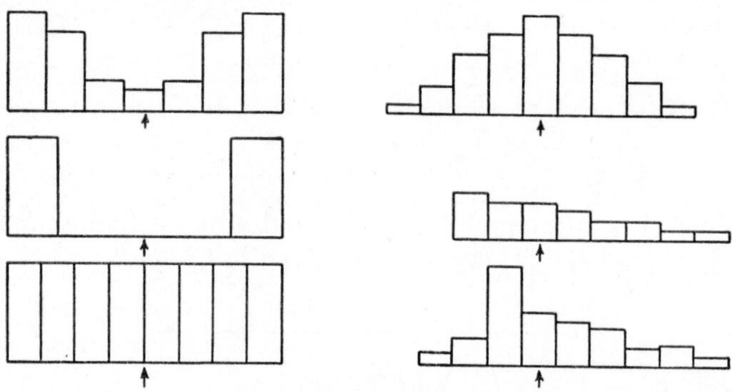

FIG. 3-1

Another type of measure which helps to clarify the shape of the distribution is a measurement which indicates how the observations are spread out from the average. Such a measure could be called a measure of dispersion, spread, or variability. It is usually desirable to have a measure which will be large if the observations are distant from the mean and small if they are close to the mean.

At first glance the sum of the deviations of the observations from the mean

$$\sum_{i=1}^{N} (X_i - \bar{X})$$

may seem to be a good measure for this purpose, but on further examination its value is seen to be always equal to zero.

For example, the arithmetic mean of the numbers 2, 3, 5, 8 is 4.5, so that the deviations from the mean are -2.5, -1.5, $+0.5$, $+3.5$. The total of these numbers is zero.

This difficulty may be overcome by squaring the deviations before they are added. The variance is defined as the sum of squares of the deviations of the observations from $\bar{X}$ divided by one less than the total number of observations. In symbols, $X_1 - \bar{X}$ is the deviation of the first observation from the mean, $X_2 - \bar{X}$ is the deviation of the second observation from the mean, and so on. Thus the variance, which we shall represent symbolically by s^2, is

$$s^2 = \frac{(X_1 - \bar{X})^2 + (X_2 - \bar{X})^2 + \cdots + (X_N - \bar{X})^2}{N - 1} = \frac{\sum_{i=1}^{N} (X_i - \bar{X})^2}{N - 1}$$

The division by $N - 1$ in place of N we shall subsequently find is necessary in order to use s^2 for the various functions it will perform in a number of statistical methods. It might be noted that many books introduce s^2 using N instead of $N - 1$ in the denominator and later adjust this by multiplying by $N/(N - 1)$.

The standard deviation is defined as the positive square root of the variance. Thus the standard deviation is given by

$$s = \sqrt{\frac{\sum_{i=1}^{N} (X_i - \bar{X})^2}{N - 1}}$$

An equivalent formula for s^2 which is simpler to use for computations is

$$s^2 = \frac{\sum_{i=1}^{N} X_i^2 - \frac{\left(\sum_{i=1}^{N} X_i\right)^2}{N}}{N - 1}$$

The variance is the difference between the sum of the squares of the observations and the quotient of the square of the sum of the observations and the number of observations, all divided by $N - 1$.

The equivalence of the two formulas for s^2 given above may be shown as follows:

$$\begin{aligned}
\sum_{i=1}^{N} (X_i - \bar{X})^2 &= \sum_{i=1}^{N} (X_i^2 - 2X_i\bar{X} + \bar{X}^2) \\
&= (X_1^2 - 2X_1\bar{X} + \bar{X}^2) + (X_2^2 - 2X_2\bar{X} + \bar{X}^2) \\
&\qquad + \cdots + (X_N^2 - 2X_N\bar{X} + \bar{X}^2) \\
&= (X_1^2 + X_2^2 + X_3^2 + \cdots X_N^2) \\
&\qquad - 2\bar{X}(X_1 + X_2 + \cdots + X_N) \\
&\qquad + (\bar{X}^2 + \bar{X}^2 + \cdots + \bar{X}^2)
\end{aligned}$$

$$= \sum_{i=1}^{N} X_i^2 - 2\frac{\sum_{i=1}^{N} X_i}{N} \sum_{i=1}^{N} X_i + N\left(\frac{\sum_{i=1}^{N} X_i}{N}\right)^2$$

$$= \sum_{i=1}^{N} X_i^2 - \frac{\left(\sum_{i=1}^{N} X_i\right)^2}{N}$$

The variance is almost the mean of the squares of the deviations (if there were an N in the denominator, it would be the arithmetic mean of these quantities). Occasionally you will see the variance referred to as the mean-square deviation and the standard deviation referred to as the root-mean-square deviation.

If the observations are arranged in a frequency table, some of the work can be shortened in a manner similar to that employed in the computation of the mean. If f_i observations have the value X_i, then, instead of adding the square of the X_i, f_i times, we multiply the square of the X_i by f_i, obtaining $f_iX_i^2$. To facilitate the work an additional column $f_iX_i^2$

TABLE 3-2

X_i	f_i	f_iX_i	$f_iX_i^2$
75	1	75	5,625
74	1	74	5,476
73	3	219	15,987
72	8	576	41,472
71	12	852	60,492
70	16	1,120	78,400
69	22	1,518	104,742
68	9	612	41,616
67	5	335	22,445
66	2	132	8,712
65	0	0	0
64	1	64	4,096
Total. .	80	5,577	389,063

$$N = \Sigma f_i = 80$$

$$\bar{X} = \frac{\Sigma f_i X_i}{N} = \frac{5{,}577}{80} = 69.7$$

$$s^2 = \frac{\Sigma f_i X_i^2 - \frac{(\Sigma f_i X_i)^2}{N}}{N - 1}$$

$$= \frac{389{,}063 - (5{,}577)^2/80}{79}$$

$$= \frac{276.4}{79} = 3.50$$

may be added to the frequency table. Then the numbers in this column can be added to give $\Sigma f_i X_i^2$. If you already have a column of $f_i X_i$, you can get the $f_i X_i^2$ by multiplying $f_i X_i$ by X_i.

The square root of 3.50 can be obtained directly from Table A-33 (in the Appendix). Direct reference to Table A-33 gives $s = 1.87$ correct to three figures. Square roots may also be computed by the method given at the foot of Table A-32.

The computations for ΣX_i^2 may be checked by replacing each X_i by $(X_i + 1)$ and computing $\Sigma(X_i + 1)^2$. The check consists in noting that

$$\Sigma(X_i + 1)^2 = \Sigma X_i^2 + 2\Sigma X_i + N$$

Some examples of other measures of dispersion are the *range, semi-quartile range, mean deviation,* and distance between P_{07} and P_{93}. The range is the distance between the smallest and largest observations and will be denoted by w. The semiquartile range is the distance between P_{25} and P_{75}. The mean deviation is the mean of the deviations of the observations from $\bar{X}$ where the deviation is taken as the positive distance between the observation and $\bar{X}$.

3-3. Effect of Uniform Change in the Observations

A few types of manipulation of the observations are sufficiently common to make it desirable to study them in some detail. In particular, adding or subtracting a constant to each observation, multiplying or dividing each observation by a constant have very specific effects upon the arithmetic mean, variance, and standard deviation.

Suppose we add 5 units to each observation. Then instead of X_1, X_2, . . . , X_N we shall have the new numbers $X_1 + 5$, $X_2 + 5$, . . . , $X_N + 5$. The mean of these new numbers will be

$$\text{New mean} = \frac{(X_1 + 5) + (X_2 + 5) + \cdots + (X_N + 5)}{N}$$

$$= \frac{1}{N}\left(\sum_{i=1}^{N} X_i + 5N\right) = \bar{X} + \frac{5N}{N} = \bar{X} + 5$$

The variance of the new numbers will be

$$\text{New variance} = \frac{\sum_{i=1}^{N} [X_i + 5 - (\bar{X} + 5)]^2}{N - 1}$$

$$= \frac{\sum_{i=1}^{N} (X_i + 5 - \bar{X} - 5)^2}{N - 1} = \frac{\sum_{i=1}^{N} (X_i - \bar{X})^2}{N - 1} = s^2$$

We see that the mean is increased by 5 units but that the variance and standard deviation are unchanged. We may state the theorem: If the increase (decrease) in each observation is a units instead of 5, the new arithmetic mean will be a units larger (smaller) than the old mean and the variance and standard deviation will not be changed.

Thus adding (or subtracting) a constant from a group of observations will add (or subtract) the same constant to the arithmetic mean but will not change the variance or standard deviation.

Suppose we multiply each observation by a constant, say, c. Then the new observations are $cX_1, cX_2, cX_3, \ldots, cX_N$. The arithmetic mean of these quantities is c times the arithmetic mean of the original observations.

$$\text{New mean} = \frac{\sum_{i=1}^{N} cX_i}{N} = \frac{c \sum_{i=1}^{N} X_i}{N} = c\bar{X}$$

The variance of the new numbers* is c^2s^2, and the new standard deviation is cs. If the observations are divided by c instead of being multiplied, then the new mean is $\bar{X}/c$, the new variance is s^2/c^2, and the new standard deviation is s/c.

Thus multiplying (or dividing) each observation by a constant will multiply (or divide) the arithmetic mean by the same constant, will multiply (or divide) the variance by the square of the constant, and will multiply (or divide) the standard deviation by the constant.

A special case is the subtraction of $\bar{X}$ from each observation. Subtracting $\bar{X}$ from each observation also subtracts $\bar{X}$ from the mean. The new mean is $\bar{X} - \bar{X} = 0$. These new observations $(X_1 - \bar{X}), (X_2 - \bar{X}), \ldots, (X_N - \bar{X})$ have the same variance as before since the subtraction of a constant from each observation does not affect the variance. Now suppose that each of these new observations is divided by the standard deviation s. Then we shall have a new set of numbers, viz.,

$$\frac{X_1 - \bar{X}}{s}, \frac{X_2 - \bar{X}}{s}, \frac{X_3 - \bar{X}}{s}, \ldots, \frac{X_N - \bar{X}}{s}$$

These new numbers still have mean zero (dividing by s affects the mean by dividing it by s, but $0/s$ is still 0). The variance will be divided by s^2.

$$\text{* New variance} = \frac{\sum_{i=1}^{N} (cX_i - c\bar{X})^2}{N-1} = \frac{\sum_{i=1}^{N} c^2(X_i - \bar{X})^2}{N-1} = \frac{c^2 \sum_{i=1}^{N} (X_i - \bar{X})^2}{N-1} = c^2s^2$$

$$\text{New standard deviation} = \sqrt{c^2s^2} = cs$$

Thus the variance of the new set of numbers is $s^2/s^2 = 1$, and the new standard deviation is $\sqrt{1} = 1$.

Coding. If the mid-points of the intervals are equally spaced, they may be replaced by the numbers 0, 1, 2, 3, . . . , or the 0 may replace an X_i near the center of the distribution and the numbers run . . . , −3, −2, −1, 0, 1, 2, 3, . . . This is called *coding* of the observations. Where the X_i are large or where the number of observations is large, coding may save considerable time in the computation of $\bar{X}$ and s^2.

In coding we subtract the score coded as zero from each observation and divide the results by the length of the class interval i. As we have seen in this section, the mean and standard deviation of the original observations are given by

$$\bar{X} = i\bar{x} + X_0$$
$$s_X = is_x$$

where $\bar{x}$ = mean of coded scores
X_0 = score coded as zero
s_X = standard deviation of original observations
s_x = standard deviation of coded observations

The computation given in Table 3-2 would appear as in Table 3-2*a* if coded with $i = 1$ and $X_0 = 70$.

3-4. Standard Scores

Scores, or grades, as was pointed out before, are essentially arbitrarily constructed types of observations. In dealing with such observations it is sometimes desirable to have (for comparison of different grades or for quick reference) scores which can be easily compared. If, for example, we know that both means are 50 and both standard deviations are 10, we may compare at a glance grades on two different examinations.

Suppose we change each score by the formula

$$Z_i = 50 + 10\,\frac{X_i - \bar{X}}{s}$$

At the end of the last section we saw that $(X_i - \bar{X})/s$ has mean 0, and we note that the Z_i will have a mean 50 units higher than 0. The $(X_i - \bar{X})/s$ was seen to have a standard deviation of 1 and the standard deviation of $10\,\dfrac{X_i - \bar{X}}{s}$ is $10 \times 1 = 10$.

We have already shown that the addition of a constant to each score does not affect the standard deviation of a distribution. Therefore, Z_i will have a mean of 50 and a standard deviation of 10. When scores are changed in this fashion, the new marks are called *standard scores*.

TABLE 3-2a

Coded score x_i	f_i	$f_i x_i$	$f_i x_i^2$
5	1	5	25
4	1	4	16
3	3	9	27
2	8	16	32
1	12	12	12
0	16	0	0
−1	22	−22	22
−2	9	−18	36
−3	5	−15	45
−4	2	− 8	32
−5	0	0	0
−6	1	− 6	36
	80	−23	283

$$N = \Sigma f_i = 80$$

$$\bar{x} = \frac{\Sigma f_i x_i}{N} = \frac{-23}{80} = -.3$$

$$\bar{X} = i\bar{x} + X_0 = 1(-.3) + 70 = 69.7$$

$$s_x{}^2 = \frac{\Sigma f_i x_i{}^2 - \dfrac{(\Sigma f_i x_i)^2}{N}}{N - 1}$$

$$= \frac{283 - (-23)^2/80}{79}$$

$$= \frac{276.4}{79} = 3.50$$

$$s_X = is_x = 1(1.87) = 1.87$$

Example 1. The computation of Z scores is illustrated below.

Original score	$X_i - \bar{X}$	$\dfrac{X_i - \bar{X}}{s}$	Z_i
60	+26	+1.42	64
43	+ 9	+ .49	55
30	− 4	− .22	48
25	− 9	− .49	45
12	−22	−1.20	38
170			

$$\bar{X} = \tfrac{170}{5} = 34$$

$$s = 18.29$$

Example 2. The use of standard scores for combining grades from examinations with different standard deviations will now be shown. Three tests are given to a large group of students. In test 1 the mean is

65, and the standard deviation is 4. In test 2 the mean is 74, and the standard deviation is 6, and in test 3 the mean is 71, and the standard deviation is 12. Two students received the following grades on the three tests:

	Student		Class mean	Class s.d.
	A	*B*		
Test 1	57	73	65	4
Test 2	76	86	74	6
Test 3	96	70	71	12
Total	229	229		
Mean	76.3	76.3		

Student *A* received one very low grade (two standard deviations below the mean), one grade slightly above the mean, and one very high grade. Student *B* received two grades that were very high (two standard deviations above the mean) and one grade close to the mean. This difference does not show up in the total of the scores. If the grades are changed to equivalent Z scores, they appear as shown below. In test 1, 57 is two standard deviations below the mean, which corresponds to $Z = 30$, etc.

	Student	
	A	*B*
Test 1	30	70
Test 2	53	70
Test 3	71	49
Total	154	189
Mean	51	63

Here the two good grades of student *B* are shown in a better light, and the averages show that his grades are relatively better than student *A*'s.

A set of means of several sets of standard scores does not constitute standard scores. They will have mean 50, but they do not, in general, have standard deviation 10. In particular the 63 for student *B* should not be interpreted as being 1.3 standard deviations above the mean.

GLOSSARY

coded score
dispersion
mean
median
range
standard deviation
standard score
variance

DISCUSSION QUESTIONS

1. Define each of the terms in the Glossary.

2. Is it possible for $\bar{X}$ and s^2 to have the same numerical value?

3. Distinguish between a measurement on an individual and a numerical quantity describing (measuring) a distribution. Give several examples of each.

4. Do the values of $\bar{X}$ and s^2 completely describe a distribution? Can you think of other measures analogous to s^2?

5. Suppose a group of scores are changed to Z scores. What happens to the percentile rank of an individual? What happens to the deviation of an individual score from the mean?

6. Suppose each measurement in a distribution is multiplied by 2. What happens to the mean of the distribution? What happens to the variance of the distribution? What happens to the standard deviation of the distribution? What happens to each of the three if 4 is added to each measurement?

7. Suppose a set of observations has mean $\bar{X}$ and variance s^2. What happens to the mean and variance if each score is divided by s and then $\bar{X}$ is subtracted from each quotient? Is the result the same if you first subtract $\bar{X}$ from each score and then divide the difference by s?

8. Give an example of a situation where the median might be a more appropriate descriptive measure than the mean.

9. Is there any difference between ΣX_i^2 and $(\Sigma X_i)^2$?

CLASS EXERCISE

Select from Table A-2 three groups of 10 numbers each. Start at some random place in the table so that each student will have a different group of numbers. Select also three groups of 10 numbers each from Table A-23. Perform the necessary computations to obtain $\bar{X}$, s^2, and s for each of the groups.

The results of this exercise will be used several times in later chapters to provide experimental verification of various theoretical statements. Therefore care should be taken in drawing the observations, and the computations should be checked.

A possible work sheet for recording the data and results is shown in Table 3-3. Columns A, B, C are for the samples from Table A-2, and the next column will be used for the combination of these three samples. Columns D, E, F are for the samples from Table A-23, and the next column will be used for the combination of these three samples. The lines below the s values will be used for computations in later chapters.

PROBLEMS

1. Compute the values of $\bar{X}$, s^2, and s for the data in the table, where the values for X represent the mid-points of intervals.

X	15	25	35	45	55	65	75	85	95	105
f	1	5	12	18	21	19	10	7	6	1

2. Compute the values of $\bar{X}$, s^2, and s for the following observations: 96, 84, 103, 88, 92, 98, 100, 96, 87, 92, 94.

3. Find Z scores for each of the mid-point values in Prob. 1.

4. Find Z scores for each of the scores in Prob. 2.

5. Three tests had the values in the table for means and standard deviations.

Test	$\bar{X}$	s
1	70	5
2	75	8
3	60	12

Student A received grades of 70, 90, 70 on the three tests, while student B received grades of 90, 70, 70. Assuming that all three tests should carry equal weight, change the grades to Z scores and average each student's scores.

6. Sketch histograms of two distributions having the same mean and total area so that one distribution has a large variance and the other has a small variance.

7. Sketch a histogram of a distribution where the mean is equal to the median. Sketch a histogram of a distribution which has two modes (bimodal). Is there any general class of distributions where the mean and median are equal?

8. The weights of a number of packages of frozen peas are given as follows: 16.1, 15.9, 15.8, 16.3, 16.2, 16.0, 16.1, 16.0, 15.9, 16.0, 16.1, 16.0, 15.9, 16.1, 16.0, 16.0.

(*a*) Make a frequency table.
(*b*) Draw a histogram.
(*c*) Find the mean.
(*d*) Find the median.
(*e*) Find the mode.
(*f*) Find the range.
(*g*) Find the variance.
(*h*) Find the standard deviation.

9. The following observations are the yields in pounds of hops. Find the mean, variance, and standard deviation.

3.4, 4.4, 4.8, 4.5, 5.1, 4.6, 5.5, 4.7, 3.5, 3.6, 4.2, 4.8, 3.4, 4.3,
5.0, 3.6, 3.5, 5.3, 4.7, 5.4, 2.2, 4.0, 4.6, 3.0, 5.3, 2.6, 4.3, 5.0,
5.8, 3.1, 2.7, 4.8, 4.0, 3.6, 5.0, 3.0, 3.2, 3.4, 5.6, 5.3, 5.8, 4.2,
4.6, 3.7, 6.0, 6.2, 5.0, 6.8, 6.0, 6.5, 4.8, 6.6, 7.0, 7.4, 5.6.

TABLE 3-3. DATA SHEET FOR SAMPLING EXPERIMENT

	From Table A-2				From Table A-23			
	A	B	C		D	E	F	
1								
2								
3								
4								
5								
6								
7								
8								
9								
10								
ΣX_i								
$\bar{X}$								
ΣX_i^2								
$\Sigma(X_i + 1)^2$								
$\Sigma X_i^2 + 2\Sigma X_i + N$								
$\Sigma X_i^2 - \frac{(\Sigma X_i)^2}{N}$								
s^2								
s								
$t = \sqrt{N}\,(\bar{X} - 0)/s$								
$\bar{X} + t_{.05}s/\sqrt{N}$								
$\bar{X} + t_{.95}s/\sqrt{N}$								
Median								
Range								
Midrange								
$\frac{s^2}{\chi_{.05}^2/\text{df}}$								
$\frac{s^2}{\chi_{.95}^2/\text{df}}$								

Section__________ Date__________

Experiments for investigation of sampling distribution of various statistics; $\bar{X}, s^2, \bar{X}_1 - \bar{X}_2$, t, etc.

Observed frequency (卌 II)	Observation (mid-point of interval)	Code	f	xf	$x^2 f$	Check $(x+1)^2 f$	Cum. per cent to upper boundary
		15					
		14					
		13					
		12					
		11					
		10					
		9					
		8					
		7					
		6					
		5					
		4					
		3					
		2					
		1					
		0					
		-1					
		-2					
		-3					
		-4					
		-5					
		-6					
		-7					
		-8					
		-9					
		-10					
		-11					
		-12					
		-13					
		-14					
		-15					
Totals							

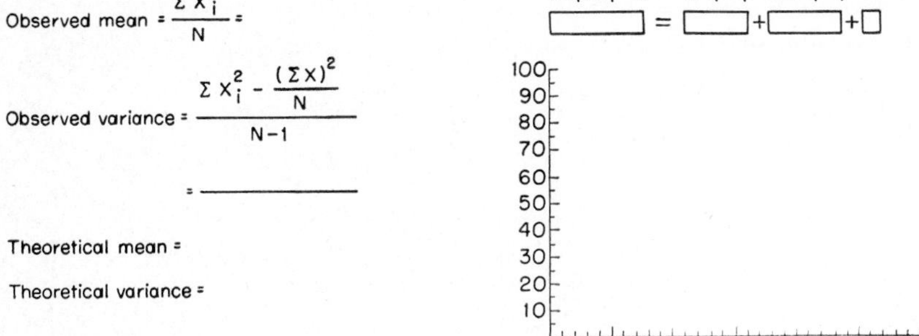

FIG. 3-2

CHAPTER 4

UNIVERSE AND SAMPLE

Any set of individuals (or objects) having some common observable characteristic constitutes a *population,* or *universe.* Any subset of a population is a *sample* from that population.

The term population may refer either to the individuals measured or to the measurements themselves. There is then a "distribution of the measurements of a sample" which we actually observe and study and a "distribution of the measurements of the universe" which may exist but usually not in observed or recorded form. One of the most important problems in statistics is to decide what information about the distribution of the population can be inferred from a study of the sample.

A third type of distribution consists of the distribution of a measurement made on each of all possible samples of a fixed size which could be taken from a universe. For example, if we took all possible samples of 10 students from a given school and computed the mean height of each sample, we should have a large number of means. These means form a distribution, which we call the *sampling distribution* of the mean of samples of size 10.

Some examples of populations and samples follow:

1. A study is to be made of the heights of the men in a certain city. A sample of 200 men is chosen, and their heights are recorded. Here the universe consists of all men in the city. The sample consists of the 200 men chosen. The measurable characteristic is height. We can form a distribution of the heights observed in the sample, but presumably the distribution of the universe is not available. If we compute the mean of the heights of the 200 men in the sample, we can think of this mean as a single observation from the distribution of means of all possible samples of 200 men.

2. An investigation is being undertaken to test the effects of a particular type of drug on tetanus. A group of rats is infected with tetanus and then treated with the drug. Then the proportion of rats recovering within a specified time interval is observed. The universe consists of all rats which will be, or could be, infected with tetanus and then given the drug. The sample consists of the group of rats actually used, and the

characteristic is either recovery or failure to recover within the specified time interval. The universe here could not be observed since we could not perform this experiment on every rat.

3. In a survey to study the manual abilities of country children (aged twelve) a manual-skills test was given to 200 country children. The universe would be all twelve-year-old country children in the locality sampled from; the sample, the 200 children taking the test.

4. A field of wheat has an area of 4,000 acres. A sample of 30 plots of size 1 square rod each is chosen, and the yields of these plots are measured. The population consists of the 640,000 individual square-rod plots, the sample is the 30 chosen, while the measurement is the yield of a plot.

5. A survey is made to determine the opinion of the people in a certain city on a proposed old-age-pension law. A sample of 500 people is questioned, and the number of favorable opinions is recorded. Here, as in example 2, the measurement is of a discrete type; we may record a 1 if the response is favorable and a 0 if unfavorable.

6. It is desired to estimate the mean score of students in a particular school on a standardized test. A sample of 10 students is chosen to take the test. The measurement is the student's score on the test.

7. Twelve seeds of a certain type of hybrid corn are planted and the yields observed. Here the population does not actually exist—it consists of all seeds of this type of corn. Probably very little seed actually exists, and whether or not much will exist in the future may depend on the outcome of this experiment.

4-1. Population, or Universe

We shall use the words population and universe interchangeably. A universe can be finite (children in a city, cows in a geographical region, electric-light bulbs manufactured during a day, etc.), or it can be infinite (all points on a line, all heights between 5 feet and 6 feet, the time required for rats to run a maze).

In many cases a universe will be finite but so large that we treat it as though it were infinite (e.g., a boxcar of grain, or the apples in an orchard).

Many populations are so scattered as to be inaccessible as a whole. For example, in studying some characteristic of all students graduated from a university it might be impractical to contact every graduate but quite reasonable to contact a sample. If the people were collected in one spot, it might be reasonable to measure every individual in the population. Similarly if it were desired to study some characteristic of railway workers, the population would be so disperse as to make any complete survey very difficult.

Most of our procedures will be based on an assumption of an infinite population. Some modifications of formulas are necessary in case the population is small compared with the size of the sample. Generally the corrections for finite population size can be ignored if the population has several hundred individuals and the size of the sample is not more than 5 per cent of the number of individuals in the population.

A different type of universe is obtained if we consider the problem of measuring the length of a field. If we measure it a large number of times, we shall get a distribution of measurements (not all alike owing to errors in measurement). The set of all possible measurements of the field which have been, or will be, or could be taken can be thought of as forming a universe. Obviously we can never observe the entire universe. Physicists in measuring the attraction of gravity, chemists in performing very accurate weighing, etc., have the same type of problem.

The various descriptive words and measurements which we have previously mentioned are applied to the distribution of the universe, as well as to other distributions. We shall be especially interested in the mean and variance. We shall denote the arithmetic mean of the universe by the Greek letter μ (mu) and the variance of the universe by the Greek σ^2 (sigma squared). The standard deviation of the universe is then denoted by σ.

Any measurable characteristic of the universe is called a parameter. μ and σ are examples of parameters.

4-2. Sample

The size of a sample, usually represented by the letter N, is the number of individuals in the sample. A sample may be any size from $N = 1$ to the number of items in the universe.

The measurements on the individuals in the sample will form a distribution which will have a mean, denoted by $\bar{X}$, and a variance, denoted by s^2. Presumably $\bar{X}$ and s^2, which we can actually measure, should give us some information about μ and σ^2, whose values are usually not known. $\bar{X}$ and s^2 are different from sample to sample, while μ and σ^2 are constant, i.e., have particular values for a particular universe.

A value computed entirely from the sample is called a *statistic*. $\bar{X}$, s^2, the median, the mode, the range of the sample are examples of statistics.

The method of choosing a sample is an important factor in determining what use can be made of the sample. If some individuals in the universe are more likely to be chosen than others, the *sample* is said to be *biased*. It has been found that subjective methods of picking individuals for a sample often (perhaps "usually" is a better word) lead to biased samples, apparently due primarily to subconscious or conscious preferences of the person making the selections. To prevent this bias and to avoid the criticism of bias even if the sample is not biased, some nonsubjective method of choosing a sample should be employed.

Random Sampling. When every individual in the population has an equal and independent chance of being chosen for a sample, the sample is called a *random sample*. Technically every individual chosen should be measured and returned to the population before another selection is made. This means, of course, that an individual can be chosen twice in the same sample. Thus, for example, to choose a *random* sample of 5 cards out of a deck of 52 cards, you should choose one card, record its value, and return it to the deck, shuffle the deck thoroughly, draw another card, record its value, and replace it in the deck, etc. If the population is large compared with the sample size, very little error will result from the procedure of not returning each individual to the population. In practice the individual is rarely returned, and in fact it is frequently impossible to do so, as in a case where the individual is changed or destroyed by the examination. In many cases care is actually taken to prevent the same individual from appearing twice in a sample. Note, however, that in Sec. 4-5, where there is a very small universe, we return each individual before drawing another.

It might well be pointed out that saying, "Every individual in the population has an equal chance of being in the sample" is not the same as saying, "Every measurement in the universe has an equal chance of being in the sample." For example, if most of the individuals in the universe have large measurements, then the large values have a better chance of being chosen for the sample.

4-3. Random Numbers

Suppose that we have a finite population from which we wish to draw a random sample of N individuals. A method of doing this would be to assign a number to each member of the population, put a set of numbered tags corresponding to the individuals into a box, and draw N tags from the box. The numbers on these N tags will correspond to the individuals to be selected. This is a satisfactory method except for the labor involved in preparing the tags and drawing them.

We can shorten this process by use of a table of *random numbers* (Table A-1). Such a table consists of numbers chosen in a fashion similar to drawing numbered tags out of a box. This table is so made that all numbers 0, 1, . . . , 9 appear with approximately the same frequency. By combining numbers in pairs we have the numbers from 00 to 99. By using the numbers three at a time we have numbers from 000 to 999, etc. Such a table could be constructed as follows: Number 10 tags 0, 1, 2, 3, 4, 5, 6, 7, 8, 9, and place them in a box. Draw one, and record its value.

Return it, and draw another, etc. We shall use the numbers from Table A-1 to select random samples.

The table should be entered in a random manner. One way is to close your eyes and place a finger on one page of the table. Either the digits under your finger can be used, or these digits may be used to locate other digits in the table. For example, 29 32 selected in this way can be taken to indicate the use of the 29th number in the 32d column of the table. This procedure may be repeated until the required number of random digits is obtained. Since the digits are thoroughly mixed in the table, the entire sample may be taken in a group once a location is determined randomly. The table is large enough to make it very unlikely that there will be much duplication in different samples.

Suppose you wish to select at random 20 items from a universe of 400 items. First, assign numbers to the 400 items in the universe. Three-place numbers are needed (400 of them), and so we agree to use three columns in the table. If the number in the table is 400 or less, take the corresponding item from the universe. If the number is more than 400, skip it. If a number comes up twice, skip it the second time (thus the sampling is slightly nonrandom). Continue reading numbers until the desired number of items, 20 in this case, have been chosen for the sample.

This method is fairly general. If the universe has between 1,000 and 10,000 members, use four columns, if between 10,000 and 100,000 use five columns, etc. For large populations this procedure has the drawback that the universe has to be numbered, and it must be relatively easy and inexpensive to find any particular individual. Modern card files and machines like the punched-card sorters may make this type of sampling practical for extremely large populations.

Sometimes when the population cannot be easily numbered, some sort of geographical numbering can be made. For example, if you wish to sample from a field of some agricultural product, you could divide the field into a large number of small rectangles by lines running north and south and lines running east and west. The rectangles are then numbered, and some of them are chosen in the manner described above.

Another example might be the choice of a sample for determining the cost-of-living index. The counties in the United States could be numbered and a sample chosen from them (actually types of sampling other than random are ordinarily used in surveys of this sort).

Suppose it is desired to investigate the effect of two drugs on mice. A random selection of 50 mice from a group of 100 mice for treatment with the first drug could be made by using the random-number table. The remainder of the mice could be given the second drug. (Sometimes other methods are preferred, and we shall discuss some of them later; for example, you might wish to guard against all the first 50 being males and the second 50 all females.)

4-4. Design of Experiments

The method of choosing a sample is called the *design of the experiment.* We have stressed the design where the observations are chosen at random, but it should be emphasized that this sampling design is by no means always the best. For some fields of application other designs will give more precise information about the particular population under investigation. It is perhaps more appropriate that these designs be studied in detail in specialized courses taken after the student has obtained a good general knowledge of statistical application. We shall not emphasize any one design (except random sampling) to any great extent.

The so-called "experiment" is usually a situation where the population does not actually exist and the purpose of the investigation is to establish something about the population if it did exist. Many agricultural, biological, medical, psychological, educational, chemical, etc., experiments are of this type. Examples 2, 7 at the beginning of this chapter are of this sort, as are problems of measuring the size of objects, the effects of fertilizers or drugs, the effects of teaching methods, the results of a particular method of chemical analysis, and so on. In situations of this type, specialized designs, where outside conditions are controlled or where groups of individuals are chosen in particular ways, may give more information than random sampling. In fact it is frequently difficult, in experimental work, to satisfy oneself that one has actually sampled in a particular manner, and considerable theory is concerned with this problem.

A second situation occurs when there is actually an existing population and we wish to determine by a "survey" some characteristic of that population. Examples 1, 3, 4 at the beginning of this chapter are examples of this type of situation. Frequently a statistical problem will involve both these situations as in example 2. In surveys a sampling design involving "stratification" of the population is often used and will, if used correctly, give more precise information about the population than random sampling. For stratification the population is subdivided into several parts, or strata, and the number of observations in the sample is apportioned among these strata. Frequently the proportion of the sample to be taken from each of the strata is fixed the same as the proportion of the population in that strata. Stratification methods have been widely used in sampling human populations, e.g., public-opinion polls and market surveys.

Very misleading results can occur if samples are not taken correctly. Probably the most publicized example is the case of the news magazine which attempted to predict the presidential election of 1936 by taking a large sample entirely from a few strata, completely ignoring the other strata. Of course, in public-opinion surveys (as in many other practical situations) there is further difficulty in actually measuring an individual. An inexperienced interviewer may easily obtain biased responses from an obliging interviewee or no response from certain classes of people.

Most of the discussion in this book is restricted to random sampling. Inferences and conclusions will be based on the assumption that the sampling has been carried out randomly.

4-5. Sampling Distributions

Any statistic (measurement on a sample) has a sampling distribution. In this section we shall stress the sampling distribution of $\bar{X}$ and s^2.

Suppose we take from a universe *all possible* samples of, say, size 10. On each sample we perform the necessary computations to find $\bar{X}$ and s^2. We should then have a universe of means (consisting of all these values of $\bar{X}$) and a universe of s^2. These have distributions which are called, respectively, the *sampling distribution of the mean* and *sampling distribution of the variance* (sometimes abbreviated to distribution of mean and distribution of variance). By examination of the sampling distribution of the mean we can tell how frequently the mean $\bar{X}$ will fall in any interval we wish to discuss. For example, we can tell how frequently it will fall within two units of the universe mean μ, between $X = 7$ and $X = 8$, etc. Let us actually record the sampling distributions of the mean and variance in a simple case and see what they look like. (Remember that in practical work it would be essentially impossible to record such distributions, and we are doing it here to show how these statistics behave in the practical situations.)

Suppose our universe consists of 6 rabbits. The weights of the rabbits in ounces are

$$X_1 = 11 \qquad X_4 = 15$$
$$X_2 = 16 \qquad X_5 = 16$$
$$X_3 = 12 \qquad X_6 = 14$$

Now suppose we take samples of size $N = 2$. There are 36 different samples possible, and they are listed in Table 4-1. Beside each one is recorded the $\bar{X}$ and the s^2 for that particular sample. Notice that it is possible for an individual to be chosen more than once in the same sample. In practice the universe will be so large that the chances of duplication will be very small.

Here our sampling distribution of the mean consists of the 36 values of $\bar{X}$. The sampling distribution of the variance consists of the 36 values of s^2. Table 4-1 shows all possible samples of size 2, with mean and variance for each. The first observation is recorded along the top, and

TABLE 4-1

	11	16	12	15	16	14
11	11 0	13.5 12.5	11.5 .5	13 8	13.5 12.5	12.5 4.5
16	13.5 12.5	16 0	14 8	15.5 .5	16 0	15 2
12	11.5 .5	14 8	12 0	13.5 4.5	14 8	13 2
15	13 8	15.5 .5	13.5 4.5	15 0	15.5 .5	14.5 .5
16	13.5 12.5	16 0	14 8	15.5 .5	16 0	15 2
14	12.5 4.5	15 2	13 2	14.5 .5	15 2	14 0

the second observation is recorded on the left. In the main part of the table the first number is the mean, and the second is the variance of the two observations in the sample. To make comparisons easier, Fig. 4-1 pictures these two distributions with the distribution of the universe.

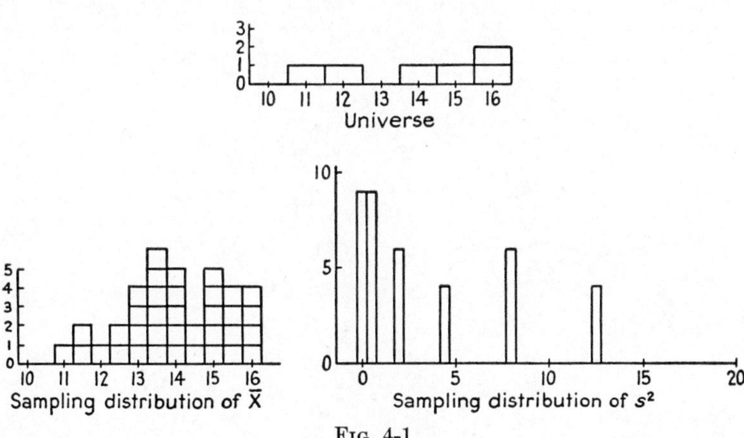

FIG. 4-1

Since we have the entire universe of 6 items, we can compute the mean,

$$\mu = \frac{11 + 16 + 12 + 15 + 16 + 14}{6} = \frac{84}{6} = 14$$

and the variance,

$$\sigma^2 = \frac{11^2 + 16^2 + 12^2 + 15^2 + 16^2 + 14^2 - (84)^2/6}{6} = \frac{22}{6} = \frac{11}{3}$$

(Note the 6 in the denominator for the computation of the variance.) We also compute the mean and variance for the distribution of $\bar{X}$ and for the distribution of s^2 (using 36, not 35, in the denominator for the variance). The computation is shown in Table 4-2. Note that the

TABLE 4-2

$\bar{X}$	f	$f\bar{X}$
16.0	4	64
15.5	4	62
15.0	5	75
14.5	2	29
14.0	5	70
13.5	6	81
13.0	4	52
12.5	2	25
12.0	1	12
11.5	2	23
11.0	1	11
	36	504

Mean $\bar{X} = \frac{504}{36} = 14$
Var. $\bar{X} = \frac{66}{36} = \frac{11}{6}$

s^2	f	$f(s^2)$
12.5	4	50
8.0	6	48
4.5	4	18
2.0	6	12
.5	8	4
0	8	0
	36	132

Mean $s^2 = \frac{132}{36} = \frac{11}{3}$

mean of the sampling distribution of $\bar{X}$ has the same value as the mean μ of the universe. Also notice that the mean of the s^2 distribution has the same value as the variance σ^2 of the universe. This second equality occurs only if we use $N - 1$ in the computation of the *sample* variance. Thus we can say that "on the average" the sample variance is equal to the variance of the universe. Suppose we had divided each sample variance by N instead of by $N - 1$. Then the mean of the distribution of variances would be much less than the variance σ^2 of the universe. Therefore, we shall use

$$s^2 = \frac{\Sigma(X_i - \bar{X})^2}{N - 1}$$

since this statistic is equal to σ^2 on the average. If the entire universe is at our disposal, then we divide by N (not $N - 1$). Thus our procedure is *if the variance is computed from a sample, the denominator is* $N - 1$; *if the variance is computed from the entire universe, the denominator is* N. Since the entire universe is rarely available, we have defined s^2 with $N - 1$ in the denominator.

Denote the variance of the universe by σ^2 and the variance of the sampling distribution of the mean by $\sigma_{\bar{X}}^2$. In the example above $(\sigma^2/\sigma_{\bar{X}}^2) = 2$, which is N, the size of the sample. This is true in general and can be written $\sigma_{\bar{X}}^2 = (\sigma^2/N)$. The variance of the distribution of s^2 does not have such a nice relationship to σ^2.

The sampling distribution of $\bar{X}$ shows the chance that $\bar{X}$ will have certain values. In the example the chance that $\bar{X} = 14$ is $\frac{5}{36}$ (5 cases in 36). As another example, we compute the chance that $\bar{X} = 13, 13.5, 14$, or 14.5 to be $\frac{17}{36}$. Compare this result with the chance that a single observation, X, is equal to 13, 13.5, 14, or 14.5. We compute

$$\frac{0 + 0 + 1 + 0}{6} = \frac{1}{6} = \frac{6}{36}$$

The four values chosen for X are near $\mu = 14$ and we can see that the mean of a sample of two observations has a greater chance than a single observation of being close to the population mean. This result is also indicated by the smaller variance $\sigma^2/2$ of the sampling distribution of $\bar{X}$ for $N = 2$.

It is a lengthy task to write down the sampling distribution for even such a small universe and such a very small sample size. For a universe of several thousand and a sample of 20 or 30 it would be essentially impossible to enumerate the individual items in the sampling distribution. We can approximate the sampling distribution in cases of this type by drawing a large number (perhaps several hundred) samples and recording the distribution observed. However, this is a tedious method of "proof," and so we must frequently fall back on the *authority* of statements of "proven" mathematical theorems. These theorems will have certain assumptions, and in applying them we must keep the assumptions, as well as conclusions, in mind. Usually these assumptions will involve either the distribution of the population or the size of the sample.

Realizing these limitations in our methods, let us draw a large number of samples from some universe and attempt to approximate the sampling distribution of the mean $\bar{X}$ and the variance s^2. In the example below we take two sample sizes ($N = 10$ and $N = 40$) to illustrate what happens with increasing N.

We shall take the occasion to introduce the use of another random-number table. This table (Table A-2) has items chosen at random from a universe which has a "normal" distribution. This normal distribution is quite important in statistical method and will be discussed in detail in the next chapter. The random-number table (Table A-1) was taken from a uniform distribution, all numbers 0, 1, 2, 3, 4, 5, 6, 7, 8, 9 being equally frequent. In Table A-2, numbers with values near zero occur fairly frequently, and numbers farther and farther away from zero occur less and less frequently. The numbers in the universe (several pages of Table A-2) have a mean of zero and a variance $\sigma^2 = 1.00(\sigma = 1.00)$. Suppose we take 200 samples of $N = 10$ and 200 of $N = 40$ and record the values of $\bar{X}$ and s^2 for each sample. We can then obtain some idea of the general shape of the sampling distributions of $\bar{X}$ and s^2.

The method of choosing samples should be fairly random. The procedure is as follows: We pick a two-digit number from Table A-1. The number is (3,6). We start on page 3, column 6, of Table A-2. Then we record the numbers in 200 sets of 10. It is not necessary to mix them up since this has been done before putting them into the table. We put these sets of 10 together, 4 at a time for 50 samples of 40 each. Then we take 150 more samples of 40 each.

Table 4-3 shows the observed means and variances corresponding to

TABLE 4-3. OBSERVED VALUES OF $\bar{X}$ AND s^2 FROM A NORMAL POPULATION WITH $\mu = 0$ AND $\sigma^2 = 1$

$\bar{X}$				s^2			
$N = 10$		$N = 40$		$N = 10$		$N = 40$	
Mid-point	Freq.	Mid-point	Freq.	Mid-point	Freq.	Mid-point	Freq.
.75	2	.425	3	.10	3	.45	3
.65	3	.375	0	.30	18	.55	16
.55	7	.325	9	.50	33	.65	16
.45	13	.275	6	.70	28	.75	21
.35	13	.225	8	.90	29	.85	27
.25	19	.175	11	1.10	26	.95	37
.15	22	.125	21	1.30	20	1.05	28
.05	24	.075	18	1.50	18	1.15	22
−.05	26	.025	30	1.70	10	1.25	12
−.15	19	−.025	36	1.90	6	1.35	12
−.25	17	−.075	16	2.10	3	1.45	6
−.35	12	−.125	14	2.30	1		
−.45	11	−.175	10	2.50	2		
−.55	5	−.225	9	2.70	1		
−.65	4	−.275	3	2.90	1		
−.75	3	−.325	4	3.10	1		
		−.375	0				
		−.425	2				
	200		200		200		200
Mean $\bar{X}$....	.009	......	.019	Mean s^2....	1.001	....	.945
Var. $\bar{X}$.....	.1035	......	.0258	Var. s^2......	.2983	....	.0579
s.d. $\bar{X}$......	.322	......	.161	s.d. s^2......	.546	....	.241

the indicated mid-points of class intervals. Figure 4-2 contains the histograms for the four frequency tables.

Some of the things we should look for in these sampling distributions are as follows:

1. The general shape of the curves.
2. The mean of the sampling distributions. From the statements in

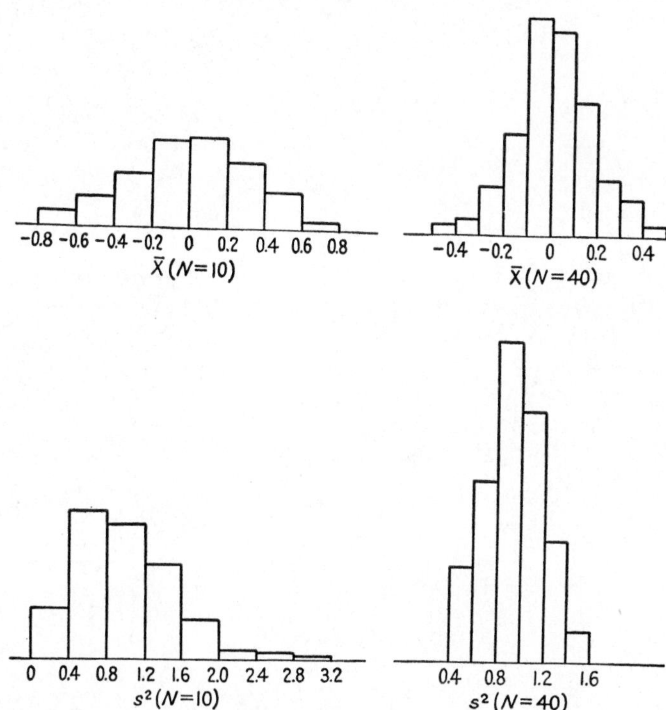

FIG. 4-2

the previous example we expect the sampling distribution of the mean $\bar{X}$ to have an average approximately equal to μ (zero here) and the sampling distribution of the variance to have an average of approximately σ^2 (1.00 here). We do not expect exact values because we do not have the entire sampling distribution, only 200 observations from it.

3. The variance of the sampling distributions of $\bar{X}$. Again from the previous examples we expect the sampling distributions of the mean to have variances approximately equal to $\frac{\sigma^2}{N}$ (which is $\frac{1.00}{10} = .1$ and $\frac{1.00}{40} = .025$ for $N = 10$ and $N = 40$, respectively).

We also record for future reference the percentiles P_{05}, P_{10}, P_{20}, P_{30}, P_{50}, P_{70}, P_{80}, P_{90}, P_{95} of the observed distribution for s^2 for $N = 10$.

The values of the percentiles for the complete sampling distribution (obtained by a mathematical process) are also recorded so that the comparison can be seen. The theoretical distribution is called the χ^2/df (chi square over degrees of freedom) distribution.

TABLE 4-4

	Observed	Theoretical
P_{05}	.28	.369
P_{10}	.39	.463
P_{20}	.52	.598
P_{30}	.64	.710
P_{50}	.92	.927
P_{70}	1.22	1.18
P_{80}	1.44	1.36
P_{90}	1.70	1.63
P_{95}	1.97	1.88

As we proceed, we shall find many occasions to approximate sampling distributions experimentally, and we shall also study several sampling distributions in enough detail to make use of mathematically obtained tables of percentiles.

4-6. Sampling without Replacement

In Sec. 4-5 the example of the 36 possible samples of size $N = 2$ taken from a population of size 6 assumed that a single animal could be obtained twice in the same sample. In most practical sampling problems the population is so large compared with the sample size that the chance of getting the same individual twice is so small that consideration of this point can be neglected. However, to see the necessary modification in the formulas if an individual cannot be chosen more than once in the same sample, we consider the 30 possible samples of size $N = 2$ if the first individual chosen for the sample is not returned to the population before the second is chosen. If the samples were recorded as in Table 4-1, the first observation recorded along the top and the second on the left, the table would appear as before except there would be no entries in the squares along the diagonal running from the upper left corner to the lower right corner of the table. Therefore the sampling distributions of $\bar{X}$ and s^2 recorded in Table 4-2 would be altered by removing the six means $\bar{X} = 11$, 16, 12, 15, 16, 14 and six zero values of s^2. Table 4-5 records the resulting sampling distributions of $\bar{X}$ and s^2. Note that, as in the case of sampling with replacement, the mean of the sampling distribution of $\bar{X}$ is μ. However, the variance of the sampling distribution of $\bar{X}$ is not the same as before. The new formula is

$$\text{Var. } (\bar{X}) = \frac{\sigma^2}{N}\left(1 - \frac{N-1}{N_p - 1}\right) = \frac{\sigma^2}{N}\left(\frac{N_p - N}{N_p - 1}\right)$$

where N_p = size of population
N = size of sample

When N is small compared with N_p, the term $(N - 1)/(N_p - 1)$ can be neglected and the formula reduces to σ^2/N. For the illustrative population var. $(\bar{X}) = \frac{11/3}{2}\left(\frac{6-2}{6-1}\right) = 1.467$.

The mean s^2 is also changed and is now given by the formula $\frac{N_p}{N_p - 1}\sigma^2$. For a large population this is very close to σ^2, as we obtained in the case of sampling with replacement. If one is sampling without replacement from a finite population, one should bear in mind that the variance of $\bar{X}$ and the mean s^2 are different from those for sampling with replacement or in sampling from an infinite population.

For the illustrative population the mean $s^2 = \frac{6}{6-1}\left(\frac{11}{3}\right) = 4.4$.

TABLE 4-5

$\bar{X}$	f	$f\bar{X}$
16.0	2	32
15.5	4	62
15.0	4	60
14.5	2	29
14.0	4	56
13.5	6	81
13.0	4	52
12.5	2	25
12.0	0	0
11.5	2	23
11.0	0	0
	30	420

Mean $\bar{X} = \frac{420}{30} = 14$

Var. $\bar{X} = \frac{44}{30} = \frac{8.8}{6} = 1.467$

s^2	f	fs^2
12.5	4	50
8.0	6	48
4.5	4	18
2.0	6	12
.5	8	4
0	2	0
	30	132

Mean $s^2 = \frac{132}{30} = 4.4$

4-7. Sampling Experiments

One of the main objectives of this book is the approach to the understanding of statistics through sampling experiments. In these experiments a sampling distribution is approximated by drawing a large number of samples from some universe. In the hope of encouraging more actual sampling experiments we shall describe here (and at other places in the text) some methods of performing such experiments.

The use of tables of random numbers (Table A-1) or tables of observations drawn from a specified normal population (Table A-2) is convenient and fast. However, students frequently have a clearer picture of the mechanism of forming a sampling distribution if they draw samples from a visible population rather than from a row of numbers on a page. Drawing from an actual population also tends to reduce the subconscious mistrust that some students may have of the arrangement of the numbers in the table.

For a situation where individuals in a population either have or do not have a certain characteristic, we use a box of beads and a paddle. The paddle is a wooden scoop with five rows of 10 holes each. By dipping the paddle into the box of beads we can obtain 5 samples of $N = 10$, or 10 samples of $N = 5$, or 1 sample of $N = 50$ individuals. The beads are small wooden spheres in two (or more) colors. Thus, for example, if there are 1,000 white beads and 500 red beads in the box, we have a population in which two-thirds of the individuals have some characteristic and one-third does not. Such a box has an advantage over tossing coins, not only in time and effort, but in the possibility of constructing (by altering the proportions of red and white beads in the box) any desired type of population.

Another device which can be employed is a box of tags (representing individuals), each tag having on it a number (representing the measurement on the individual). The tags may be small, round paper tags with metal rims such as those used in marking prices on merchandise. If there are a large number of tags in the box (i.e., in the universe), samples of 10 or so can be drawn at once and all 10 values recorded before returning the tags to the box. If the number of tags in the box is small, it is better to return each observed tag before drawing another. Usually the distribution of numbers on the tags is made up to be an approximately "normal" distribution (as described in Chap. 5). Table A-22 gives six possible sets of numbers for tags. Sets 1, 2, 3, 4, 5 represent approximately normal distributions with means and standard deviations as marked. Set 6 is a uniform distribution in which each measurement has the same frequency. For example, to construct a universe from set 1, take 200 tags, mark 1 of them 5, 3 of them 4, 10 of them 3, and so on.

For the experiments in this chapter only one such set is used. However, in later chapters we shall describe experiments using several sets at once. To keep them separate, the sets are recorded in different colors as noted in the table.

Models and Assumptions. It should be emphasized that tables of random numbers or prepared boxes of tags or beads are *ideal* populations where no assumptions need be made. In using Table A-2, for example, we may be sure that the population is "normally" distributed and that observations are drawn at random from this population. Such ideal populations are *models* used only to demonstrate certain mathematical theorems. In practical problems, where assumptions must be made concerning a population, we should be reasonably certain that such assumptions are satisfied before using statistical procedures based on these assumptions or should use statistical procedures which are little affected by the truth of the assumptions that have been made.

GLOSSARY

biased sample
design of experiment
parameter
population
random numbers
random sample
sample
sample size
sampling distribution
statistic
survey
universe

DISCUSSION QUESTIONS

1. What three types of distributions were presented in this chapter? How do these three types differ?

2. Suppose a population consists of the four measurements $X_1 = 2$, $X_2 = 4$, $X_3 = 6$, $X_4 = 8$. How many random samples of size 3 could be chosen from this population? List these samples, and compute the mean and median for each sample. Form the sampling distribution of the mean and the sampling distribution of the median for samples of size 3 from this population. Which of these distributions has the smaller variance? How do the means of these two distributions compare with the population mean? Does the variance of each of these distributions equal σ^2/N? If you had a single sample of three observations, which measurement, the mean or the median, would be more likely to be close to the population mean? Do you think this is a general rule, or do you think that the answer to this last question would depend upon the form of the distribution of the population?

3. Distinguish between a parameter and a statistic. Are these constants? What are two uses of a statistic?

4. Why do we not measure parameters directly?

5. How many random samples of size 3 could be taken from a population of 100 individuals? From a population of 1,000 individuals? How many samples of size $N = 100$ could be taken from a population of 1,000,000 individuals?

6. Discuss methods of obtaining random samples (except for replacement) from the following populations. Give for each a possible measurement which might be made on individuals in the sample:

(*a*) Students in a school.
(*b*) Oranges on a tree.
(*c*) People in a city.

(*d*) Fir trees in a forest.
(*e*) Houses in a county.
(*f*) A day's production of electric-light bulbs from a factory.
(*g*) The wheat in a freight car.
(*h*) Children in a certain hospital during 1956.
(*i*) All graduates of some college.
(*j*) The fish in a river.

7. What happens to the variance of the sampling distribution of the mean $\sigma_{\bar{X}}^2$ if the sample size is doubled? What happens to the standard deviation of the sampling distribution of the mean if the sample size is doubled?

8. If you observe a *single* sample mean $\bar{X} = 12$, how can there be a distribution of means?

9. What information do you get from the sampling distribution of any statistic?

10. What might be meant by the statement "In a sample of size $N = 40$ you can count on $\bar{X}$ being only one-half as far from the population mean as in a sample of size $N = 10$"? Does this mean that in every sample of size 40 the sample mean is only one-half as far from μ as the mean of any sample of size 10?

11. Is a sample mean ever equal, usually equal, or always equal to the population mean?

12. Define each of the terms in the Glossary.

13. Suppose that a single measurement is made of the length of a field. Can this be thought of as a sample? If so, from what population? Is it possible to estimate the population variance from these data?

14. We sometimes ask whether two school classes are significantly different, based on the results of some tests. In what populations are we interested?

15. If a sample is obtained by selecting every tenth item, what possible bias could result? Give examples. Why is this not a random sample?

16. Suppose it is desired to estimate the mean family size in a certain town. Would the recording of the family size of a random selection of high-school students be a reasonable way to obtain data?

CLASS EXERCISES

1. Collect the observed values of $\bar{X}$ and s^2 for the samples of size $N = 10$ drawn from Table A-2 (Class Exercise, Chap. 3) into distributions. Draw histograms, and compute the mean $\bar{X}$, the mean s^2, and the variance of $\bar{X}$. Compare these values with the theoretical values.

2. Proceed as in Exercise 1 for the samples drawn from Table A-23.

3. Each student collects the three samples of size 10 from Table A-2 into one sample of size 30 and computes the $\bar{X}$ and s^2 for this sample. Then the results are collected into a distribution of values of $\bar{X}$ for $N = 30$ and into a distribution of values of s^2 for $N = 30$. Compute the mean $\bar{X}$, the mean s^2, and the variance of $\bar{X}$, and compare these numbers with the theoretical values.

4. Compute for each of the samples drawn from Table A-2 the values of the median and of the range, w. Collect the results into distributions, and compute the mean median, the mean range, and the variance of the medians. Compare the estimated sampling distribution of the mean with that of the median. Compare the estimated sampling distribution of s^2 with that of w.

5. Consider the observations 1, 2, 3, 4, 5 as a population. Draw a histogram, and find the mean and variance of the population. From this population draw all possible samples, with replacement, of size 2. Find the mean and variance of the sampling distribution of the means and the mean of the sampling distribution of the variance. Compare these values with the mean and variance of the universe.

6. Consider the population of Exercise 5, and proceed as described there, except sample without replacement.

PROBLEMS

1. Use the table of random numbers to select 10 individuals from the 80 measurements on page 8. Describe exactly how you entered the table and how you decided which individuals to take for the sample. Compute the mean $\bar{X}$ and the variance s^2 for the sample you selected, and compare them with μ and σ^2.

2. Use the random-number table to select 10 individuals from the distribution of s^2 for samples of size 10 recorded in Table 4-3. Describe exactly how you entered the table and how you decided which individuals to take for the sample. Find the mean of the 10 s^2 values selected, and compare with σ^2.

3. Suppose 500 samples of size 20 each are to be taken from Table A-2 and $\bar{X}$ and s^2 recorded for each. Approximately what values would you expect to find for (*a*) the mean $\bar{X}$, (*b*) the variance of the $\bar{X}$'s, and (*c*) the mean of the 500 values of s^2? *Ans.* $\mu = 0$; $\sigma^2/20 = .05$; $\sigma^2 = 1$.

4. A population of tags is formed with the distribution of numbers in Table 2-1. Suppose 1,000 random samples of size 5 each are taken from the population and $\bar{X}$ and s^2 recorded for each sample. Approximately what values would you expect to find for (*a*) the mean $\bar{X}$, (*b*) the variance of the $\bar{X}$'s, (*c*) the mean of the s^2's? *Ans.* $\mu = 60.7$; $\sigma^2/5 = (276.4/80)/5 = .691$; $\sigma^2 = 276.4/80 = 3.455$.

5. Suppose in a population of 1,000 tags 500 are marked 1 and 500 are marked 0. Verify $\mu = .5$, $\sigma^2 = .25$. Suppose 100 random samples of size 10 are taken from the population and $\bar{X}$ is recorded for each sample. Approximately what values would you expect to find for (*a*) the mean of the $\bar{X}$'s, (*b*) the variance of the $\bar{X}$'s. *Ans.* $\mu = [500(1) + 500(0)]/1{,}000 = .5$,

$$\sigma^2 = [500(1^2) + 500(0^2) - 500^2/1{,}000]/1{,}000 = .25;$$

$\mu = .5$; $\sigma^2/10 = .025$.

CHAPTER 5

THE NORMAL DISTRIBUTION

One of the most important frequency distributions in statistics is the normal distribution. Many of the procedures in later chapters will be based on a knowledge of this distribution. Its physical appearance is that of a symmetrical bell-shaped curve, extending infinitely far in both positive and negative directions. Its use is the same as that of any other distribution curve. The relative frequency with which a variable will take on values between two points is the area under the curve between the two points on the horizontal axis. It is well to note that not all symmetrical bell-shaped distributions are normal distributions, and the words *normal distribution* refer to the fact that the area under the curve is distributed in a specified manner which will be discussed later. The word normal used in referring to a distribution is used in this sense throughout this text and not as the opposite of abnormal.

5-1. Equation of the Normal Curve

The equation of the normal curve is

$$Y = \frac{1}{\sigma\sqrt{2\pi}} e^{-\frac{1}{2}\left(\frac{X-\mu}{\sigma}\right)^2}$$

where π = a constant (approximately 3.1416)

e = a constant (approximately 2.7183)

σ = a parameter (it is equal to the standard deviation of the distribution; different normal curves may have different standard deviations and thus different values for σ; however, for a given distribution σ is constant)

μ = a parameter (it is equal to the mean of the distribution; different normal curves may have different means, hence different values for μ; however, for a given distribution μ is constant)

X = abscissa, measurement or score marked on horizontal axis

Y = ordinate, height of curve corresponding to an assigned value of X

The total area between this curve and the X axis is one square unit. Thus the area under the curve between the points, say, $X = a$ and $X = b$ is equal to the proportion of cases which lie between the two points. It is very important, therefore, to be able to find the area under sections of the curve.

It is sometimes desirable to construct a normal-distribution curve which has the same area as a given histogram. In this case the equation is

$$Y = \frac{Ni}{\sigma\sqrt{2\pi}} e^{-\frac{1}{2}\left(\frac{X-\mu}{\sigma}\right)^2}$$

where N = number of cases observed

i = length of class interval used to draw the histogram

The area under such a curve is Ni square units. If the histogram is drawn with the proportion of observations in each interval as the height of that interval, then the N is replaced by 1 and the area under the curve is i square units.

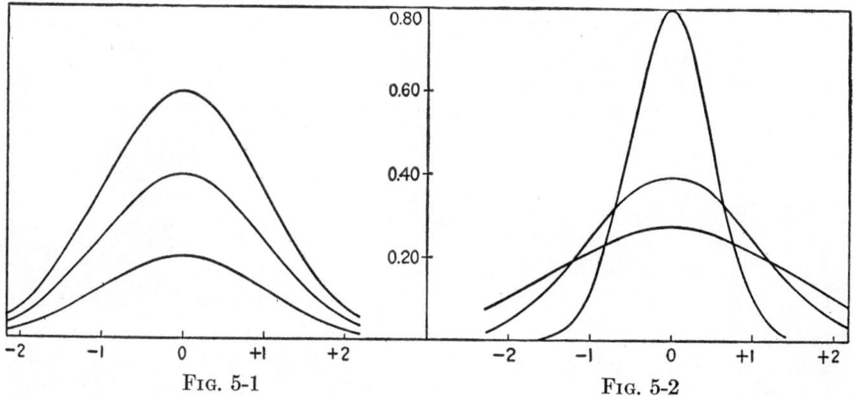

FIG. 5-1 FIG. 5-2

Figures 5-1 and 5-2 indicate the shape of the normal curve. In Fig. 5-1 the three curves each have the same mean μ and the same standard deviation σ, but different total areas Ni. The area under each of the three curves in Fig. 5-1 is distributed the same proportionately to the total area under the curve. For example, the area between μ and $\mu + \sigma$ is in each case 34.13 per cent of the area under the curve.

In order to facilitate comparison of different normal curves, as well as to keep the concept of "distribution" as having total area 1, we shall usually draw the curves with total area 1. This is particularly advantageous since the amount of area between any two values is also the proportion of the total area.

Figure 5-2 compares normal curves with the same area. The three curves drawn each have the same mean μ but different standard deviations σ. A curve with area concentrated closely about the mean has a smaller value of σ, while a curve with area less concentrated about the mean has a larger value of σ.

Normal curves all extend infinitely far both to the right and to the left. They are all symmetrical about $X = \mu$, that is, about the mean. They are all concave downward for X within 1σ of the mean and concave upward for X farther than 1σ from the mean. The proportion of area under a normal curve between any two values is completely determined by μ and σ.

5-2. An Example of the Normal Distribution

One of the most useful applications of the normal distribution is in the sampling distribution of the mean. To demonstrate in an actual case, we shall construct a universe and approximate the sampling distribution of the mean experimentally.

Suppose our universe contains an equal frequency of quantities ranging from 60 to 69. To correspond to the scores in our experiment, we take 300 tags, 30 labeled 60, 30 labeled 61, and so on, to 69. We place the tags in a box, mix them thoroughly, and draw a sample of two tags ($N = 2$). We compute the mean of the scores on the two tags. We repeat this 200 times (200 samples of size $N = 2$), record the results in a frequency table (Table 5-1), and draw a histogram (Fig. 5-3). The same procedure is carried out for samples of size 4, 8, and 16. Note that $Ns_{\bar{X}}^2$ is approximately equal to σ^2. Why is it not exactly equal to σ^2?

The top histogram in Fig. 5-3 is the frequency distribution of the universe. The approximation to the bell-shaped curve may be noted. The universe does not have a normal distribution, but the sampling distribution of the means tends to be more normal than the universe. The following theorem states the situation more explicitly:

If the distribution of the universe has a finite variance, the sampling distribution of the means of random samples will be approximately normal if the sample size is sufficiently large.

For most practical examples the universe will have a finite variance, and thus this condition is not very restrictive. The "sufficiently large" is more troublesome since it depends upon the distribution of the universe, which is usually unknown. If, however, the distribution of the universe is exactly normal, then the sampling distribution of the mean of any size sample, even as small as $N = 1$ or $N = 2$, will be exactly normal. If the population is reasonably symmetric and not too disperse, a moderate sample size will usually make the distribution approximately normal.

Our use of "approximately normal" is, so far, largely intuitive. We say that a histogram is approximately normal when the areas of the rectangles are approximately equal to the corresponding areas under a normal curve. In Sec. 5-5 there is discussed a simple method of examining a set of data for marked deviations from normality.

For the above examples it can be seen that the mean of the sample means falls fairly close to the mean of the universe, μ, in every case. A

TABLE 5-1. FREQUENCY DISTRIBUTION OF OBSERVED MEANS OF OBSERVATIONS DRAWN FROM A UNIFORM POPULATION WITH $\mu = 64.5$ AND $\sigma^2 = 8.25$

$N = 1$ (universe)		$N = 2$		$N = 4$		$N = 8$		$N = 16$	
X	f	$\bar{X}$	f	$\bar{X}$	f	$\bar{X}$	f	$\bar{X}$	f
69	30	68.75	9	68.50	3	67.250	2	66.1875	3
68	30	67.75	12	67.75	5	66.625	4	65.8750	5
67	30	66.75	23	67.00	4	66.000	26	65.5625	21
66	30	65.75	37	66.25	21	65.375	36	65.2500	27
65	30	64.75	33	65.50	38	64.750	40	64.9375	24
64	30	63.75	38	64.75	35	64.125	43	64.6250	25
63	30	62.75	22	64.00	53	63.500	30	64.3125	35
62	30	61.75	13	63.25	25	62.875	15	64.0000	26
61	30	60.75	13	62.50	8	62.250	3	63.6875	18
60	30			61.75	8	61.625	1	63.3750	15
								63.0625	1
	300		200		200		200		200
Mean $\bar{X}$	...	.....	64.66	.....	64.63	......	64.57	....	64.58
Var. $\bar{X}$.	...	.....	4.173	.....	1.868	......	1.105	....	.509
$s_{\bar{X}}$.....	...	.....	2.043	.....	1.367	......	1.051	....	.714
$Ns_{\bar{X}}^2$...	...	.....	8.35	.....	7.47	......	8.84	....	8.14

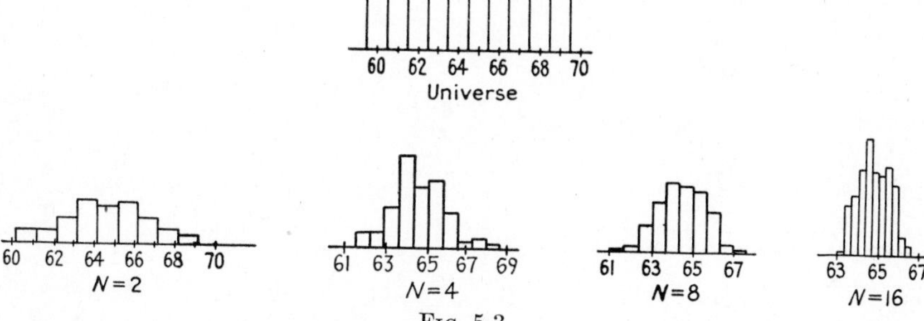

FIG. 5-3

statistic whose sampling distribution has a mean equal to some universe parameter is an *unbiased estimate* of that parameter.

For example, as was pointed out in Chap. 4, the arithmetic mean of a sample is an unbiased estimate of μ, and s^2 is an unbiased estimate of the population variance σ^2. If we use a statistic which is an unbiased estimate of a parameter we shall estimate the parameter correctly "on the average." This does not say that we are likely to be close to the correct value of the parameter. The chance of being close depends not only upon the center of the sampling distribution but also upon the dispersion of the distribution. The standard deviation is frequently used to measure dispersion and, in the case of an unbiased statistic, a small standard deviation indicates a large chance of being close.

5-3. The Cumulative Normal Distribution

The cumulative-distribution function gives the relative frequency with which observations will fall below (to the left of) any specified value. This relative frequency is the area under the distribution curve from minus infinity to the specified value.

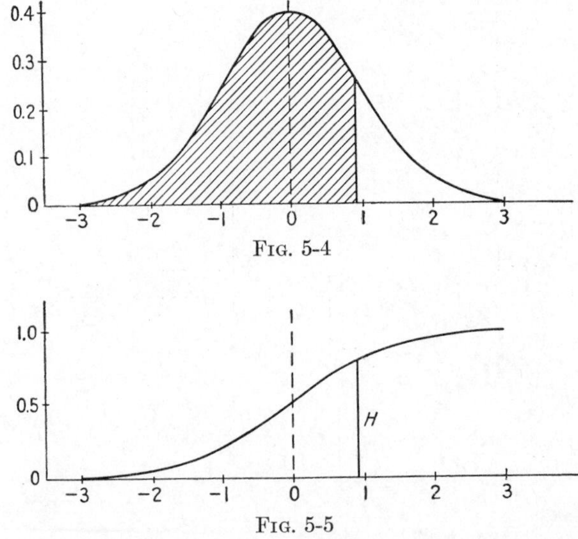

FIG. 5-4

FIG. 5-5

In the case of the normal distribution the areas under the curve from minus infinity to the point $(X - \mu)/\sigma$ have been tabled (Table A-4). This table is entered with the value of $z = \dfrac{X - \mu}{\sigma}$, and the cumulated area is read from the area column. Note that μ and σ are constant and X is the variable; however, the table must be entered by way of the deviation of X from the mean measured in σ units. The advantage of this method is that the same table can be used for any value of μ and σ.

The height H indicated in Fig. 5-5 is numerically equal to the area shaded under the normal curve in Fig. 5-4 and thus gives the frequency with which observations less than or equal to any given value of X will occur.

5-4. Areas under the Normal Curve

The area under the normal curve between the points $X = a$ and $X = b$ $(a < b)$ gives the relative frequency with which cases fall between a and b. To find this area, first find the area from minus infinity to $X = b$, then find the area from minus infinity to $X = a$, and subtract the second area from the first.*

Example 1. In a normal distribution $\mu = 30$, $\sigma = 5$. What proportion of cases fall between 20 and 35?

Answer.

$$X = 20 \text{ gives } \frac{X - \mu}{\sigma} = \frac{20 - 30}{5} = -2.0$$

$$X = 35 \text{ gives } \frac{X - \mu}{\sigma} = \frac{35 - 30}{5} = 1.0$$

Table A-4 gives the area to the left of -2.0 to be .0228 and the area to the left of 1.0 to be .8413. Thus, the area (proportion of cases) between $X = 20$ and $X = 35$ is $.8413 - .0228 = .8185$. 81.85 per cent of cases are between 20 and 35 (see Fig. 5-6).

Example 2. Between what values does the central 95 per cent of all the area under the normal curve lie?

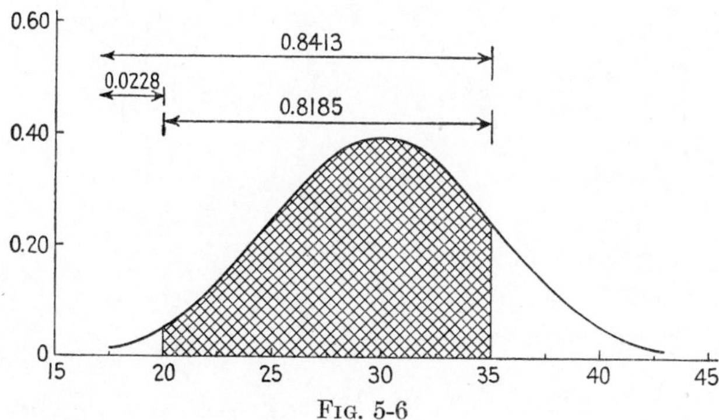

FIG. 5-6

* The mathematical notation for the area between $X = a$ and $X = b$ is given by use of an integral sign.

$$\text{Area} = \int_a^b \frac{1}{\sigma\sqrt{2\pi}} e^{-\frac{1}{2}\left(\frac{X-\mu}{\sigma}\right)^2} dx$$

Actually in this case the integral sign is useful only as a symbol, and the area must be computed by approximate methods.

Answer. Table A-4 shows that 2.5 per cent (half of 5 per cent) of the area is below $\frac{X - \mu}{\sigma} = -1.96$ (or $X - \mu = -1.96\sigma$, or $X = \mu - 1.96\sigma$) and 2.5 per cent lies above $\frac{X - \mu}{\sigma} = 1.96$. Thus 95 per cent of the area lies between $X = \mu - 1.96\sigma$ and $X = \mu + 1.96\sigma$. If, for example, $\mu = 7$ and $\sigma = 2$, then the middle 95 per cent of the area is between $X = 3.08$ and $X = 10.92$.

Example 3. In a normal distribution $\mu = 163$, $\sigma = 12$. Where are P_{10}, P_{50}, and P_{95}?

Answer. P_{10} is a point having 10 per cent of the area below it. Table A-4 shows this point to be $\frac{X - 163}{12} = -1.28$ [or $X = 163 + 12(-1.28)$], and thus $P_{10} = 148$. Similarly $P_{50} = 163$, and $P_{95} = 183$.

Example 4. Samples of 25 items were taken from a normal distribution with $\mu = 50$ and $\sigma = 10$. What proportion of the sample means would lie between 48 and 52?

Answer. From Chap. 4 we know that the mean of the sampling distribution of the $\bar{X}$'s is the same as the mean of the universe; thus, $\mu_{\bar{X}} = 50$. We also know that $\sigma_{\bar{X}}^2 = (\sigma^2/N) = \frac{100}{25} = 4$, so that $\sigma_{\bar{X}} = 2$. As we have indicated in Sec. 5-2, the sampling distribution of the mean of samples from a normal universe is a normal distribution. Thus, we can make use of Table A-4 with $\mu = 50$ and $\sigma = 2$. The area below 48 is obtained by entering Table A-4 with the value $\frac{X - \mu}{\sigma} = \frac{48 - 50}{2} = -1.0$. The area below 52 is obtained by using $\frac{X - \mu}{\sigma} = \frac{52 - 50}{2} = +1.0$. These areas are .1587 and .8413, and the area between 48 and 52 is $.8413 - .1587 = .6826$. Hence 68 per cent of sample means may be expected to lie between 48 and 52. If we choose a single sample, we have a 68 per cent chance of finding the $\bar{X}$ between 48 and 52.

Example 5. Some values from Table A-4 are used frequently enough to make them worthy of special note. Between what two points does the central 50 per cent of the cases in a normal distribution fall? The central 99 per cent?

Answer. $\frac{X - \mu}{\sigma} = -.674$ has 25 per cent of the area below it, and $\frac{X - \mu}{\sigma} = +.674$ has 75 per cent of the area below it. Thus, 50 per cent of the area lies between $\mu - .674\sigma$ and $\mu + .674\sigma$.

The middle 99 per cent falls between $\mu - 2.576\sigma$ and $\mu + 2.576\sigma$. These central areas can also be obtained directly from Table A-3.

5-5. Normal-probability Paper

By changing the vertical scale on the graph of the cumulative-normal-distribution curve, it is possible to have the cumulative-normal-distribution curve take on the shape of a straight line. This can be visualized if we think of the curve as plotted on an elastic sheet and the sheet stretched in an appropriate fashion. Figure 5-7 shows the cumulative-normal-distribution curve and indicates the stretching necessary. To the left of the mean the cumulative curve should be pulled down, and on the right of the mean it should be pulled up until it coincides with the dotted line.

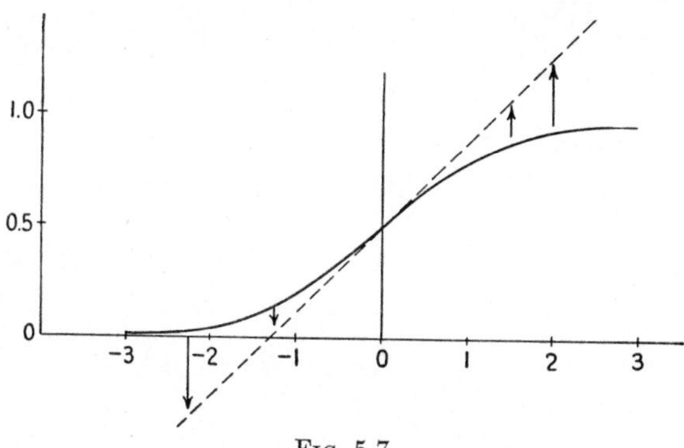

FIG. 5-7

This, of course, means that the scale on the vertical axis is changed. Special paper, scaled appropriately, can be purchased. It is called *probability paper*, although a more appropriate term would be *normal-probability paper*, since it is made to use with the normal distribution. In Fig. 5-8 is shown a sheet of this type of graph paper. The horizontal axis is marked for a mean of 100 and a standard deviation of 8 units. The line drawn represents the cumulative normal distribution with $\mu = 100$ and $\sigma = 8$.

Note that percentiles can be read directly from the right-hand scale of this graph. To find P_{20}, for example, look for 20 on the vertical scale, then move horizontally until you meet the cumulative-distribution line. Then read the horizontal scale directly under this point.

The values recorded in Table A-4 can also be read from this paper by using z scores on the horizontal scale. At least two percentile values must be known to draw the line, but once the line is drawn any percentile can be read from it. Thus, if we want the value of P_{70}, we find 70 on the vertical scale, move horizontally to the line, and read the z score directly below the intersection. The student should verify, from Fig. 5-8, that this procedure gives the same value, $z = .525$, as Table A-4. To find the percentile rank of $z = -1.5$, we find the height of the line above $z = -1.5$ to be 7.

Probability paper may also be used to indicate whether the distribution

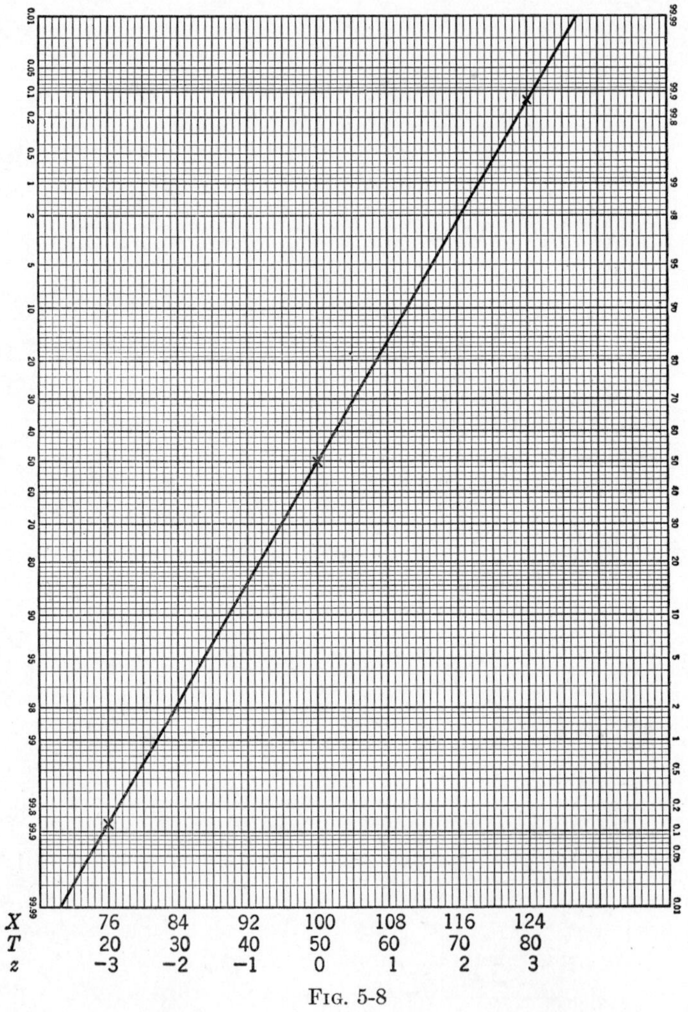

FIG. 5-8

of a given sample is approximately normal. This is done by plotting the cumulative distribution of the sample upon the probability paper and then noting how closely this curve approximates a straight line. If the curve is approximately a straight line, the distribution is approximately normal. If it deviates considerably from a straight line, then the distribution is not normal. The fact that the sample distribution gives a curve which is not a straight line is an indication that the population from which it came is not normal.

We have plotted, on normal-probability paper, the cumulative curves for 200 observations of $\bar{X}$ and s^2 for samples of size 10. These results are

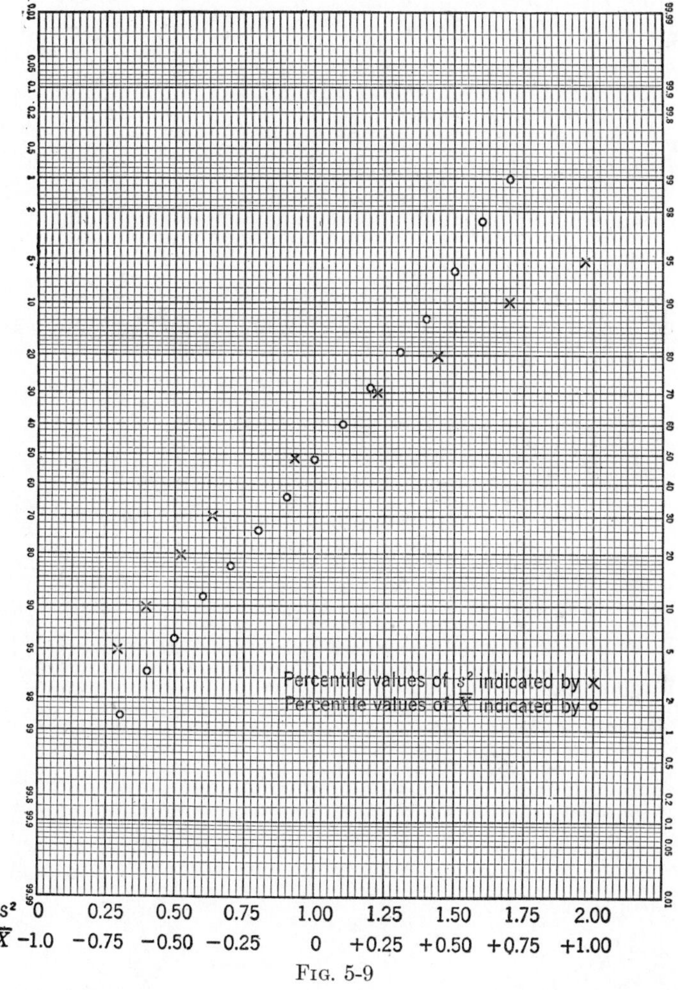

FIG. 5-9

recorded in Table 4-3. Upon examining these curves (Fig. 5-9) we note that the distribution of $\bar{X}$ is approximately a straight line, while that of s^2 is markedly curved. This gives empirical evidence, or proof, of our statement that the sampling distribution of the mean is approximately normal and indicates that the distribution of s^2 is not normal.

5-6. Standardized Normal Scores (T Scores)

It is common practice in educational and psychological studies to standardize the scores of examinations. Knowing that a student's score on an examination is 63 gives no information about the comparative standing of the student. Also, saying that a man is 70 inches tall does not in itself indicate whether he is exceptionally tall, or of medium height, or short. In no case does a single measurement give us a great deal of information. A single measurement selected from a known distribution tells us much more, for then we can say whether the item picked is exceptionally large or small. In fact, we can say what proportion of cases fall above or below it. Many times it is difficult to look at an entire distribution, and we should like some way of designating a single score (measurement) so that its value tells at a glance whether it is a comparatively large or small value. Z scores, introduced in Chap. 3, perform this function to a certain extent. A Z score of 70 is two standard deviations above the mean and thus probably a very high score. We still would not know exactly what proportion of the cases are above 70. If the distribution is normal, there are about 2.3 per cent of the scores above a Z score of 70. In a normal distribution there are

50 % above a Z score of 50
16 % above a Z score of 60
7 % above a Z score of 65
2.3% above a Z score of 70
.6% above a Z score of 75
.1% above a Z score of 80

Thus, a Z score in a *normal distribution* gives us considerable information. This indicates a need for a normalized Z score. Such scores, called T scores, are computed in the following manner: Suppose a proportion p of the observed cases fall below a particular value of the variable. We shall assign to $(T - 50)/10$, $(T - \mu)/\sigma$, a value from the normal table (Table A-4) such that a proportion p of the area of the normal curve lies to the left of that value. Thus, if a value is larger than 90 per cent of the cases observed, we shall say

$$\frac{T - 50}{10} = 1.28 \qquad \text{or} \qquad T - 50 = 10(1.28)$$

and thus the T score for this variable is $T = 50 + 10(1.28) = 63$. Three examples which illustrate this method of finding T scores are given below.

T **Score for Grades.** Suppose the following table of grades and frequencies is given. What T score would be assigned to each grade?

Grade	*Frequency*
A	12
B	18
C	30
D	15
F	5
	80

Below (to the left of) the center of the F rectangle in the histogram there are 2.5 units out of a total of 80 units of area. This is based on the premise that 2.5 of the 5 F grades were below the middle. Thus the proportion of cases below the center grade of F is 2.5/80 = .03125, and this corresponds to $\frac{T-50}{10} = -1.9$. In the area column in Table A-4 we find that .03125 lies between .0287, the entry for $\frac{T-\mu}{\sigma} = -1.90$ and .0322, the entry for $\frac{T-\mu}{\sigma} = -1.85$. The approximate value -1.9 is sufficiently accurate to find T to the nearest integer. Thus the T score for a grade of F is $T = 50 + 10(-1.9) = 31$. Below the D center there are 12.5 units of area (5 from the F and one-half of the 15 D's). The proportion of cases below a D is 12.5/80 = .156. Table A-4 gives approximately $\frac{T-50}{10} = -1.0$ and $T = 50 + 10(-1.0) = 40$. A form outlining the complete calculations for this problem is shown in Table 5-2.

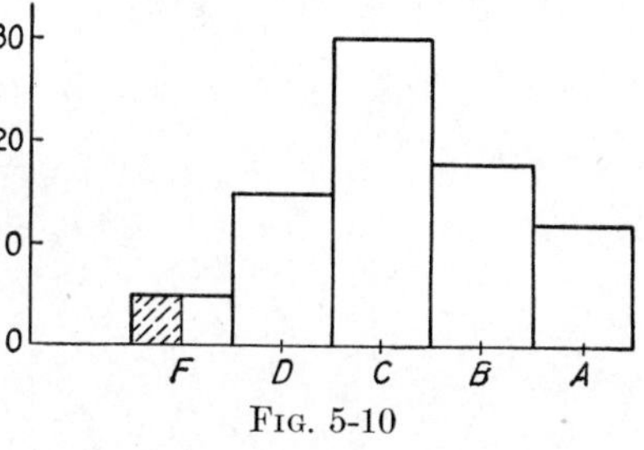

FIG. 5-10

TABLE 5-2

Grade	Freq.	Cum. freq. to mid-point	Cum. prop. to mid-point	$\frac{T-50}{10}$ (from Table A-4)	T score
A	12	74	.925	+1.4	64
B	18	59	.738	+ .6	56
C	30	35	.438	− .2	48
D	15	12.5	.156	−1.0	40
F	5	2.5	.031	−1.9	31
	80				

T Scores for Ranks. Suppose that a group of scores have been assigned ranks (i.e., the highest score is assigned rank 1, the next highest rank 2, etc.). These ranks can be thought of as grades with one score to each grade, and the T score for each rank can be computed by the method illustrated above. For example, suppose that five scores have been given a rank order. Table 5-3 shows the computations to find the T scores:

TABLE 5-3

Rank	Freq.	Cum. freq. to mid-point	Cum. prop. to mid-point	$\frac{T-50}{10}$	T
1	1	4.5	.9	+1.3	63
2	1	3.5	.7	+ .5	55
3	1	2.5	.5	0	50
4	1	1.5	.3	− .5	45
5	1	.5	.1	−1.3	37

T Scores for Data Arranged in a Frequency Table. T scores for numerical data are obtained in exactly the same way as T scores for grades. Table 5-4 shows the computation and the results.

TABLE 5-4

X	Freq.	Cum. freq. to mid-point	Cum. prop. to mid-point	$\frac{T-50}{10}$	T
18.5	5	37.5	.94	+1.6	66
17.5	6	32.0	.80	+ .8	58
16.5	8	25.0	.63	+ .3	53
15.5	12	15.0	.38	− .3	47
14.5	7	5.5	.14	−1.1	39
13.5	2	1.0	.03	−1.9	31

T scores can be read from normal-probability paper which has been marked with $\mu = 50$ and $\sigma = 10$ on the horizontal scale and has the corresponding cumulative line drawn. The line drawn on Fig. 5-8 can be used for this purpose if the T scale marked on the horizontal is used.

To find T scores by use of this paper, find the cumulative proportion as was done in the examples above, and then read the score from the horizontal scale.

The student should verify for the last example that corresponding to $X = 17.5$, which has a cumulative proportion of .80, the point on the line is above $T = 59$.

The use of this prepared paper omits the reference to Table A-4, the multiplication by 10, and the addition of 50.

5-7. Fitting a Normal Curve to a Histogram

In this section we discuss the "fitting" of a normal curve to some given data. This means writing the equation of, and drawing the graph of, a normal curve having the same mean and standard deviation as the given data. It is worth noting that a normal curve can be fitted to any histogram. Whether or not the curve accurately pictures the frequency distribution is another matter. The "fit" may be good or bad.

If $\bar{X}$ is the mean and s the standard deviation of the sample, the equation of the curve is

$$Y = \frac{iN}{s}\left[\frac{1}{\sqrt{2\pi}} e^{-\frac{1}{2}\left(\frac{X-\bar{X}}{s}\right)^2}\right]$$

The value of the factor in brackets is given in Table A-3. This table is entered with values of $(X - \bar{X})/s$, and the ordinate column gives the value of $\frac{1}{\sqrt{2\pi}} e^{-\frac{1}{2}\left(\frac{X-\bar{X}}{s}\right)^2}$. This value must be multiplied by iN/s to give the height of the curve for a histogram of total area iN.

The example in Table 5-5 shows the method of finding points on the curve. We have drawn a normal curve with the same mean and standard deviation as the observed distribution of $\bar{X}$ for samples of size 40 as recorded in Table 4-3. For this distribution we have $\bar{X} = .02$, $s = .16$, $i = .05$, $N = 200$, $(iN/s) = 62.5$.

Enough values of X should be chosen to permit sketching a smooth curve to the accuracy desired. In this example the mean was taken for

TABLE 5-5

X	$\frac{X - \bar{X}}{s}$	$\frac{1}{\sqrt{2\pi}} e^{-\frac{1}{2}\left(\frac{X-\bar{X}}{s}\right)^2}$ (from Table A-3)	$Y = \frac{iN}{s} \times$ (col. 3) $= 62.5 \times$ (col. 3)
.50	3.0	.004	.3
.42	2.5	.018	1.1
.34	2.0	.054	3.4
.26	1.5	.130	8.1
.18	1.0	.242	15.1
.10	.5	.352	22.0
.02	0	.399	24.9
−.06	− .5	.352	22.0
−.14	−1.0	.242	15.1
−.22	−1.5	.130	8.1
−.30	−2.0	.054	3.4
− 38	−2.5	.018	1.1
−.46	−3.0	.004	.3

one value of X, and then points were taken on either side of the mean at intervals of $.5\sigma$. The computation is simplified by this procedure, but we must compute the X values in the first column in Table 5-5 to use for plotting the points on the curve. For example, when $\frac{X - \bar{X}}{s} = 2.0$, we have $X = .34$.

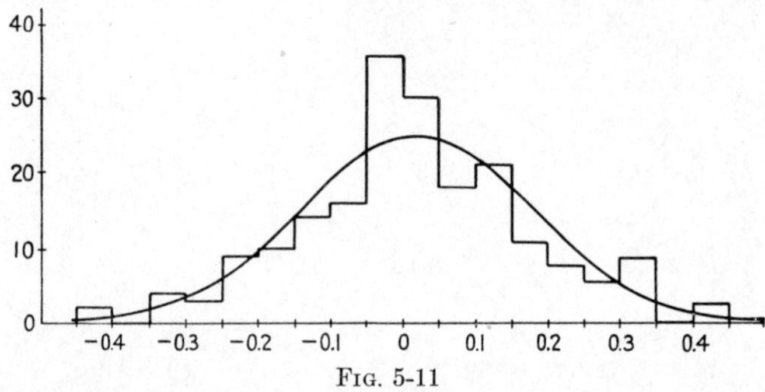

Fig. 5-11

5-8. Sampling from a Dichotomous (Yes or No) Population

Frequently populations can be divided into two groups on the basis of some characteristic. For example, a population of animals may be divided into males and females, a population of voters can be divided into those voting for a Republican candidate and those voting for other candidates (or those voting yes on a proposition and those voting no), a population of diseased people can be divided into those recovering and those who do not, a population of projectiles divided into those which are defective and those which are not.

We can record observations of this type in a manner similar to that used for continuous measurements if we assign the number 1 ($X = 1$) to each member of the population belonging to one group (say, group A) and the number zero ($X = 0$) to the members belonging to the other group (say, group B). If we take a sample from the population, the sum of these assigned numbers $\sum_{i=1}^{N} X_i$, which is the sum of 1s and 0s, will be the number in the sample belonging to group A and the mean $\bar{X}$ of the 1s and 0s will be the proportion of the sample belonging to group A. As noted earlier in this chapter, the sampling distribution of $\bar{X}$ from any population with a finite variance will be approximately normal if the sample size is sufficiently large and the variance of the sampling distribution is σ^2/N. These results apply to our present problem.

For illustration, we construct a population of 1,000 red beads and 1,000 white beads. We assign the number 1 to the red beads and the number 0 to the white beads. The population frequency distribution is recorded in

TABLE 5-6

X	f	fX	fX^2
1	1,000	1,000	1,000
0	1,000	0	0
Total........	2,000	1,000	1,000

$$\mu = \frac{1{,}000}{2{,}000} = .5$$

$$\sigma^2 = \frac{1{,}000 - \frac{(1{,}000)^2}{2{,}000}}{2{,}000} = .25$$

$$\sigma = \sqrt{.25} = .5$$

Table 5-6 and shows the computation of the mean and variance.

To approximate the sampling distribution of $\bar{X}$, we take 100 samples of size $N = 10$ each and record the number ΣX_i and the proportion $\bar{X}$ of red beads for each. The experiment is repeated with 100 samples of size $N = 20$ and 100 samples of size $N = 40$. The results are in Table 5-7. Note that the mean of the $\bar{X}$'s is in each case close to $\mu = .5$ and the variance is about equal to $\sigma^2/N = .25/N$.

TABLE 5-7. OBSERVED PROPORTIONS OF RED BEADS IN SAMPLES OF SIZES 10, 20, AND 40 FROM A POPULATION CONTAINING 50 PER CENT RED BEADS ($\mu = .5$ AND $\sigma^2 = .25$)

$N = 10$			$N = 20$			$N = 40$		
No. red	Prop. ($\bar{X}$)	f	No. red	Prop. ($\bar{X}$)	f	No. red	Prop. ($\bar{X}$)	f
10	1.0	0	16	.80	1	28–29	.7125	2
9	.9	0	15	.75	1	26–27	.6625	5
8	.8	7	14	.70	5	24–25	.6125	9
7	.7	11	13	.65	10	22–23	.5625	16
6	.6	22	12	.60	12	20–21	.5125	24
5	.5	20	11	.55	16	18–19	.4625	24
4	.4	18	10	.50	15	16–17	.4125	10
3	.3	14	9	.45	13	14–15	.3625	8
2	.2	6	8	.40	10	12–13	.3125	2
1	.1	2	7	.35	7			
0	0	0	6	.30	5			
			5	.25	3			
			4	.20	2			
Mean $\bar{X}$...	.493			.500			.503	
Var. $\bar{X}$....	.0291			.0161			.0074	
N var. $\bar{X}$..	.291			.322			.296	

The three distributions in Table 5-7 are pictured in Fig. 5-12 as histograms with normal curves sketched over them.

Formulas giving μ and σ^2 for a population containing a proportion p of 1s and a proportion $1 - p$ of 0s are $\mu = p$ and $\sigma^2 = p(1 - p)$. This result was given for $p = \frac{1}{2}$ in Table 5-6. Table 5-8 records values of p and $\sigma^2 = p(1 - p)$, $\sigma = \sqrt{p(1 - p)}$ taken from Table A-28. Note that there is little variation in σ for proportions between .3 and .7. Therefore, if p is between .3 and .7, even though we do not know exactly where,

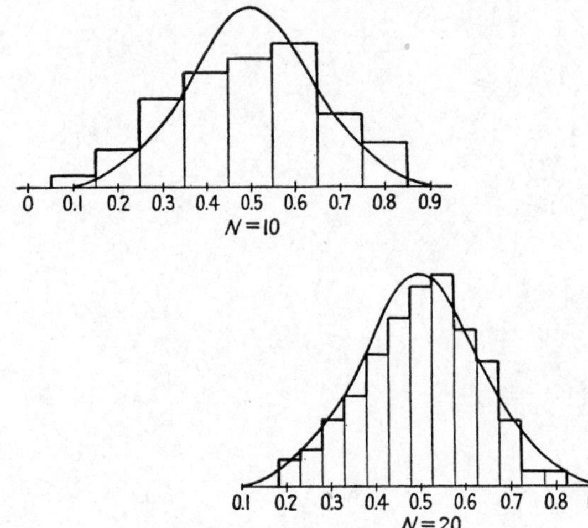

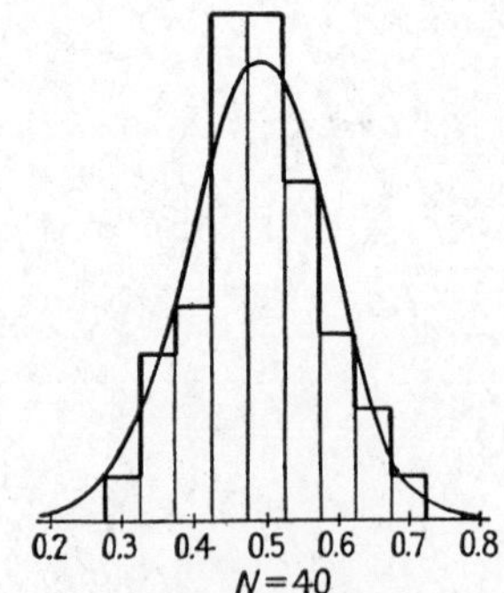

FIG. 5-12

we may use $\sigma = .5$, which will be at least as large as σ and not be in error by more than 10 per cent. Also in Table 5-8 are values of $.5/\sqrt{N}$ for several values of N.

We shall apply these formulas for μ and σ^2, together with the assumption that the sample proportion $\bar{X}$ is approximately normal, in an example.

Example. Suppose a sample of $N = 100$ people is taken from a population containing 50 per cent men and 50 per cent women. What is the chance that the proportion of men in the sample will be between .48 and .52, that is of the number of men being 48, 49, 50, 51, 52?

Answer. We note that $\mu = .5$, $\sigma = \sqrt{(.5)(.5)} = .5$, and

$$\sigma_{\bar{X}} = \frac{.5}{\sqrt{100}} = .05$$

Since we are using a continuous distribution to approximate the distribution of observed proportions, we shall obtain better accuracy if we consider that the number of men is between 47.5 and 52.5, a range of five

TABLE 5-8

p	$\sigma^2 = p(1-p)$	$\sigma = \sqrt{p(1-p)}$	$1/\sigma$
.1 or .9	.09	.30	3.33
.2 or .8	.16	.40	2.50
.3 or .7	.21	.46	2.18
.4 or .6	.24	.49	2.04
.5	.25	.50	2.00

N	$.5/\sqrt{N}$	N	$.5/\sqrt{N}$	N	$.5/\sqrt{N}$
10	.1581	50	.0707	500	.02236
15	.1291	100	.0500	1,000	.01581
20	.1118	200	.03536	5,000	.00707
25	.1000	300	.02887	10,000	.00500
40	.0791	400	.02500	1,000,000	.00050

units corresponding to the five quantities 48, 49, 50, 51, 52. The reason for this correction can easily be seen from Fig. 5-12, where normal curves have been drawn over the discrete distributions. By referring to the pictures for $N = 10$ and $N = 20$ in Fig. 5-12 (where the data have not been grouped into larger intervals) we can see that the chance of $\bar{X}$ having any particular value is represented by a rectangle which extends halfway to the next possible value for $\bar{X}$. Since it is the area of these rectangles which we wish to approximate, we must find the area under the normal curve which corresponds to the rectangles. In the figure for $N = 10$ the rectangle for $\bar{X} = .5$ extends from .45 to .55, and in the figure for $N = 20$ the rectangle for $\bar{X} = .5$ extends from .475 to .525. Returning to our example, we note that the five rectangles corresponding to 48, 49, 50, 51,

52 for $N = 100$ will extend from 47.5 to 52.5 or for the proportion $\bar{X}$ from .475 to .525.

The normal deviates z for .475 and for .525 are

$$\frac{\bar{X} - \mu}{\sigma_{\bar{X}}} = \frac{.475 - .5}{.05} = -.5$$

and

$$\frac{\bar{X} - \mu}{\sigma_{\bar{X}}} = \frac{.525 - .5}{.05} = +.5$$

Table A-3 gives the area between $z = -.5$ and $z = +.5$ to be .3829, which is the chance of $\bar{X}$ falling between .475 and .525 or of the number of men being 48, 49, 50, 51, 52. As an additional example, consider a sample of $N = 25$ from the same population. Let us find the chance of the number of men being 12 or 13, that is, either $\bar{X} = .48$ or $\bar{X} = .52$. We consider the number of men being between 11.5 and 13.5, or the proportion $\bar{X}$ between .46 and .54. The values of z corresponding to $\bar{X} = .46$ and .54 are $-.4$ and $+.4$, which from Table A-3 gives a .3108 chance of $\bar{X}$ being .48 or .52. For larger values of N the chance that $\bar{X}$ takes on some value from .48 to .52 increases. For example, for $N = 400$ the chance is .6047.

5-9. Normal Populations

Many practical problems have statistical answers based on the "assumption" that the distribution of the population is normal. As was noted before, the truth of this assumption may be checked by plotting the sample cumulative-percentage points on normal-probability paper. Frequently in practice the variable of interest is not normally distributed. It may be possible, however, to modify the measuring device in such a way that the distribution is at least approximately normal. If the entire population is measured, T scores may be computed to "normalize" the population, but this normalization is of dubious value for a sample.

Often a research worker has sufficient data and enough experience with his material to be able to specify the type of transformation of measurement which will give a normally distributed variable. Sometimes there are general classes of problems for which a standard change of variable is employed. For example, in dosage-response or sensitivity experiments it often happens that the logarithm of the dosage concentration is approximately normally distributed. Section 10-9 discusses various types of transformations frequently used.

GLOSSARY

cumulative normal distribution
curve fitting
normal curve
normal-probability paper
T score
unbiased estimate

DISCUSSION QUESTIONS

1. Suppose we multiplied by 6 every number in Table A-2 and then added 20 to each new number. Describe the resulting distribution. Is it still a normal distribution?

2. What is a normal distribution? How many normal curves are there?

3. How many parameters determine a normal distribution?

4. Is there always 95 per cent of the area under a normal curve between $X = -1.96$ and $X = 1.96$?

5. Is a normal curve always bell-shaped? Is a bell-shaped distribution curve always a normal curve?

6. What use of the standard deviation has been emphasized in this chapter?

7. How do you interpret the area under a section of a normal curve?

8. What is a method of checking to see whether or not a sample is approximately normally distributed?

9. Can a sample be exactly normally distributed?

10. Why would one wish to "fit" a normal curve to a histogram? Is there any other way to accomplish the same purpose?

11. Explain the difference between the standard deviation of the sampling distribution of single observations and the standard deviation of the sampling distribution of means. Why is the standard deviation of means especially useful?

12. Distinguish between a Z score of 60 and a T score of 60.

13. What property does normal-probability paper have?

14. What distributions can you expect to be approximately normal? Describe experiments to "prove" your answer. Is the word prove used correctly here?

15. Define each term in the Glossary.

16. What justification is there for the use of T scores?

CLASS EXERCISES

1. Using a box of 500 white beads and 1,000 red beads, draw samples of size $N = 20$. Form an estimated sampling distribution of the number of red beads in a sample, as was done in Sec. 5-8. Verify that the mean of the sampling distribution is two-thirds of 20. Plot the observed cumulative distribution on normal-probability paper, and verify that the distribution is approximately normal.

2. Plot the estimated sampling distribution of $\bar{X}$, of the samples of size $N = 10$ from Table A-2 drawn for the Class Exercise in Chap. 3, on normal-probability paper, and verify that the distribution is approximately normal (actually since the population is normal the sampling distribution of $\bar{X}$ is exactly normal).

3. Perform the operations described in Exercise 2 with the samples from Table A-23.

4. Perform the operations described in Exercise 2 with the samples of size 30 from Table A-2.

5. Draw, on normal-probability paper, the observed distributions of s^2 for samples of size 10 and of size 30 from Table A-2. Verify that the distribution for samples of size 30 is closer to a normal distribution than the distribution for samples of size 10.

PROBLEMS

1. In a normal distribution $\mu = 30$, and $\sigma = 5$. Find:

(*a*) The area below 24.

(*b*) The area between 24 and 36.
(*c*) The area between 30 and 40.
(*d*) The area above 37.
(*e*) The point that has 95 per cent of the area below it.
(*f*) The two points containing the middle 90 per cent of the area.

2. In a normal distribution $\mu = 47.6$, and $\sigma = 16.2$. Find:
(*a*) The chance of a single observation being larger than 50.
(*b*) Two points such that a single observation has 97 per cent chance of falling between them.
(*c*) P_{10}, P_{30}, and P_{99}.
(*d*) Standard (z) scores for 63.8 and 39.5.

3. In a normal population $\mu = 100$, and $\sigma = 12$. (*a*) What is the chance that a sample of 36 items has a mean less than 102? (*b*) What are two points such that the chance of a mean of 36 items, lying between the two points, is .95? (*c*) Same as (*b*), but .99 instead of .95.

4. In a normal distribution $\mu = 43$, $\sigma = 15$. Use normal-probability paper to draw the cumulative-frequency curve, and read from this paper the values of P_{10}, P_{50}, P_{75}, P_{90}, P_{99}.

5. Plot on normal-probability paper the normal cumulative distribution with $\mu = 0$, $\sigma = 1$. Read from the curve the area between 0 and 2, the area between -1.5 and 2.5. Check these values by using Table A-4.

6. Find T scores for the ranks of seven scores.

7. Find T scores for the following distribution:

Test score	*Frequency*
95	2
90	3
85	5
80	6
75	8
70	12
65	8
60	6

8. Fit a normal curve to the histogram of the data in Prob. 7. Draw both the histogram and the fitted curve on the same set of coordinate axes.

9. Plot on normal-probability paper the observed cumulative distributions of $\bar{X}$ and s^2 from Class Exercise 1, Chap. 4. Check to see whether or not they agree in mean, variance, and type of distribution as stated in the text for the sampling distributions of $\bar{X}$ and s^2.

10. A test is standardized with mean 80 and standard deviation 5. If the population which was used to standardize was normal, what proportion of the population would have grades over 90? Less than 75?

11. The mean life of stockings used by an army was 40 days, with a standard deviation of 8 days. Assume the life of the stockings follows a normal distribution. If 100,000 pairs are issued, how many would need replacement after 35 days? After 46 days?

12. For the data in Prob. 9, Chap. 3, draw the cumulative-frequency distribution on normal-probability paper. Would you say that these data came from a normal population?

13. In Class Exercise 1 of this chapter, $p = \frac{2}{3}$. What are the mean and variance of the population, assuming the red beads to be labeled 1 and the white beads 0?

What are the mean and standard deviation of the sampling distribution of $\bar{X}$'s of samples of size 20 taken from this population? *Ans.* $\frac{2}{3}$, $\frac{2}{9}$; $\frac{2}{3}$, .105.

14. In a box of 1,000 nuts 500 have a left-hand thread, and 500 have a right-hand thread. What is the chance that a sample of 25 will contain fewer than 10 nuts with a left-hand thread? Fewer than 8? Between 10 and 15 inclusive?

15. A sample of 3,600 voters is selected. Using the 1 and 0 labeling for yes and no answers, what is the chance that $\bar{X}$ will differ from the population proportion by less than .05? By less than .01? (Assume the approximate value .5 for σ.)

CHAPTER 6

VARIOUS MEASURES OF CENTRAL VALUE AND DISPERSION

In the early part of Chap. 3 the arithmetic mean was introduced as a measure of central value, and the variance was introduced as a measure of dispersion. Then mention was made of several other measures which might be used in place of the mean and variance. We shall present these measures in more detail here and compare them with the mean and variance.

6-1. Other Measures of Central Value

When mention is made of an average, it is generally assumed that the arithmetic mean is intended. However, other measures are frequently used, and therefore any statement of average should indicate whether or not it is the arithmetic mean. The *median* (P_{50}) is often quoted in place of the mean as an average. The median is the middle value in any group of observations. Hence, for the distribution 10, 12, 14, 18, 19, the median is 14. If there are an even number of observations, we obtain the median by finding the mean of the two middle values. For the distribution 10, 12, 14, 18, 19, 21 the median is $(14 + 18)/2 = 16$. This score is central in the sense that half the observations yield values which are larger and half which are smaller. In many cases there will be little difference between the mean and the median, but they may differ widely. Consider the situation where a majority of salaries are at a comparatively low level and there are a few very large salaries. Here the mean salary may be twice as large as the median salary. It is obvious in such a case that a report giving the average salary may be very misleading unless we know whether the mean or median is being used.

The *mode* is the value of the observation occurring most frequently. For discrete measurements one has only to notice which value has occurred in greatest numbers. For continuous measurements it is necessary to group the data into a frequency table in order to determine the mode. For example, notice that in Fig. 2-2 the mode is 69 inches (the mid-point of the interval having the largest number of cases). If the data were grouped into different intervals we might obtain a different value for the mode.

The *midrange* is a point halfway between the largest and smallest observations. For example, the midrange of the four values 22, 23, 23, 26 is $(22 + 26)/2 = 24$.

The *percentile estimate* $(P_{25} + P_{75})/2$ is sometimes used when there are a large number of observations. Of course, the mean of any two symmetrically placed percentiles may be used as a measure of central value.

6-2. Comparison of Mean and Median

The various definitions in the preceding paragraph make it clear that a choice of appropriate descriptive statistics should be made. This section will deal specifically with the mean and median. Similar discussions of the other measures will be given in Chaps. 15 and 16.

If a measure of central value is being chosen only to describe a set of numbers, a choice between the mean and median is mainly determined by the interpretation put on the concept of "central." Thus, for example, in buying a large number of bags of grain the mean weight of 100 bags is essentially as useful to the buyer as the weights of the individual bags. On the other hand, in a discussion of amounts of money spent by families for milk it may be more useful (from the over-all health viewpoint if not from the dairy's) to know a median, which specifically pinpoints the dividing line between the upper and lower 50 per cent of the families, rather than the mean, which indicates the total amount spent.

There is also the question of the relative effort or difficulty in finding the mean value or the median value. If we have an unarranged collection of numbers, it will probably be as easy to compute with a machine the mean (and the variance also) as it is to arrange the numbers in a frequency table. However, if the numbers are arranged in order of size or in a frequency table, the median can be found by inspection in several seconds, while computation of the mean would perhaps still require several minutes. An example where saving time is of value occurs in systematic sampling where small samples are taken at frequent time intervals. If lengthy computations with each sample can be avoided, one person can carry out concurrently the inspection of a number of different facets of a manufacturing process. Furthermore if the median is used, measurement of every item in the sample may sometimes be avoided. For example, in observing heights of small groups of people the middle person can often be noted by visual inspection, and the single measurement of his height would determine the median of the group. Of course, the measurement of height is simple, but many types of measurement are difficult and a considerable saving in effort and time may be obtained by measuring only one item in each sample.

The value of a small increase in the ease of computation of the median over the computation of the mean should be considered only in the light of the whole problem. The effort required to set up an experiment, to collect the observations, and to interpret the results is usually great and often quite expensive. The actual computation carried out (at least in using techniques described in this book) seldom requires more than a few hours at the outside, and though this may sound tedious, it comprises a small part of the total time spent. Actually most of the computations discussed can be carried out in a few minutes.

Aside from the above comments it is important in choosing the mean or median to consider the possibility that a statistic (measured on a sample) will be used to estimate a parameter (measured on a population). Of course, it seems reasonable to use a sample median to estimate a population median and a sample $\bar{X}$ to estimate a population μ. However, let us suppose that we think the population mean and median are approximately equal and consider whether to use the sample mean or the sample median as an estimate of μ.

We noted in Chap. 4 that the sampling distribution of $\bar{X}$ has variance σ^2/N. If the population is normal, the variance of the sampling distribution of medians is given by σ^2/NE, where values of E, called the relative efficiency of the median compared with the mean, are given in Table A-8*b*(4). Thus for samples of size 4 the variance of the median is $\sigma^2/4(.838) = \sigma^2/(3.35)$, and for samples of size 10 it is $\sigma^2/(7.23)$. For large sample sizes the value $E = .64$ should be used. Note that for normal populations the $\bar{X}$ distribution has a smaller variance, thus a smaller spread, and consequently (this is the important point) a single observed mean has a greater chance of being close to μ than does a single observed median. This statement does not guarantee that for each sample the mean will be closer than the median to the population mean.

Although the variances for median and mean are different for the same sample size, they may be made equal if different sample sizes are used. If we equate the two variances, using N_1 as the size of the sample from which the median is computed and N_2 the equivalent sample size using the mean, we have

$$\frac{\sigma^2}{.637N_1} = \frac{\sigma^2}{N_2}$$

Since the same σ^2 appears on both sides of the equation, we can find the sample size N_1 which corresponds to any value of N_2 by solving the equation

$$.637N_1 = N_2$$

In particular if we take $N_1 = 1{,}000$, we obtain $N_2 = 1{,}000(.637) = 637$. Therefore, if we measure precision by the variance of the sampling distribution, we obtain the same precision from a sample mean based on 637 observations as we do from a sample median based on 1,000 observations.

Approximate determination of the relative efficiency can be obtained from sampling experiments such as were described in Chaps. 4 and 5. To illustrate, we take 200 samples, each of size $N = 10$, from Table A-2, and record the median of each sample in Table 6-1, using the same class interval as in the experiment recorded in Table 4-3. The values of $\bar{X}$ are copied from Table 4-3, and the slightly greater spread of the median distribution can be noted. The observed variance of the 200 medians is .1398, which can be compared with the value from the formula $\sigma^2/(7.23) = .138$. The ratio of the observed variance of means to the observed variance of medians is $.1035/.1398 = .740$, which agrees fairly well with the value .723 recorded in Table A-8*b*(4).

TABLE 6-1. OBSERVED VALUES OF $\bar{X}$ AND MEDIANS FOR 200 SAMPLES OF SIZE 10, EACH FROM A NORMAL POPULATION WITH $\mu = 0$ AND $\sigma^2 = 1$

Mid-point	Freq. of $\bar{X}$'s	Freq. of medians
.95	0	1
.85	0	1
.75	2	3
.65	3	4
.55	7	7
.45	13	8
.35	13	21
.25	19	12
.15	22	21
.05	24	23
−.05	26	23
−.15	19	14
−.25	17	17
−.35	12	13
−.45	11	9
−.55	5	9
−.65	4	6
−.75	3	5
−.85	0	2
−.95	0	1

	Theoretical	Observed
Mean $\bar{X}$	$\mu = 0$	.009
Var. $\bar{X}$	$\sigma^2/N = .1$	.1035
Mean med.	$\mu = 0$	−.013
Var. med.	$\sigma^2/NE = .1383$	.1398
Efficiency	$.1/.1383 = .723$	.740

6-3. Efficiency and Unbiasedness in Estimating μ

With several measures of average and dispersion available we must decide which to use. In the practical situation we make several observations and hope from the analysis of these data to estimate the population values. Let us write down two criteria it would seem reasonable to require of a statistic for this purpose:

1. The statistic should on the average give the "right" answer (population value);
2. The statistic should give us values which "most of the time" are close to the "right" answer.

This first criterion states that the sampling distribution of our statistic should have its mean* equal to the population value it is expected to estimate. The sampling distribution of an average should have its mean at μ, the population mean. The sampling distribution of an estimate of the variance should have its mean at σ^2, the population variance.

The second criterion states that the sampling distribution of an average should be concentrated near μ. Likewise, the sampling distribution of an estimate of the variance should be concentrated near σ^2.

Usually both these criteria are investigated for any statistic. It is not sufficient that a statistic give the right answer on the average if it is frequently very distant from that value. Therefore, the second criterion should also be applied. In fact, the second criterion might be considered as the only criterion necessary for a statistic to satisfy.

If a statistic, "on the average," gives the "right" answer, we say it is *unbiased*. If a statistic gives values which are concentrated more closely about the right value than values from any other statistic, we say it is *efficient*. The two requirements above could be stated:

1. *The statistic should be unbiased.*
2. *The statistic should be efficient.*

In the previous chapter it was noted that the mean of the sampling distribution of $\bar{X}$ is μ and its variance is σ^2/N. If the sampling distribution were obtained for samples from a normal population (with mean μ and variance σ^2) for the median, midrange, and $(P_{25} + P_{75})/2$, it would be discovered that the mean is μ in each case, so that none of these statistics is biased. However, as in the case of the median discussed in the last section, it would be discovered that the variances of these other sampling distributions are larger than for the arithmetic mean. In fact, the arithmetic mean is efficient.

These results are true for observations from a normal population. The mean is not the efficient estimate of the population mean for various other

* Other averages than the arithmetic mean might well be used, *e.g.*, the median of the sampling distribution.

populations. In particular, if the population is uniform with equal frequencies in each interval, the midrange has greater relative efficiency than the mean. However, our attention will be confined here to normal populations.

We shall define the efficiency of other unbiased estimates relative to the efficient estimate by the ratio of the variances of the sampling distributions of the efficient estimate and the estimate being compared.

To compare the efficiencies of the median, midrange, and $(P_{25} + P_{75})/2$, we divide the variance of the sampling distribution of the mean by the variance of each of the sampling distributions of these other statistics. The values are developed mathematically on the assumption that the universe has a normal distribution and are tabulated in Table A-8*b*(4). The symbol ∞ in the column for sample size is used to indicate very large sample sizes. The efficiencies can be summarized as follows:

The efficiencies of these statistics are high for very small sample sizes. The efficiency of the median, which is .70 *for samples of* 5, *slowly declines toward* .64 *as the sample size increases. The efficiency of* $(P_{25} + P_{75})/2$ *slowly declines from about* .84 *for samples of* 10 *to* .81 *for very large samples. The efficiency of the midrange drops off fairly rapidly and approaches zero for large sample sizes* (.77 *for samples of* 5, .54 *for samples of* 10).

It can be shown that the efficiencies are approximately the ratio of the sample sizes which will give equal precision in the estimate. For example, an efficiency of .80 indicates that the mean of a sample of, say, 80 items will have as much accuracy as the substitute estimate would have when determined from a sample of 100 items. This was shown for the median in Sec. 6-2.

We may use the concept of efficiency as an aid in designing statistical studies. We can weigh the importance of using a statistic that is easy to compute or rapid to obtain against the loss in precision of the estimate or the effort of obtaining more observations to preserve a certain degree of precision.

6-4. Other Measures of Dispersion

Many statistical studies report results, using other measures of dispersion than the sample variance or standard deviation. We shall give several examples and then discuss their comparative value as an estimate of dispersion. It will be seen that for certain applications the other estimates have advantages.

The *mean deviation* is usually defined as the arithmetic mean of the distances of each observation from the mean. The distances here are all taken as positive. More accurately, this statistic should be called the *mean absolute deviation from the mean.* One may also compute a mean deviation using deviations from the median. We shall use the *mean deviation from the median.*

To illustrate the computation of the mean deviation, we shall compute its value for a sample of 5 items, 50, 52, 57, 54, 56. The median is 54.

TABLE 6-2

Deviation	Deviation	Absolute deviation
50 − 54	−4	4
52 − 54	−2	2
57 − 54	3	3
54 − 54	0	0
56 − 54	2	2
		11

$$\text{Mean deviation} = \frac{11}{5} = 2.2$$

The range, w, is the distance between the largest and smallest observations. For example, the range of the observations 10, 12, 14, 18, 19, 21 is $w = 21 - 10 = 11$. Usually the range is used as a measure of dispersion only for a small number of observations. There is some objection to the use of the range as a measure of dispersion since it can be greatly affected by a single value which may be removed a considerable distance from all other values observed. For a large number of observations the percentile estimate $(P_{93} - P_{07})$ is sometimes used as an estimate of dispersion. In this way 7 per cent of the observations at each end are disregarded.

The mean deviation, the range, and the percentile estimate must all be adjusted to be unbiased estimates of σ, since the means of their sampling distributions are not equal to σ.

6-5. Efficiency and Unbiasedness in Estimating Dispersion

We noted in Chap. 4 that the mean of the sampling distribution of $s^2 = \Sigma(X_i - \bar{X})^2/(N - 1)$ is equal to the population variance σ^2. This is true for random samples from any population, and so s^2 is always an unbiased estimate of σ^2. Usually we shall use s to estimate σ, and it should be noted that s is a biased estimate of σ. For normal populations a factor can be used to give an unbiased estimate of σ. The unbiased estimates for $N = 2, 3, 4$ are $1.253s$, $1.128s$, and $1.085s$, respectively. For larger values of N we can use the estimate $\left[1 + \frac{1}{4(N - 1)}\right]s$. These correction factors are listed in Table A-8*b*(1). They are to be used only for samples from approximately normal populations; other factors apply for other population distributions. This result is in contrast to the above statement that the mean s^2 equals σ^2 for *any* population distribution.

The mean deviation, range, and $P_{93} - P_{07}$ are also biased estimates of σ and must be corrected appropriately for different populations. For normal populations we note from Table A-4 that for large samples $P_{93} = \mu + 1.476\sigma$ and $P_{07} = \mu - 1.476\sigma$; so $P_{93} - P_{07}$ is approximately 2.952σ. Thus an unbiased estimate of σ is

$$(P_{93} - P_{07})/2.952 = .339(P_{93} - P_{07})$$

The correction factors for the range and mean deviation vary with N and are given, for normal populations, in Table *A*-8*b*. For example, we can see from the table that for samples of size 10 the range must be multiplied by .325 to give an unbiased estimate of σ. In other words, the mean range is $1/.325 = 3.08$ standard deviations.

We have recorded in Table 6-3 the values of the range w and the values of s observed for a number of samples from a normal population having $\sigma^2 = 1$. The mean of the observed values of w is 3.0425 standard deviations, which agrees fairly well with the correct value 3.08 noted above. When the values of w are multiplied by .325, the observed mean is .984, which is close to the theoretical 1σ ($\sigma = 1$). The values of s after being multiplied by $1 + \frac{1}{4 \times 9} = 1.028$ to remove the bias have a mean of 1.015, which is also close to the theoretical value.

Even in very large samples the range is often used as a very rough estimate of the standard deviation. For normal populations the entire sample for a wide range of sample sizes will be contained in an interval of about four to six standard deviations. For example, in the distribution given in the first column of Table 4-3 the entire distribution is contained in an interval of length 1.6 units. We may state a rough estimate of the standard deviation as about $1.6/4 = .4$ or $1.6/6 = .27$. In this case the standard deviation is actually .322.

After adjusting the estimates to remove bias we can compare the relative efficiencies of the various estimates. Strictly, the most efficient estimate of σ^2 is $\Sigma(X - \mu)^2/N$. However, μ is in general unknown; so no further consideration will be given to this estimate other than to state that the relative efficiency of s^2 with respect to this statistic is $1 - 1/N$. The other estimates of dispersion are compared for relative efficiency with the unbiased estimate based on s as mentioned above. These efficiencies are given in Table A-8*b*(4). We can see that the efficiency of the mean deviation for samples of size 10 or less is .89 or greater. The efficiency of the range estimate is high for very small sample sizes (.955 for $N = 5$) but decreases to .850 for $N = 10$ and to .700 for $N = 20$. The efficiency of the range estimate approaches zero as the sample size increases indefinitely.

Referring again to the sampling distribution reported in Table 6-3, we see that the ratio of the variances of the distribution of $1.028s$ and $.325w$ is $.0645/.0685 = .942$, which, although larger than the efficiency of the range $E = .850$ noted above, still indicates that the estimate based on s has a smaller variance than the estimate based on w.

TABLE 6-3. OBSERVED VALUES OF w, kw, AND cs FOR 200 SAMPLES OF SIZE 10, EACH FROM A NORMAL POPULATION WITH $\mu = 0$ AND $\sigma = 1$

k is chosen so that the mean of the sampling distribution of kw is σ and for samples of size 10 is $k = .325$. c is chosen so that the mean of the sampling distribution of cs is σ, and for samples of size 10 is $c = 1.028$.

Distribution of w		Distribution of kw and cs		
Mid-point	Freq.	Mid-point	Freq. of $.325w$	Freq. of $1.028s$
6.0	1	1.9	2	1
5.5	1	1.7	0	2
5.0	1	1.5	12	9
4.5	11	1.3	25	29
4.0	24	1.1	46	65
3.5	36	.9	64	55
3.0	50	.7	44	31
2.5	42	.5	7	7
2.0	29	.3	0	1
1.5	5	.1	0	0
	200		200	200

	Theoretical	Observed
Mean w	3.08	3.0425
Mean $.325w$	1.000	.984
Var. $.325w$	.0671	.0685
Mean $1.028s$	1.000	1.015
Var. $1.028s$	.0570	.0645

The efficiencies of some estimates, for example, the estimates obtained from the mean deviation and the percentile difference $P_{93} - P_{07}$, approach a constant value as we consider larger and larger sample sizes. These constants are .88 in the case of the mean deviation and .65 in the case of the percentile difference. The variance of the estimate based on s for large sample sizes is given in Table A-8b(1) as $\sigma^2/2N$. We can write the variances of the unbiased estimates based on the mean deviation and the estimate obtained from the percentile difference in the form $\sigma^2/2NE$, that is, $\sigma^2/2N(.88)$ and $\sigma^2/2N(.65)$, respectively.

Most methods to be discussed in this text will be based on $\bar{X}$ and s^2 because they are efficient for normal populations. There are circumstances when it is more convenient or is even necessary to use estimates other than the sample mean and variance, and a detailed study of these statistics will be made in Chaps. 15 and 16, including the special uses where the disadvantages outlined here are overcome by other considerations.

6-6. Confidence-interval Estimate of the Mean

Since estimates do vary in precision, it is important that an estimate be accompanied by a statement which describes the precision of the estimate, or "how close" the estimate may be to the quantity which it is desired to estimate. Confidence intervals provide a method of stating the precision of an estimate.

We have seen from the investigation of the sampling distribution of $\bar{X}$ in the previous chapter that the mean is μ, the standard deviation $\sigma/\sqrt{N}$, and that it is normal in shape. Therefore, we can use the normal table to find the proportion of the time we can expect to obtain a sample mean within a certain distance of μ. For example, we can say that 95 per cent of the time $(\mu - \bar{X})$ will be between $-1.96\sigma/\sqrt{N}$ and $1.96\sigma/\sqrt{N}$. This fact can be written in an inequality,

$$\frac{-1.96\sigma}{\sqrt{N}} < \mu - \bar{X} < \frac{1.96\sigma}{\sqrt{N}}$$

Now, suppose we add $\bar{X}$ to each term in this inequality. We then have

$$\bar{X} - \frac{1.96\sigma}{\sqrt{N}} < \mu < \bar{X} + \frac{1.96\sigma}{\sqrt{N}}$$

If we wish to use 99 per cent in place of 95 per cent, the value 1.96 must be replaced by 2.58. The intervals, of course, must be longer in order to include μ a larger per cent of the time. For example, suppose that σ is known and we collect 16 observations to estimate the population mean. The average of these observations is, say, 15.70; the known σ is 2.80. If we write the above inequality with these values substituted, we obtain

$$15.70 - \frac{1.96(2.80)}{\sqrt{16}} < \mu < 15.70 + \frac{1.96(2.80)}{\sqrt{16}}$$
$$15.70 - 1.37 < \mu < 15.70 + 1.37$$
$$14.33 < \mu < 17.07$$

We can state our result thus: 95 per cent of the intervals obtained in this way will include μ; in this case the interval is from 14.33 to 17.07. This is called a 95 per cent *confidence interval.* The values at the ends of the interval are called *confidence limits.* If we had obtained a sample mean of 15.20, we should have obtained an interval extending from 13.83 to 16.57. If we had obtained a mean of 17.0, our interval would extend from 15.63 to 18.37. Remember that the population mean has a certain value, unknown in this case. We are computing an interval, based on the sample mean, which has a 95 per cent chance of containing the population mean. Of course, it is not known for any particular determination that the mean is actually included. We know only that, if we repeatedly estimate μ in this way, we shall include μ in our intervals 95 per cent of the time.

It will be convenient to denote the factors obtained from the normal table by z_α to represent the 100α percentile. In this notation $z_{.025} = -1.96$ and $z_{.975} = +1.96$. The $100(1 - \alpha)$ per cent confidence interval can be written $\bar{X} + z_{\frac{1}{2}\alpha}\sigma/\sqrt{N} < \mu < \bar{X} + z_{1-\frac{1}{2}\alpha}\sigma/\sqrt{N}$.

It is necessary to know the population σ to estimate μ as just shown. s is an estimate of σ and could be substituted for σ, but the factor 1.96 would no longer ensure 95 per cent confidence limits. It will be necessary to investigate the sampling distribution of $\dfrac{\bar{X} - \mu}{s/\sqrt{N}}$ to see how it differs from the sampling distribution of $\dfrac{\bar{X} - \mu}{\sigma/\sqrt{N}}$. This will be done in Chap. 9.

6-7. Confidence-interval Estimates of σ^2 and σ

The estimation of σ^2 by confidence limits is based on the sampling distribution of s^2. Certain percentiles of the distribution of s^2/σ^2 were obtained in Chap. 4. For example, for samples of size 10 two percentiles experimentally obtained were $P_{05} = .28$ and $P_{95} = 1.97$. As in the case of the normal distribution these percentiles can be obtained more precisely from a table of the sampling distribution. The percentiles of the sampling distribution of s^2/σ^2 are in Table A-6*b* and are called the percentiles of the χ^2/df distribution (read "chi square over degrees of freedom"). The percentile values are different for different sample sizes, and this table gives, for samples of size 10, $P_{05} = .369$, $P_{95} = 1.88$. These values are in the columns headed 5.0 and 95 and on the line stating the number used in the denominator of s^2. This is $N - 1$, or, for this example, 9. This number is called *degrees of freedom.* Therefore, 90 per cent of the time,

$$.369 < \frac{s^2}{\sigma^2} < 1.88$$

and

$$\frac{1}{.369} > \frac{\sigma^2}{s^2} > \frac{1}{1.88}$$

so that, multiplying by s^2, we obtain

$$\frac{s^2}{.369} > \sigma^2 > \frac{s^2}{1.88}$$

and have 90 per cent confidence limits for the estimation of σ^2. Suppose for a sample of 10 items the sample variance is computed to be 300. The limits for 90 per cent confidence are 300/.369 and 300/1.88. These limits are 813 and 160. In general, the 90 per cent confidence limits are

$$\frac{s^2}{P_{05}} > \sigma^2 > \frac{s^2}{P_{95}}$$

where the percentile values indicated are obtained from the χ^2/df distribution in Table A-6*b*. If confidence limits are desired for other than 90 per cent confidence, different percentile values must be used.

Confidence limits for σ may be obtained directly from the confidence limits for σ^2 by taking the square root of the three terms in the inequality. For our example we have

$$\sqrt{\frac{s^2}{.369}} > \sigma > \sqrt{\frac{s^2}{1.88}}$$

or

$$\sqrt{813} > \sigma > \sqrt{160}$$

and, obtaining the square roots from Table A-33, we have

$$28.5 > \sigma > 12.6$$

In addition to the use of confidence intervals as estimates of population values, the lengths of the confidence intervals for estimating the mean and the variance could be used to compare the various measures of mean and dispersion. The statistic which yields the shortest confidence interval could be termed the "best," and a rating of any other statistic could be obtained by comparing the length of its confidence interval with that of the "best" estimate. In fact, this procedure is made use of in theoretical investigations of these various statistics.

6-8. Estimation of a Proportion

The method used for estimating means and variances may also be used to estimate the proportion of individuals in a population having a certain characteristic, for example, to estimate from a sample of registered voters the proportion of all registered voters in favor of a certain candidate.

In Sec. 5-8 we noted that a proportion of a sample having a stated characteristic could be treated as a special case of a mean $\bar{X}$ by assigning the score 1 to the individuals having the characteristic and the score 0 to those not having the characteristic. The mean of these scores is the statistic $\bar{X}$, which for large sample sizes has an approximately normal sampling distribution with mean p, the proportion in the population, and standard deviation $\sigma/\sqrt{N} = \sqrt{p(1 - p)/N}$. The fact that the standard deviation depends on the unknown p is troublesome, and further attention will be given to this point later. For this chapter we shall be satisfied by noting:

1. That, whatever the value of p, the quantity $p(1 - p)$ is never larger than .25; so if we use $.5/\sqrt{N}$ instead of $\sigma/\sqrt{N}$, we shall be using a number no smaller than the true standard deviation, or

2. That, if N is moderately large, there is little error in replacing $\sqrt{p(1 - p)/N}$ by $\sqrt{\bar{X}(1 - \bar{X})/N}$.

These approximations seem more reasonable if we note how little $\sqrt{p(1 - p)}$ changes for considerable changes in p. This point was discussed in Sec. 5-8.

Using either of the procedures, we can now form approximate confidence intervals for p in the same manner as for the mean μ in Sec. 6-6.

As an example using the observed $\bar{X}$ in the standard-deviation formula, suppose a sample of 500 people was interviewed and 200 of them stated they were in favor of a certain candidate for president. Approximate 95 per cent confidence limits for the population proportion in favor of the candidate are given by

$$\frac{200}{500} - 1.96\sqrt{\frac{.4(.6)}{500}} < p < \frac{200}{500} + 1.96\sqrt{\frac{.4(.6)}{500}}$$

or

$$.357 < p < .443$$

The use of .5 as an approximate value for the standard deviation will give an interval $.356 < p < .444$, which is little different from the interval using the observed $\bar{X}$.

Further attention is given to the estimation of proportions in Chap. 13.

6-9. Estimates Using Inefficient Statistics

Statistics such as the median and range, although somewhat inefficient as estimators, often have advantages in time or effort and may be used to form confidence-interval estimates in a very similar manner to those based on $\bar{X}$ and s^2. This section discusses four examples of inefficient statistics in confidence-interval estimates of parameters. For normal populations these methods will usually give longer confidence intervals than those based on $\bar{X}$ and s^2. In particular cases, however, the speed of computation or the use of simpler sampling designs may make them advantageous.

Example 1. *Range as an Estimate of* σ. For small samples from a normal population percentiles of the distribution of the range divided by the population standard deviation, w/σ, are recorded in Table A-8b(1). We can form a confidence-interval estimate of σ by stating that the observed range divided by σ is between certain percentile limits. For example, suppose that in a sample of five observations we find $w = 15.3$. The 2.5 and 97.5 per cent limits of w/σ for $N = 5$ are .85 and 4.20. Thus we estimate σ by the interval $.85 < 15.3/\sigma < 4.20$, which gives $3.64 < \sigma < 18.0$.

Example 2. *Confidence Interval for μ Based on Medians.* It is sometimes convenient to take a number of small samples, compute an inefficient statistic for each, and average the values for all the samples. Suppose we measure the medians of 200 samples of five observations each. If our original population is normal, the variance of the population of medians for samples of size 5 is $\sigma^2/NE = \sigma^2/5(.697) = \sigma^2/3.48$, so that we can estimate the unknown σ^2 by multiplying the observed variance of the medians by 3.48. Suppose on the other hand that the original population variance is known to be 100; we can then use the 200 medians to estimate the population mean μ. The mean of the 200 medians can be assumed to have an approximately normal sampling distribution with mean equal to the population mean μ and a variance which is $\sigma^2/3.48$ divided by 200. The confidence limits for μ are

$$\bar{X} + z_{\frac{1}{2}\alpha}\sqrt{\frac{28.7}{200}} < \mu < \bar{X} + z_{1-\frac{1}{2}\alpha}\sqrt{\frac{28.7}{200}}$$

Example 3. *Estimates of μ and σ^2 Based on Means.* If a collection of $\bar{X}$'s of samples of size N are available, they may be used to estimate the mean and variance of the original population. (In this example only the estimation of the variance is inefficient.) Suppose we have 500 samples of four observations each from a population and the means $\bar{X}_1, \bar{X}_2, \ldots,$ $\bar{X}_{500}$ have been recorded. The mean $\bar{X} = \sum_1^{500} \bar{X}_i/500$ is the mean of a sample of $500 \times 4 = 2{,}000$ observations, and we can estimate μ by the interval

$$\bar{X} + z_{\frac{1}{2}\alpha}\frac{\sigma}{\sqrt{2{,}000}} < \mu < \bar{X} + z_{1-\frac{1}{2}\alpha}\frac{\sigma}{\sqrt{2{,}000}}$$

If, for example, $\bar{X} = 70.0$ and $\sigma = 10$ then 95 per cent confidence limits are

$$70.0 - 1.96\frac{10}{\sqrt{2{,}000}} < \mu < 70.0 + 1.96\frac{10}{\sqrt{2{,}000}}$$

or

$$69.56 < \mu < 70.44$$

If σ^2 is not known, we compute the variance $s_{\bar{X}}^2$ of the 500 values $\bar{X}_i$, which is an estimate of $\sigma^2/N = \sigma^2/4$, the variance of $\bar{X}$'s for samples of size 4. As in the last section we refer to Table A-6b to form a confidence-interval estimate for σ^2. Reference is made to the table for 499 degrees of freedom. Suppose we observe $s_{\bar{X}}^2 = 2.30$ and thus estimate $\sigma^2 = 4(2.30) = 9.20$. A 90 per cent confidence-interval estimate of σ^2 is

$$.898 < \frac{s_{\bar{X}}^2}{\sigma^2/4} < 1.11$$

or

$$\frac{4(2.30)}{1.11} < \sigma^2 < \frac{4(2.30)}{.898}$$

Example 4. *Confidence Interval for σ Based on Mean Range.* The mean of the ranges of a number of small samples can be used to estimate σ as in the following example: Suppose that we have 200 samples of size $N = 4$ from a normal population and have recorded the range w_i of each. An unbiased estimate of σ is $.486\bar{w} = .486 \sum_{1}^{200} w_i/200$. The factor .486 is obtained from Table A-8b(1) for the range of four observations. Also note from Table A-8b(1) that the variance of the range estimate $.486w$ is $.183\sigma^2$. Now $.486\bar{w}$ is the mean of 200 observations from the population of range estimates and thus has a variance $.183\sigma^2/200$. Since $\bar{w}$ is the mean of a fairly large sample of ranges, we can assume that it is normally distributed; so we can compute confidence limits for σ from

$$.486\bar{w} + z_{\frac{1}{2}\alpha}\sqrt{\frac{.183\sigma^2}{200}} < \sigma < .486\bar{w} + z_{1-\frac{1}{2}\alpha}\sqrt{\frac{.183\sigma^2}{200}}$$

obtaining

$$\frac{.486\bar{w}}{1 + z_{1-\frac{1}{2}\alpha}\sqrt{\frac{.183}{200}}} < \sigma < \frac{.486\bar{w}}{1 - z_{1-\frac{1}{2}\alpha}\sqrt{\frac{.183}{200}}}$$

If the observed $.486\bar{w} = 21.3$, the observed 95 per cent confidence limits for σ are

$$\frac{21.3}{1 + 1.96\sqrt{\frac{.183}{200}}} < \sigma < \frac{21.3}{1 - 1.96\sqrt{\frac{.183}{200}}}$$

or

$$20.1 < \sigma < 22.6$$

6-10. Sample Size Required to Estimate with Desired Precision

Since larger samples provide estimates of greater precision, we can attain whatever precision we desire by taking samples sufficiently large.

In Sec. 6-6 we estimated the difference $\mu - \bar{X}$ as being between $z_{\frac{1}{2}\alpha}\sigma/\sqrt{N}$ and $z_{1-\frac{1}{2}\alpha}\sigma/\sqrt{N}$, where z is the normal deviate read from Table A-3 or A-4. If we specify the maximum desired distance, d, between the sample mean $\bar{X}$ and the population mean μ, we find the required sample size $N = [z_{1-\frac{1}{2}\alpha}\sigma/d]^2$. The confidence interval will then have length $2d$. As an example, suppose that a population has standard deviation 3 inches and we wish to estimate μ to the nearest $\frac{1}{2}$ inch with 95 per cent confidence. Using $d = \frac{1}{2}$, $\sigma = 3$, $z = 1.96$, we require $N = [1.96(3)/\frac{1}{2}]^2 = 139$ observations from the population. If we take 139 observations, the 95 per cent confidence interval for μ will be $\bar{X} - \frac{1}{2} < \mu < \bar{X} + \frac{1}{2}$.

As another example, suppose we are conducting a public-opinion poll and wish from a random sample to estimate the proportion in the population with a certain opinion and wish to be 99 per cent sure of being accurate to the nearest 1 per cent. Using the approximate value .25 for $\sigma^2 = p(1 - p)$, or .5 for σ, we state that a sample of size

$$N = \left[\frac{2.58(.5)}{.01}\right]^2 = 16{,}641$$

would be sufficient. If p is actually not close to .5, σ^2 would be smaller than .25 and a smaller N would be sufficient.

We can also specify the required sample size to estimate σ^2 correctly within a certain percentage. For example, if we use a 95 per cent confidence interval, we obtain from Table A-6*b* the 2.5 and the 97.5 percentiles of s^2/σ^2. If the limits are to be within, say, 10 per cent of σ^2, we need to find approximately .90 in the 2.5 column and approximately 1.10 in the 97.5 column. By reference to the table we can see that about 740 or 750 degrees of freedom are required. Therefore a sample variance with about 750 degrees of freedom is required. The sample size is given by $N = (\text{df}) + 1$.

GLOSSARY

best estimate
confidence interval
confidence limits
mean deviation
median
midrange
mode
range
statistical efficiency
unbiased

DISCUSSION QUESTIONS

1. Define each of the terms in the Glossary.

2. Give examples of situations where it might be practical to take a larger number of observations and use an inefficient estimating statistic. Situations of this type might occur if it is easy and inexpensive to obtain observations and results are needed in a short period of time, or if it is easy to order the individuals and difficult to measure any particular one.

3. Is it easier to find the median or the mean?

4. Describe an experiment illustrating the proportion of confidence intervals for estimating μ in a normal population which actually cover μ.

CLASS EXERCISES

1. From the observed distribution of the median as recorded in Class Exercise 4, Chap. 4, estimate the efficiency of the median compared with the mean for samples of size 10 from a normal population. Compare this estimated efficiency with the theoretical efficiency .71.

2. Compute the midrange for the samples of size 10 drawn from Table A-2 (Class Exercise, Chap. 3). Collect the computed values into a distribution, and compute the mean and variance. Compare the results with the theoretical values given in Table A-8*b*(4). Estimate the efficiency of the midrange for samples of size 10 from a normal population.

3. Each student computes 90 per cent confidence limits for μ from the value of $\bar{X}$ observed in each of the three samples of size 10 from Table A-2. Assume $\sigma = 1$. Count, for all students in the class, the number of these intervals which actually cover μ. Note that the intervals change location from sample to sample but that all the intervals are of the same length.

4. Each student computes 90 per cent confidence limits for σ^2 from the sample variances computed for the three samples of size 10 from Table A-2. Count the number of these intervals, for all students in the class, which actually cover σ^2. Note that the intervals not only change position from sample to sample but also change in length.

PROBLEMS

1. For the data given at the top of page 8, find (*a*) the median, (*b*) the midrange (*c*) the range.

2. Compute for the data of Prob. 9, Chap. 3, (*a*) the median, (*b*) the midrange, (*c*) the range.

3. Problem 17, Chap. 9, gives data for two samples labeled *A* and *B*. Compute for each sample (*a*) the median, (*b*) the midrange, (*c*) the range, (*d*) an unbiased estimate of σ based on the range.

4. For what size sample will the sampling distribution of the mean have the same dispersion as the sampling distribution of the median of 20 observations?

5. If data collected for determining the median cost 10 cents per observation and data collected for computing the mean cost 15 cents per observation, would it be more economical to take a sample of 100 cases and measure $\bar{X}$ or a sample sufficiently large to provide a median as precise as $\bar{X}$?

6. An experimenter has the choice of finding $\bar{X}$ for 163 observations or the median for 200. Which will give him the more precise estimate of μ?

7. A sample of 1,000 cases has $P_{93} = 16.1$ and $P_{07} = 10.3$. Estimate μ and σ. Assuming the efficiency of $.3388(P_{93} - P_{07})$ relative to s is $E = .65$ and the variances for $.3388(P_{93} - P_{07})$ and s are approximately $\sigma^2/2NE$ and $\sigma^2/2N$, respectively, for what size sample would s be as precise as the percentile estimate?

8. If P_{25} and P_{75} are observed in a sample of 1,000 observations from a normal population, how can unbiased estimates of μ and σ be constructed?

9. If it is known that the variance of the length of life of electric-light bulbs is 2,500, and if we obtain a mean life of 500 hours for a sample of 25 bulbs, determine a 95 per cent confidence-interval estimate of the population mean.

10. A sample of 40 observations from a population with $\sigma = 3$ inches has $\bar{X} = 64.2$ inches. Give 90 per cent confidence limits for μ. Give 99.9 confidence limits for μ.

11. Suppose it is desired to estimate the variance of the number of seeds of a certain plant when grown in a new environment. For 20 plants $\Sigma(X_i - \bar{X})^2 = 6{,}000$. What is the 90 per cent confidence-interval estimate of σ^2?

12. In Table 3-2 the mean of a sample of 80 observations is $\bar{X} = 69.7$. If $\sigma^2 = 3.50$, estimate μ with a 95 per cent confidence interval. Using $s^2 = 3.50$, estimate σ^2 with a 95 per cent confidence interval.

13. The first 200 babies born in January were 120 boys and 80 girls. Estimate by an 80 per cent confidence interval the population proportion of male births.

14. Of 1,000 people treated with a new drug 200 showed an allergic reaction. Estimate with a 90 per cent confidence interval the proportion in the population from which the sample is taken who would show an allergic reaction.

15. In Table 6-1 the mean median of 200 samples of size 10 each was observed to be $-.013$. Use this result to estimate μ with a 99 per cent confidence interval, assuming $\sigma^2 = 1$.

16. In Table 4-3 are recorded $\bar{X}$'s of samples of size 10 and 40. Using the $\bar{X}$'s of samples of size 10, (*a*) estimate μ with a 95 per cent confidence interval, (*b*) estimate σ^2 (not $\sigma_{\bar{X}}^2$) with a 90 per cent confidence interval. Do the same, using the $\bar{X}$'s of samples of size 40.

17. What size sample should be taken from a population with $\sigma = 3$ inches to give a 90 per cent confidence interval for μ of length 1 inch? A 99 per cent confidence interval of length $\frac{1}{2}$ inch?

18. What size sample should be taken from a population to estimate p to the nearest 1 per cent with 98 per cent confidence?

19. What sample size should be taken so that a 90 per cent confidence interval for the variance will not be in error by more than 20 per cent, i.e., so that s^2/σ^2 is between .80 and 1.20 approximately?

CHAPTER 7

STATISTICAL INFERENCE

In previous chapters we have been concerned with the description of observations and with the *estimation* of certain characteristics of the population from which a sample is drawn. Here, we shall investigate how these procedures can be used to make *decisions.*

7-1. Statistical Hypothesis

In geometry it might be stated as a hypothesis that the sum of the angles of a triangle is 180°. By accepted procedures of *proof* we decide whether this hypothesis is true or false. In this case we have a mathematical proof of the hypothesis, and when we have completed the proof, we are *certain* as to whether the hypothesis is true or false. In sciences other than mathematics there may be proposed a hypothesis or theory concerning some universe or population of individuals. This we call a *statistical hypothesis*, and the only way to be absolutely certain about its truth or falsity may be to examine the entire population concerned. This is frequently impractical (or impossible), and we are forced to take a sample from the population and use the sample to make a decision as to whether the hypothesis is true or false. *The process of using the sample to "test" whether the hypothesis is true* (*or false*) *is called a statistical proof of the truth* (*or falsity*) *of the hypothesis.* Unfortunately there is no "certainty" that a mistake will not be made. In fact there are two types of mistakes either of which we may make. If it happens that the hypothesis stated is true, we might call it false (type 1, or α, error), or if it happens that the hypothesis stated is false, we might call it true (type 2, or β, error.) The frequency with which mistakes are made is, of course, very important to us and we shall see that this frequency can be controlled to a certain extent.

Examples of hypotheses which can be subjected to statistical test are as follows:

1. This group of observations is a sample from a population with mean equal to μ:

   a. These electric-light bulbs are of standard quality (average length of life μ equal to some specified value μ_0).

   b. The average number of bacteria killed by test drops of a germicide is equal to some standard number.
   c. The average intelligence of this class is equal to the average of all students.

2. This group of observations is a sample from a population with variance σ^2:

   a. This class is just as variable in intelligence as the usual class.
   b. This machine produces axles of more uniform diameter than the allowable variation σ^2.
   c. The growing period for this hybrid of corn is more variable than the growing period of other hybrids.

3. These two groups are from populations with the same average ($\mu_1 = \mu_2$):

   a. Method A is better than method B for teaching algebra.
   b. Steel made by method A is harder than steel made by method B.
   c. Penicillin is more effective than streptomycin in the treatment of disease X.

Hypotheses of other types involving more than two means and variances, those involving proportions and hypotheses concerning association, etc., will be introduced later.

Our decision as to whether we shall accept or reject a hypothesis will be based on the information we obtain by making observations and by what risk we are willing to take that our decision may be wrong. We shall state our hypothesis (e.g., state a value for a population parameter). We collect a number of observations (our sample) and examine the results obtained to see whether or not they are similar to the population stated in our hypothesis. If there is close agreement, we shall accept the hypothesis. If the agreement is poor, we shall reject the hypothesis. To decide whether or not there is close agreement, we shall usually compute some statistic and compare the particular value obtained with the sampling distribution for this statistic under the assumption that the hypothesis is true.

7-2. Level of Significance, α

The procedure for testing any of the hypotheses stated above can be illustrated by the use of the sampling distribution of $\bar{X}$. Suppose the hypothesis is stated that the population mean is 50, $\mu = 50$. The statistic $\bar{X}$ is computed for a sample of N observations. It can be seen from the sampling distribution of $\bar{X}$ that a sample mean far removed from 50 will rarely occur if our hypothesis is true. Therefore, if the computed $\bar{X}$ is close to 50, we shall accept the hypothesis. If the computed $\bar{X}$ is very different from 50, we shall reject our hypothesis.

In order to find the explicit relationship between the size of the deviation and the likelihood of this deviation, we refer to the sampling distribution of $\bar{X}$. Suppose the sample is $N = 25$ observations from a normal population with standard deviation 10. From our study of Chaps. 5 and 6 we know that we can assume that the sampling distribution is normal with standard deviation $\sigma_{\bar{X}} = \sigma/\sqrt{N} = \frac{10}{5} = 2$. If the mean of the population is $\mu = 50$, then the mean of the sampling distribution of $\bar{X}$ is also 50. This sampling distribution is pictured in Fig. 7-1.

We now choose the values of $\bar{X}$ which will cause us to reject the hypothetical value, $\mu = 50$. Suppose, for example, we decide to reject $\mu = 50$ if $\bar{X}$ is more than $1.960\sigma_{\bar{X}} = 1.960(2) = 3.920$ units from 50. That is,

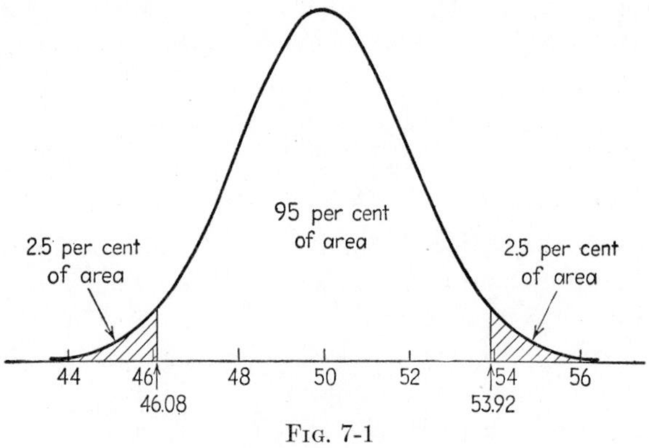

FIG. 7-1

reject $\mu = 50$ if $\bar{X}$ is less than 46.08 or if $\bar{X}$ is more than 53.92, and accept $\mu = 50$ if $\bar{X}$ is between these two values. Table A-4 shows that 2.5 per cent of the area under the sampling distribution in Fig. 7-1 corresponds to values of $\bar{X}$ less than 46.08 [reference to the table is made with $z = (46.08 - 50)/2 = -1.960$] and 2.5 per cent corresponds to values of $\bar{X}$ greater than 53.92. Thus, if $\mu = 50$, we have a 5 per cent ($\alpha = .05$) chance that a sample $\bar{X}$ is less than 46.08 or is greater than 53.92, causing us to reject the true hypothesis.

For illustration, we consider a sampling experiment in which we draw successive samples of $N = 25$ observations each from a population of tags with mean 50 and standard deviation 10. Approximately 5 per cent of the samples will have an $\bar{X}$ less than 46.08 or an $\bar{X}$ greater than 53.92, and for these samples the above rule for decision leads to the error of rejecting 50 as the true mean. For approximately 95 per cent of the samples $\bar{X}$ will be between 46.08 and 53.92, and for these cases we shall correctly decide to accept $\mu = 50$. It should be recognized that here the hypothesis is correct, but nevertheless we definitely expect to be wrong in our conclusion about the hypothesis a certain per cent of the time, in this case,

5 per cent. Of course, in actual applied problems we must usually decide to accept or reject the hypothesis on the basis of a single sample of observations and thus run a 5 per cent risk in each single conclusion.

The possible values of $\bar{X}$ which cause rejection of the hypothesis make up the *rejection region*, or *critical region*. In this case the critical region of the test of the hypothesis $\mu = 50$ is $\bar{X} < 46.08$ and $\bar{X} > 53.92$. The chance of finding a single sample which has $\bar{X}$ in this critical region *if the hypothesis* $\mu = 50$ *is true* is 5 per cent. This chance is called the *level of significance* of the test and is usually denoted by the Greek letter α.

Since the value of α may be chosen by the experimenter and its choice will in part determine the acceptance or rejection of the hypothesis, it should be fixed before the experiment is begun. If it is a matter of serious concern when a true hypothesis is rejected, the risk α of making this error should be made small. If it is of great concern that a hypothesis be rejected if there is only little evidence against it, we may wish to choose α larger. A convention frequently followed is to state the result *significant* if the hypothesis is rejected with $\alpha = .05$ and *highly significant* if it is rejected with $\alpha = .01$.

In Sec. 7-5 we shall vary the size of α and consider the effect on the critical region.

7-3. Second Type of Error, β

In addition to the possible α error of rejecting the hypothesis when it is true, there is also the possibility of the β error of accepting the hypothesis when it is false. We use the notation β error as the error itself and β as the chance of making the error, as above, where we used α error as the type of mistake which could be made and α as the chance of making the mistake. For a fixed number N of observations we shall find that, if we choose α as we please, β will then be determined. Also for fixed N a decrease in α will increase β. If we wish to decrease both α and β, we must increase the number of observations.

As an illustration of the β error, consider the test in Fig. 7-1 where we agreed to reject the value $\mu = 50$ if $\bar{X}$ was greater than 53.92 or less than 46.08. The shaded area in Fig. 7-1 corresponds to the value of α and is 5 per cent of the total area under the curve. Now suppose that the hypothesis is not true, and as a specific example suppose $\mu = 52$. The mean of the sampling distribution of $\bar{X}$ will then be 52, and its standard deviation as before will be equal to two units. Figure 7-2 shows this sampling distribution of $\bar{X}$, with the shaded area being the chance of our rejecting $\mu = 50$. Since the samples are from a population with $\mu = 52$, rejection of $\mu = 50$ would not be an error. The size of the shaded area is $1 - \beta$, and, of course, β is the size of the unshaded area.

The size of the unshaded area is found by the method of Chap. 5 as follows: Compute

$$z_1 = \frac{46.08 - 52}{2} = -2.96 \qquad \text{and} \qquad z_2 = \frac{53.92 - 52}{2} = +.96$$

Refer to Table A-4 to find $\beta = .8314 - .0015 = .8299$, or 83 per cent. Therefore, if it happens that the sample comes from a population with a mean equal to 52 (instead of the suggested value 50), the rule of decision we have used with $\alpha = .05$ will result in an 83 per cent chance of accepting 50, that is, an 83 per cent chance of not recognizing that 50 is incorrect.

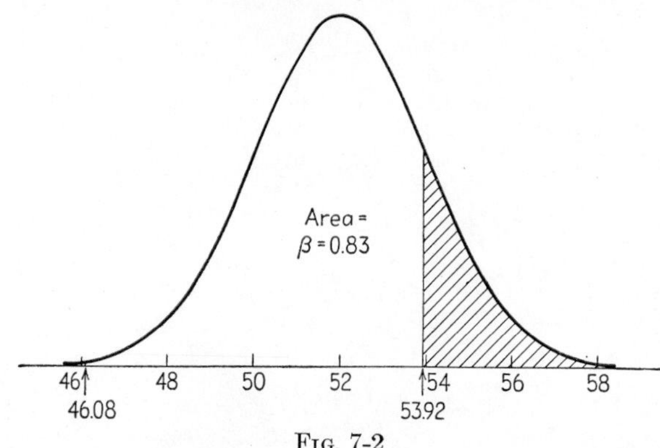

FIG. 7-2

For illustration, we consider a sampling experiment. From a population with mean 52 and $\sigma = 10$ draw successive samples of size $N = 25$. Approximately 83 per cent of the samples will have $\bar{X}$ between 46.08 and 53.92, and in those cases we would make the error of accepting $\mu = 50$. Approximately 17 per cent of the samples will have $\bar{X}$ less than 46.08 or greater than 53.92, and in those cases we would correctly conclude that the mean is not 50. The statements of the two alternative conclusions are as follows:

1. If $\bar{X}$ is greater than 53.92 or less than 46.08, we shall reject the hypothesis that $\mu = 50$. If μ is 50, we shall make such a decision (wrong, of course) 5 per cent of the time. Thus $\alpha = .05$.

2. If $\bar{X}$ is between 46.08 and 53.92, we shall accept the hypothesis that $\mu = 50$. If actually $\mu = 52$, we shall accept $\mu = 50$ (again a wrong decision) 83 per cent of the time. Thus $\beta = .83$.

It should be noted that other values than 52 might have been used in the above illustration. Discussion on this point is deferred to Sec. 7-8.

The summary of our procedure for testing a hypothesis is:

1. We do not know the population mean μ.
2. We state a hypothesis that the mean is 50.

3. We wish to reject the hypothesis when there are results whose chance of occurring when the hypothesis is true is only 5 per cent. (In this example we rejected the hypothesis when $\bar{X} < 46.08$ or when $\bar{X} > 53.92$.)

4. We compute $\bar{X}$ from a sample of 25 observations in order to decide whether to accept or reject this hypothesis.

5. If we observe an $\bar{X}$ less than 46.08 or greater than 53.92, we reject the hypothesis; if we observe an $\bar{X}$ between these values, we accept the hypothesis.

This is an example of the procedure for testing a hypothesis statistically. In many statistical applications the second type of error β is not controlled, but even there the experimenter should be aware that this error exists and have some idea of how large it might be.

7-4. Test of Statistical Hypothesis

Since the same procedure used for the experiment on means will be used in general, it will be stated again here separated from that problem.

1. Statement of the hypothesis.

2. Ideally α and β are specified. These will determine the number of observations we must take for computing the statistic we have chosen. More frequently in practice α and N are specified.

3. Determine which resulting values of some statistic, called the *critical region,* will cause us to reject the hypothesis and which values will cause us to accept the hypothesis.

4. Compute the value of the statistic from the observed values obtained experimentally.

5. Accept or reject the hypothesis, depending on whether the value obtained for the statistic is outside or inside the critical region.

7-5. Effect of Changes in α on the Critical Region and on β

As above, suppose our population is normal, with $\sigma = 10$, and we wish to test a hypothetical mean $\mu = 50$. We noted that, using a random sample of 25 observations and rejecting this hypothesis if $\bar{X}$ is more than 1.96 standard-deviation units, that is, 3.92 units, from 50 gives a 5 per cent level of significance. Once 1.96 is chosen, we find $\alpha = .05$ from Table A-4 or conversely, if we choose $\alpha = .05$, the critical region ($\bar{X}$ more than 1.96 standard deviations from 50) is found using the same table. Since we may choose any value α we wish, we shall consider the effects of different choices of α.

We can see from Fig. 7-1 that if α is chosen smaller than 5 per cent the critical values of $\bar{X}$ will be farther from 50 than 1.96 standard-deviation units. For example, if we choose $\alpha = .01$, we determine two values such that the area under the sampling distribution of $\bar{X}$ to the left of one value is .005 and to the right of the other is .005. From Table A-4 we see that these values are $\mu - 2.576\sigma_{\bar{X}} = 50 - 2.576(2) = 44.848$ and $\mu + 2.576\sigma_{\bar{X}} = 55.152$. Thus the 1 per cent critical region is any $\bar{X}$ less than 44.848 or greater than 55.152. These values are pictured in Fig. 7-3.

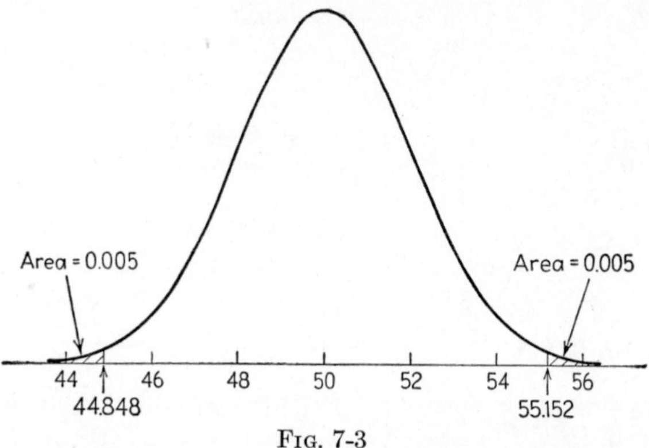

FIG. 7-3

We shall restrict our discussion for the time being to the two values $\alpha = .05$ and $\alpha = .01$ for the level of significance. It is clear that any other level may be used. In general, the smaller the α risk one is willing to take, the farther the critical region will be from the suggested mean.

Now again as in Sec. 7-3 suppose the sample actually comes from the population with mean 52. Using the $\alpha = .01$ test of the hypothesis $\mu = 50$, we shall accept $\mu = 50$, thus making a β error, if $\bar{X}$ is between

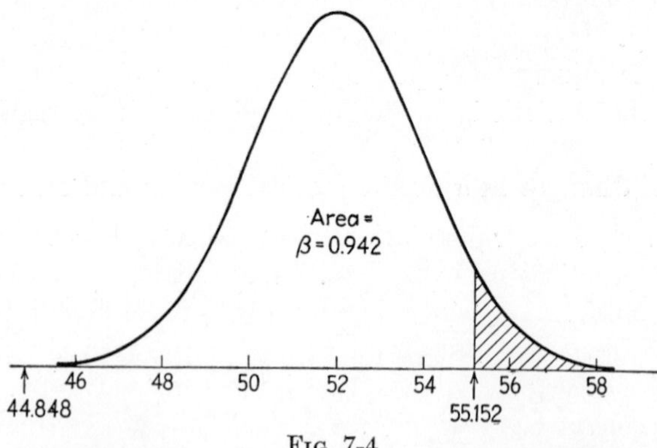

FIG. 7-4

44.848 and 55.152. The sampling distribution of $\bar{X}$ is now considered normal with mean 52 and standard deviation 2; so β is the area under this normal curve between 44.848 and 55.152. To find β, we compute $z_1 = (44.848 - 52)/2 = -3.576$ and $z_2 = (55.152 - 52)/2 = 1.576$ and refer to Table A-4 to obtain $\beta = .942 - .000 = .942$. β is the unshaded area in Fig. 7-4.

Note that a smaller risk (.01 instead of .05) of rejecting a true hypothesis ($\mu = 50$) results in a larger risk (.942 instead of .830) of not recognizing the hypothesis as false when some alternative hypothesis ($\mu = 52$ in this case) is true. The observation that β increases as α decreases is true in general, and the experimenter may wish to vary the level of significance of his test to cause a corresponding change in β. A small value of α is certainly desirable, but taking α too small may result in a β so large that we seldom recognize the hypothesis to be false when it is false.

7-6. Effect on the Critical Region of Varying N

So far in this chapter we have considered an example of only one sample size, $N = 25$. Since $\sigma_{\bar{X}} = \sigma/\sqrt{N}$ changes when N is changed, the critical region will also change for different values of N. Since N enters into the formula $\sigma_{\bar{X}}$ in the denominator, an increase in sample size will cause a decrease in $\sigma_{\bar{X}}$.

In the example with $\sigma = 10$ and the hypothetical mean equal to 50, we agreed to accept at the $\alpha = .05$ level if a sample $\bar{X}$ for a sample of 25 observations was between 46.08 and 53.92, that is, if $\bar{X}$ was within $1.96\sigma_{\bar{X}}$ of the suggested mean 50. If we had a sample of size 100, then $\sigma_{\bar{X}} = 10/\sqrt{100} = 1$ and we would expect 95 per cent of the samples to have a mean $\bar{X}$ within $1.96\sigma_{\bar{X}} = 1.96$ units of the population mean μ. Thus the $\alpha = .05$ critical region would be values of $\bar{X}$ less than $50 - 1.96 = 48.04$ and values of $\bar{X}$ greater than $50 + 1.96 = 51.96$. For the same level of significance the acceptance region is smaller for larger sample sizes. The interval is shortened by the appropriate amount to account for the fact that there is a better chance that the mean $\bar{X}$ of a large sample will be closer to μ than the mean of a smaller sample.

Table 7-1 shows a set of critical regions for various values of N, and $\alpha = .05, .01$. If z_α represents, as in Chap. 6, the 100α percentile of the

TABLE 7-1. CRITICAL REGIONS FOR TESTING $\mu = 50$, GIVEN $\sigma = 10$, REJECTING IF $\bar{X}$ IS NOT CLOSE TO 50

N	$\alpha = .05$		$\alpha = .01$	
	$\bar{X} <$ $50 - 1.960\sigma_{\bar{X}}$	$\bar{X} >$ $50 + 1.960\sigma_{\bar{X}}$	$\bar{X} <$ $50 - 2.576\sigma_{\bar{X}}$	$\bar{X} >$ $50 + 2.576\sigma_{\bar{X}}$
1	30.40	69.60	24.24	75.76
3	38.68	61.32	35.13	64.87
5	41.23	58.77	38.48	61.52
10	43.80	56.20	41.85	58.15
25	46.08	53.92	44.85	55.15
50	47.23	52.77	46.36	53.64
100	48.04	51.96	47.42	52.58
400	49.02	50.98	48.71	51.29
1,000	49.38	50.62	49.19	50.81

unit normal distribution as given in Table A-4, the critical region for testing the hypothesis $\mu = \mu_0$ at the α level of significance is

$$\bar{X} < \mu_0 + z_{\frac{1}{2}\alpha} \frac{\sigma}{\sqrt{N}} \qquad \text{and} \qquad \bar{X} > \mu_0 + z_{1-\frac{1}{2}\alpha} \frac{\sigma}{\sqrt{N}}$$

7-7. Effect on β of Changes in α and N

We have noted in the previous sections that:

1. Changing α from .05 to .01 had the effect of increasing β if N remained fixed.

2. Keeping α fixed and increasing N increased the size of the critical region (i.e., a smaller deviation from the hypothesis was considered significant).

We shall now consider the effect on β of increasing N when α is fixed. In Table 7-1 we have recorded critical regions for testing the hypothesis that a population which has $\sigma = 10$ has a mean $\mu = 50$. The regions are recorded for several values of N and for $\alpha = .05, .01$. Suppose as in Sec. 7-3 a sample is drawn from a population with mean 52 in place of the hypothetical value 50. We can compute as in Sec. 7-3 the value of β corresponding to each of the 18 examples (two values of α and nine values of N). For $N = 25$ we have already found $\beta = .830$ for $\alpha = .05$ and $\beta = .942$ for $\alpha = .01$. Table 7-2 lists the values of β for $\mu = 52$ corresponding to the sample size and the values of α used in Table 7-1.

TABLE 7-2. VALUES OF β FOR ALTERNATIVE $\mu = 52$ IN TESTING THE HYPOTHESIS $\mu = 50$

N	$\alpha = .05$	$\alpha = .01$
1	.945	.988
3	.936	.985
5	.927	.912
10	.903	.973
25	.830	.942
50	.707	.877
100	.484	.717
400	.021	.077
1,000	.00001	.0001

We note that, for a fixed alternative and some fixed level of significance, α, the chance β of not declaring a false hypothesis false decreases as N increases. We can now summarize the results: If a single alternative to the hypothesis is stated, a statistical test will have the property that:

For α fixed choosing N smaller increases β, and choosing N larger decreases β.

For N fixed choosing α smaller increases β, and choosing α larger decreases β.

7-8. Dependence of β on the Alternative Considered

Thus far we have considered the single alternative $\mu = 52$. Other alternatives will have other values of β. Suppose again that we are testing the hypothesis $\mu = 50$ with $\sigma = 10$ and $\alpha = .05$ with a sample of $N = 25$ observations. The critical region from Table 7-1 calls for rejection of the hypothesis if $\bar{X}$ is not between 46.08 and 53.92. Now, if in fact $\mu = 53$, we compute, as in Sec. 7-3, $z_1 = (46.08 - 53)/2 = -3.46$ and $z_2 = (53.92 - 53)/2 = .46$ and from Table A-4 we find

$$\beta = .677 - .000 = .677$$

This value of β for $\mu = 53$ is smaller than $\beta = .830$ for $\mu = 52$. We, of course, expect our test to have less chance of failing to reject $\mu = 50$ when the observations are from a population with $\mu = 53$ than when they are from a population with $\mu = 52$. In other words, we expect to have a greater chance of rejecting $\mu = 50$ when a sample is drawn from a population with $\mu = 53$ than when it is drawn from a population with mean

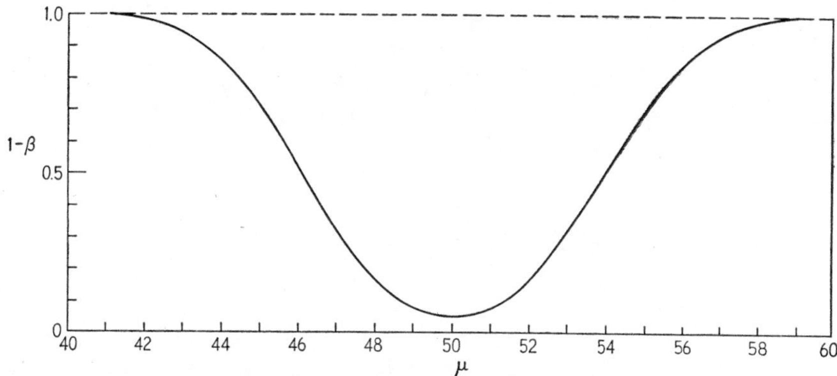

FIG. 7-5. The power curve for test of the hypothesis $\mu = 50$ with $\sigma = 10$ and $\alpha = .05$ with a sample of 25 observations. This is the chance that $\bar{X}$ is not between 46.08 and 53.92 when samples are drawn from a population with mean μ.

$\mu = 52$. For any fixed N and α we can compute β for a series of values of μ. For the example carried throughout this chapter with $N = 25$ and $\alpha = .05$, the computed values of β were plotted to draw the curve in Fig. 7-5, with μ on the horizontal axis and $1 - \beta$ on the vertical axis. The curve is called the *power* curve for the statistical test used. More details on these concepts are given in Chap. 14.

7-9. One-sided Tests

In some cases it will be desirable to reject a hypothetical mean only if the observed $\bar{X}$ is unusually distant in one direction, e.g., if an unusually large value of $\bar{X}$ is observed. If the hypothesis states $\mu = 50$, with

$\sigma = 10$, $N = 25$, $\alpha = .05$, we may use as a critical region values of $\bar{X}$ greater than $50 + 1.645\sigma/\sqrt{N} = 50 + 1.645(2) = 53.39$.

From Table A-4 we take the quantity 1.645 since there is a 95 per cent chance that $z = (\bar{X} - 50)/2$ is less than 1.645 if actually $\bar{X}$ is from a population with $\mu = 50$. Figure 7-6 shows the distribution of $\bar{X}$ if the hypothesis is correct with the critical region indicated.

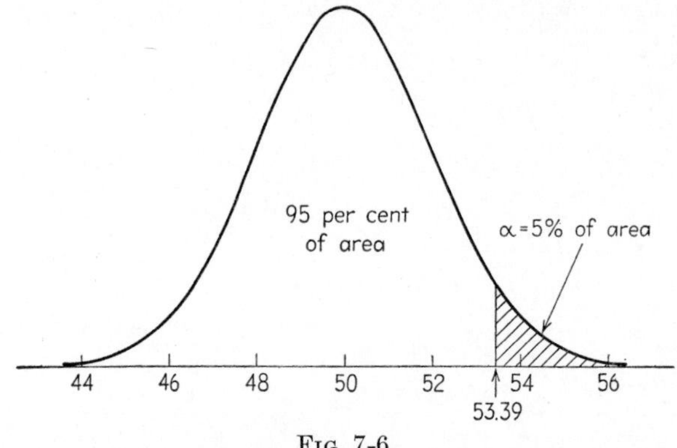

FIG. 7-6

The discussion of the effects on the β error for changes in α and sample size can be investigated for this one-sided critical region in a manner similar to that discussed in Secs. 7-3 to 7-8 for the two-sided critical region. If in fact $\mu = 52$, the sampling distribution of $\bar{X}$ has mean 52. This distribution is in Fig. 7-7, and the area representing the β error is

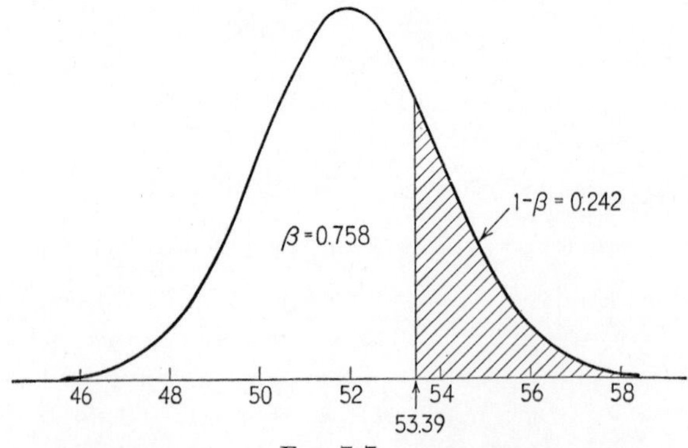

FIG. 7-7

shown. The chance β of accepting $\mu = 50$ when actually $\mu = 52$ is the unshaded area. The value of β is computed as in Sec. 7-3 by noting that, for $\bar{X} = 53.39$, $z = (53.39 - 52)/2 = 1.39/2 = .70$. From Table A-4 we see that the area is $\beta = .758$. The same conclusions summarized in Sec. 7-7 hold for one-sided tests.

In using the one-sided critical region we are really considering only alternative population means which are larger than 50. This fact may be indicated in the statement of the hypothesis as $\mu \leq 50$, which is read "μ is less than or equal to 50." It is assumed here that values of μ less than 50 are acceptable and the values of $\bar{X}$ which are noted as critical are unusually large values only.

Obviously the above discussion could be restated using a critical region consisting only of small values of $\bar{X}$ to test the hypothesis $\mu \geq 50$.

Some examples where one-sided critical regions seem reasonable are as follows:

1. Drinking water may be tested for bacteria count and rejected only if the bacteria count is too high.
2. A new fertilizer may be tested for crop yield and the old fertilizer rejected only if a significantly higher yield results with the new.
3. Cores of concrete may be tested for strength and rejected only if they are unusually low in strength.
4. Contents of peanut-butter jars labeled "Eight ounces net weight" may be weighed and the product rejected as being improperly packaged only if the weight is too low.

7-10. Testing a Hypothesis in a Dichotomous Population

In Sec. 5-8 we considered the sampling distribution of $\bar{X}$ for samples of size N taken from a population containing a proportion p of individuals marked 1 and a proportion $1 - p$ of individuals marked 0. We noted that the sampling distribution of $\bar{X}$ has a mean equal to p and a standard deviation equal to $\sqrt{p(1 - p)/N}$ and that the distribution of $\bar{X}$ is approximately normal for large N. These results can be used to test a hypothetical value of p. Suppose we wish to test the hypothesis that a certain population of flies grown in a laboratory is 50 per cent male and 50 per cent female. This is a test of the hypothesis $p = .50$. Suppose we take a random sample of 100 flies from the population and observe 40 males. Would this result lead to a rejection of the hypothesis of $p = .50$ at the .05 level of significance? Here $N = 100$, $\bar{X} = .40$, $\alpha = .05$, and $z = (\bar{X} - \mu)/\sigma_{\bar{X}} = (.40 - .50)/.05 = -2.0$. A two-sided test would reject if $\bar{X}$ were more than 1.96 standard-deviation units from the hypothetical mean; therefore, we reject the hypothesis in this case. Also a hypothesis of $p \geqq .50$ would be rejected for an observed $\bar{X} = .40$ since the rejection region is any $\bar{X}$ less than

$$\mu - 1.645\sigma_{\bar{X}} = .50 - 1.645(.05) = .50 - .082 = .418$$

GLOSSARY

α error
β error
critical region
level of significance
statistical hypothesis
statistical proof

DISCUSSION QUESTIONS

1. What are the two kinds of inference we are studying? What is a statistical inference?

2. Does our use of the words *statistical proof* agree with the definition of the word *proof* in the dictionary?

3. What are the two types of errors which we might make in testing hypotheses? Why, in a particular problem, can we make only one? Would it be an advantage if we knew which error we might make?

4. How can the chances of making either type of error be made very small?

5. To which type of error does the level of significance refer?

6. Is the chance of making a β error equal to 1 minus the chance of making an α error? Explain.

7. Distinguish between assumption and hypothesis.

CLASS EXERCISE

Suppose that you believe that you are sampling from the population represented in Table A-2 but that you actually are sampling from the population in Table A-23. You wish to test the hypothesis that the population mean is zero at the 5 per cent level of significance. Assuming that $\sigma^2 = 1$, determine a test and a critical region. Then, using the samples from Table A-23, approximate the chance, or relative frequency, of accepting your false hypothesis (i.e., the β error).

PROBLEMS

1. Check the values in Table 7-1 for $N = 50$, and compute similar limits for $N = 64$, $\alpha = .05$, and for $N = 64$, $\alpha = .01$.

2. We wish to test the hypothesis that the mean weight of a population of people is 140 pounds. Using $\sigma = 15$ pounds, $\alpha = .05$, and a sample of 36 people, find (*a*) the values of $\bar{X}$ which would lead to rejection of the hypothesis and (*b*) the β error if $\mu = 150$ pounds. Use a two-sided test.

3. We wish to test the hypothesis that the mean IQ of a student body is 100. Using $\sigma = 15$, $\alpha = .01$, and a sample of 100 students, determine the critical region for a two-sided test.

4. Suppose in a sample of 100 people the mean height $\bar{X}$ was observed to be 67.0 inches. If the hypothetical height of the population is 66.0 inches and $\sigma = 3$ inches, would you reject $\mu = 66.0$ with $\alpha = .05$? With $\alpha = .01$? With $\alpha = .001$? Use a two-sided test.

5. Determine, for $\alpha = .10$, $N = 36$, $\sigma = 5$, values of $\bar{X}$ which would cause rejection of $\mu = 50$, using a two-sided test.

6. In which of the following cases would you reject the hypothetical value of μ. using a two-sided test?

(*a*) $N = 25$, $\sigma = 2$, $\alpha = .05$, $\mu = 50$, $\bar{X} = 51.0$.
(*b*) $N = 100$, $\sigma = 2$, $\alpha = .01$, $\mu = 67$, $\bar{X} = 66.5$.
(*c*) $N = 2{,}500$, $\sigma = 2$, $\alpha = .01$, $\mu = 1.60$, $\bar{X} = 1.70$.
(*d*) $N = 3{,}600$, $\sigma = .5$, $\alpha = .01$, $\mu = .50$, $\bar{X} = .51$.
(*e*) $N = 4$, $\sigma = .5$, $\alpha = .05$, $\mu = .50$, $\bar{X} = .75$.

7. (*a*) Compute the critical region for the hypothesis discussed in Table 7-1 for $N = 100$, $\alpha = .10$, using a two-sided test.

(*b*) For this case, compute β for the values $\mu = 51$, $\mu = 52$, $\mu = 53$, $\mu = 54$. Draw figures analogous to Figs. 7-1 and 7-3, shading the corresponding areas.

(*c*) Draw a curve showing values of $1 - \beta$ for this value of α.

(*d*) Read from the curve the values of $1 - \beta$ for $\mu = 50.5$ and $\mu = 51.5$.

8. What values of $\bar{X}$ for a sample of $N = 400$ from a population containing a proportion p of 1s and a proportion $1 - p$ of 0s would be in the critical regions for tests of the hypotheses $p = .50$, $p = \frac{1}{3}$, $p = .25$ if two-sided tests with $\alpha = .01$ were used? If one-sided tests with $\alpha = .05$ were used?

9. Would an observed proportion of .30 in a sample of $N = 900$ be in the critical region for a two-sided test of the hypothesis $p = \frac{1}{3}$ at the 5 per cent level of significance?

CHAPTER 8

THE VARIANCE: ESTIMATION AND TESTS OF HYPOTHESES

In some types of research it is of great importance to study the variability of some measurement. This importance may be illustrated in the following examples. The problem of teaching a class which is homogeneous in ability is much different from the problem of teaching a class in which abilities differ widely, even though both classes are of similar ability on the average. In the manufacture of links for a chain, not only should the links have a sufficient strength on the average, but it is essential that the variability about that average be small.

We shall develop procedures for testing statistically whether two estimates of variability are significantly different.

8-1. Sampling Distributions of s^2 and F

As was noted in Chap. 6 the sampling distribution of s^2/σ^2, computed from random samples from a normal population, is called a χ^2/df distribution with $(N - 1)$ degrees of freedom, indicated by $\chi^2/\text{df}(N - 1)$. Several percentiles of this distribution are given in Table A-6*b*. We shall use this distribution to test various hypothetical statements about the value of σ^2. The graphs in Fig. 8-1 show the shapes of certain χ^2/df distribution curves.

Suppose we have two random samples drawn from a normal population. We shall let X_{1i} be the ith observation in the first sample and X_{2i} be the ith observation in the second sample. Let N_1 be the number of observations in the first sample and N_2 the number in the second. Then the means and variances of the two samples are as follows:

$$\bar{X}_1 = \frac{\Sigma X_{1i}}{N_1} \qquad s_1^2 = \frac{\Sigma(X_{1i} - \bar{X}_1)^2}{N_1 - 1}$$

$$\bar{X}_2 = \frac{\Sigma X_{2i}}{N_2} \qquad s_2^2 = \frac{\Sigma(X_{2i} - \bar{X}_2)^2}{N_2 - 1}$$

The statistic F given by the formula

$$F = \frac{s_1^2}{s_2^2}$$

has a sampling distribution called the F distribution. There are two sample variances involved and two sets of degrees of freedom, $N_1 - 1$ in the numerator of the F and $N_2 - 1$ in the denominator. Each pair of degrees of freedom determines an F distribution, and to indicate which is intended, we shall write $F(N_1 - 1, N_2 - 1)$, where the first number in parentheses is the number of degrees of freedom in the numerator and the second is the number of degrees of freedom in the denominator.

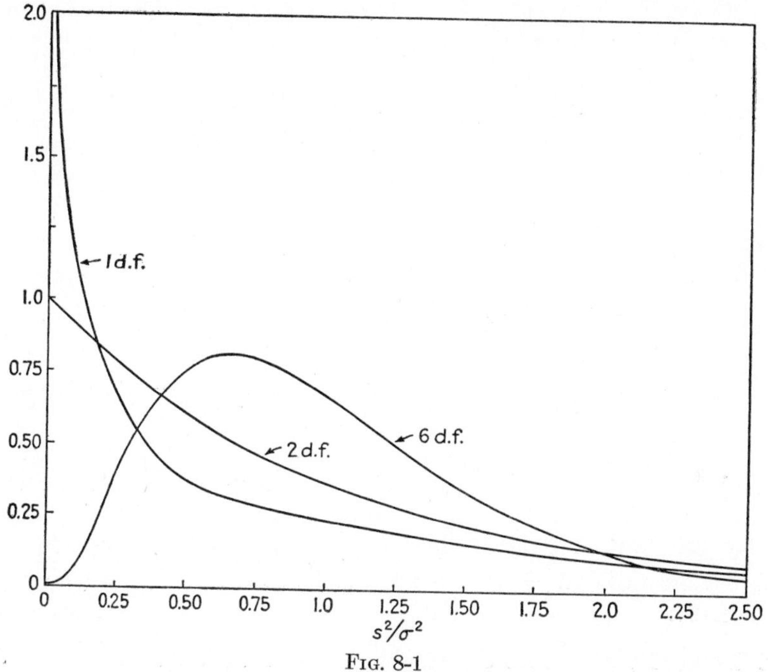

FIG. 8-1

Table A-7 gives critical values of $F(N_1 - 1, N_2 - 1)$. This table must be entered with three values, the appropriate percentage level, the number of degrees of freedom in the numerator, and the number of degrees of freedom in the denominator. Two separate tables, A-7*a* and A-7*b*, are given for cumulative proportions of 95 per cent, 99 per cent ($F_{.95}$, $F_{.99}$). These tables are also labeled 5%, 1%, and these percentages refer to the proportion of the area under the curves to the right of the values given in the tables. The number of degrees of freedom in the numerator of the F ratio is at the top of the tables, and the number of degrees of freedom in the denominator is in the left-hand column. Thus, for example, if $N_1 - 1 = 10$ and $N_2 - 1 = 12$, we could read from the tables that 1 per cent of the area under the $F(10,12)$ curve is to the right of 4.30, 5 per cent is to the right of 2.75, etc. The chance of $F = (s_1^2/s_2^2)$ being larger than 2.75 is .05, etc. Note that the distribution of $F(10,12)$ is different from the distribution of $F(12,10)$, and correspondingly different numbers appear in the table under 12 and across from 10 from those appearing under 10 and across from 12.

Table A-7*c* lists these percentiles as well as a number of other percentiles. The percentiles for each distribution are given in single groups. For example, suppose we wish to find percentiles for the ratio of two variances, the variance in the numerator having 4 degrees of freedom and the variance in the denominator having 8 degrees of freedom. We enter the table in the column headed $\nu_1 = 4$, and, moving down the left-hand side of the table to $\nu_2 = 8$, we can read $F_{.95}(4,8) = 3.84$. Similarly $F_{.50}(4,8) = .915$, $F_{.10}(4,8) = .253$, $F_{.50}(12,15) = .989$, $F_{.95}(2,\infty) = 3.00$, etc. Two F-distribution curves are sketched in Fig. 8-2.

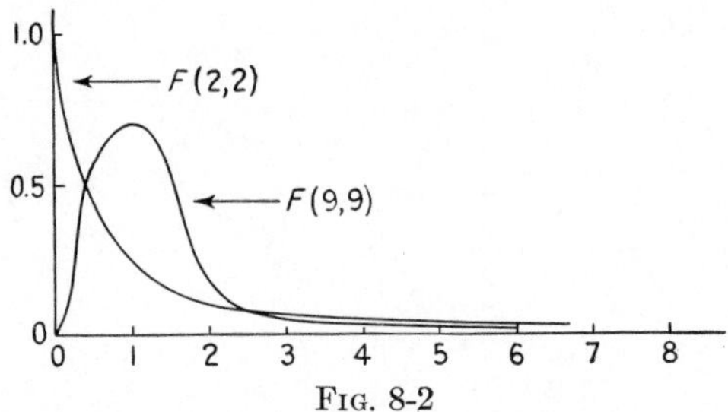

FIG. 8-2

It might be noted that ∞ degrees of freedom corresponds to a case where the value of s^2 is equal to σ^2, and the $F(N-1,\infty)$ distribution is the same as the distribution of s^2/σ^2, thus a χ^2/df distribution. Therefore the critical values of $F(N-1,\infty)$ are the same as those of $\chi^2/\text{df}(N-1)$ in Table A-6*b*.

8-2. Tests of Hypotheses Concerning a Single Variance

Suppose the hypothesis is made that the variance σ^2 of a normal population has some fixed value, say, σ_0^2. Our procedure to "test" this statement will be to draw a random sample from the population and compute the value of s^2 for this sample. If the observed s^2 is markedly smaller or markedly larger than the supposed variance σ_0^2, we shall reject that value as a reasonable value for σ^2. The criterion of "how much larger or how much smaller" will be based on the sampling distribution of s^2/σ_0^2. If, *and only if*, the hypothesis of $\sigma^2 = \sigma_0^2$ is true, the sampling distribution of s^2/σ_0^2 is a χ^2/df distribution. By using this distribution, therefore, we can specify the level of significance α and control the chance of rejecting the hypothesis when it is actually true.

The form below indicates the steps in testing this hypothesis. We shall abbreviate the word hypothesis to H, followed by the particular hypothetical statement to be tested.

1. $H: \sigma^2 = \sigma_0^2$.

2. Choose the level of significance α. Commonly used values are $\alpha = .01, .05, .10$.

3. The statistic used to test this hypothesis is $\chi^2/\text{df} = s^2/\sigma_0^2$.

4. Assuming that the observations are a random sample from a normally distributed population which does have $\sigma^2 = \sigma_0^2$, then percentiles of the sampling distribution of this statistic are given in Table A-6*b*.

5. The critical region is $s^2/\sigma_0^2 < \chi_{\frac{1}{2}\alpha}^2/\text{df}(N-1)$ and

$$s^2/\sigma_0^2 > \chi_{1-\frac{1}{2}\alpha}^2/\text{df}(N-1)$$

where $\chi_{\frac{1}{2}\alpha}^2/\text{df}(N-1)$ is the value from Table A-6*b* which has a proportion $\frac{1}{2}\alpha$ of the cases in the sampling distribution to the left of the value and $\chi_{1-\frac{1}{2}\alpha}^2/\text{df}(N-1)$ is the value which has a proportion of $1 - \frac{1}{2}\alpha$ of the cases to the left. For example, if $\alpha = .10$ and $N = 10$, then $\chi_{.05}^2/\text{df}(9) = .369$ and $\chi_{.95}^2/\text{df}(9) = 1.88$.

6. Compute the statistic s^2/σ_0^2, and reject the hypothesis if the value is in the critical region or accept the hypothesis if the value is not in the critical region.

Example 1. A standard examination has been given for several years with $\mu = 70$ and $\sigma^2 = 9$. A school using this examination for the first time gave it to a group of 25 students who obtained a mean of $\bar{X} = 71$ and a variance of $s^2 = 12$. Is there reason to doubt that the scores of all the students in the school would have a variance of 9?

1. $H: \sigma^2 = 9$.
2. $\alpha = .10$.
3. The statistic used is $(\chi^2/\text{df}) = (s^2/\sigma_0^2) = (s^2/9)$.
4. If the assumptions in the above form hold, we can refer to Table A-6*b* for critical values.
5. The critical region is $s^2/9 < .577$ and $s^2/9 > 1.52$.
6. Here $(s^2/9) = \frac{12}{9} = 1.33$, which is not in the critical region, and so we do not have sufficient reason to doubt, at the 10 per cent level of significance, the statement that $\sigma^2 = 9$.

One-sided Alternatives. Frequently statistical problems are concerned with the rejection of hypotheses on variances only when the sample indicates that the parameter involved is actually larger than the hypothetical value.

For example, it might be satisfactory to manufacture an article with variance 5 but unsatisfactory if the variance is much larger than 5. If the variance is much greater than 5, we would wish to retool our machinery, but if the variance is 5 *or is less than* 5, we would wish to continue production without change. To test this hypothesis, we would reject only if $s^2/5$ is significantly large. To indicate this situation, we state as a hypothesis $\sigma^2 \leq 5$, where the "less than or equal to" sign reminds us to reject only if $s^2/5$ is large. We use $\sigma^2 = 5$ as a hypothetical value and use the sampling distribution of $s^2/5$, that is, $\chi^2/\text{df}(N-1)$, to determine a critical region corresponding to a given level of significance α. Then, if $\sigma^2 = 5$, we have a chance α of saying that σ^2 is larger than 5, while if σ^2 is actually less than 5, we have an even smaller chance than α of saying that σ^2 is larger.

Situations such as the above consider "one-sided" alternatives; i.e., values on only one side of $\sigma_0{}^2$ are cause for rejection, while the situation described first considers a "two-sided" alternative hypothesis. Note that the example in Chap. 7 considered one- and two-sided hypotheses concerning the mean μ.

The outline below indicates steps in testing a one-sided hypothesis. The hypothesis $\sigma^2 \geq \sigma_0{}^2$ is tested in a similar fashion except that it is rejected only if $s^2/\sigma_0{}^2$ is small.

1. $H: \sigma^2 \leq \sigma_0{}^2$.
2. Choose the level of significance α.
3. Use the statistic $\chi^2/\text{df} = (s^2/\sigma_0{}^2)$ to test the hypothesis.
4. If the observations are a random sample from a normal population and if the hypothesis is true, then this statistic has a $\chi^2/\text{df}(N-1)$ distribution as given in Table A-6*b*.
5. For a critical region take values of $s^2/\sigma_0{}^2$ larger than $\chi^2_{1-\alpha}/\text{df}(N-1)$ as given in Table A-6*b*.
6. Compute the value of the statistic, and accept or reject the hypothesis.

Example 2. A certain type of light bulb whose burning time is measured in hours has a variance of 10,000. A sample of 20 new-type light bulbs is observed to have $s^2 = 12{,}000$. Is this reason to believe, at the 5 per cent level of significance, that the variance of the new type is more than 10,000?

1. $H: \sigma^2 \leq 10{,}000$. This is stated in this fashion so that if we reject we have sufficient reason to believe that $\sigma^2 > 10{,}000$.
2. $\alpha = .05$.
3. Use $s^2/10{,}000$.
4. If the assumptions above hold, the sampling distribution of this statistic is $\chi^2/\text{df}(19)$.
5. Reject if $\dfrac{s^2}{10{,}000} > \chi_{.95}{}^2/\text{df}(19) = 1.59$.
6. Here $(s^2/10{,}000) = 1.2$, and so we do not have justification, at the 5 per cent level of significance, to reject the hypothesis.

8-3. Tests of Hypotheses Concerning the Variances of Two Populations

The F distribution can be used to test the hypothesis that the variances $\sigma_1{}^2$ and $\sigma_2{}^2$ of two normally distributed populations are equal. It is not necessary to assume that the two populations have equal means. To test this hypothesis, our procedure is to take a random sample from each population and compute the ratio of the sample variances, $F = (s_1^2/s_2^2)$. If this ratio is smaller or larger than would be expected by chance, say, 95 per cent of the time, we reject the hypothesis that $\sigma_1^2 = \sigma_2^2$. The F-distribution tables give values exceeded a certain proportion of the time. If we assign one-half of the 5 per cent rejection region to large values of F and one-half to small values, we shall reject the hypothesis of equal variances if $F > F_{.975}(N_1 - 1, N_2 - 1)$ or if $F < F_{.025}(N_1 - 1, N_2 - 1)$. For example, if our samples have 13 and 11 cases, respectively, then there is a 2.5 per cent chance that $s_1^2/s_2^2 > F_{.975}(12,10) = 3.62$ and a 2.5 per cent chance that $s_1^2/s_2^2 < F_{.025}(12,10) = .297$. These values are obtained from Table A-7*c*. If we agreed to reject if either of these results occurs, we would test the hypothesis at the 5 per cent level of significance.

The list below indicates steps in testing the hypothesis of equal variances.

1. $H: \sigma_1^2 = \sigma_2^2$.
2. Choose α.
3. Use the statistic $F = (s_1^2/s_2^2)$ to test the hypothesis.
4. If the observations are random samples from normal populations and if the hypothesis is true, then the sampling distribution of this statistic is $F(N_1 - 1, N_2 - 1)$.
5. Reject if $F > F_{1-\frac{1}{2}\alpha}(N_1 - 1, N_2 - 1)$ or if $F < F_{\frac{1}{2}\alpha}(N_1 - 1, N_2 - 1)$.
6. Compute the F from your sample, and reject or accept the hypothesis.

Example. We wish to test whether the yields of two types of wheat have the same variances. We observe $s_1^2 = 17$ for the weights of 15 plots of one type of wheat and $s_2^2 = 29$ for the weights of 12 plots of the second type. Is there reason to doubt, at the 10 per cent level of significance, that the population variances are equal?

1. $H: \sigma_1^2 = \sigma_2^2$.
2. $\alpha = .10$.
3. Use $F = (s_1^2/s_2^2) = \frac{17}{29} = .586$.
4. If the assumptions listed above are satisfied, the sampling distribution of this statistic is $F(14,11)$.
5. Reject if $F > 2.74$ or if $F < .391$. Note that these values are the 95 per cent and 5 per cent values of $F(14,11)$.
6. F is not in the critical region, and so we accept the hypothesis.

One-sided Alternatives. We can also test hypotheses of the type $\sigma_1^2 \leq \sigma_2^2$. The procedure is similar to that above except that we would reject only if the ratio s_1^2/s_2^2 is larger than $F_{1-\alpha}(N_1 - 1, N_2 - 1)$.

8-4. Values of β for Tests Involving Variances

In the two-sided test of the hypothesis $H: \sigma^2 = \sigma_0^2$ we agree to accept the hypothesis if s^2/σ_0^2 is between

$$P_{\frac{1}{2}\alpha} = \chi_{\frac{1}{2}\alpha}^2/\text{df}(N - 1) \qquad \text{and} \qquad P_{1-\frac{1}{2}\alpha} = \chi_{1-\frac{1}{2}\alpha}^2/\text{df}(N - 1)$$

That is, when

$$P_{\frac{1}{2}\alpha} < \frac{s^2}{{\sigma_0}^2} < P_{1-\frac{1}{2}\alpha}$$

This is equivalent to accepting if

$$\frac{{\sigma_0}^2}{\sigma^2} P_{\frac{1}{2}\alpha} < \frac{s^2}{\sigma^2} < \frac{{\sigma_0}^2}{\sigma^2} P_{1-\frac{1}{2}\alpha}$$

If σ^2 is the correct value, i.e., if the sample is actually taken from a population with this value of σ^2, then the chance that the inequality holds is given by the $\chi^2/\text{df}(N - 1)$ distribution and can be found, at least approximately, from Table A-6*b*.

Example. Suppose we are testing the hypothesis H: $\sigma^2 = 9$ with $N = 25$, $\alpha = .10$ as in Example 1 of Sec. 8-2. We shall accept $\sigma^2 = 9$ if $s^2/9$ is between .369 and 1.88 with risk $\alpha = .10$ of rejecting a true hypothesis. Now suppose that the sample is taken from a population with $\sigma^2 = 18$, that is, from a population with a variance twice as large. We now compute the value of β (the chance of accepting $\sigma^2 = 9$) for this alternative. Note that the statement that $s^2/9$ is between .369 and 1.88 is equivalent to the statement that $s^2/18$ is between $\frac{1}{2}(.369) = .185$ and $\frac{1}{2}(1.88) = .94$. We have multiplied each term by ${\sigma_0}^2/\sigma^2 = \frac{1}{2}$. Since $s^2/18$ has a $\chi^2/\text{df}(24)$ distribution under the alternative hypothesis, we can use the line for 24 df in Table A-6*b*. There is less than .0005 chance of $s^2/18$ being less than .185 and .45 chance of $s^2/18$ being less than .94; so the chance of accepting the hypothesis $H: \sigma^2 = 9$ when actually $\sigma^2 = 18$ is approximately $\beta = .45$.

Example. Suppose we are testing the hypothesis $H: \sigma^2 \leq 10{,}000$ with $N = 20$ and $\alpha = .05$ as in Example 2 of Sec. 8-2. We shall accept this hypothesis if $s^2/10{,}000$ is less than 1.59. Now suppose that actually σ^2 is 30,000, that is, three times the hypothetical value. Note that $s^2/10{,}000$ less than 1.59 is equivalent to $s^2/30{,}000$ less than $1.59(\frac{1}{3}) = .53$. The chance that this inequality holds is read from Table A-6*b* for $20 - 1 = 19$ df and is approximately .05. Therefore for the alternative $\sigma^2 = 30{,}000$ our test has $\beta = .05$. If we wish to find the alternative σ^2 which corresponds to a particular value of β, $\beta = .50$, we solve for the σ^2 which makes $1.59(10{,}000/\sigma^2) = .965$, the 50th percentile of the χ^2/df distribution. Here, $\sigma^2 = 1.59(10{,}000)/.965 = 16{,}500$.

Similarly, if we are testing the hypothesis that two populations have equal variances H: ${\sigma_1}^2 = {\sigma_2}^2$, we accept the hypothesis if $F = {s_1}^2/{s_2}^2$ is between two percentiles of the F distribution,

$$F_{\frac{1}{2}\alpha}(N_1 - 1, N_2 - 1) < \frac{{s_1}^2}{{s_2}^2} < F_{1-\frac{1}{2}\alpha}(N_1 - 1, N_2 - 1)$$

If σ_1^2 is not equal to σ_2^2, then the quantity $(s_1^2/\sigma_1^2)/(s_2^2/\sigma_2^2)$ has the F distribution with $N_1 - 1$ and $N_2 - 1$ degrees of freedom. Therefore, in order to find the β error, we change the above inequality into one which is equivalent by multiplying each term by σ_2^2/σ_1^2 as follows,

$$\frac{\sigma_2^2}{\sigma_1^2} F_{\frac{1}{2}\alpha}(N_1 - 1, N_2 - 1) < \frac{s_1^2/\sigma_1^2}{s_2^2/\sigma_2^2} < \frac{\sigma_2^2}{\sigma_1^2} F_{1-\frac{1}{2}\alpha}(N_1 - 1, N_2 - 1)$$

and the chance of this occurring can be read, at least approximately, from Table A-7*c*.

Example. Suppose we are testing the hypothesis that $\sigma_1^2 = \sigma_2^2$, using samples of size $N_1 = 16$ and $N_2 = 12$ with $\alpha = .10$ as in the example of Sec. 8-3. Suppose actually $\sigma_1^2 = 2\sigma_2^2$, that is, the first variance is twice as large as the second. We accept $\sigma_1^2 = \sigma_2^2$ if s_1^2/s_2^2 is between .398 and 2.72, which is equivalent to $\frac{1}{2}s_1^2/s_2^2$ being between $.398/2 = .199$ and $2.72/2 = 1.36$, and the chance that this is so can be obtained from Table A-7*c* for 15 and 11 df as $.68 - .00 = .68$.

8-5. Estimation of Variances Using Several Samples

If two or more samples are from the same population or from different populations having equal variances, σ^2, then the variances of the several samples, one from each population, can be pooled or averaged to give an estimate of σ^2. The formula for this estimate if there are k samples is

$$s_p^2 = \frac{(n_1 - 1)s_1^2 + (n_2 - 1)s_2^2 + \cdots + (n_k - 1)s_k^2}{n_1 + n_2 + \cdots + n_k - k}$$

This s_p^2 is an unbiased estimate of σ^2. If the populations have normal distributions, not necessarily the same means, the sampling distribution of s_p^2/σ^2 is a $\chi^2/\text{df}(n_1 + n_2 + \cdots + n_k - k)$ distribution. In this case 90 per cent confidence limits for σ^2 are

$$\frac{s_p^2}{\chi_{.95}^2/\text{df}(\Sigma n_i - k)} < \sigma^2 < \frac{s_p^2}{\chi_{.05}^2/\text{df}(\Sigma n_i - k)}$$

Another method of estimating σ^2 is to group all the observations into one sample and compute the variance of this single set of numbers. This procedure is valid only if the separate populations have the same mean. Otherwise this estimate will tend to be somewhat larger than σ^2. As an example of this situation, consider an extreme case where one population has mean 0, and a second population has mean 10, and each has variance $\sigma^2 = 1$. Individuals in a sample from the first population would cluster around 0, while individuals in a sample from the second population would cluster around 10. If the two samples were combined into one group, the mean would be about 5 and the variance of the single set would be approximately 25, much larger than $\sigma^2 = 1$. This is an extreme case, of course, but it indicates that grouping several samples into a single sample to estimate variance may be considerably less reliable than averaging the several sample variances.

Still another method of estimating σ^2 was discussed in Sec. 6-9. The variance of the means of several samples each of size N is computed. This variance is an estimate of $\sigma_{\bar{X}}^2 = \sigma^2/N$. Thus we may estimate σ^2 by multiplying the variance of the means by N. Again this method is valid if the samples come from populations having the same mean, but the estimate tends to be too large if the population means are unequal. This fact is used in the analysis-of-variance techniques in Chap. 10.

GLOSSARY

chi-square distribution
$\chi^2/\mathrm{df}(N)$
confidence limits for σ^2
F distribution
$F_\alpha(N_1,N_2)$
pooled estimate of σ^2

DISCUSSION QUESTIONS

1. When does s^2 have a χ^2/df distribution?

2. Explain the reasoning and assumptions used in forming a confidence interval for estimating σ^2 from s^2.

3. How many F distributions are represented in Table A-7?

CLASS EXERCISES

1. For the six samples drawn for the Class Exercise, Chap. 3, compute s_p^2, and also compute the variance of all 60 observations. Collect the results of all the students, and verify the statement that s_p^2 is an unbiased estimate of σ^2 but that the variance of the combined groups is generally much larger than σ^2.

2. From the observed values of s^2 for samples of size 10 from Table A-2 verify that if you were testing the hypothesis $\sigma^2 = 1$ at the 5 per cent level of significance you would have rejected this hypothesis 5 per cent of the time.

PROBLEMS

1. What values of s^2 from a sample of N observations from a normal population would cause you to reject the hypothetical value σ_0^2 in each of the following cases:

(*a*) $N = 21, \sigma_0^2 = 100, \alpha = .01$, two-sided test.
(*b*) $N = 50, \sigma_0^2 \leq 15, \alpha = .05$, one-sided test.
(*c*) $N = 12, \sigma_0^2 = 20, \alpha = .05$, two sided test.
(*d*) $N = 61, \sigma_0^2 = 30, \alpha = .05$, two-sided test.
(*e*) $N = 38, \sigma_0^2 \geq .016, \alpha = .10$, one-sided test.

2. If a sample of 25 observations has $s^2 = 12.6$, would you accept or reject at the 5 per cent level of significance the hypothesis $\sigma^2 = 20$? The hypothesis $\sigma^2 \geq 20$?

3. Suppose two samples of 12 and 25 individuals, respectively, have $s_1^2 = 20$ and $s_2^2 = 12$. Test for equality of variances at the 10 per cent level of significance.

4. For each of the following cases test the hypothesis $\sigma_1^2 = \sigma_2^2$:

(*a*) $N_1 = N_2 = 16, s_1^2 = 50, s_2^2 = 16, \alpha = .05$.

(b) $N_1 = 41$, $N_2 = 13$, $s_1^2 = 15.6$, $s_2^2 = 6.3$, $\alpha = .01$.
(c) $N_1 = 60$, $N_2 = 120$, $s_1^2 = 8.0$, $s_2^2 = 17.0$, $\alpha = .02$.

5. In order to time events accurately, it is important to have a timepiece which gains or loses a constant amount so that appropriate allowance may be made. The following data given in seconds show the daily gain or loss for two timepieces. Is one significantly more variable than the other?

A	−46	−37	−51	−50	−38	−46	−42	−43	−40	−39
B	96	88	96	102	92	98	103	94	91	97

6. A mixture is considered thoroughly mixed if samples selected randomly from the mixture are very much the same. A certain ingredient was measured for eight samples each from mixtures produced by methods A and B. The variances are $s_A^2 = 24.2$, $s_B^2 = 37.3$. Are methods A and B equally effective?

7. For Prob. 1 compute the value of β if the true value of σ^2 for the corresponding five cases is (a) 50, (b) 20, (c) 10, (d) 15, (e) .004.

8. A one-sided hypothesis $\sigma^2 \leq 16$ is to be tested at the 5 per cent level of significance. What size sample should be used to give $\beta = .50$ if the sample is actually drawn from a population with $\sigma^2 = 32$?

9. Compute for Prob. 4 the value of β if the true value of σ_1^2/σ_2^2 for the corresponding three cases is (a) 2, (b) .5, (c) 2, instead of the hypothetical value $\sigma_1^2/\sigma_2^2 = 1$.

10. Compute for the data in Prob. 6 the chance that the hypothesis of equal variance will be rejected if actually one variance is twice the other. Use $\alpha = .05$.

11. Suppose two samples from the same population with 12 and 35 observations, respectively, have $s_1^2 = 16.0$ and $s_2^2 = 18.0$. Pool these values, and estimate σ^2 with a 95 per cent confidence interval.

12. Suppose 10 samples of 9 observations each have variances as follows: 23.5 30.6, 29.3, 27.5, 27.5, 26.3, 29.8, 30.7, 22.3, 26.5. Form a pooled estimate of σ^2, and use it to give 90 per cent confidence limits for σ^2.

CHAPTER 9

THE MEAN: ESTIMATION AND TESTS OF HYPOTHESES

In this chapter we continue the discussion started in Chap. 7 of estimating and testing hypotheses concerning the means of populations. First, we summarize the results covered there. Second, the necessary modification of these tests when σ is not known will be discussed. We then present the problem of comparing the means of two populations, problems connected with the analysis of observations drawn in pairs, and methods of estimating population means with confidence intervals.

9-1. Comparison of Sample Mean and Population Mean when σ^2 Is Known

Suppose we believe that the mean μ of a universe has some specified value, say, μ_0. Also suppose we believe (or are willing to assume) that the universe variance has some known value σ^2. Then it is common to assume that the sampling distribution of

$$z = \frac{\bar{X} - \mu_0}{\sigma/\sqrt{N}}$$

is a normal distribution with mean zero and unit standard deviation (μ_0, σ, N are constant). This is true if the hypothesis ($\mu = \mu_0$) is true and if the universe has a normal distribution, and is approximately correct for large-size samples even though the universe is not normal.

With this in mind we would be surprised when values of $\dfrac{\bar{X} - \mu_0}{\sigma/\sqrt{N}}$ very much different from zero occur (perhaps larger than 2 or less than -2). Such values tend to throw doubt on or disprove the hypothesis. If we think sufficient doubt is cast upon the hypothesis, we "reject it," i.e., make the statement "The hypothesis is not true." If we think that little doubt is cast upon the hypothesis we "accept it," i.e., make the statement "This sample is not inconsistent with the hypothesis."

Note the greater strength of the rejecting statement as compared with the accepting statement. If we reject, we think that we have definite reason to disbelieve the hypothesis, while if we accept, we say only that there is "not sufficient evidence to doubt." Although the rejecting statement is strong, we realize that we may still reject the hypothesis when it is actually true. We are able to control this type of error (the chance of rejecting the hypothesis when it is true) at any chosen *level of significance* α.

HYPOTHESIS. *Universe mean is equal to a specified number when σ^2 is known.*

1. H: Universe mean $\mu = \mu_0$ (some given number) when universe variance $= \sigma^2$ (σ^2 known).

2. Decide on the level of significance α, the chance of rejecting the hypothesis if it is true.

3. Decide upon the statistic to be used for testing this hypothesis, in this case, $z = \dfrac{\bar{X} - \mu_0}{\sigma/\sqrt{N}}$.

4. Find the sampling distribution of the statistic under the assumption that the hypothesis is true. Here assume $z = \dfrac{\bar{X} - \mu_0}{\sigma/\sqrt{N}}$ has a normal distribution with mean equal to zero and variance equal to 1.

5. Decide upon a *critical region*, those values of the statistic which would cause us to reject the hypothesis. The chance of the statistic falling in the critical region if the hypothesis is true should be exactly α. In this case we find in Table A-4 the values of $z_{\frac{1}{2}\alpha}$ and $z_{1-\frac{1}{2}\alpha}$ such that a proportion of $\frac{1}{2}\alpha$ of the cases will be larger than $z_{1-\frac{1}{2}\alpha}$ and a proportion $\frac{1}{2}\alpha$ of the cases will be smaller than $z_{\frac{1}{2}\alpha}$. Then the critical region consists of all values of z below $z_{\frac{1}{2}\alpha}$ and above $z_{1-\frac{1}{2}\alpha}$. If $\alpha = .05$, then the critical region is below $z_{.025} = -1.96$ and above $z_{.975} = +1.96$. If the observed statistic $\dfrac{\bar{X} - \mu_0}{\sigma/\sqrt{N}}$ is less than -1.96 or greater than 1.96, we reject the hypothesis. If $\alpha = .01$, the points are $z_{\frac{1}{2}\alpha} = -2.58$ and $z_{1-\frac{1}{2}\alpha} = +2.58$.

6. Compute the value of the statistic from the sample, and see whether or not it falls in the critical region.

7. Make a statement accepting or rejecting the hypothesis. If the statistic has a value in the critical region, we reject; if not, we accept.

Example 1. A standard intelligence examination has been given for several years with an average score of 80 and a standard deviation of 7. A group of 25 students are taught with special emphasis on reading skill. If the 25 students obtained a mean grade of 83 on the examination, is there reason to believe that the special emphasis changes the results on the test?

1. H: Mean of students taught by new method $= 80$, $\sigma = 7$.

2. $\alpha = .05$. (This choice is arbitrary, of course, and is set by the experimenter before the data are examined.)

3. $z = \dfrac{\bar{X} - \mu_0}{\sigma/\sqrt{N}}$.

4. Assume that z has normal distribution with zero mean and variance equal to 1.

5. The critical region for $\alpha = .05$ is $z < -1.96$ and $z > 1.96$.

6. $z = \dfrac{83 - 80}{7/\sqrt{25}} = \dfrac{3}{7/\sqrt{25}} = \dfrac{3\sqrt{25}}{7} = 2.14$. This is greater than 1.96, and so we reject the hypothesis that the scores of the students taught by the special method still have the same mean of 80.

We reason that if the mean of the population of students taught by the new method is 80 then there is less than 5 per cent chance that a mean of 25 scores would be as far away as 83. Thus there is sufficient reason to doubt the statement that the mean is 80.

HYPOTHESIS. *Universe mean is not greater than a specified number when σ^2 is known.*

Many problems arise where we are chiefly interested in the possibility that the mean may be too large. For example, we might wish to test whether or not a particular type of fertilizer increases the yield of wheat. If it does not, we continue using the old type of fertilizer. Another problem would be whether or not a certain chemical increases the melting point of lead. If it decreased the melting point, we would not add it. We usually state the hypothesis in these cases as $\mu \leq \mu_0$ to take advantage of the strength of the rejecting statement. Thus, if we reject, we have a certain degree of assurance that the mean μ is larger than μ_0. In computations we use μ_0 as the hypothetical mean. The less than or equal to sign reminds us that values of $\bar{X}$ which are less than or equal to μ would not be cause for rejection. If the true mean μ does equal μ_0, the chance of rejecting the hypothesis is controlled at the value α. If the true mean μ is actually less than μ_0, the chance of rejecting the hypothesis is less than α.

Our procedure for testing a hypothesis of this sort is as follows:

1. $H: \mu \leq \mu_0$.

2. Choose α.

3. Use $z = \dfrac{\bar{X} - \mu_0}{\sigma/\sqrt{N}}$ as a statistic to test the hypothesis. Note that we shall not want to reject if z happens to be negative.

4. Assume that the sampling distribution of $z = \dfrac{\bar{X} - \mu_0}{\sigma/\sqrt{N}}$ is normal with mean $= 0$, variance $= 1$.

5. Here the critical region will be z greater than $z_{1-\alpha}$ ($z > z_{1-\alpha}$), where $z_{1-\alpha}$ is the value (from Table A-4) above which a proportion α of the observations will fall.

6. Compute the value of $z = \dfrac{\bar{X} - \mu_0}{\sigma/\sqrt{N}}$, and reject the hypothesis if $z > z_{1-\alpha}$ and accept it if $z < z_{1-\alpha}$.

Example 2. A certain manufacturing process produces 12.3 units per hour. This yield has a variance $\sigma^2 = 2.0$. A new process is suggested which is expensive to install but would be worthwhile if production could be increased to an average of at least 13.0 units per hour. In order to decide whether or not to make the change, 14 new machines are tested. They produce a mean of 13.3 units per hour.

1. H: Mean yield from new machines ≤ 13.0. If we have sufficient reason to doubt this, we shall buy the machines.

2. $\alpha = .25$. α tells us that the chance of investing in the new machines when they produce at a rate no greater than 13.0 units per hour is .25. The manufacturer is willing to take a risk of this size.

3. $z = \dfrac{\bar{X} - \mu_0}{\sigma/\sqrt{N}} = \dfrac{\bar{X} - 13}{1.4/\sqrt{14}}$.

4. Assume z has a normal distribution.

5. Reject the hypothesis if $z > z_{.75} = .67$ (from Table A-4).

6. $z = \dfrac{13.3 - 13}{1.4/\sqrt{14}} = \dfrac{.3\sqrt{14}}{1.4} = \dfrac{.3(3.74)}{1.4} = \dfrac{1.122}{1.4} = .80$. This is greater than .67, and so the new machines should be purchased.

HYPOTHESIS. *Universe mean is not less than a specified number when σ^2 is known.*

The procedure for testing this hypothesis is the same as in the previous paragraph except that the critical region will be z less than z_α (from Table A-4).

9-2. Comparison of Sample Mean and Population Mean when σ^2 Is Unknown (the t Distribution)

It was noted in Sec. 9-1 that the sampling distribution of $\dfrac{\bar{X} - \mu}{\sigma/\sqrt{N}}$ is often a normal distribution; however, there is the disadvantage that the value of σ is usually not known. It seems natural to replace σ with s and use $t = \dfrac{\bar{X} - \mu}{s/\sqrt{N}}$ instead of z. In order to do this, we must know the sampling distribution of t. Even though on the average s^2 is equal to σ^2, s^2 is actually less than σ^2 more than half the time (see the distribution of s^2 in Chap. 4). This might lead us to suspect that the sampling distribution of the statistic t (here we are thinking of μ as known) would be slightly more spread out than a normal distribution. If N is very large, s^2 will be very close to σ^2 and we might believe that for large N the sampling distribution of $t = \frac{\bar{X} - \mu}{s/\sqrt{N}}$ will differ little from the distribution of $z = \frac{\bar{X} - \mu}{\sigma/\sqrt{N}}$ (i.e., normal).

A proof by experiment of the above statements would proceed much like the examples in Chap. 4. Suppose we have a normally distributed universe. This universe could be the numbers in Table A-2 which we used in Chap. 4, or it could be a universe of tags bearing numbers which have an approximately normal distribution. (Any finite universe, of course, can have only an approximately normal distribution.) We draw many samples of, say, $N = 3$, then many samples of $N = 5$, then of $N = 10$, and compute for each sample the value of $t = \frac{\bar{X} - \mu}{s/\sqrt{N}}$ (μ would be known since we have the universe). If we form the histograms of the

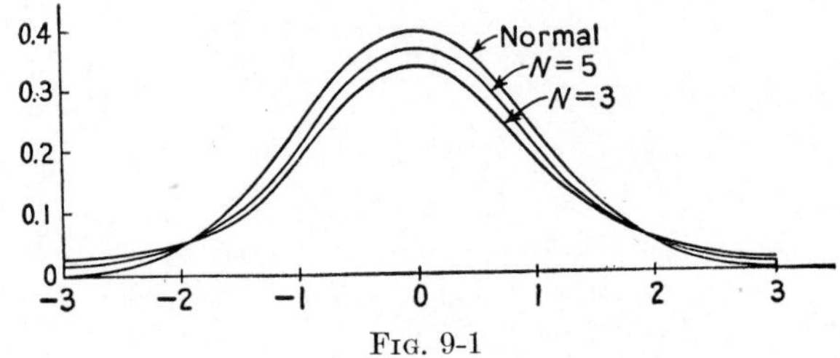

FIG. 9-1

observed distributions, we see that, with increasing N, they approach a normal distribution with variance 1 and mean 0. In Fig. 9-1 are sketched t-distribution curves for $N = 3$, 5, and a normal curve with $\mu = 0$, $\sigma^2 = 1$.

Inspecting these curves we see that to include any *given* per cent of the area under the curves the interval must be longer for the smaller size samples. For example, to include 95 per cent of the area the interval must extend from -4.30 to $+4.30$ for the $N = 3$ curve, from -2.78 to $+2.78$ for $N = 5$, and from -1.960 to $+1.960$ for the normal distribution.

Table A-5 gives several percentiles of several t distributions. The percentiles are indicated at the top of the table, and the particular distributions are indicated down the left-hand side of the table under "df" (degrees of freedom). The number of degrees of freedom is exactly the same as the number of degrees of freedom used in estimating the variance ($N - 1$ for our present example).

Here, as well as in previous cases, the term *degrees of freedom* has a mathematical implication of the number of independent variables involved (number of dimensions), but for our purposes the term will be used only to tell us where to look for tabled numbers. The number of degrees of freedom must be given for each type of problem we study.

Some examples in the use of the t table follow:

1. For $N = 10$ in the column marked $t_{.95}$ across from $N - 1 = 9$ we read that 95 per cent of observations of $\dfrac{\bar{X} - \mu}{s/\sqrt{N}}$ will be less than 1.83.

Values of t_α for α less than .50 are negative and are obtained by using the percentile indicated at the foot of the table and prefixing a minus sign to the value obtained from the table.

2. For $N = 10$, 5 per cent of observations of $\dfrac{\bar{X} - \mu}{s/\sqrt{N}}$ will be less than $t_{.05} = -1.83$ (above $t_{.05}$ and across from $N - 1 = 9$).

3. For $N = 30$, 99 per cent of the observations of $\dfrac{\bar{X} - \mu}{s/\sqrt{N}}$ will be between -2.76 and $+2.76$ (in the column titled $t_{.005}$ and $t_{.995}$ and across from $N - 1 = 29$).

4. For $N = 3$, 5 per cent of the observations of t either exceed 4.30 or are less than -4.30.

We shall use the notation $t_\alpha(\text{df})$ to indicate the value just larger than a proportion α of the t distribution with the indicated number of degrees of freedom. In this notation the above values will be written:

1. $t_{.95}(9) = 1.83$.
2. $t_{.05}(9) = -1.83$.
3. $t_{.995}(29) = 2.76$; $t_{.005}(29) = -2.76$.
4. $t_{.975}(2) = 4.30$; $t_{.025}(2) = -4.30$.

HYPOTHESIS. *Universe mean is equal to a specified constant when σ^2 is not known.*

Our procedure in testing this hypothesis is as follows:

1. H: $\mu = \mu_0$.
2. Choose α.
3. Use the statistic $t = \dfrac{\bar{X} - \mu_0}{s/\sqrt{N}}$.
4. If the universe has a normal distribution and if the hypothesis is true, the statistic t has a $t(N - 1)$ distribution.
5. The critical region is $t < t_{\frac{1}{2}\alpha}(N - 1)$ and $t > t_{1-\frac{1}{2}\alpha}(N - 1)$ where these values are read from Table A-5.
6. Compute the value of t from the sample, and reject the hypothesis if the observed t is less than $t_{\frac{1}{2}\alpha}(N - 1)$ or if it is greater than $t_{1-\frac{1}{2}\alpha}(N - 1)$, and otherwise accept the hypothesis.

Example 1. A certain type of rat shows a mean gain in weight of 65 grams during the first 3 months of life. Twelve rats were fed a particular diet from birth until age 3 months, and the following weight gains were observed: 55, 62, 54, 58, 65, 64, 60, 62, 59, 67, 62, 61. Is there reason to believe at the 5 per cent level of significance that the diet causes a change in the amount of weight gained?

1. $H: \mu = 65$.
2. $\alpha = .05$.
3. $t = \dfrac{\bar{X} - 65}{s/\sqrt{12}}$.
4. We assume this statistic has a t distribution with 11 degrees of freedom.
5. Reject if $t < -2.20$ or if $t > 2.20$.
6. $t = \dfrac{\bar{X} - 65}{s/\sqrt{12}} = \dfrac{\sqrt{12}}{3.8406}(60.75 - 65) = -3.83$. t is less than -2.20, and so we reject the hypothesis.

HYPOTHESIS. *Universe mean is not greater than a specified number when σ^2 is not known.*

The modifications of the above procedure necessary to test this hypothesis are contained in the following procedure:

1. $H: \mu \leq \mu_0$.
2. Decide on α.
3. Use $t = \dfrac{\bar{X} - \mu_0}{s/\sqrt{N}}$ as a statistic to test the hypothesis.
4. Assuming that the universe has a normal distribution, then this statistic has a $t(N - 1)$ distribution.
5. The critical region is $t > t_{1-\alpha}$. We are interested in rejecting our hypothesis only when t is large, say, larger than $t_{1-\alpha}$, which gives us the chosen level of significance α.
6. Compute the value of t, and reject the hypothesis if the observed t is greater than or equal to $t_{1-\alpha}$, or accept the hypothesis if the observed t is less than $t_{1-\alpha}$.

Example 2. A certain type of hormone, to be injected into hens, is said to increase the mean weight of eggs .3 ounce. A sample of 30 eggs has an arithmetic mean .4 ounce above the preinjection mean and a value of s equal to .20. Is this enough reason to accept the statement that the mean increase is .3 ounce?

1. $H: \mu \leq .3$.
2. Choose α, say, $\alpha = .05$.
3. $t = \dfrac{\bar{X} - .3}{s/\sqrt{N}}$.
4. We assume this statistic has a t distribution with
$$N - 1 = 30 - 1 = 29 \text{ degrees of freedom}$$
5. Reject if $t > t_{.95}(29) = 1.70$.

6. $t = \dfrac{.4 - .3}{.20/\sqrt{30}} = .5\sqrt{30} = 2.75$, which is larger than 1.70, and so we reject the hypothesis that $\mu \leq .3$. The statement that the mean increase is more than .3 ounce is accepted. It might be noted here that factors such as the possibility that hormones react differently on different hens have not been considered. If such possibilities exist (as they probably do in this case), we should apply an appropriately designed experiment to test for hormone effects. Examples of this type can sometimes be handled by analysis-of-variance techniques described in Chap. 10.

HYPOTHESIS. *Universe mean is not less than a specified constant when σ^2 is not known.*

This is the same as the preceding case, except that the critical region is $t < t_\alpha$.

9-3. Tests of Hypotheses Concerning the Means of Two Populations

Suppose we have two samples, one from each of two populations. We might wish to know whether the means of the two populations are equal. We will denote the two population means by μ_1 and μ_2 and the two population variances by σ_1^2 and σ_2^2. To compare μ_1 and μ_2, we take a sample of N_1 observations from the first population, a sample of N_2 observations from the second population, and compute the respective means $\bar{X}_1$ and $\bar{X}_2$. Then, to test the hypothesis that $\mu_1 - \mu_2 = 0$, we use the statistic $\bar{X}_1 - \bar{X}_2$ and reject the hypothesis if this difference is significantly far from zero. The sampling distribution of $\bar{X}_1 - \bar{X}_2$ is, for large sample sizes, approximately normal with mean $\mu_1 - \mu_2$ and with variance $(\sigma_1^2/N_1) + (\sigma_2^2/N_2)$. Thus, if $\mu_1 - \mu_2 = 0$, we may assume that the sampling distribution of the statistic $z = (\bar{X}_1 - \bar{X}_2)/\sqrt{(\sigma_1^2/N_1) + (\sigma_2^2/N_2)}$ is approximately as given in Table A-4, and this table can be used to determine a critical region.

To illustrate these statements, we have taken samples of sizes $N_1 = N_2 = 1$ from Table A-2 and computed $\bar{X}_1 - \bar{X}_2$ for each pair of samples. In all, 200 such pairs of samples were taken, and the results are recorded in Table 9-1. Note that the mean of the differences $\bar{X}_{1i} - \bar{X}_{2i}$ agrees approximately with the theoretical value zero, and the observed variance is also close to the value

$$\frac{\sigma_1^2}{N_1} + \frac{\sigma_2^2}{N_2} = 1 + 1 = 2$$

given by the formula. To test agreement of the observed mean with the theoretical mean, we can compute $z = \dfrac{.1125 - 0}{\sqrt{2}/\sqrt{200}} = 1.125$ and see that the difference is not significant at the 5 per cent level of significance.

TABLE 9-1. RESULTS OF 200 OBSERVATIONS OF DIFFERENCES $\bar{X}_{1i} - \bar{X}_{2i}$ OF MEANS OF SAMPLES OF SIZES $N_1 = N_2 = 1$ FROM NORMAL POPULATIONS WITH $\mu_1 = \mu_2 = 0$ AND $\sigma_1^2 = \sigma_2^2 = 1$

Mid-point of $(\bar{X}_1 - \bar{X}_2)$	*Freq.*
3.5	3
3.0	4
2.5	4
2.0	14
1.5	22
1.0	18
.5	25
0	31
− .5	24
−1.0	16
−1.5	20
−2.0	10
−2.5	7
−3.0	2
	200

	Observed	Theoretical
Mean $(\bar{X}_1 - \bar{X}_2)$..	.1125	$\mu_1 - \mu_2 = 0$
Var. $(\bar{X}_1 - \bar{X}_2)$....	1.978	$\sigma_1^2/1 + \sigma_2^2/1 = 2$

HYPOTHESIS. *Means of two populations are equal, assuming that they have the same σ^2 when σ^2 is known.*

1. $H: \mu_1 = \mu_2$, given $\sigma_1^2 = \sigma_2^2 = \sigma^2$.
2. Decide on α.
3. Use the statistic $z = \dfrac{\bar{X}_1 - \bar{X}_2}{\sigma\sqrt{(1/N_1) + (1/N_2)}}$.
4. If the universe is normally distributed, the sampling distribution of z is normal; or, in most cases, if the sample sizes N_1 and N_2 are large, the sampling distribution of z is approximately normal.
5. The critical region is $z < z_{\frac{1}{2}\alpha}$ and $z > z_{1-\frac{1}{2}\alpha}$.

Example 1. Two astronomers recorded observations on a certain star. The 12 observations obtained by the first astronomer have a mean reading of 1.20. The 8 observations obtained by the second astronomer have a mean of 1.15. Past experience has indicated that these astronomers obtain readings with a variance of about .40. Does the difference between the two results seem reasonable?

1. $H: \mu_1 = \mu_2, \sigma^2 = .40, \sigma = \sqrt{.40} = .6325$.
2. Choose $\alpha = .01$.
3. Use $z = \dfrac{\bar{X}_1 - \bar{X}_2}{\sigma\sqrt{(1/N_1) + (1/N_2)}}$.

4. We assume that z has a normal distribution with mean 0 and variance 1.

5. Reject if $z < -2.58$ or if $z > 2.58$.

6. $z = \dfrac{1.20 - 1.15}{(.6325)\sqrt{\frac{1}{12} + \frac{1}{8}}} = .17$, which is between -2.58 and $+2.58$, and so we accept the hypothesis. Thus this difference does not seem unreasonable.

HYPOTHESIS. *Mean of one population is less than or equal to the mean of another population when σ^2 is known.*

Problems involving inequality of the means of two populations often arise. As in Sec. 9-1, the statement of the hypothesis is in the form $H: \mu_1 \leq \mu_2$ where we consider the equality $\mu_1 = \mu_2$ is in question, and the less than or equal to sign is to remind us that we will reject only if $\bar{X}_1$ is significantly larger than $\bar{X}_2$.

1. $H: \mu_1 \leq \mu_2$, given $\sigma_1^2 = \sigma_2^2 = \sigma^2$, and the value of σ^2 is known.
2. Choose α.
3. The statistic to use here is $z = \dfrac{\bar{X}_1 - \bar{X}_2}{\sigma\sqrt{(1/N_1) + (1/N_2)}}$.
4. We assume this statistic has a normal distribution with mean zero and unit variance.
5. We would not wish to reject the hypothesis if $\bar{X}_1$ turns out less than $\bar{X}_2$, and so for a critical region take $z > z_{1-\alpha}$.
6. Compute the statistic, and reject or accept the hypothesis.

HYPOTHESIS. *Two populations have the same mean when σ^2 is not known.*

1. $H: \mu_1 = \mu_2$. It is known that $\sigma_1^2 = \sigma_2^2 = \sigma^2$, but the value of σ^2 is unknown.
2. Choose α.
3. For a statistic to test this hypothesis use

$$t = \frac{\bar{X}_1 - \bar{X}_2}{s_p\sqrt{(1/N_1) + (1/N_2)}}$$

where s_p^2 is the pooled mean-square estimate of σ^2 given by

$$s_p^2 = \frac{\sum X_{1i}^2 - \frac{(\Sigma X_{1i})^2}{N_1} + \sum X_{2i}^2 - \frac{(\Sigma X_{2i})^2}{N_2}}{N_1 + N_2 - 2}$$

$$= \frac{(N_1 - 1)s_1^2 + (N_2 - 1)s_2^2}{N_1 + N_2 - 2}$$

where ΣX_{1i}^2 = sum of squares in first sample
ΣX_{2i}^2 = sum of squares in second sample
ΣX_{1i} = sum of observations in first sample
ΣX_{2i} = sum of observations in second sample

This s_p^2 is the same pooled estimate discussed in Chap. 8.

4. If both populations have normal distributions with the same mean and the same variance, then this statistic has the $t(N_1 + N_2 - 2)$ distribution with percentiles recorded in Table A-5.

5. The rejection region is $t < t_{\frac{1}{2}\alpha}(N_1 + N_2 - 2)$ and

$$t > t_{1-\frac{1}{2}\alpha}(N_1 + N_2 - 2)$$

6. Compute t, and reject or accept the hypothesis.

Example 2. Two new types of rations are fed to pigs. It is desired to test whether one or the other of the types is better. A sample of 12 pigs is fed type A ration, and a sample of 12 pigs is fed type B ration. The gains in weight are recorded below.

Type A..............	31	34	29	26	32	35	38	34	30	29	32	31
Type B..............	26	24	28	29	30	29	32	26	31	29	32	28

1. $H: \mu_1 = \mu_2$.
2. $\alpha = .05$.
3. Use $t = \dfrac{\bar{X}_1 - \bar{X}_2}{s_p\sqrt{(1/N_1) + (1/N_2)}}$.
4. If the two populations have normal distributions with the same mean and the same variance, then this statistic has a t distribution with $12 + 12 - 2 = 22$ df.
5. Reject if $t < -2.07$ or if $t > 2.07$.

For type A, $\bar{X}_1 = 31.7500$, $\Sigma X_{1i}{}^2 - \dfrac{(\Sigma X_{1i})^2}{12} = 112.25$.

For type B, $\bar{X}_2 = 28.6667$, $\Sigma X_{2i}{}^2 - \dfrac{(\Sigma X_{2i})^2}{12} = 66.64$.

$$s_p{}^2 = \frac{112.25 + 66.64}{12 + 12 - 2} = 8.131$$

$$s_p = \sqrt{8.131} = 2.85$$

6. $t = \dfrac{\bar{X}_1 - \bar{X}_2}{s_p\sqrt{\frac{1}{12} + \frac{1}{12}}} = \dfrac{3.083\sqrt{6}}{2.85} = 2.65$. This is larger than 2.07, and so we reject the hypothesis.

HYPOTHESIS. *Mean of one population is less than or equal to the mean of a second population when σ^2 is unknown.*

This problem is a combination of those in previous examples. We use the same test statistic as above, but we shall reject only if t is larger than $t_{1-\alpha}(N_1 + N_2 - 2)$.

Example 3. Two types of paint are to be tested. Type I is somewhat cheaper than type II. The test consists in giving scores to the paints after they have been exposed to certain weather conditions for a period of 6 months. Five samples of each type of paint are scored as follows:

Type I..........	85	87	92	80	84
Type II.........	89	89	90	84	88

We should like to adopt type I, the cheaper one, unless we have definite reason to believe that type II is better. If we state as a hypothesis that $\mu_2 \leq \mu_1$, our chance of adopting type II when the paints are equally good will be controlled at α.

1. H: $\mu_2 \leq \mu_1$.
2. $\alpha = .05$.
3. $t = \dfrac{\bar{X}_1 - \bar{X}_2}{s_p \sqrt{(1/N_1) + (1/N_2)}}$.
4. Assume this statistic has a t distribution with $N_1 + N_2 - 2$ degrees of freedom.
5. Reject if $t < t_{.05}$, that is, if $t < -1.86$. We reject here if t is negative ($t < -1.86$) since that would lead us to believe that $\mu_2 > \mu_1$.
6. $\bar{X}_1 = 85.6$, $\Sigma X_{1i}^2 - \dfrac{(\Sigma X_{1i})^2}{5} = 77.2.$

$$\bar{X}_2 = 88.0,\ \Sigma X_{2i}^2 - \frac{(\Sigma X_{2i})^2}{5} = 22.0.$$

$$s_p^2 = \frac{77.2 + 22.0}{8} = 12.4$$

$$s_p = 3.52$$

$t = \dfrac{85.6 - 88.0}{3.52 \sqrt{\frac{1}{5} + \frac{1}{5}}} = -1.08.$ We therefore accept the hypothesis.

HYPOTHESIS. *Two populations have the same mean (variances not equal).* Suppose that we wish to compare the means of two normally distributed populations having variances σ_1^2 and σ_2^2. As before, denote the observations by X_{1i}, X_{2i} and the sample sizes by N_1 and N_2. The sampling distribution of the statistic

$$z = \frac{(\bar{X}_1 - \bar{X}_2) - (\mu_1 - \mu_2)}{\sqrt{(\sigma_1^2/N_1) + (\sigma_2^2/N_2)}}$$

is normal with mean 0 and variance 1. This is approximately true for sufficiently large values of N_1 and N_2 even if the populations are not normal.

If the values of σ_1 and σ_2 are known, they are substituted into the formula and observed values of z can be compared with the normal distribution in Table A-4.

If the values of σ_1 and σ_2 are not known but the experimenter feels that there is evidence that each population is normally distributed, then he may wish to use the statistic obtained by substituting the observed s_1 and s_2 for σ_1 and σ_2, obtaining the statistic

$$t = \frac{(\bar{X}_1 - \bar{X}_2) - (\mu_1 - \mu_2)}{\sqrt{(s_1^2/N_1) + (s_2^2/N_2)}}$$

which, if the assumptions of normality are correct, has approximately a t distribution with f degrees of freedom where

$$f = \frac{\left(\frac{s_1^2}{N_1} + \frac{s_2^2}{N_2}\right)^2}{\frac{\left(\frac{s_1^2}{N_1}\right)^2}{N_1 + 1} + \frac{\left(\frac{s_2^2}{N_2}\right)^2}{N_2 + 1}} - 2$$

This value of f will not be an integer, and interpolation in the t table may be necessary for exact significance levels; however, usually the closest value in the table is sufficient.

If there is evidence that σ_1 and σ_2 are not equal, a more convenient sampling design and analysis sometimes results from pairing the observations from the two populations, as described in the next section.

9-4. Pairing Observations

In sampling from two populations it sometimes happens that extraneous factors cause a significant difference in means, whereas there was no difference in the effects we are trying to measure.

For example, if we are interested in whether one of two different teaching methods is better than the other, we might take two groups of students and teach one group by one method and the other group by the second method. If one of the groups was composed of better students (or more mature, or better trained in basic subjects, etc.) than the other group, the results of the experiment may not reflect the effectiveness of the teaching method.

Another example is as follows: In an experiment to test which of two types (A or B) of fertilizers is the better, two plots of wheat are planted at each of 10 experiment stations. One of the two plots has fertilizer A and the other fertilizer B. If the averages of the 10 having type A are compared with the averages of the 10 having type B, part of the difference observed (if any) may be due to the different types of soil or different weather conditions instead of different fertilizers. Another possibility is that the fertilizers cause a difference but this difference is obscured by the other factors.

One design for experiments which sometimes overcomes part of the above difficulty is the device of taking the observations in pairs. We try to make sure that the two members of any pair are alike in all respects except that which we are trying to measure. This is an ideal, of course, and we are limited by the availability of pairs which are similar and by our ability to choose similar pairs.

Thus, in the first example, pairs of students of approximately equal ability are taken, and one member of each pair is taught by one method, and the other is taught by the second method. In the second example, each pair of plots would have approximately the same types of soil, weather conditions, etc.

Suppose we let X_{i1} be the first member of the ith pair and X_{i2} be the second member. We have, say, N pairs of observations,

$$(X_{11},X_{12}),\ (X_{21},X_{22}),\ (X_{31},X_{32}),\ \ldots\ ,\ (X_{N1},X_{N2})$$

If we take differences $X_{i1} - X_{i2} = d_i$, we shall have a set of N observations, each observation being a difference between two original observations. There may be certain extraneous factors affecting some of the individuals, but we hope (and assume) that it affects each member of any one pair in exactly the same manner. We also assume that the effect is essentially one of increasing (or decreasing) each of the means by some constant so that the subtraction has removed the effect.

We wish to test the hypothesis that $\mu_1 = \mu_2$. This hypothesis states that there is no difference between treatments, i.e., no difference within pairs. There is probably a difference from pair to pair, but we hope that this has been eliminated by our use of $X_{i1} - X_{i2}$. To test the above hypothesis, we note that, if the hypothesis is true, the differences $X_{i1} - X_{i2}$ would come from a set of numbers with mean zero. Thus we can test the hypothesis that the $X_{i1} - X_{i2}$ come from a universe with mean zero, $\mu = 0$. This is done exactly the same as in Sec. 9-2 (t test with $N - 1$ degrees of freedom).

Another advantage of this method is that *we need not assume the two variances* σ_1^2 *and* σ_2^2 *to be equal or that the values of* X_{i1} *and* X_{i2} *are independent.* Previous to this section it has been assumed that the observations are independent, i.e., that each single observation corresponds to an individual randomly selected.

If there are no extraneous effects, then we actually lose information by pairing. This loss results in an increase in the probability of accepting the hypothesis when it is false. The increase is slight, however, if the sample sizes are moderately large, say, greater than 10. The level of significance is not affected. This point is discussed further in Chap. 14.

With only $N - 1$ degrees of freedom in the estimate of σ^2 we accept larger differences in $\bar{X}_1 - \bar{X}_2$ than we might accept if we had $2N - 2$ degrees of freedom. Of course, if there are extraneous effects (as in the examples above), we may be forced to pair and take the risk of a loss in precision.

Example 1. In a study of learning 10 boys and 10 girls were chosen at random from a freshman class. Scores were obtained measuring their ability to learn nonsense syllables. Since the experimenter suspected the variation to be different for boys and girls (σ_1^2 not equal to σ_2^2), he decided to pair the data. The analysis shown here is appropriate for a random pairing of the subjects. However, it is possible that pairing the subjects on IQ, for example, will effect a reduction in population variance and thus make it easier to discover any differences in ability. The observations and analysis are recorded below.

	Pair number									
	1	2	3	4	5	6	7	8	9	10
Boys	28	18	22	27	25	30	21	21	20	27
Girls	19	38	42	25	15	31	22	37	30	24
Difference	9	−20	−20	2	10	−1	−1	−16	−10	3

$\Sigma d_i = -44$; $\Sigma d_i^2 = 1{,}352$; $\bar{d} = -4.4$; $s_d^2 = [1{,}352 - (44)^2/10]/9 = 128.7$.

1. $H: \mu_1 = \mu_2$, that is, mean learning score for boys equals mean learning score for girls.

2. $\alpha = .01$.

3. $t = \dfrac{\bar{d} - 0}{s/\sqrt{N}} = \dfrac{-4.4}{\sqrt{128.7}/\sqrt{10}} = -1.2$. (Note that $\bar{X}_1 - \bar{X}_2 = \bar{d}$ and that s^2 is the variance of the differences.)

4. If the populations have normal distributions, then this statistic has a t distribution with $10 - 1 = 9$ degrees of freedom.

5. Reject if $t < -3.25$ or if $t > 3.25$.

6. $t = -1.2$; so we accept the hypothesis. This experiment does not indicate a difference in ability to learn nonsense syllables for boys and girls.

Example 2. A certain stimulus is to be tested for its effect on blood pressure. Twelve men have their blood pressure measured before and after the stimulus. The results are as shown in Table 9-2. Is there reason to believe that the stimulus would, on the average, raise blood pressure five points?

The pairing was necessary here since two observations are made on the same individual. The sample consists of 12 individuals with two measurements on each.

1. $H: \mu_2 - \mu_1, \leq 5$ (or mean of differences is 5).

2. $\alpha = .05$.

3. $t = \dfrac{\bar{X}_2 - \bar{X}_1 - 5}{s/\sqrt{12}}$. ($\bar{X}_2 - \bar{X}_1$ is the same as the mean of the differences. The student should check this. The s is the standard deviation of the differences.)

4. If the populations have normal distributions and if extraneous effects are additive, then this statistic has a t distribution with

$$12 - 1 = 11 \text{ degrees of freedom}$$

5. Reject if $t > +1.80$.

6. We compute $s^2 = [414 - (22)^2/12]/11 = 33.97$, $s = 5.83$, $t = \dfrac{1.833 - 5}{5.83/\sqrt{12}} = \dfrac{-3.167}{1.68} = -1.9$. We therefore accept the hypothesis.

TABLE 9-2

Man	Before	After	Increase d_i	d_i^2
1	120	128	+8	64
2	124	131	+7	49
3	130	131	+1	1
4	118	127	+9	81
5	140	132	−8	64
6	128	125	−3	9
7	140	141	+1	1
8	135	137	+2	4
9	126	118	−8	64
10	130	132	+2	4
11	126	129	+3	9
12	127	135	+8	64
			22	414

9-5. Confidence Limits for Means

In Sec. 6-6 confidence limits for the mean μ of a population were given in case the population variance was known. The confidence limits were

$$\bar{X} + \frac{z_{\frac{1}{2}\alpha}\sigma}{\sqrt{N}} \quad \text{and} \quad \bar{X} + \frac{z_{1-\frac{1}{2}\alpha}\sigma}{\sqrt{N}}$$

where $z_{\frac{1}{2}\alpha}$, $z_{1-\frac{1}{2}\alpha}$ = percentiles from Table A-4
$\bar{X}$ = sample mean
σ^2 = population variance
N = sample size

If we compute such limits from a sample, the chance of the interval covering μ is $1 - \alpha$. If in a series of problems we have occasion to make many such statements as "The mean μ is between these limits," we shall have, in the long run, a proportion α of false statements.

If the value of σ is unknown, then the confidence limits for μ are

$$\bar{X} + \frac{t_{\frac{1}{2}\alpha}s}{\sqrt{N}} \qquad \text{and} \qquad \bar{X} + \frac{t_{1-\frac{1}{2}\alpha}s}{\sqrt{N}}$$

where $t_{\frac{1}{2}\alpha}$, $t_{1-\frac{1}{2}\alpha}$ are read from Table A-5 for the given α and $N - 1$ degrees of freedom.

The interpretation of these limits is the same as in the case where σ was known. The confidence intervals for μ when σ is unknown are somewhat longer. Thus we can estimate the distance of $\bar{X}$ from the population mean μ better in case σ is known. This does not mean that $\bar{X}$ falls closer to μ in cases where σ is known but that we have a *better idea* of where $\bar{X}$ will fall.

Confidence limits for μ when σ is known are of constant length. As successive samples are taken, the intervals fall in different positions but they are always of length $2z_{1-\frac{1}{2}\alpha}\sigma/\sqrt{N}$. If σ is not known, the intervals formed using $t_{1-\frac{1}{2}\alpha}$ will vary in position from one sample to another and also vary in length, since their lengths depend upon s, which, of course, varies from one sample to another. In either case the intervals will cover the true value of μ a fixed proportion of the time, and thus the degree of confidence we have in any one such interval covering μ is established.

Just as in Sec. 9-2, the use of the t distribution is restricted to cases where the distribution of the population is approximately normal. Even for nonnormal populations the use of Table A-5 will be approximately correct if the sample is sufficiently large.

Confidence Limits for the Difference between Two Means. If we have two populations with means μ_1 and μ_2, we can estimate the difference between μ_1 and μ_2 by the following confidence limits when σ is known:

$$\bar{X}_1 - \bar{X}_2 + z_{\frac{1}{2}\alpha}\sigma\sqrt{\frac{1}{N_1} + \frac{1}{N_2}} \qquad \bar{X}_1 - \bar{X}_2 + z_{1-\frac{1}{2}\alpha}\sigma\sqrt{\frac{1}{N_1} + \frac{1}{N_2}}$$

If σ is not known, $z_{\frac{1}{2}\alpha}$ must be replaced by $t_{\frac{1}{2}\alpha}$ and σ by s_p. The number of degrees of freedom is $N_1 + N_2 - 2$.

In case the observations of two samples are paired, confidence limits for the difference in means are as follows:

$$\bar{X}_1 - \bar{X}_2 + t_{\frac{1}{2}\alpha}s\sqrt{\frac{1}{N}} \qquad \bar{X}_1 - \bar{X}_2 + t_{1-\frac{1}{2}\alpha}s\sqrt{\frac{1}{N}}$$

Here s^2 is the variance of the differences (as in Sec. 9-4), and the t values are read from Table A-5 corresponding to α and $N - 1$ degrees of freedom.

It might be noted that confidence intervals cover values of parameters which would be "accepted" in problems of testing hypotheses. For example, if $\bar{X} = 3$, $s = 1$, $N = 20$, $\alpha = .05$, then $t_{1-\frac{1}{2}\alpha} = 2.09$. Ninety-five per cent confidence limits are

$$3 - \frac{2.09}{\sqrt{20}} = 2.53 \qquad \text{and} \qquad 3 + \frac{2.09}{\sqrt{20}} = 3.47$$

Any hypothetical value of μ between these limits would be accepted at the 5 per cent level of significance.

9-6. Sampling of Intact Groups

Suppose the universe consists of a number of intact and homogeneous groups and our sampling procedure is such that we take at random several complete groups in our sample.

For illustration, consider the case where our sample consists of 12 groups of 17 individuals each. We must be very careful to note that we do not have a random sample of $17 \times 12 = 204$ cases, but rather a random sample of 12 groups. Thus, to test hypotheses about, or to estimate, the mean of the universe, we should not use the 204 cases directly but rather use the 12 group means. Suppose we wished to test the hypothesis that the population mean is equal to some number μ_0. We would use the 12 group means $\bar{X}_1, \bar{X}_2, \ldots, \bar{X}_{12}$ and compute from them an estimate of the variance of all the group means. If $\bar{X}$ denotes the observed mean of the 204 cases, this estimate of variance is

$$s^2 = \frac{\sum_{i=1}^{12} (\bar{X}_i - \bar{X})^2}{11} = \frac{\sum_{i=1}^{12} \bar{X}_i^2 - \frac{(\Sigma \bar{X}_i)^2}{12}}{11}$$

The statistic used to test the above hypothesis is $t = \dfrac{\bar{X} - \mu_0}{s/\sqrt{12}}$, and the critical region (for $\alpha = .05$, $k - 1 = 11$ df) is $t < -2.20$ and $t > 2.20$. In case the groups are of unequal size, we must weight the group means. Suppose there are k groups and the number of individuals in each group is $n_1, n_2, \ldots, n_k$. Let $\bar{X}_1, \bar{X}_2, \ldots, \bar{X}_k$ be the group means, and let $\bar{X}$ be the mean of all the observations. The total number of individual observations is $N = \sum_{i=1}^{k} n_i$. $\bar{X}$ is computed from the $\bar{X}_i$ according to the formula

$$\bar{X} = \frac{\sum_{i=1}^{k} n_i \bar{X}_i}{N} = \frac{\Sigma T_i}{N} = \frac{T}{N}$$

(since $n_i\bar{X}_i = T_i$ is the sum of all observations in the ith group and $T = \sum_{i=1}^{k} n_i\bar{X}_i$ is the sum of all the observations). The estimate of the variance in the population is

$$s^2 = \left[\frac{\sum_{i=1}^{k} \frac{n_i k}{N}(\bar{X}_i - \bar{X})^2}{k-1}\right] = k\left[\frac{\sum_{i=1}^{k}\left(\frac{T_i^2}{n_i}\right) - \frac{T^2}{N}}{N(k-1)}\right]$$

The estimate of the variance of $\bar{X}$ is then s^2/k.

This problem sometimes arises in sampling classes of school children when each class is taken as a unit. Another example is the collection of data from family groups.

9-7. Tolerance Limits

We have found that confidence limits may be determined so that the interval between these limits will cover a population parameter with a certain confidence, i.e., a certain proportion of the time. Sometimes it is desirable to obtain an interval which will cover a fixed *portion of the population distribution* with a specified confidence. These intervals are called *tolerance intervals,* and the end points of these intervals are called *tolerance limits.* For example, it is of considerable interest to a manufacturer to estimate what proportion of manufactured articles will have dimensions in a given range. Tolerance intervals may be of the form $\bar{X} \pm Ks$, where K is determined so that the interval will cover a proportion P of the population with confidence γ. Confidence limits for μ are also in the form $\bar{X} \pm ks$. However, we determined k so that the confidence interval would cover the population mean μ a certain proportion of the time. It is obvious that the interval must be longer to cover a large portion of the distribution than is necessary for it to cover the single value μ. Table A-16 gives values of K for $P = .75, .90, .95, .99, .999$ and $\gamma = .75, .90, .95, .99$ and for many different sample sizes N. For example, if $\bar{X} = 14.0$ and $s = 1.5$, $N = 18$, we can estimate that the interval $\bar{X} \pm Ks = 14.0 \pm 3.702(1.5) = 14.0 \pm 5.553$, or the interval 8.447 to 19.553 will contain 99 per cent of the population with confidence 95 per cent. The values for K in Table A-16 are computed assuming that observations are from normal populations.

9-8. Control Charts

In this section we shall describe a simple graphical device which is useful in keeping track of production quality. This device is a quality-control chart. Control here implies that some static condition exists and not that we are actually improving or changing the quality. If the quality does improve or change significantly, we say that we no longer have "control" and we depend upon our device to detect the change. In the past most of the applications of this method have been in engineering; however, the techniques are being adopted in many other fields. We shall give examples of the use of several quality-control charts.

Control Chart for Means and Ranges. Suppose that an article which should have size μ is being produced. We shall take a sample of N of these articles every day and compute the mean of the observations. This we shall record on a graph as in Fig. 9-2. On the vertical axis we have a

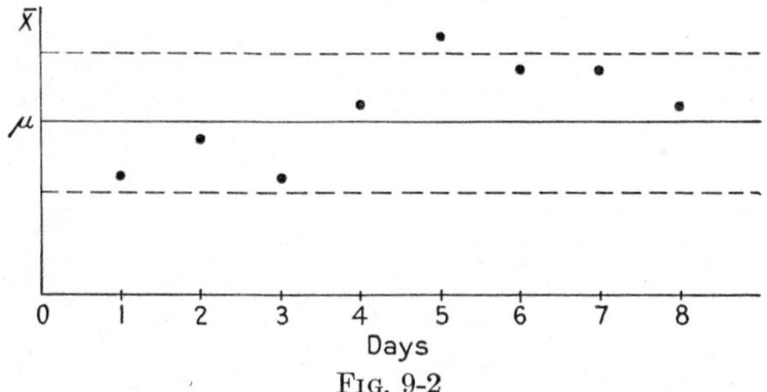

FIG. 9-2

scale for observed values of $\bar{X}$. On the horizontal axis we have a scale for days, or the time at which the sample was taken. A solid horizontal line is drawn through the assumed mean, and two parallel dotted lines are drawn, one above and one below the solid line. We shall observe the mean of a sample every day and plot it on the graph. If the point is between the dotted lines, we say that the manufacturing process is in control and take no further action. If the point is above the upper or below the lower dotted line, we say that the procedure is out of control and we attempt to find the factor which is causing the extreme observations. In the example in the figure the process was out of control on the fifth day.

We wish the chance to be very small of saying that there is lack of control (i.e., a change in mean) when actually the static condition still exists. We control the chance of this happening by the distance between the dotted lines. If we assumed a normal distribution of means, we could draw the lines at $\mu + 1.96\sigma/\sqrt{N}$ and $\mu - 1.96\sigma/\sqrt{N}$ for 5 per cent chance of making such a mistake. In practice it is customary to use $3\sigma/\sqrt{N}$ as control lines. These, for a normal distribution, give a chance of .27 per cent of deciding erroneously that there is a lack of control. The chance of this kind of error corresponds to the level of significance in testing hypotheses.

Usually another control chart to record dispersion is kept simultaneously with the control chart for means. The dispersion is usually measured by the sample standard deviation s or by the sample range R. Because of the speed and ease with which it can be computed, R is more widely used. Actually for small samples R is fairly efficient. A control chart for R has the same general appearance as one for $\bar{X}$. The range is scaled on the vertical axis and days or time of observation on the horizontal. There are upper and lower control lines as before. Each sample range is plotted as it is observed and the process inspected if the sample range is outside the control lines.

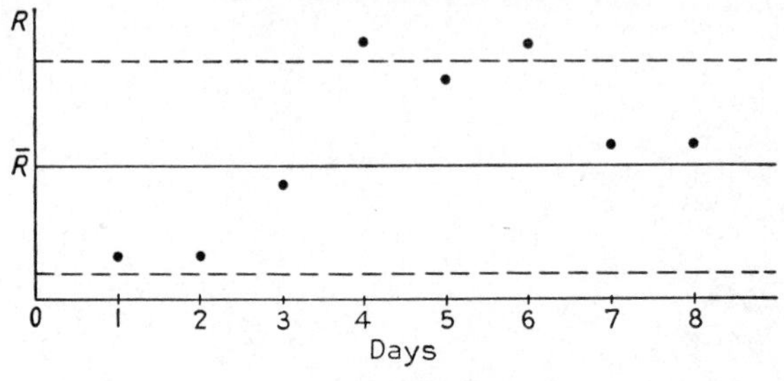

FIG. 9-3

The control lines for the range are found by use of Table 9-3. If $\bar{R}$ denotes the standard or hypothetical range,* then the control limits are $D_L\bar{R}$ and $D_U\bar{R}$, where D_L and D_U are read across from the sample size N. These multipliers are computed to give 1 per cent chance of the sample range exceeding D_U or being less than D_L. They are the .5 and the 99.5 percentiles of the sampling distribution of the statistic R, and $\bar{R}$ is the mean of this distribution. These values are based on the assumption that the measurements have a normal distribution.

Frequently σ is not known, and the mean range $\bar{R}$ is used to measure $3\sigma/\sqrt{N}$ limits for the control chart for means. Control limits $\mu \pm A_2\bar{R}$ can be used instead of $\mu \pm 3\sigma/\sqrt{N}$, with values of A_2 as given in Table 9-3. The factor A_2 includes the $3/\sqrt{N}$ and also a factor which, in a normal population, is such that $A_2\bar{R} = 3\sigma/\sqrt{N}$.

Frequently the mean of a large number of samples is treated as μ, and the mean range of these samples is treated as $\bar{R}$. Then the control lines are drawn and the charts used to indicate whether the production is in control.

Example. In 1955 a department in a store reported weekly its overtime pay. For the entire year the mean monthly overtime pay was 21.3 per cent. Every month the range of the four weekly reports was computed. The mean of these 12 ranges was 12.1 per cent.

* We have used the bar above a symbol to represent the mean value as obtained from a sample. This use of $\bar{R}$ here is inconsistent but is standard notation in quality-control work. The sample range is denoted by w elsewhere in this book since w is the usual notation in other than quality-control applications.

TABLE 9-3. MULTIPLIERS FOR CONTROL CHARTS

N	D_L	D_U	A_2
2	.009	3.52	1.88
3	.100	2.58	1.02
4	.185	2.26	.73
5	.254	2.09	.58
6	.308	1.97	.48
7	.351	1.90	.42
8	.386	1.84	.37
9	.415	1.79	.34
10	.441	1.76	.31
11	.463	1.72	.29
12	.482	1.70	.27
13	.498	1.68	.25
14	.511	1.66	.24
15	.524	1.64	.22

Control limits on monthly ($N = 4$) mean overtime and range are

$$\bar{X}: 21.3 \pm .73(12.1) \qquad R: .185(12.1) \text{ to } 2.26(12.1)$$
$$12.5 \text{ to } 30.1 \qquad 2.20 \text{ to } 27.3$$

During 1956 the $\bar{X}$ and R values in the table were recorded. $\bar{X}$ is out of control for January, March, and September. R is out of control for May.

	Jan.	Feb.	Mar.	Apr.	May	June	July	Aug.	Sept.	Oct.	Nov.	Dec.
$\bar{X}$	12.1	15.8	10.2	18.6	19.2	12.6	13.8	12.6	31.0	18.6	20.3	28.6
R	13.6	12.3	6.5	26.0	29.0	17.1	12.3	10.3	13.6	12.3	23.0	19.1

Other uses of control charts in management are control of output and quality of clerical help, sales performance in various fields, production by skilled labor, etc.

GLOSSARY

control chart for means
control chart for the range
degrees of freedom
intact groups
paired observations
t distribution
tolerance limits

DISCUSSION QUESTIONS

1. What assumptions are made about the population when an experiment is carried out and analyzed by use of a t test?

2. Describe two types of situations where a paired-observation experiment should be used. Give several examples of each type. What assumptions are made about the populations in a paired-observation experiment?

3. Why in testing a one-sided hypothesis is the rejection region entirely on one side of the hypothetical value?

4. Would there be any objection to using the rejection region

$$\mu_0 - \frac{.125\sigma}{\sqrt{N}} < \bar{X} < \mu_0 + \frac{.125\sigma}{\sqrt{N}}$$

to test the hypothesis $\mu = \mu_0$ at the 10 per cent level of significance?

5. If it is not necessary to pair observations and you decide to pair, do you have a different level of significance than if you did not pair? Discuss the effect of pairing on your chance of making a correct inference both in the case where you should pair and in the case where it is not necessary.

6. What use do we make of the words degrees of freedom?

7. Give an example of a situation where you might wish to sample by intact groups.

8. Explain the difference between tolerance intervals and confidence intervals.

9. Why are the control limits for R given in this chapter better than $\bar{R} \pm 3\sigma_R$?

CLASS EXERCISES

1. For each of the samples of size $N = 10$ drawn from Table A-2 compute the value of $t = \dfrac{(\bar{X} - 0)\sqrt{10}}{s}$, and verify that less than 95 per cent fall between -1.96 and $+1.96$ ($\mu - 1.96\sigma$ and $\mu + 1.96\sigma$). Compute P_{95} for the observed distribution of t values, and compare it with $t_{.95}$ (9) from Table A-5.

2. For each of the samples of size $N = 10$ drawn from Table A-23 find 90 per cent confidence limits for μ (that is, $\bar{X} + t_{.05}s/\sqrt{10}$, $\bar{X} + t_{.95}s/\sqrt{10}$). What proportion of these observed intervals covered the population mean?

3. Each student draws three samples of size $N = 10$ from Table A-24. He takes one of these samples and one of the samples he has previously drawn from Table A-2 and computes the value of $\dfrac{\bar{X}_1 - \bar{X}_2}{s_p\sqrt{(1/N_1) + (1/N_2)}}$. Repeat this for each of the other two samples, combining each with one of the samples drawn from Table A-2. For how many of these experiments is the hypothesis that the two populations have the same mean rejected at the 5 per cent level of significance?

Using the data collected above, repeat the analysis by pairing the observations, and again observe the proportion of cases where the hypothesis of equal means is rejected.

Table A-24 records observations from a normal universe with zero mean and variance equal to 2. Here the two populations do have equal means, and this experiment will indicate the effect of unequal variances upon an experiment.

PROBLEMS

In each problem state the hypothesis you wish to test, assumptions made, level of significance; show computations; and state conclusions. In each problem give 95 per cent or 99 per cent confidence limits for the mean or difference in means.

1. Twenty plots of ground were planted with corn. On 10 a new type of phosphorus fertilizer was applied. The yields are recorded below. Is there a significant difference between the yields (at the 5 per cent level)?

	1	2	3	4	5	6	7	8	9	10
Control..............	6.1	5.8	7.0	6.1	5.8	6.4	6.1	6.0	5.9	5.8
Phosphorus..........	5.9	5.7	6.1	5.8	5.9	5.6	5.6	5.9	5.7	5.6

2. On an examination a class of 18 students had a mean of 70 with $s = 6$. Another class of 21 had a mean of 77 with $s = 8$, on the same examination. Is there reason to believe that one class is significantly better than the other? Consider the classes as samples from some universe. What might the universe be?

3. A machine is set to turn out ball bearings having a radius of 1 centimeter (allowable error $\pm .01$ centimeter). A sample of 10 ball bearings produced by this machine has a mean radius of 1.004 centimeters with $s = .003$. Is there reason to suspect the machine is turning out ball bearings having a mean radius greater than 1.0 centimeter?

4. A fertilizer mixing machine is set to give 10 pounds of nitrate for every 100 pounds of fertilizer. Ten 100-pound bags are examined. The percentages of nitrate are as follows: 9, 12, 11, 10, 11, 9, 11, 12, 9, 10. Is there reason to believe that the mean is not equal to 10 per cent?

5. A tire manufacturer wished to test two types of tires. Fifty type *A* tires had a mean life of 24,000 miles with $s^2 = 6{,}250{,}000$. Forty type *B* tires had a mean life of 26,000 miles with $s^2 = 9{,}000{,}000$. Is there a significant difference between the two sample means?

6. A sample of 25 workmen showed an average increase in wages of 45 cents per hour with $s = 10$ cents. Give 90 per cent confidence limits for the mean wage increase in the population from which the sample was drawn. State assumptions used.

7. The following data give paired yields of two varieties of wheat. Each pair was planted in a different locality. Test the hypothesis that the mean yields are equal. Find a 90 per cent confidence interval for the difference in the mean yields.

I	45	32	58	57	60	38	47	51	42	38
II	47	34	60	59	63	44	49	53	46	41

Explain why pairing is necessary in this problem.

8. For the data in Prob. 4 determine an interval such that you have 99 per cent confidence of it covering 90 per cent of the population.

9. If a certain machined part is accurate within $\pm .2$ inch, it is usable. A random sample of 10 such parts showed deviations from the exact size as follows: $+.08$, $-.11$, $+.04$, $-.01$, $-.07$, $+.04$, $-.02$, $+.03$, $+.12$, $-.10$. About what proportion of the population sampled from can you be 95 per cent confident of finding between $-.20$ and $+.20$?

10. In the manufacturing of parts the following data were obtained for the daily number defective for a production of 100 parts per day. Construct a control chart with the first 20 readings, and see whether or not the production goes out of control after that point.

22	25	15	26	31	22	17	26
23	20	28	32	43	18	16	36
21	16	29	26	18	24	28	42
17	14	26	33	26	24	32	36
38	26	25	30	21	16	18	34

11. (*a*) Construct a control chart for $\bar{X}$ for the following data on the blowing time of fuses, samples of 5 being taken every hour. (*b*) If these are the first data taken on this product, would you say that the process seemed to be under control and hence that the mean and range from these data could be used for future control? (*c*) If it is known that previous control existed with a mean and standard deviation about equal to these sample values, would these data justify some action on the part of the engineer in charge at any time? Each set of 5 has been arranged in order of magnitude.

42	42	19	36	42	51	60	18	15	69	64	61
65	45	24	54	51	74	60	20	30	109	91	78
75	68	80	69	57	75	72	27	39	113	93	94
78	72	81	77	59	78	95	42	62	118	109	109
87	90	81	84	78	132	138	60	84	153	112	136

12. For each of the six hypotheses below complete the following:
(*a*) The statistic used to test this hypothesis is ______________.
(*b*) The critical region is ______________.
(*c*) The hypothesis is ______________ (rejected or accepted).
1. $H: \mu = 5$, given $N = 25$, $\bar{X} = 6$, $s = 2$, $\alpha = .05$.
2. $H: \sigma_1^2 = \sigma_2^2$, given $N_1 = 13$, $N_2 = 16$, $s_1^2 = 100$, $s_2^2 = 300$, $\alpha = .02$.
3. $H: \sigma^2 \geq 200$, given $N = 25$, $s^2 = 80$, $\alpha = .01$.
4. $H: \mu_1 \leq \mu_2$, given $N_1 = N_2 = 18$, $\sigma_1^2 = \sigma_2^2 = .49$, $\bar{X}_1 = 17$, $\bar{X}_2 = 13$, $\alpha = .05$.
5. $H: \mu_1 = \mu_2$, given $N_1 = N_2 = 21$, $s_1^2 = 86.5$, $s_2^2 = 126.3$, $\bar{X}_1 = 63.7$, $\bar{X}_2 = 67.0$, $\alpha = .05$.

13. A cigarette manufacturer wished to advertise that the nicotine content of his cigarettes had an average less than 24 milligrams. A laboratory made five determinations of the nicotine content in milligrams as 26, 28, 22, 23, 29.

(*a*) Would the manufacturer feel safe at the 5 per cent level in making the above claim for his product? Carry out the solution, stating assumptions and conclusions in the same general fashion as in the text.

(*b*) How could the manufacturer make an α error (type I error)? What is the chance of his doing so? What would be the consequences of making an error of this kind?

(*c*) How could the manufacturer make a β error (type II error)? What is the chance of his doing so? What would be the consequences of such an error?

14. A manufacturer of flashlight batteries claims that his batteries will operate continuously for an average life of at least 20 hours with a certain type of bulb. A government testing laboratory experimented with five batteries, obtaining the following burning times: 19, 18, 22, 20, 17.

(*a*) Would the laboratory feel safe at the 5 per cent level in saying that the manufacturer's claim is correct? Carry out the solution, stating assumptions and conclusions in the same general fashion as in the text.

(*b*) How could the laboratory make an α error (type I error)? What is the chance of its doing so? What would be the consequences of such an error?

(*c*) How could the laboratory make a β error (type II error)? What is the chance of its doing so? What would be the consequences of such an error?

15. An experiment was performed using seven hop plants. One half of each plant was pollinated, and the other half of the plant was not pollinated. The yield of the seed of the hop plants is tabulated as follows:

Plant number	Weight of seed (grams per 10 grams of hops)	
	Pollinated	Nonpollinated
1	0.78	0.21
2	0.76	0.12
3	0.43	0.32
4	0.92	0.29
5	0.86	0.30
6	0.59	0.20
7	0.68	0.14

(*a*) Determine at the 5 per cent level whether the pollinated half of the plant gives a higher yield in seed than the nonpollinated half. State the assumptions and hypotheses to be tested, and carry through the computations to make a decision.

(*b*) How can the experimenter make an α error? What are the consequences of his doing so?

(*c*) How can the experimenter make a β error? What are the consequences of his doing so?

(*d*) Give 90 per cent confidence limits for the difference in mean yields.

16. The machinery for producing a certain wire is set up in such a way that the mean tensile strength should be 260 pounds, allowing a standard deviation of 1 pound. To ascertain that the machinery is set up properly, a number of wires are tested. Their tensile strengths in pounds are as follows: 265, 259, 263, 264, 260, 259, 261, 262, 264, 259. Determine whether the machinery needs adjustment in order to meet the standards.

17. The following data give readings in foot-pounds of the impact strength on two kinds of insulating material. Determine whether there is any difference in uniformity or in mean strength between the two kinds of material.

A	*B*
1.25	1.01
1.16	.89
1.33	.97
1.15	.95
1.23	.94
1.20	1.02
1.32	.99
1.28	1.06
1.21	.98

18. A group of 50 boys and a group of 50 girls were given a test in arranging different-shaped blocks. The times are recorded in the frequency table below. Analyze the data. If this was an industrial experiment, give a 90 per cent confidence interval for the mean saving in time if girls perform the task rather than boys.

	Time (seconds)											
	40	41	42	43	44	45	46	47	48	49	50	51
Freq. of girls	1	4	3	6	12	9	9	3	1	1	1	
Freq. of boys	...	...	3	2	6	10	12	7	3	4	2	1

CHAPTER 10

ANALYSIS OF VARIANCE

In this chapter procedures will be developed for testing for differences among the means of two or more populations. In Sec. 8-5 it was noted that if means of subgroups are greatly different the variance of the combined groups is much larger than the variances of the separate groups. The analysis of differences in means will be based on this fact.

Circumstances frequently make it necessary to design an experiment in such a way that several variables or populations can be studied simultaneously. If we wish to investigate the differences among five means by performing a t test on each pair of means, there would be ten t values to compute. There are several reasons why it is not good statistical procedure to do this. First, if we use a 5 per cent critical value and then test a number of means in this manner, the level of significance will be much larger than 5 per cent for testing the hypothesis of no difference in means as a group, since, even though all samples are from the same population, 5 per cent of the t values will exceed the critical value on the average. It can be shown that the chance that some one or more of 10 independent t values will exceed $t_{.95}$ is .40. If the above hypothesis of all five means equal is rejected when some one of the ten t values exceeds $t_{.95}$, this hypothesis will be rejected with a chance which may be many times the level of significance .05.

In addition to the disadvantage of a materially increased level of significance α there is the loss of precision in estimating the variance if we use only those measurements in the two groups being compared. This can be improved by using a pooled variance, but the α still remains indefinite.

The examples in the next section illustrate some types of experimental design which are analyzed with analysis-of-variance methods. As will be seen in the following sections, the analysis rests on a separation of the variance of all the observations into parts, each part measuring variability attributable to some specific source, e.g., to internal variation of the several populations, to variations from one population to another, etc., and the phrase analysis of variance refers to this breakdown of the sample variance. Note, however, that the basic question concerns a comparison of the means of the several populations, and the parts of the sample variance are analyzed for this purpose. It will be seen that there are a number of ways of completing the analysis, depending on the specific conclusions desired; for example, one may wish an omnibus test of the hypothesis that all populations have equal means, or one may wish to compare individual populations to find if any one has a significantly greater mean.

10-1. Examples and Discussion of Several Problems

Example 1. *Single Classification.* The simplest application of analysis-of-variance procedures is to the problem of estimating or testing hypotheses about the means $\mu_1, \mu_2, \ldots, \mu_k$ of k populations and is referred to as a single classification problem. The case $k = 2$ was discussed in detail in Chap. 9, where the difference $\mu_1 - \mu_2$ was estimated by a confidence interval and where the hypothesis $\mu_1 = \mu_2$ was tested. All individuals are classified into exactly one of the k populations, or categories. It should be emphasized that the k categories exhaust the cases in which there is interest and are not merely a sample from a larger number of categories. (Such cases are mentioned in Examples 4 and 5.) In order to distinguish this type of example from those to be discussed later, the present example is called a "fixed-constants model" or a "model I" experiment.

Examples of the classification of individuals of a population on a single variable are as follows:

(*a*) We have five ($k = 5$) teaching methods and a group of school children. We imagine five hypothetical populations, each consisting of all the children taught by one of the methods, and are interested in comparing the mean amount of material learned by each group (as measured by an examination) using the respective five methods.

(*b*) We have three cities ($k = 3$) and are interested in comparing the mean incomes of the inhabitants of each of the three cities. In this case the populations actually exist at present. In the previous example the populations may not ever exist except in the mind of the experimenter.

(*c*) We have four varieties of wheat ($k = 4$) and imagine a population of yields of each variety. We are interested in comparing the mean yields of the four varieties.

Example 2. *Two Classifications.* In this example individuals are categorized on two characteristics. Each individual will belong to exactly one category for each variable. One of the characteristics is arbitrarily called the first variable and has, say, c categories, and the other variable is called the second and has, say, r categories. In Table 10-1 the first variable is placed at the top and is also referred to as a column variable. Thus there are c categories for the first variable and c columns in the table. The second variable appears as rows in the table, and thus the table has r rows corresponding to the r categories of the second variable. Table 10-1 represents the case $c = 3$ and $r = 4$. We may consider each

TABLE 10-1. TWO-WAY CLASSIFICATION

		First-variable categories			
		1	2	3	
Second-variable categories	1	μ_{11}	μ_{21}	μ_{31}	$\mu_{\cdot 1}$
	2	μ_{12}	μ_{22}	μ_{32}	$\mu_{\cdot 2}$
	3	μ_{13}	μ_{23}	μ_{33}	$\mu_{\cdot 3}$
	4	μ_{14}	μ_{24}	μ_{34}	$\mu_{\cdot 4}$
		$\mu_{1\cdot}$	$\mu_{2\cdot}$	$\mu_{3\cdot}$	$\mu_{\cdot\cdot}$

of the $c \cdot r = 3 \cdot 4 = 12$ cells as separate populations, each individual belonging to one and only one of the 12. We are interested in how the means of these 12 populations differ from one another. In the table the means of the separate populations are labeled μ_{ij}, with the first subscript referring to the column and the second to the row. For example, μ_{23} is the mean of the population of individuals belonging to category 2 of the column variable of classification and to category 3 of the row variable of classification. On the right side of the table are recorded $\mu_{\cdot j}$ defined as the mean of μ_{ij} for that row, for example, $\mu_{\cdot 1} = (\mu_{11} + \mu_{21} + \mu_{31})/3$, and at the bottom of the table $\mu_{i\cdot}$, for example, $\mu_{1\cdot} = (\mu_{11} + \mu_{12} + \mu_{13} + \mu_{14})/4$, defined as the mean of the μ_{ij} for that column. The mean of all 12 values $\mu_{11}, \mu_{12}, \ldots, \mu_{34}$ is written as $\mu_{\cdot\cdot}$ in the lower right-hand corner of the table. If the 12 populations are of equal size, then $\mu_{\cdot 1}$ is the mean of the population consisting of all individuals in the first row (category 1 of variable 2), $\mu_{2\cdot}$ is the mean of the population in the second column, etc.

As in the first example, it is supposed that the c and r categories exhaust all categories of interest for the first (column) and second (row) variables, respectively, and neither is considered as a sample of categories for the particular variable, i.e., this is still a fixed-constants or model I situation.

Examples of the classification of individuals by two characteristics are as follows:

(*a*) We have the children of three schools ($c = 3$), and four teaching methods ($r = 4$), to investigate. Note here that for the fixed-constants model we suppose that we are interested in only three schools and, specifically, do not plan to infer from our results anything about a larger group of schools. We may wish here to compare the schools, to compare the teaching methods, or possibly to see whether there is some interacting effect which a particular school has with a particular method.

(*b*) We have three cities ($c = 3$) and have divided the employed people into groups by sex ($r = 2$). We may wish to compare the mean income for men with the mean income for women, to compare the mean incomes for the three cities, and also to see whether there is some interaction, e.g., a particular city having an unusually large or small mean income for either men or women but not both.

(*c*) We have four varieties of wheat ($c = 4$) and three sources of fertilizer ($r = 3$) and are interested in discovering whether a combination of a particular variety of wheat with fertilizer from a particular source will result in a larger mean yield than the other combinations. Or, as before, we may also be interested in whether some one source of fertilizer is over-all better than the others. ("Over-all" here indicates that it is to be used with all four varieties of wheat.)

Example 3. *Several Classifications.* The previous example can be extended to cases where individuals are classified on more than two variables. For example, we may consider all people in three cities classified as to (*a*) the city in which they live, (*b*) sex, and (*c*) having income over or under $3,000 per year. The original population is divided into 12 subpopulations; men in city 1 earning under $3,000, men in city 1 earning over $3,000, women in city 1 earning under $3,000, etc. We may wish to consider whether the mean per cent of income spent on medicine was the same for the three cities, for the two income groups, for the two sexes, or possibly whether some interaction was present.

Example 4. *Components of Variance.* A situation which appears to be similar to the single-variable, model I problem in Example 1 occurs if the k populations examined are actually not the entire set of populations existing but rather a sample from the larger group. This is referred to as a *components-of-variance* model, and although the arithmetic of the analysis is the same as the fixed-constants case, the interpretations differ. Here, in addition to the problem of comparing the means $\mu_1, \ldots, \mu_k$ of the chosen populations we have the problem of inference beyond them to the class of populations sampled from.

Examples of this situation are as follows:

(*a*) We have a group of 50 schools and choose samples of students from 5 of them ($k = 5$). We are interested in estimating means or testing hypotheses about the means of the 50 schools and wish to use the data from the 5 schools chosen for this purpose.

(*b*) We have a group of 200 cities and choose samples of people from 10 of the cities ($k = 10$). We are interested in estimating the mean or variance of the mean incomes of the 200 cities.

(*c*) We have a fertilizer which may be used for 10 types of wheat. We choose 3 types ($k = 3$) from the 10 and wish to estimate the mean yield if the fertilizer was used on all 10 types. Note that since there is a single fertilizer we still have only one variable of classification.

Example 5. *Components with Two Variables, Mixed Model.* Components-of-variance situations also occur if there are two variables of classification. If the categories for both variables are samples from larger groups of categories we refer to it as a components-of-variance situation. However, if all categories are used for one variable, and the categories for the other are a sample of categories, we refer to the situation as a *mixed-model* problem. Examples of the two situations are as follows:

(*a*) Components of variance. We have a group of 50 schools and 12 age groups of students. We choose 5 schools ($c = 5$) and 2 age groups ($r = 2$) and measure samples of students in the 2 age groups from each of the 5 schools. Our measurements might be learning skill, or money spent for comics, or growing rate, etc. We are interested in an inference to the entire group of 50 schools and to all 12 age groups. For example, we may wish to determine whether the mean learning skill for all 50 schools is above a given norm, basing our inference on the data from the 5 schools.

(*b*) Components of variance. We have a group of 200 cities and 15 income categories of workers. We choose samples of workers from 20 cities ($c = 20$) and from 3 chosen income categories ($r = 3$) and measure the amount of education for each worker. We are interested in an inference comparing the mean amounts of education of workers in the 200 cities and an inference comparing the mean amounts of education of workers in the 15 income categories. As noted in Example 3, we may also be interested in whether there is evidence of an interaction of city and income level; i.e., it may be that in some cities a particular income classification has a mean level of education which is unusually high or low.

(*c*) Mixed model. We have exactly four types of wheat ($c = 4$) and 60 general locations in a state in which to grow wheat. We choose 5 locations at random ($r = 5$) and grow each of the four types of wheat at each of the 5 locations. Since all the types of wheat are present in our experiment, but only a sample of locations, we have a mixed-model experiment.

Probably in most scientific investigations an attempt is made to consider factors other than the one specifically under study. The methods illustrated above which arrange the factors into general classifications are often useful for this purpose since they permit a study at each category level of each variable. This type of experimentation is contrary to the method of holding all factors constant except for the one under study. To illustrate this point, we list the following examples:

Suppose we wish to compare two methods of teaching a certain subject and select test groups which have the same proportion of boys and girls who are equal in intelligence, of equal ages, etc. An experiment conducted by one teacher or in one school, however, is subject to the criticism that this certain teacher may be efficient with a certain method or that the superiority of a certain method may be due to the particular school involved. It is clear that an experiment of this sort should involve several schools and several teachers in each school. Depending on the problem being studied, it may be better to include more schools even with one teacher per school. Thus, to investigate a particular phenomenon, we do not really wish to "hold constant" all other variables, but to show that the phenomenon exists independent of the other variables.

Suppose we wish to investigate the effect of several treatments on a group of white rats. For example, suppose four groups of rats are given four different concentrations of an injection and the performance of the rats in running a maze is observed. If we can determine that there is a significant difference in the performance of the different groups but we discover in a study of the records that there is also a significant difference in the ages of the rats in the four groups, this experiment must be declared inconclusive. It is easy to see, then, that it would be desirable to remove the chance that a difference in age, training, sex or a difference in previous experiments to which they have been subjected would produce changes which might be concluded either to be the result of our treatments or to cause so much variability in the results that any effects of our treatments are completely masked.

If we wish to compare the yield of several hybrids of corn, we must consider the important variables such as planting time, soil fertility, amount of fertilizer, etc. Either these variables must be controlled, or the experiment must be designed in such a way that the effects of planting time, fertility, etc., can be estimated and separated from the effect on yield of the difference among the hybrids themselves. It will probably be necessary to use several planting times and to plant the corn with different amounts of fertilizer, etc., in order to estimate these effects.

If we wish to decide whether some additional treatment makes soil pipe more resistant to corrosion, we should like to be sure that the improvement, if any exists, is valid for several different types of soil before this treatment is generally adopted.

A study of various ways of treating delinquent children should include cases from various educational, economic, regional groups, etc.

In cases where the important variables can be held constant, as in the laboratory, simpler statistical procedures are possible. When the circumstances are such that these variables cannot be controlled, a statistical procedure must be developed which will take into account these various changes. However, even in cases where the important variables can be controlled, it may be prohibitively expensive to do so. Further, there is always the possibility that the values at which the variables have been fixed cause a different result to occur in our experiment from that which might occur for other values of these variables. Also, it is sometimes very difficult to create the same experimental situation every time we wish to repeat our experiment on one or two more items.

The time factor is frequently the chief factor in causing us to design an experiment which will study a number of treatments and materials simultaneously. It often takes a whole year to perform one experiment in biology or agriculture. In many sciences a whole generation or several generations are required, so that it is important to have a single experiment as complete as possible.

An important point to bear in mind in designing experiments is that in using a mean $\bar{X}$ of observations to estimate a population mean μ our precision depends on the size of the variance σ^2/N of the sampling distribution of $\bar{X}$. If σ^2/N is small, either because N is large or because σ^2 is small, then our estimate will be more precise. The population σ^2 consists of two parts, the actual variability of the members of the population and the variability introduced by lack of complete precision in measuring the sampled members of the population. This second portion of σ^2 may be reduced by refining the measuring instruments or improving the experimental apparatus. From an economic point of view careful consideration should be given to the appropriate balance between the number of observations and the precision of each. In some cases we may wish to reduce σ^2, and in some cases it is simpler to increase N.

This chapter presents only an introduction to statistical methods applicable to experiments of the type described above. The analyses will cover the following topics:

Single variable of classification:

1. Fixed constants, model I:
   a. Test of hypothesis of equal means in Sec. 10-2.
   b. Contrasts or comparisons in Sec. 10-3.
2. Components-of-variance model in Sec. 10-8.

Two variables of classification:

1. Fixed constants, model I:
   a. Test of hypothesis of equal means in terms of row, column, and interaction effects in Secs. 10-4 and 10-5.
   b. Contrasts or comparisons in Sec. 10-6.
2. Components-of-variance model in Sec. 10-8.

Three variables of classification, Latin square in Sec. 10-7.

Section 10-9 contains a discussion of extensions and assumptions.

10-2. Single Variable of Classification, Model I

In this design every individual belongs to one and only one of k distinct populations with means labeled $\mu_1, \mu_2, \ldots, \mu_k$. We wish to make inferences concerning the sizes of these means. In this section we shall develop a test of the hypothesis that *all* k means are equal. In the next section tests for and estimates of more detailed comparisons among the means will be developed, for example, estimates of $\mu_1 - \mu_2$, $\mu_1 - \mu_3$, etc.

A random sample of individuals will be taken from each population, n_1 from the first population, n_2 from the second, and so on, to n_k individuals from the kth population. We shall compute from the means $\bar{X}_{1.}$, $\bar{X}_{2.}$, . . . , $\bar{X}_{k.}$ of the samples an estimate of the variance σ^2 of each of the k populations to compare with the pooled variance s_p^2 obtained from the variances of the k samples.

For convenience we shall refer to the different categories, which may represent different schools, classes, hybrids, fertilizers, stages of learning, dosages of penicillin, economic groups, number of children in family, age groups, color of eyes, metals of different atomic-weight classes, different classes of polymers, etc. It might be noted that if the categories represent different treatments given to individuals the populations differ only in treatment given. In this case we could select a number of individuals and randomly assign an equal number to each of the categories.

To simplify the presentation further, only three categories, $k = 3$, will be considered. The changes necessary to include more groups will be pointed out. Suppose we have observed five individuals at random from

TABLE 10-2

	Category			
	A	B	C	
	X_{11}	X_{21}	X_{31}	
	X_{12}	X_{22}	X_{32}	
	X_{13}	X_{23}	X_{33}	
	X_{14}	X_{24}	X_{34}	
	X_{15}	X_{25}	X_{35}	
Total	T_{1+}	T_{2+}	T_{3+}	T_{++} = Grand total
Mean	$\bar{X}_{1\cdot}$	$\bar{X}_{2\cdot}$	$\bar{X}_{3\cdot}$	$\bar{X}_{..}$ = Grand mean

$$T_{1+} = X_{11} + X_{12} + X_{13} + X_{14} + X_{15}, \text{ etc.}$$
$$T_{++} = T_{1+} + T_{2+} + T_{3+}$$
$$\bar{X}_{1\cdot} = \frac{T_{1+}}{5}, \text{ etc.}$$
$$\bar{X}_{..} = \frac{T_{++}}{15}$$

each category. X_{ij} is the measurement on the jth individual being chosen from the ith category. The data may be arranged as in Table 10-2 and the totals and averages computed as indicated. Thus, T_{1+} is the total of all the observations in the first column, T_{2+} the total for the second column, and T_{3+} the total for the third column. T_{++} is the total of all the column totals, which of course is equal to the total of all the observations.

The hypothesis to be tested is as follows: There is no difference in means among the categories. (The three groups of five are all drawn from populations with the same mean.) The choice of the level of significance should be made before the experiment is conducted.

We shall estimate the population σ^2 in two ways and then compare these two estimates.

We shall estimate σ^2:

1. By forming a pooled estimate of σ^2 as was done in Chap. 8.

$$s_p^2 = \frac{\sum_{j=1}^{n_1} (X_{1j} - \bar{X}_{1\cdot})^2 + \sum_{j=1}^{n_2} (X_{2j} - \bar{X}_{2\cdot})^2 + \sum_{j=1}^{n_3} (X_{3j} - \bar{X}_{3\cdot})^2}{n_1 + n_2 + n_3 - 3} \tag{1}$$

where n_1, n_2, n_3 are the number of cases in category A, B, C, respectively, and, for the data above, $n_1 = n_2 = n_3 = 5$.

2. By computing the variance of the means directly and multiplying by the sample size n, as was done in Chap. 6. The variance of the means is an estimate of σ^2/n. Therefore, the variance of the means multiplied by n is an estimate of σ^2. This estimate is

$$s_M^2 = n \frac{\sum_{i=1}^{k} (\bar{X}_{i\cdot} - \bar{X}_{\cdot\cdot})^2}{k - 1} \tag{2}$$

where k = number of categories or treatments ($k = 3$ in this case)
n = number of measurements in each category ($n = 5$ in this case)

When the number of observations is not the same in all categories, this estimate is

$$s_M^2 = \frac{\sum_{i=1}^{k} n_i (\bar{X}_{i\cdot} - \bar{X}_{\cdot\cdot})^2}{k - 1} \tag{2'}$$

These two quantities, s_p^2 and s_M^2, may be tested for significant difference by using the F ratio. If the groups are from populations having unequal means, the second estimate (2) or (2′) will usually be considerably larger than estimate (1). We wish to reject the hypothesis of no difference in means if the observed means are more disperse than we would expect when they are all obtained from the same population. We wish to reject the hypothesis only if they are *significantly more* disperse. Therefore we always place this second estimate in the numerator and reject the hypothesis of equal means if the F ratio obtained exceeds the critical value of the F table for $k - 1$ and $\Sigma n_i - k$ degrees of freedom (for this example, 2 and 12 degrees of freedom). This use of the F table has been justified mathematically for normal populations.

As was noted in Chaps. 8 and 9, an alternate computing formula for s_p^2 is

$$s_p^2 = \frac{\sum_j X_{1j}^2 - \frac{(\Sigma X_{1j})^2}{n_1} + \sum_j X_{2j}^2 - \frac{(\Sigma X_{2j})^2}{n_2} + \sum_j X_{3j}^2 - \frac{(\Sigma X_{3j})^2}{n_3}}{n_1 + n_2 + n_3 - 3}$$

or, rearranging the terms and replacing the total of the ith column $\sum_j X_{ij}$ by T_{i+}, we can write

$$s_p^2 = \frac{\sum_i \sum_j X_{ij}^2 - \left(\frac{T_{1+}^2}{n_1} + \frac{T_{2+}^2}{n_2} + \frac{T_{3+}^2}{n_3}\right)}{\sum_i n_i - 3}$$

The numerator is referred to as the *within-groups sum of squares*, and the pooled variance s_p^2 is sometimes called the *within-groups mean square*, or *within-groups variance*. The denominator is referred to as the number of *degrees of freedom* in s_p^2. The general formula for s_p^2 if there are k categories can be written

$$s_p^2 = \frac{\Sigma\Sigma X_{ij}^2 - \Sigma(T_{i+}^2/n_i)}{\Sigma n_i - k}$$

In a similar manner the estimates (2) or (2′) can be rearranged to give as a computing formula

$$s_M^2 = \frac{\frac{T_{1+}^2}{n_1} + \frac{T_{2+}^2}{n_2} + \frac{T_{3+}^2}{n_3} - \frac{T_{++}^2}{N}}{3 - 1}$$

where $T_{++} = \Sigma\Sigma X_{ij}$ = total of all observations
$N = \Sigma n_i$ = total number of observations

The numerator is called the *sum of squares for means* (or *between categories*), and s_M^2 is called the *mean square for* (or *between*) *categories*. The computing formula for s_M^2 if there are k categories is

$$s_M^2 = \frac{\sum_{i=1}^{k} \frac{T_{i+}^2}{n_i} - \frac{T_{++}^2}{N}}{k - 1}$$

The number of degrees of freedom for s_M^2 is $k - 1$.

Note that if the numerators of s_p^2 and s_M^2 are added the result is

$$\sum \sum X_{ij}^2 - \frac{T_{++}^2}{N}$$

which when divided by the degrees of freedom $N - 1$ is exactly the computing formula for the variance of the entire set of observations. The breakdown of the total sum of squares into two parts can be conveniently recorded in a table, as shown in Table 10-3. The last column of Table 10-3 will be discussed later in this section.

TABLE 10–3. ANALYSIS-OF-VARIANCE TABLE FOR ONE VARIABLE

	Sum of squares	df	Mean square	Estimate of
Means..........	$\sum \frac{T_{i+}^2}{n_i} - \frac{T_{++}^2}{N}$	$k - 1$	s_M^2	$\sigma^2 + n\sigma_m^2$
Within..........	$\sum \sum X_{ij}^2 - \sum \frac{T_{i+}^2}{n_i}$	$N - k$	s_p^2	σ^2
Total.........	$\sum \sum X_{ij}^2 - \frac{T_{++}^2}{N}$	$N - 1$		

The computations are simple to perform. The following data are fictitious and introduced only to illustrate the computation. The data are presented in four categories to illustrate the changes necessary in the formulas for a different number of categories.

The hypothesis of no difference in categories (equal means) will be tested at the 5 per cent level of significance.

TABLE 10-4

	Category				
	A	*B*	*C*	*D*	
	7	6	8	7	
	2	4	4	4	
	4	6	5	2	
				5	
Total	13	16	17	18	64

Computation. Category means:

$$\left(\frac{13^2}{3} + \frac{16^2}{3} + \frac{17^2}{3} + \frac{18^2}{4}\right) - \frac{64^2}{13} = 319 - 315.08 = 3.92$$

Within:

$$7^2 + 2^2 + 4^2 + 6^2 + 4^2 + 6^2 + 8^2 + 4^2 + 5^2 + 7^2 + 4^2 + 2^2 + 5^2 - \left(\frac{13^2}{3} + \frac{16^2}{3} + \frac{17^2}{3} + \frac{18^2}{4}\right) = 37.00$$

Total:

$$7^2 + 2^2 + 4^2 + 6^2 + 4^2 + 6^2 + 8^2 + 4^2 + 5^2 + 7^2 + 4^2 + 2^2 + 5^2 - \frac{64^2}{13} = 356 - 315.08 = 40.92$$

In the computation unnecessary detail has been included for clarity. If a calculating machine is used for computation, portions of the computation may be cumulated directly in the dials of the machine. Since the sum of the first two values obtained is equal to the third, we need compute only two of the three quantities.

TABLE 10-5. ANALYSIS OF VARIANCE

	Sum of squares	df	Mean square	F ratio
Category means	3.92	3	1.31	$F = \frac{1.31}{4.11} = .32$
Within.............	37.00	9	4.11	$F_{.95}\,(3,9) = 3.86$
Total............	40.92	12		

The analysis-of-variance table (Table 10-3) has been almost universally accepted as the particular form for reporting the computation results. The number of degrees of freedom among categories in this table is $(k - 1)$, in this case 3, or one less than the number of categories. The degrees of freedom for the pooled estimate of the variance (sum of squares within groups) is $(\Sigma n_i - k)$, in this case 9. The number of degrees of freedom for the total is $(N - 1)$, in this case 12. Note that the degrees of freedom for the two estimates of variance total to $N - 1$. The row of totals in the analysis-of-variance table is used only for computation of other numbers in the table. The numbers in the mean-square column are obtained by dividing the corresponding sum of squares by the degrees of freedom. The two mean squares obtained are the two estimates of variance s_M^2 and s_p^2. The mean square obtained from the means is always placed in the numerator of the F ratio since we wish to declare the means significantly different only if they are significantly more spread out than would be expected for samples from the same population. For the particular data above, the hypothesis of equal means would be accepted since the observed F is less than $F_{.95}\,(3,9) = 3.86$.

Hypothesis and Assumptions. The hypothesis we are testing with the above analysis of variance is that the samples are from populations with the same mean, that is, $\mu_1 = \mu_2 = \mu_3 = \mu_4$. The computation up to the test of significance gives valid results for estimating the variances, if the samples are randomly chosen from populations having approximately equal variances. However, the test of significance using the F distribution in the analysis of variance above is known to be valid if the observations are from normally distributed populations with equal variances. Investigation has shown that the results of the analysis are changed very little by moderate violations of the assumptions of normal distribution and equal variance. If a considerable amount of experimentation is involved, these assumptions can be checked from the data gathered.

Outline of Analysis-of-variance Test for Single Variable of Classification

1. H: $\mu_1 = \mu_2 = \cdots = \mu_k$. The means of the k categories are all equal.
2. Choose the level of significance α.
3. The statistic used is F, the ratio of the mean square for means to the mean square for within groups.
4. Assuming the observations are randomly selected from normal populations with $\sigma_1^2 = \sigma_2^2 = \cdots = \sigma_k^2$ (homogeneous variance) and that the hypothesis is true, the distribution of F is $F(k - 1, \Sigma n_i - k)$ as given in Table A-7.
5. The critical region is $F > F_{1-\alpha}(k - 1, \Sigma n_i - k)$.
6. Compute F, and accept or reject the hypothesis.

Often it can be assumed from past experience or from an examination of the data that the assumption of homogeneous variance is satisfied. If the variances are not homogeneous, it may be possible to transform the observations so that this assumption will be satisfied (see Sec. 10-9).

If the hypothesis $\mu_1 = \mu_2 = \cdots = \mu_k$ is true, both s_p^2 and s_M^2 are unbiased estimates of σ^2, the variance of the individual populations. If in fact the hypothesis is not true and some of the μ_i's are unequal, then, assuming for simplicity that there is an equal number n of observations from each population, s_M^2 will have a sampling distribution with mean equal to $\sigma^2 + n\sigma_m^2$, where $\sigma_m^2 = \sum_{i=1}^{k} (\mu_i - \bar{\mu})^2/(k - 1)$. However, the within-groups variance s_p^2 is still an unbiased estimate of σ^2. These mean values are listed in the last column of Table 10-3. If the n_i are not equal, $n\sigma_m^2$ is replaced by a more complicated expression.

The value of σ_m^2 may be estimated by subtracting the within-groups variance from the mean square for means and dividing by n. Thus $(s_M^2 - s_p^2)/n$ is an unbiased estimate of $[(\sigma^2 + n\sigma_m^2) - \sigma^2]/n = \sigma_m^2$.

To illustrate the meaning of σ_m^2, consider 10 observations from each of six populations, each having $\sigma^2 = 1$. Suppose the means of the six populations are $\mu_1 = \mu_2 = \mu_3 = 0$ and $\mu_4 = \mu_5 = \mu_6 = 2$. Then $\bar{\mu} = 1$, and

$\sigma_m^2 = \frac{6}{5} = 1.20$. Therefore the mean square for means s_M^2 estimates $\sigma^2 + n\sigma_m^2 = 1 + 10(1.20) = 13$, and s_p^2 estimates $\sigma^2 = 1$. In the usual situation the μ_i's are not known, and we estimate their dispersion from the formula $(s_M^2 - s_p^2)/n$.

10-3. Individual Comparisons in the One-variable Case

If the hypothesis $\mu_1 = \mu_2 = \cdot \cdot \cdot = \mu_k$ is rejected by the methods of the previous section, we conclude that there are differences among the means. The test, however, indicates very little about the nature of the differences. The procedure introduced in this section provides a method for examining in a single experiment a wide variety of possible differences, including those suggested by the data itself. It is based on the range of the k observed means, i.e., the difference between the smallest and largest observed means.

In the preceding section the total sum of squares was separated into two parts, one involving the variance of the observed means and the other the within-groups sum of squares. The two portions were used in a test of the hypothesis that the several populations have equal means. If the observed means are close together, we accept the hypothesis; if they are significantly dispersed, we reject the hypothesis. In the test we used the variance of the observed means $\bar{X}_{1\cdot}, \bar{X}_{2\cdot}, \ldots, \bar{X}_{k\cdot}$ to measure their dispersion.

The range w is also a measure of dispersion and can be used to measure the dispersion of the k means. A test of the hypothesis of equal means can be made by comparing the range of the means to the within-groups sum of squares. This can be done with the test statistic $q = \dfrac{w}{s_p/\sqrt{n}}$, where s_p^2 is the pooled or within-groups mean square and n is the size of each sample. The denominator $s_p/\sqrt{n}$ is an estimate of $\sigma/\sqrt{n}$, the standard deviation of $\bar{X}$'s for samples of size n from the same population.

Several percentiles of the sampling distribution of the statistic q are given in Table A-18, where k is the number of means and ν = df, the number of degrees of freedom in s_p^2. The heading in Table A-18 is $q = w/s$, which is the ratio for k single observations ($n = 1$) from a normal population. The statistic is modified by the factor $\sqrt{n}$ to apply it to the means of n observations each.

Suppose we have four observations ($n = 4$) from each of three populations ($k = 3$); then the pooled variance has $12 - 3 = 9$ df. We read in Table A-18 that $q = \dfrac{w}{s_p/\sqrt{4}}$ has a 95 per cent chance of being less than 3.95 and a 99 per cent chance of being less than 5.43. An $\alpha = .05$ critical region for testing the hypothesis that the three populations have equal means consists of values of q greater than 3.95, and an $\alpha = .01$ critical region consists of values of q greater than 5.43. If, for example, the observed means are $\bar{X}_{1.} = 2.25$, $\bar{X}_{2.} = 4.00$, $\bar{X}_{3.} = 4.50$ and the pooled variance is $s_p^2 = 4.41$, then the observed $q = \dfrac{2.25}{(2.10)/2} = 2.14$ and this is less than 3.95. Thus we do not reject the hypothesis of equal means at the 5 per cent level of significance.

Extension to Other Hypotheses. The preceding analysis was presented as a test of the hypothesis that the k population means $\mu_1, \mu_2, \ldots, \mu_k$ are equal. We may also use the q table to estimate or to test simultaneously hypotheses about all possible differences of the means of the type $\mu_1 - \mu_2$, $\mu_1 - \mu_3$, $\mu_4 - \mu_2$, etc., as well as all possible linear expressions of the form $a_1\mu_1 + a_2\mu_2 + \cdots + a_k\mu_k$, where $a_1 + a_2 + \cdots + a_k = 0$, and where for convenience we shall make the sum of the positive a's equal to 1. Such forms are called *contrasts*, or *comparisons*, among the means $\mu_1, \mu_2, \ldots, \mu_k$.

Tests for contrasts are based on the following theorem:

For random samples from k normal populations with the same variance the chance that all comparisons simultaneously satisfy

$$\frac{-q_{1-\alpha}s_p}{\sqrt{n}} < (a_1\bar{X}_{1.} + a_2\bar{X}_{2.} + \cdots + a_k\bar{X}_{k.}) - (a_1\mu_1 + a_2\mu_2 + \cdots + a_k\mu_k) < \frac{q_{1-\alpha}s_p}{\sqrt{n}}$$

is equal to $1 - \alpha$, *where the value of* $q_{1-\alpha}$ *is read from Table* A-18.

For example, consider the observations on three populations given above: $k = 3$, $n = 4$, $\bar{X}_{1.} = 2.25$, $\bar{X}_{2.} = 4.00$, $\bar{X}_{3.} = 4.50$, and $s_p^2 = 4.41$. For 95 per cent confidence in our statements we use $q_{.95} = 3.95$ from Table A-18 for $k = 3$ and df $= 9$. Using the notation $q_{1-\alpha}(k,\nu)$, we have $q_{.95}(3,9) = 3.95$. We first compute $q_{1-\alpha}s_p/\sqrt{n} = 3.95(2.10)/\sqrt{4} = 4.15$. We may now say with 95 per cent confidence of being correct in all statements that

$$\bar{X}_{1.} - \bar{X}_{2.} - 4.15 < \mu_1 - \mu_2 < \bar{X}_{1.} - \bar{X}_{2.} + 4.15$$
$$-5.90 < \mu_1 - \mu_2 < 2.40$$

and

$$\bar{X}_{1.} - \bar{X}_{3.} - 4.15 < \mu_1 - \mu_3 < \bar{X}_{1.} - \bar{X}_{3.} + 4.15$$
$$-6.40 < \mu_1 - \mu_3 < 1.90$$

and

$$\bar{X}_{2.} - \bar{X}_{3.} - 4.15 < \mu_2 - \mu_3 < \bar{X}_{2.} - \bar{X}_{3.} + 4.15$$
$$-4.65 < \mu_2 - \mu_3 < 3.65$$

and

$$\frac{\bar{X}_{1.} + \bar{X}_{2.}}{2} - \bar{X}_{3.} - 4.15 < \frac{\mu_1 + \mu_2}{2} - \mu_3 < \frac{\bar{X}_{1.} + \bar{X}_{2.}}{2} - \bar{X}_{3.} + 4.15$$
$$-5.53 < \frac{\mu_1 + \mu_2}{2} - \mu_3 < 2.77$$

and

$$\frac{\bar{X}_{1\cdot} + \bar{X}_{3\cdot}}{2} - \bar{X}_{2\cdot} - 4.15 < \frac{\mu_1 + \mu_3}{2} - \mu_2 < \frac{\bar{X}_{1\cdot} + \bar{X}_{3\cdot}}{2} - \bar{X}_{2\cdot} + 4.15$$

$$-4.77 < \frac{\mu_1 + \mu_3}{2} - \mu_2 < 3.53$$

and

$$\frac{\bar{X}_{2\cdot} + \bar{X}_{3\cdot}}{2} - \bar{X}_{1\cdot} - 4.15 < \frac{\mu_2 + \mu_3}{2} - \mu_1 < \frac{\bar{X}_{2\cdot} + \bar{X}_{3\cdot}}{2} - \bar{X}_{1\cdot} + 4.15$$

$$-2.15 < \frac{\mu_2 + \mu_3}{2} - \mu_1 < 6.15$$

and so on, for as many contrasts as we can, or wish to, write down.

This is a most useful result since it makes possible confidence statements about differences suggested by the data rather than about only a particular difference stated in a hypothesis before data are collected. Usually exploratory collections of data can be used to suggest hypotheses that may be tested by a future experiment, which is then carried out to decide whether to reject or to accept the hypotheses. Using the q statistic in this case makes it possible to look for unexpected results in the data and then to use the same data to establish significance. It should be emphasized in this connection that if a certain single comparison is of major interest a shorter confidence interval may be obtained for this comparison by using percentiles of t from Table A-5 to form the interval

$$t_{\frac{1}{2}\alpha} s_p \sqrt{\frac{\Sigma a_i^2}{n}} < (a_1\bar{X}_{1\cdot} + a_2\bar{X}_{2\cdot} + \cdots + a_k\bar{X}_{k\cdot}) - (a_1\mu_1 + a_2\mu_2 + \cdots + a_k\mu_k) < t_{1-\frac{1}{2}\alpha} s_p \sqrt{\frac{\Sigma a_i^2}{n}}$$

However, the level of confidence applies only to this single statement and not to repeated single statements. For example, one could have 90 per cent confidence in a joint conclusion about two independent statements by using $\alpha = .051$ in the above formula for each comparison.

Computations for a number of contrasts can be recorded conveniently in tabular form. The coefficients $a_1, a_2, \ldots, a_k$ corresponding to $\bar{X}_{1\cdot}, \bar{X}_{2\cdot}, \ldots, \bar{X}_{k\cdot}$ are listed for each contrast of interest in a table like Table 10-6. Although only six contrasts are listed, we note again that any others may be added to the table with no loss of confidence in the final conclusions provided the q statistic is used. The numerical results for the example discussed above are given in Table 10-7. In this example there is no evidence, using the q statistic at the 5 per cent level, to reject a zero value for any of the six contrasts listed.

Assuming that we shall estimate only one particular contrast and no other, we may use the t statistic. Suppose the single contrast chosen in advance of the experiment to be the third one listed in Table 10-7. We could then state the 95 per cent confidence limits for $\mu_2 - \mu_3$ as $-.50 \pm (2.26)(2.10)\sqrt{\frac{2}{4}}$ or $-.50 \pm 3.36$.

TABLE 10-6. EXAMPLES OF CONTRASTS AMONG THREE GROUPS

$\bar{X}_{1\cdot}$	$\bar{X}_{2\cdot}$	$\bar{X}_{3\cdot}$	Confidence limits	Population contrast
1	−1	0	$(\bar{X}_{1\cdot} - \bar{X}_{2\cdot}) \pm \frac{qs_p}{\sqrt{n}}$	$\mu_1 - \mu_2$
1	0	−1	$(\bar{X}_{1\cdot} - \bar{X}_{3\cdot}) \pm \frac{qs_p}{\sqrt{n}}$	$\mu_1 - \mu_3$
0	1	−1	$(\bar{X}_{2\cdot} - \bar{X}_{3\cdot}) \pm \frac{qs_p}{\sqrt{n}}$	$\mu_2 - \mu_3$
$\frac{1}{2}$	$\frac{1}{2}$	−1	$\left(\frac{\bar{X}_{1\cdot} + \bar{X}_{2\cdot}}{2} - \bar{X}_{3\cdot}\right) \pm \frac{qs_p}{\sqrt{n}}$	$\frac{\mu_1 + \mu_2}{2} - \mu_3$
$\frac{1}{2}$	−1	$\frac{1}{2}$	$\left(\frac{\bar{X}_{1\cdot} + \bar{X}_{3\cdot}}{2} - \bar{X}_{2\cdot}\right) \pm \frac{qs_p}{\sqrt{n}}$	$\frac{\mu_1 + \mu_3}{2} - \mu_2$
−1	$\frac{1}{2}$	$\frac{1}{2}$	$\left(\frac{\bar{X}_{2\cdot} + \bar{X}_{3\cdot}}{2} - \bar{X}_{1\cdot}\right) \pm \frac{qs_p}{\sqrt{n}}$	$\frac{\mu_2 + \mu_3}{2} - \mu_1$

Some writers advocate making multiple comparisons of the type discussed in this section with a much larger value of α. This, of course, improves the chance of recognizing cases where some one of the hypotheses tested is not true, but it should be recognized that it also increases the chance of saying a true hypothesis is false.

TABLE 10-7. NUMERICAL EXAMPLE FOR CONTRASTS AMONG THREE GROUPS

2.25	4.00	4.50	Confidence limits	Population contrast
1	−1	0	-1.75 ± 4.15	$\mu_1 - \mu_2$
1	0	−1	-2.25 ± 4.15	$\mu_1 - \mu_3$
0	1	−1	$-\ .50 \pm 4.15$	$\mu_2 - \mu_3$
$\frac{1}{2}$	$\frac{1}{2}$	−1	-1.38 ± 4.15	$\frac{\mu_1 + \mu_2}{2} - \mu_3$
$\frac{1}{2}$	−1	$\frac{1}{2}$	$-\ .62 \pm 4.15$	$\frac{\mu_1 + \mu_3}{2} - \mu_2$
−1	$\frac{1}{2}$	$\frac{1}{2}$	2.00 ± 4.15	$\frac{\mu_2 + \mu_3}{2} - \mu_1$

10-4. Two Variables of Classification, Single Observation

This section will present the analysis of an experiment designed to study populations of individuals classified by two characteristics.

Experiments can be conducted in such a way that several variables may be studied in the same experiment. For each variable a number of categories or levels may be chosen for study. If an equal number of observations is made for all possible combinations of levels (one level from each variable), the experiment is called a *factorial experiment.* In an experiment with two (or more) variables it sometimes happens that all combinations of both variables cannot be studied. Thus, for example, we might have three experimental teaching methods to test and 10 groups of students from which to choose. Assignment of the methods to 6 of the groups of students could be made at random with two replications of each method. This is called a completely randomized design. If three groups of students at each of five schools were assigned the three methods randomly in each school, the experiment would be called a *randomized-block* design. The schools in this example are referred to as blocks. Other examples of experiments with several variables follow.

In studying the yield of different grain hybrids we may wish to investigate at the same time the effect of varying fertility on the yields of these hybrids.

The sociologist in studying family size may wish to investigate the effects of city size and region of the country. Average size of family could be computed for five categories of city size in each of, say, six regions of the country and the results investigated for significant differences in size of family for different city sizes independent of region of the country and for significant differences in size of family for different regions of the country independent of city size.

An experiment in teaching methods might be designed with two variables of classification, different classes and different schools, and the average score obtained on an examination might be observed.

Often one of the variables of classification is important as a control; i.e., we wish to confirm that that variable does not affect the measurements. For example, the amount of eye pigment in drosophila might be measured for each of several hybrids for three or four different conditions of environment (food, temperature, etc.).

In this section we shall consider only the case where one observation is made for each combination of levels, i.e., a factorial experiment. Our observations can be recorded as in the 12 cells of Table 10-8.

T_{1+} is the total of the observations in the first column, T_{+1} is the total of those in the first row, etc., T_{++} is the total of all the observations. The $\bar{X}_{i\cdot}$'s are the means of the columns, the $\bar{X}_{\cdot j}$'s the means of the rows, and $\bar{X}_{\cdot\cdot}$ the grand mean. c is the number of columns, and r is the number of rows.

The variation of the observations in this table is caused not only by the population variance and the basic experimental errors which are always present but also by differences which may be due to a difference in treatments (first variable of classification) or a difference in varieties (second variable of classification).

The development of the analysis-of-variance procedure for this two-way table of observations will be illustrated numerically.

TABLE 10-8

First variable

		A	B	C	D	Total	Mean
Second variable	a	X_{11}	X_{21}	X_{31}	X_{41}	T_{+1}	$\bar{X}_{\cdot 1}$
	b	X_{12}	X_{22}	X_{32}	X_{42}	T_{+2}	$\bar{X}_{\cdot 2}$
	c	X_{13}	X_{23}	X_{33}	X_{43}	T_{+3}	$\bar{X}_{\cdot 3}$
Total		T_{1+}	T_{2+}	T_{3+}	T_{4+}	T_{++}	
Mean		$\bar{X}_{1\cdot}$	$\bar{X}_{2\cdot}$	$\bar{X}_{3\cdot}$	$\bar{X}_{4\cdot}$		$\bar{X}_{\cdot\cdot}$

In the previous case of a single variable of classification an estimate of the variance was obtained from the means of the columns. Here we shall also estimate the variance from the row means. The computation is illustrated for the following data for four treatments A, B, C, D and three varieties a, b, c. The sum of squares we shall use in the estimate of the population variance obtained from column means is computed as before,

$$\frac{(13)^2}{3} + \frac{(16)^2}{3} + \frac{(17)^2}{3} + \frac{(14)^2}{3} - \frac{(60)^2}{12} = 303.33 - 300 = 3.33$$

TABLE 10-9

	A	B	C	D	T_{+i}
a	7	6	8	7	28
b	2	4	4	4	14
c	4	6	5	3	18
T_{i+}	13	16	17	14	60

Similarly the sum of squares for estimating the population variance from the row means is

$$\frac{(28)^2}{4} + \frac{(14)^2}{4} + \frac{(18)^2}{4} - \frac{(60)^2}{12} = 326 - 300 = 26.00$$

The total sum of squares is

$$7^2 + 2^2 + 4^2 + 6^2 + \cdots + 3^2 - \frac{(60)^2}{12} = 336 - 300 = 36.00$$

It may be noted that these formulas are all similar. The denominator in every term is the number of items which have been added into the total which appears in the numerator.

The analysis of variance is shown in Table 10-10. The residual sum of squares is obtained by subtracting the sums of squares for row means

TABLE 10-10. ANALYSIS OF VARIANCE

	Sum of squares	df	Mean square
Row means	26.00	2	13.00
Column means	3.33	3	1.11
Residual	6.67	6	1.11
Total	36.00	11	

and column means from the total sum of squares. Since there are three row means, there are 2 degrees of freedom for rows. There are four columns and thus 3 degrees of freedom for column means. The degrees of freedom for residual is obtained by subtraction, $11 - 2 - 3 = 6$. We can form an F ratio to test the difference among rows for significance by comparing the estimate of variance from row means with the residual variance, which is an estimate of variance independent of the differences in means of both rows and columns.

$$F = \frac{13.00}{1.11} = 11.7 \qquad F_{.95}(2,6) = 5.14$$

We then reject the hypothesis of no difference among means of different rows.

A test can also be made for the difference among means of the different columns independent of any difference in rows.

$$F = \frac{1.11}{1.11} = 1.00 \quad F_{.95}(3,6) = 4.76$$

We accept the hypothesis of no difference in means of the columns.

The above example indicates the computing procedure for the analysis of variance for a two-way table. The following analysis of the same data, although more lengthy, will perhaps make the above analysis easier to understand. First the table of data is bordered with row and column means and the deviation of these means from the grand mean. The

	A	B	C	D	T_{+j}	$\bar{X}_{\cdot j}$	$\bar{X}_{\cdot j} - \bar{X}_{\cdot\cdot}$
a	7	6	8	7	28	7.0	2.0
b	2	4	4	4	14	3.5	−1.5
c	4	6	5	3	18	4.5	− .5
T_{i+}	13	16	17	14	60		
$\bar{X}_{i\cdot}$	4.333	5.333	5.667	4.667		5.00	
$\bar{X}_{i\cdot} - \bar{X}_{\cdot\cdot}$	−.667	.333	.667	−.333			

estimate of variance from column means is

$$\frac{r\Sigma(\bar{X}_{i\cdot} - \bar{X}_{\cdot\cdot})^2}{c-1} = \frac{3}{3}[(-.667)^2 + (.333)^2 + (.667)^2 + (-.333)^2] = 1.11$$

as was also obtained from the computing formulas and given in the analysis-of-variance table. Likewise the estimate of variance from row means is

$$\frac{c\Sigma(\bar{X}_{\cdot j} - \bar{X}_{\cdot\cdot})^2}{r-1} = \frac{4}{2}[(2.0)^2 + (-1.5)^2 + (-.5)^2] = 13.00$$

The residual sum of squares will be obtained by computing the sum of squares of all the observations after the differences in row and column means have been "removed." Let us change the values of our observations so that all row means are the same by adding or subtracting the same amount from each value in a row. Thus, we subtract 2.0 from each value in the first row, add 1.5 to each value in the second row, and add .5 to each value in the third row. Note that the column means and the grand mean are unchanged.

	A	B	C	D	T_{+j}	$\bar{X}'_{\cdot j}$
a	5.0	4.0	6.0	5.0	20	5.0
b	3.5	5.5	5.5	5.5	20	5.0
c	4.5	6.5	5.5	3.5	20	5.0
T_{i+}	13	16	17	14	60	
$\bar{X}_{i\cdot}$	4.333	5.333	5.667	4.667		5.00

Now, in a similar manner, change the values obtained so that the column means will be the same. Add .667 to each observation in the first column, subtract .333 from each observation in the second column, subtract .667 in the third column, and add .333 in the fourth column. The

	A	B	C	D	T_{+j}	$\bar{X}'_{\cdot j}$
a	5.667	3.667	5.333	5.333	20	5.0
b	4.167	5.167	4.833	5.833	20	5.0
c	5.167	6.167	4.833	3.833	20	5.0
T_{i+}	15	15	15	15	60	
$\bar{X}'_{i\cdot}$	5.0	5.0	5.0	5.0		5.0

remaining variation of the values in the table is not due to differences in row and column means since all row and column means are now the same.

Computing the variance of the values corrected for differences in means, we obtain

$$(5.667)^2 + (4.167)^2 + (5.167)^2 + (3.667)^2 + \cdots + (3.833)^2 - \frac{(60)^2}{12} = 6.67$$

This is recorded in the analysis-of-variance table as the residual sum of squares. If the variables are additive (see end of this section), the residual sum of squares measures experimental errors which are not explained by differences in row means or differences in column means. Note that the two sums of squares for means and the value just obtained add up to the total sum of squares: $36.00 = 3.33 + 26.00 + 6.67$.

The 12 residual values in the last table have been corrected for three row means, which themselves must average $\bar{X}_{..}$, and four column means, which themselves must average $\bar{X}_{..}$, resulting in a loss of 2 and 3 degrees of freedom in addition to a loss of 1 degree of freedom for the grand mean. The degrees of freedom for this sum of squares of residuals is $(c - 1)(r - 1) = 6$, and this sum of squares divided by the degrees of freedom is an unbiased estimate of σ^2 which is independent of any differences there might be in means for "treatments" or "varieties." In the above numerical example the X_{ij} were "corrected" as follows:

$$X_{ij} - (\bar{X}_{i\cdot} - \bar{X}_{..}) - (\bar{X}_{\cdot j} - \bar{X}_{..})$$

The relation which we noted in the numerical example above is true in general:

$$\sum_j \sum_i (X_{ij} - \bar{X}_{..})^2 = \sum_j \sum_i [X_{ij} - (\bar{X}_{i\cdot} - \bar{X}_{..}) - (\bar{X}_{\cdot j} - \bar{X}_{..}) - \bar{X}_{..}]^2 + r \sum_i (\bar{X}_{i\cdot} - \bar{X}_{..})^2 + c \sum_j (\bar{X}_{\cdot j} - \bar{X}_{..})^2$$

where the values of i run from 1 to c and the values of j from 1 to r. The proof of this equation can be obtained from the computing form of each of the four terms in the equation as follows: As discussed in Sec. 10-2, the sum on the left can be written as

$$S_T = \sum \sum X_{ij}^2 - \frac{T_{++}^2}{cr}$$

and the last two terms on the right can be written as

$$S_c = \frac{\Sigma T_{+j}^2}{c} - \frac{T_{++}^2}{cr}$$

and

$$S_r = \frac{\Sigma T_{i+}^2}{r} - \frac{T_{++}^2}{cr}$$

The new term on the right is first written as

$$S_R = \sum_i \sum_j (X_{ij} - \bar{X}_{i\cdot} - \bar{X}_{\cdot j} + \bar{X}_{\cdot\cdot})^2$$

and then, after some manipulation, as

$$S_R = \sum_i \sum_j X_{ij}^2 - \frac{\Sigma T_{i\cdot}^2}{r} - \frac{\Sigma T_{\cdot j}^2}{c} + \frac{T_{\cdot\cdot}^2}{cr}$$

It can be seen that the computing forms of the three sums of squares on the right add up to the computing form of the sum of squares on the left. Thus the residual sum of squares S_R can be found by computing the total sum of squares S_T and subtracting from it S_c and S_r, the sums of squares for the column and row means.

Outline of Analysis-of-variance Test for Two Variables of Classification, Single Observation

1. HYPOTHESIS 1. *The c column effects are zero.* The test of this hypothesis is made independent of the row effects.

HYPOTHESIS 2. *The r row effects are zero.* The test of this hypothesis is made independent of the column effects.

2. Choose the level of significance.
3. The statistic used is F: for Hypothesis 1 the ratio of the mean square for column means to the residual mean square; for Hypothesis 2 the ratio of the mean square for row means to the residual mean square.
4. Assuming the observations are randomly selected from normal populations with homogeneous variance and that the row and column effects are additive, percentiles of the F distribution are given in Table A-7.
5. The critical region for Hypothesis 1 is

$$F > F_{1-\alpha}[c - 1,(r - 1)(c - 1)]$$

The critical region for Hypothesis 2 is

$$F > F_{1-\alpha}[r - 1,(r - 1)(c - 1)]$$

6. Compute F ratios, and accept or reject the hypotheses.

Hypotheses and Assumptions. As an indication of the assumptions underlying the analysis of variance in this case, assume that the population means for the 12 cells in the above layout are of the following sort: We suppose the mean for the first cell to be $\mu_{11} = \mu + r_1 + c_1$, where μ is the same for all cells, r_1 is the same for all cells in row 1, and c_1 is the same for all cells in column 1. The mean for the second cell in the first row is $\mu_{21} = \mu + r_1 + c_2$, and so on, to the fourth cell in the third row, where the mean is $\mu_{43} = \mu + r_3 + c_4$. As an example, consider the means for the 12 cells as illustrated in Table 10-11, for which $\mu = 50$ and the row "effects" for the means are $r_1 = 0$, $r_2 = 5$, $r_3 = -5$, the column "effects" for the means are $c_1 = 7$, $c_2 = -2$, $c_3 = 4$, $c_4 = -9$. These effects will always be taken so that their sum is zero. This can always be done since μ can be changed, if necessary. We select one observation from each population as indicated in Table 10-11, i.e., one from a normal popula-

TABLE 10-11

57 (50 + 0 + 7)	48 (50 + 0 − 2)	54 (50 + 0 + 4)	41 (50 + 0 − 9)
62 (50 + 5 + 7)	53 (50 + 5 − 2)	59 (50 + 5 + 4)	46 (50 + 5 − 9)
52 (50 − 5 + 7)	43 (50 − 5 − 2)	49 (50 − 5 + 4)	36 (50 − 5 − 9)

tion with mean 57, one from a normal population with mean 48, etc. It is assumed that the variance σ^2 of each population is the same. In this example, neither Hypothesis 1 nor Hypothesis 2 is true. If, for example, there were no column effects, i.e., if Hypothesis 1 is true, the second number added to 50 in Table 10-11 would be zero in every case. Since in practice we do not know the population values for any of the cells, we shall use the analysis of variance to test for differences in the c's and in the r's.

We see then that the computation in Table 10-10, and immediately following, tests the following two hypotheses:

HYPOTHESIS 1. *There are no column effects* ($c_1 = c_2 = c_3 = c_4 = 0$).

HYPOTHESIS 2. *There are no row effects* ($r_1 = r_2 = r_3 = 0$).

When the experiment is designed as above, we may test the hypothesis stating that all c_i's are zero, independent of whether or not there are row effects. Likewise we may test the hypothesis stating that all r_j's are zero, independent of whether or not there are column effects. We must assume, however, that these effects are *additive*, i.e., that the mean of the cell in the ith column and jth row can be written as $\mu_{ij} = \mu + r_i + c_j$. This is an assumption since any arbitrary set of 12 cell means written in a 3×4 table may not satisfy this condition. One interpretation of additivity is that the row and column effects do not *interact*, i.e., do not have an effect in combination different from the sum of their separate effects.

It might be noted that analyses of variance are frequently made without full assurance that the variables do not interact. Such analyses may lead to useful results, but caution should be exercised since little is known about the effects of interaction on the results of the analysis.

Table 10-12 shows the analysis-of-variance table for two-way classification with single observation, including the population value estimated by the computed mean square. σ^2 is the variance of each of the rc populations; σ_c^2 and σ_r^2 are $\Sigma c_i^2/(c-1)$ and $\Sigma r_j^2/(r-1)$, respectively. If there is a significant column (or row) effect, σ_c^2 (or σ_r^2) may be estimated as shown at the end of Sec. 10-2.

TABLE 10-12. ANALYSIS-OF-VARIANCE TABLE FOR TWO-WAY CLASSIFICATION WITH SINGLE OBSERVATION

	Sum of squares	df	Mean square	Estimate of
Column means....	$\sum \frac{T_{i+}^2}{r} - \frac{T_{++}^2}{rc} = S_c$	$c-1$	$\frac{S_c}{(c-1)}$	$\sigma^2 + r\sigma_c^2$
Row means..	$\sum \frac{T_{+j}^2}{c} - \frac{T_{++}^2}{rc} = S_r$	$r-1$	$\frac{S_r}{(r-1)}$	$\sigma^2 + c\sigma_r^2$
Remainder..	$S_T - S_c - S_r = S_R$	$(c-1)(r-1)$	$\frac{S_R}{(c-1)(r-1)}$	σ^2
Total.....	$\sum\sum X_{ij}^2 - \frac{T_{++}^2}{rc} = S_T$	$rc-1$		

10-5. Two Variables of Classification, Repeated Measurements

The best estimate of experimental error (population σ^2) for use in investigating differences in means is obtained from measurements repeated under similar conditions. Suppose, in the study of yield of corn, two variables of classification are treatments and varieties and, for every combination of treatment and variety, the corn is planted in several plots. We say the experiment has been *replicated*, or repeated. This replication will enable us to analyze the data more fully. The analysis is a combination of the two procedures presented thus far. The data will appear as in Table 10-13 if there are two rows, three columns, and

TABLE 10-13

	A	B	C
a	X_{111}	X_{211}	X_{311}
	X_{112}	X_{212}	X_{312}
	X_{113}	X_{213}	X_{313}
b	X_{121}	X_{221}	X_{321}
	X_{122}	X_{222}	X_{322}
	X_{123}	X_{223}	X_{323}

TABLE 10-14

	A	B	C
a	T_{11+}	T_{21+}	T_{31+}
b	T_{12+}	T_{22+}	T_{32+}

three replications.* First, this set of data can be considered to be samples of size 3 each from six populations and can be analyzed as in Sec. 10-2 of this chapter. That is, we test the hypothesis that the means of the six populations are equal by comparing the variance of the observed means in the six cells with the within-groups variance. If we reject the hypothesis that the six means are equal (and perhaps even in the case where we accept the hypothesis), we shall wish to look further into the type of differences in the means, using the methods either of Sec. 10-3 or of Sec. 10-4. In this section we shall continue the approach of Sec. 10-4 and in the next section analyze a similar problem with contrasts as in Sec. 10-3. We now record the six totals as in Table 10-14 and consider these data to be the single observations classified in a two-way table as in Sec. 10-4, proceeding with the computations as performed there, except that each denominator in the computing formulas is the number of observations in each total and not merely the number of rows or columns.

In Table 10-15 we have recorded an example of data collected as above.

TABLE 10-15

	A	B	C	
	4	2	5	
a	7	3	6	
	5	2	4	
	9	8	10	
b	8	7	8	
	8	5	7	
				108

Totals

	A	B	C	
a	16	7	15	38
b	25	20	25	70
	41	27	40	108

The analysis of variance is carried out as in Sec. 10-2 and recorded in Table 10-16.

We compute

Sum of squares for total:

$$4^2 + 7^2 + 5^2 + 9^2 + 8^2 + 8^2 + 2^2 + \cdots + 7^2 - \frac{(108)^2}{18} = 744 - 648 = 96$$

Sum of squares for subtotals from six populations as described above:

$$\frac{16^2}{3} + \frac{25^2}{3} + \frac{7^2}{3} + \frac{20^2}{3} + \frac{15^2}{3} + \frac{25^2}{3} - \frac{(108)^2}{18} = 726.67 - 648 = 78.67$$

* Only the case of an equal number of replications in each cell will be considered here. The analysis must be modified for an unequal number of replications.

TABLE 10-16. ANALYSIS OF VARIANCE

	Sum of squares	df	Mean square	F ratio
Between six means.....	78.67	5	15.73	10.9
Within.................	17.33	12	1.44	$F_{.95}(5,12) = 3.11$
Total................	96.00	17		

The significant F ratio indicates that there is evidence that the means of the six populations are unequal. We now analyze the cell totals as in Sec. 10-4, recording the results in Table 10-17.

We compute

Sum of squares for rows:

$$\frac{38^2}{9} + \frac{70^2}{9} - \frac{(108)^2}{18} = 704.89 - 648 = 56.89$$

Note that the totals 38 and 70 are each totals of 9 of the original observations. The total 108 is the sum of all 18 original observations. Sum of squares for columns:

$$\frac{41^2}{6} + \frac{27^2}{6} + \frac{40^2}{6} - \frac{(108)^2}{18} = 668.33 - 648 = 20.33$$

TABLE 10-17. ANALYSIS OF VARIANCE

	Sum of squares	df	Mean square
Row means.	56.89	1	56.89
Column means..........	20.33	2	10.17
Interaction..............	1.45	2	.72
Subtotal..............	78.67	5	
Within groups...........	17.33	12	1.44
Total..................	96.00	17	

The sum of squares for "interaction" in Table 10-17 is the same as the residual sum of squares in the two-way analysis of variance of single observations and is obtained as in Sec. 10-4, that is,

$$78.67 - 56.89 - 20.33 = 1.45$$

The degrees of freedom are also determined as in Secs. 10-2 and 10-4. The subtotal sum of squares corresponds to the sum of squares for means in Table 10-16.

The term *interaction* is used in this analysis in place of "residual," since we have a further estimate of the variance, "within groups," to use in a test for those differences among means which cannot be accounted for by constant shifts in row means and column means, as was illustrated in the previous section. These remaining effects are called interactions.

Note that we have a breakdown of the total sum of squares into four parts: the within-groups sum of squares, which measures the variances of the six individual populations, the sum of squares of row means, which measures the variability from one row to another, the analogous sum of squares for column means, and the sum of squares for interaction, which measures the lack of additivity of row and column effects.

From this point on, the analysis definitely depends on whether we are interested in main effects, i.e., differences in row (or column) means averaged over all columns (or rows), or whether we are interested in which combination of row and column (main effect plus interaction) produces a very large or very small result. As an example, where main effects are of interest, suppose that the two rows a and b refer to two breeds of cattle and the three columns A, B, and C refer to three types of diet. The observations are weight gains of individual steers that were individually fed, and there are 18 steers in all in the experiment, 3 of each breed with each type of diet. We suppose that a single diet will be used for both breeds and thus are interested in the type which is over-all best. If it is considered possible to supply different diets to different breeds, the interest is not in main effects but in which diet is best for each breed. If we are to choose a single breed and a single diet for best results in the future, we are interested in the best combination of breed and diet. In order to introduce these considerations into the analysis, we temporarily leave our example to give the relationship between the numbers in the analysis-of-variance table and the various parameters to be estimated.

The statement of the assumptions and tests of hypotheses underlying our problem is as follows:

1. We assume that the observations in the ith column and jth row are random samples from a normal population with mean $\mu + c_i + r_j + I_{ij}$, where μ is the same for all cells, c_i is the same for all cells in the ith column, r_j is the same for all cells in the jth row and where the I_{ij}'s may be different for each i and j. We can suppose with no loss in generality that $\sum_i c_i = 0$, $\sum_j r_j = 0$, and $\sum_i I_{ij} = 0$ for each j, and $\sum_j I_{ij} = 0$ for each i, since if these sums are not zero we may make them zero by redefining μ.

2. We assume that the variance σ^2 is the same for each of the normal populations.

Although we are introducing as assumptions normality and equal variance (both of which may be tested), the fact that the cell means are written in terms of a grand mean, row, column, and interaction effects implies no assumption since this places no restriction on the means of the individual populations. In Sec. 10-4, where the I_{ij} are assumed to be zero, a restriction was imposed.

The various statistics in the analysis-of-variance table (Table 10-17) are unbiased estimates of certain functions of the population means as recorded in Table 10-18. We suppose there are n observations from each cell of a two-way classification of c columns and r rows. X_{ije} is the eth observation from the population in the ith column and jth row. As before, σ^2 is the variance of each of the rc populations, $\sigma_c^2 = \Sigma c_i^2/(c - 1)$ and $\sigma_r^2 = \Sigma r_j^2/(r - 1)$ and $\sigma_I^2 = \Sigma\Sigma I_{ij}^2/(c - 1)(r - 1)$. We see from Table 10-18 that if we are interested in the inequality of the c_i's we can compare the mean square for columns with the within-groups mean square and, if the ratio is much larger than unity, conclude that the c_i's are not equal, that is, σ_c^2 is not equal to zero. Similarly we divide the mean square for rows by the within-groups mean square, to test for inequality of the row effects, and divide the interaction mean square by the within-groups mean square, to test for inequality of the I_{ij}'s.

TABLE 10-18. ANALYSIS OF VARIANCE WITH ESTIMATES

	Sum of squares	df	Mean square	Estimate of
Column means....	$rn\Sigma(\bar{X}_{i..} - \bar{X}_{...})^2 = S_c$	$c - 1$	$\dfrac{S_c}{(c-1)}$	$\sigma^2 + rn\sigma_c^2$
Row means..	$cn\Sigma(\bar{X}_{.j.} - \bar{X}_{...})^2 = S_r$	$r - 1$	$\dfrac{S_r}{(r-1)}$	$\sigma^2 + cn\sigma_r^2$
Interaction..	$S_s - S_c - S_r = S_I$	$(c-1)(r-1)$	$\dfrac{S_I}{(c-1)(r-1)}$	$\sigma^2 + n\sigma_I^2$
Subtotal..	$n\Sigma\Sigma(\bar{X}_{ij.} - \bar{X}_{...})^2 = S_s$	$rc - 1$		
Within......	$S_T - S_s = S_w$	$rc(n-1)$	$\dfrac{S_w}{rc(n-1)}$	σ^2
Total.....	$\Sigma\Sigma\Sigma(X_{ije} - \bar{X}_{...})^2 = S_T$	$rcn - 1$		

With these general results in mind we return to the example in Table 10-17. To look for interaction, we compare .72 with 1.44, getting $F = .72/1.44 = .5$, which gives no indication that σ_I^2 is greater than zero. For the row effects $F = 56.89/1.44 = 39.5$, which, since it is larger than $F_{.95}(1,12) = 4.75$, is significant at the $\alpha = .05$ level. For the columns, $F = 10.17/1.44 = 7.06$, which is also significant at the $\alpha = .05$ level. Thus we have no evidence of lack of additivity but significant differences in both row and column effects.

It may be noted in Table 10-18 that if $\sigma_I^2 = 0$ then both the lines labeled "Interaction" and "Within" give unbiased estimates of σ^2. This indicates that a combination of the two may improve the estimate of σ^2. A suggested procedure which has some theoretical justification (see References, page 357) is to average, or pool, interaction and within sums of squares if the ratio of the interaction and within-mean squares is less than twice the 50th percentile of the F distribution. Using this rule, we would pool in our example since the ratio is .72, which is less than $2F_{.50}(2,12) = 2(.735) = 1.470$. To pool, we add the sum of squares for "Interaction" to the sum of squares for "Within" to get a "Residual" sum of squares and then add the respective degrees of freedom to get the degrees of freedom for "Residual." For our example the residual mean square is $18.78/14 = 1.34$. This residual mean square is now used as a denominator in testing for row or column main effects. The results are shown in Table 10-19.

TABLE 10-19. ANALYSIS OF VARIANCE

	Sum of squares	df	Mean square
Rows	56.89	1	56.89
Columns	20.33	2	10.17
Residual	18.78	14	1.34
Total	96.00	17	

To test for row effects, we compute,

$$F = \frac{56.89}{1.34} = 42.5 \qquad F_{.95}(1,14) = 4.60$$

This value is significant, and we reject the hypothesis of equal row means. To test for column effects, we compute,

$$F = \frac{10.17}{1.34} = 7.59 \qquad F_{.95}(2,14) = 3.74$$

This is also significant at the 5 per cent level.

It should be emphasized that the level of significance in the above analysis is for the case where it has been agreed before collecting data to perform a single test. If we proceed beyond the first test, the chance of rejecting at least one true hypothesis will increase, probably in the order of the size of $1 - (1 - \alpha)^h$, where h tests are performed at the α level of significance. This formula applies to completely unrelated tests and is known to be an upper bound for this case. Instead of performing several tests on the data as above and in Table 10-17 and then proceeding to estimate the differences in the means of the several cell populations, it is recommended that the procedures outlined in Secs. 10-3 and 10-6 be used.

10-6. Two-by-Two Factorial Design, Individual Comparisons

As noted in Sec. 10-5, a factorial experiment has an equal number of observations (replications) for every combination of categories in the variables of classification. This type of experiment, as well as many other types, may be analyzed by setting up comparisons as in Sec. 10-3. We illustrate this for the case where there are two variables with two categories each. This case is called a two-by-two (2 × 2) factorial experiment where the numbers 2 × 2 denote the number of categories in each variable. In this terminology a 3 × 4 × 5 factorial experiment would involve three variables, the first having three categories, the second having four categories, and the third having five categories. The example in Sec. 10-4 is a 3 × 4 factorial experiment, and the example in Sec. 10-5 is a 2 × 3 factorial experiment replicated three times.

As an example, suppose that we have two populations of people, say, men and women, and two methods of teaching, say, methods *A* and *B*. We use each teaching method on three men and three women (12 people in all) and record a final examination score for each. The data are recorded in Table 10-20 in the same manner as recorded in Sec. 10-5, and the corresponding analysis of variance is in Table 10-21. In Table 10-22 are some of the possible contrasts among the observed means. As in Sec. 10-3, these contrasts are in the form $a_{11}\bar{X}_{11\cdot} + a_{12}\bar{X}_{12\cdot} + a_{21}\bar{X}_{21\cdot} + a_{22}\bar{X}_{22\cdot}$, where $a_{11} + a_{12} + a_{21} + a_{22} = 0$ and the sum of the positive a_{ij}'s is unity. This table shows how it is possible to use the cell means to estimate the average difference between men and women for the two teaching methods (main effects) and also the degree to which a particular method is good or poor for either sex. If, as in the example in Sec. 10-5, a single teaching method is to be used for both men and women, the experimenter is interested in main effects. If a different method could be used for men from that for women, the experimenter is interested in which method is

TABLE 10-20. DATA FOR 2 × 2 FACTORIAL

	A	*B*
Men	5	5
	8	5
	9	6
Women	11	7
	14	8
	15	6

Totals

	A	*B*	
Men	22	16	38
Women	40	21	61
	62	37	99

best for men and which method is best for women. If, as in some types of industrial job placement, the experimenter is interested in the best single combination of sex and teaching method, then he wishes to find that combination having the largest mean.

TABLE 10-21. ANALYSIS OF VARIANCE

	Sum of squares	df	Mean sq.	F ratio
Rows	$\frac{5{,}165}{6} - 816.75 = 44.08$	1	44.08	17.63
Columns	$\frac{5{,}213}{6} - 816.75 = 52.08$	1	52.08	20.83
Interaction	$110.25 - 44.08 - 52.08 = 14.09$	1	14.09	5.64
Subtotal	$\frac{2{,}781}{3} - 816.75 = 110.25$	3		
Within	$130.25 - 110.25 = 20.00$	8	2.50	
Total	$947 - 816.75 = 130.25$	11		

In Table 10-21 all three F ratios are larger than $F_{.95}(1,8) = 5.32$. Therefore, if the experiment were designed to investigate any one of the three effects, row, column, or interaction, we may declare significance at the 5 per cent level. However, it is not clear that one can state significance at the 5 per cent level for all three simultaneously.

We may look at any or all contrasts by the use of the q statistic. Some of these contrasts are listed in Table 10-22. For example, line 1 shows the contrast $\frac{1}{2}\bar{X}_{11\cdot} + \frac{1}{2}\bar{X}_{21\cdot} - \frac{1}{2}\bar{X}_{12\cdot} - \frac{1}{2}\bar{X}_{22\cdot}$, which measures the mean difference for men and women. We note that the contrasts in lines 2, 5, 6, 7, 10 are significant since the confidence limits do not cover zero. These contrasts are column (teaching) main effects, difference in methods for women, difference for sex for method A, difference between method B for men and method A for women, and difference for method A for women and the average of the three other cells. Some interpretations are:

From contrast 2. If a single teaching method is to be used for both men and women, method A should be used.

From contrasts 4 and 5. If different methods may be used for men and for women, for method A it can be said from contrast 5 that this experiment demonstrates that women perform better than men. By contrast 4 we can see that this is not demonstrated for method B.

From contrasts 6 and 8. If one can choose to train only men or only women, then only in the case of the women is it conclusive that method A will obtain superior results.

From contrasts 5, 6, and 7 together. The combination of women and method A results in significantly higher examination scores than any of the other three combinations.

From contrast 10. The combination of women and method A is better than the average of the other three combinations. In this example this result could be inferred from contrasts 5, 6, and 7 taken together.

TABLE 10-22. INDIVIDUAL COMPARISONS IN A 2 × 2 FACTORIAL EXPERIMENT

	$\bar{X}_{11.} = \frac{22}{3}$	$\bar{X}_{21.} = \frac{16}{3}$	$\bar{X}_{12.} = \frac{40}{3}$	$\bar{X}_{22.} = \frac{21}{3}$	$\Sigma a_{ij}\bar{X}_{ij.} \pm q_{.95}s/\sqrt{n}$	Estimate of —
1	$\frac{1}{2}$	$\frac{1}{2}$	$-\frac{1}{2}$	$-\frac{1}{2}$	-3.83 ± 4.13	$r_1 - r_2$, row main effect, difference for men and women
2	$\frac{1}{2}$	$-\frac{1}{2}$	$\frac{1}{2}$	$-\frac{1}{2}$	4.17 ± 4.13	$c_1 - c_2$, column main effect, difference for methods
3	$\frac{1}{2}$	$-\frac{1}{2}$	$-\frac{1}{2}$	$\frac{1}{2}$	-2.17 ± 4.13	$2I_{11}$, interaction effect
4	1	−1	0	0	2.00 ± 4.13	Difference of methods for men
5	0	0	1	−1	6.33 ± 4.13	Difference of methods for women
6	1	0	−1	0	-6.00 ± 4.13	Difference for men and women using method A
7	0	1	−1	0	-8.00 ± 4.13	Difference of method B for men and A for women
8	0	1	0	−1	-1.67 ± 4.13	Difference for men and women using method B
9	1	0	0	−1	$.33 \pm 4.13$	Difference of method A for men and B for women
10	$-\frac{1}{3}$	$-\frac{1}{3}$	1	$-\frac{1}{3}$	6.78 ± 4.13	Difference of method A for women and average of three other cells

$q_{.95}(4,8) = 4.53$; $s = \sqrt{2.50} = 1.58$; $qs/\sqrt{n} = 4.53(1.58)/\sqrt{3} = 4.13$.

10-7. Latin Square

The design will be given for a 4 × 4 Latin square as an illustration. As before, we shall lay out a plan showing two variables of classification. If there are the same number of categories for each, we may superimpose a third variable of classification represented by A, B, C, D in such a way that each category appears once and only once in each row and column. It is easily seen that the design presented is not the only one available for four rows and columns; there are 576 in all. The experimenter may

TABLE 10-23

	I	II	III	IV
1	*A*	*B*	*C*	*D*
2	*D*	*A*	*B*	*C*
3	*C*	*D*	*A*	*B*
4	*B*	*C*	*D*	*A*

wish to pick one at random from all the possibilities. For squares with five rows and columns there are 161,280 different squares.

Suppose a number of children are divided into four equal groups and four lists of words are divided into four tests of different types. The scores are the number of words each group spells correctly in each test which were spelled incorrectly previously. Since there may be some difference in the results of the experiment depending on the order in which the tests are presented to the children, we shall use the Latin square and let A, B, C, D represent the separate tests in each list. The words were all spelled from dictation in the previous test. The four tests are as follows:

A, multiple choice
B, second dictation
C, wrongly spelled word
D, skeleton word

The results are as shown in Table 10-24.

Sums of Squares. Columns (groups):

$$\frac{(207)^2}{4} + \frac{(214)^2}{4} + \frac{(196)^2}{4} + \frac{(219)^2}{4} - \frac{(836)^2}{16} = 43{,}755.5 - 43{,}681 = 74.5$$

Rows (lists):

$$\frac{(219)^2}{4} + \frac{(226)^2}{4} + \frac{(177)^2}{4} + \frac{(214)^2}{4} - \frac{(836)^2}{16} = 44{,}040.5 - 43{,}681 = 359.5$$

Treatments (tests):

$$\frac{(326)^2}{4} + \frac{(176)^2}{4} + \frac{(157)^2}{4} + \frac{(177)^2}{4} - \frac{(836)^2}{16} = 48{,}307.5 - 43{,}681 = 4{,}626.5$$

Total:

$$81^2 + 38^2 + 31^2 + \cdots + 81^2 - \frac{(836)^2}{16} = 49{,}348 - 43{,}681 = 5{,}667$$

TABLE 10-24. DATA FROM A SPELLING EXPERIMENT*

Groups of Children

Lists of words	1	2	3	4	Total
1	*A* 81	*B* 41	*C* 44	*D* 53	219
2	*D* 38	*A* 97	*B* 42	*C* 49	226
3	*C* 31	*D* 43	*A* 67	*B* 36	177
4	*B* 57	*C* 33	*D* 43	*A* 81	214
Total	207	214	196	219	836

Tests

	A	*B*	*C*	*D*	
Total	326	176	157	177	836

* Data from *British Journal of Educational Psychology,* vol. 11 (1941), p. 135.

TABLE 10-25. ANALYSIS OF VARIANCE

	Sum of squares	df	Mean square	*F* ratio*
Columns (groups)	74.5	3	24.8	.25
Rows (lists)	359.5	3	119.8	1.18
Treatments (tests)	4,626.5	3	1,542.2	15.25
Residual	606.5	6	101.1	
Total	5,667.0	15		

* F ratios for columns, rows, and treatments are to be compared with $F_{.95}(3,6) = 4.76$.

It can be seen that the only variance which is significantly large compared with the residual variance is the treatments or tests variance. We conclude, then, that the groups of children are of similar ability and the lists are of equal difficulty but that the four tests which make up each list are significantly different.

The same assumptions of normal distribution for the observations and of the effects being additive are necessary here for the tests of significance to be valid. As in the two-way design with one observation per cell, this design will not measure interaction, and it should be used only if it can be assumed that no interaction exists.

Generalizations of the Latin square are also used. For example, suppose four treatments of a different type, say, α, β, γ, δ, were superimposed on the Latin square. We would have what is called a *Greco-Latin* square. This superimposition may be performed so that each treatment of the first type appears with each treatment of the second type. Each treatment of each type appears just once in each row and column. A third

$A\alpha$	$B\beta$	$C\gamma$	$D\delta$
$B\gamma$	$A\delta$	$D\alpha$	$C\beta$
$C\delta$	$D\gamma$	$A\beta$	$B\alpha$
$D\beta$	$C\alpha$	$B\delta$	$A\gamma$

type of treatment may be superimposed and analyzed in a similar manner when there are five or more classifications for each variable.

10-8. Components-of-variance Model

Single Variable of Classification. In Example 4 of Sec. 10-1 the terminology single-variable components of variance was introduced for the model in which k categories are chosen from a parent population of categories and we wish to make inferences to the whole population of categories. A concept equivalent to the selection of categories is the selection of the means $\mu_1, \mu_2, \ldots, \mu_k$ of the chosen categories from a population of means. Let μ and $\sigma_m{}^2$ be the mean and variance of the means of the parent population of categories. A category is itself a population, and from each one selected we shall draw a sample of size n_i. We assume that all categories have the same variance σ^2 and wish to estimate the quantities μ, $\sigma_m{}^2$, and σ^2. We shall also test the hypothesis that $\sigma_m{}^2 = 0$. Although the formula for $\sigma_m{}^2$ is the same as used in the fixed-constants model, where it was a parameter based only on the categories from which samples were taken, here it involves all category means, including the means of those categories from which no samples were taken.

As an example, suppose we select at random five men ($k = 5$) from a population of men and measure each man's height three times ($n_i = 3$). The categories selected are the five men. The samples drawn from the selected categories are the three measurements on each. Then μ is the mean and $\sigma_m{}^2$ is the variance of the heights of the population of men. The set of three measurements for each man can be considered to be a sample of 3 from the population of all possible measurements of the height of the man. The variance of each of these populations of measurements is σ^2. The three measurements will vary depending on the degree of precision of the measuring device or on slight variations in the position or posture of the person being measured. For the measurements described σ^2 would be quite small, perhaps .01 square inch, and $\sigma_m{}^2$ would be comparatively large, perhaps about 9 square inches. It is clear in this example that taking many measurements on each person is of little value since most of the variation is between people rather than between repeated measurements of (within) each person.

Test of Hypothesis of Equal Means. Since we know that people do vary in height, we know that σ_m^2 is not zero and so in this case would not wish to test the hypothesis $\sigma_m^2 = 0$. However, the same test procedure outlined in Sec. 10-2 is appropriate here also. To test the hypothesis that all category means are equal, we divide s_M^2 by s_p^2 and reject the hypothesis if the ratio is larger than $F_{1-\alpha}(k - 1, N - k)$.

Estimation of σ^2, σ_m^2, and μ. Table 10-26 contains an example of data collected as described above. The computations are carried out exactly the same as for the fixed-constants model and are recorded in Table 10-27. Note that the first, second, and third measurements do not form a second variable of classification since the order of measurement should have no influence on the result. Note also that in this example, as in all other problems of this chapter, we are assuming the repeated measurements are independent determinations.

TABLE 10-26. EXAMPLE FOR ONE-VARIABLE COMPONENTS-OF-VARIANCE MODEL

Measurement	Man 1	Man 2	Man 3	Man 4	Man 5	
1	65.4	68.7	63.1	70.3	66.0	
2	65.3	68.7	63.2	70.2	66.1	
3	65.5	68.9	63.3	70.1	65.8	
T_{i+}	196.2	206.3	189.6	210.6	197.9	$T_{++} = 1{,}000.6$

As in the fixed-constants model, $s_p^2 = .013$ is an unbiased estimate of σ^2, and $(s_M^2 - s_p^2)/3 = 23.25/3 = 7.75$ is an unbiased estimate of σ_m^2. An unbiased estimate of μ is $\bar{X} = \Sigma\bar{X}_{i\cdot}/k = 66.71$.

TABLE 10-27. COMPONENTS-OF-VARIANCE ANALYSIS

	Sum of squares	df	Mean square	Estimate of
Men.........	93.00	4	$s_M^2 = 23.25$	$\sigma^2 + 3\sigma_m^2$
Within.......	.13	10	$s_p^2 = .013$	σ^2
Total......	93.13	14		

Confidence intervals for the parameters depend on further assumptions concerning the populations. If measurement errors are normally distributed, then s_p^2/σ^2 has a χ^2/df distribution with $N - k$ degrees of freedom. Thus Table A-6*b* can be used to estimate σ^2 by confidence intervals. For the example, $N - k = 10$, and a 95 per cent confidence-interval estimate of σ^2 is $.325 < .013/\sigma^2 < 2.05$ or $.0063 < \sigma^2 < .40$.

If in addition the category means are normally distributed, then

$$F = \frac{s_M^2/(\sigma^2 + 3\sigma_m^2)}{s_p^2/\sigma^2}$$

has an $F(4,10)$ distribution and Table A-7 can be used to give confidence limits for σ_m^2/σ^2. This is done by setting

$$F_{\frac{1}{2}\alpha}(k - 1, N - k) < \frac{s_M^2/(\sigma^2 + n\sigma_m^2)}{s_p^2/\sigma^2} < F_{1-\frac{1}{2}\alpha}(k - 1, N - k)$$

and rearranging terms to find the limits

$$\frac{s_M^2}{ns_p^2F_{1-\frac{1}{2}\alpha}(k - 1, N - k)} - \frac{1}{n} < \frac{\sigma_m^2}{\sigma^2} < \frac{s_M^2}{ns_p^2F_{\frac{1}{2}\alpha}(k - 1, N - k)} - \frac{1}{n}$$

If the term on the left of the inequality is negative, it is usually replaced by zero since σ_m^2 is never negative. This same rule may be followed in computing the estimate of σ_m^2 from $(s_M^2 - s_p^2)/3$, but the resulting estimate will not then be unbiased.

The sampling distribution of $\bar{X} = \Sigma\bar{X}_{i\cdot}/k$ is approximately normal if the sample sizes taken from the k populations are large and exactly normal for any size sample if the measuring errors as well as the population of means are normal. The mean $\bar{X}$ is μ, and the variance of $\bar{X}$ is $\frac{\sigma_m^2}{k} + \frac{\sigma^2}{k^2}\sum\frac{1}{n_i}$, where n_i is the size of the sample from the ith category. For this example $k = 5$, and all n_i's $= 3$; so the variance of $\bar{X}$ is $(3\sigma_m^2 + \sigma^2)/15$. An estimate of this variance is $s_M^2/15$. The statistic $z = (\bar{X} - \mu)/\sqrt{s_M^2/15}$ is approximately distributed as in Table A-4, allowing the computation of confidence intervals for μ.

In the example $\bar{X} = 66.71$, $s_M^2 = 23.25$, and approximate 95 per cent confidence limits for μ are $66.71 \pm 1.96\sqrt{23.25/15}$ or $64.27 < \mu < 69.15$.

If the n_i's are not equal, s_M^2 is an unbiased estimate of $\sigma^2 + n'\sigma_m^2$, where $n' = (N - \Sigma n_i^2/N)/(k - 1)$. In this case the estimate of the variance of $\bar{X}$ is $\frac{s_M^2 - s_p^2}{n'k} + s_p^2\sum\frac{1}{n_i}\Big/k^2$. Note that if the n_i's are not equal $\bar{X} = \Sigma\bar{X}_{i\cdot}/k$ is not the direct mean of all N observations.

Two Variables of Classification. In the single-variable case the analysis-of-variance table is the same for the components model and for the fixed-constants model, and the difference arises in the interpretation of σ_m^2. In the two-variable case where the c columns and r rows each consist of samples from larger groups of categories, the table differs from the fixed-constants model only in the column headed "Estimate of." This column, shown in Table 10-28, gives the parameters which the mean squares estimate. The remainder of the table is the same as Table 10-18 and is not repeated here. As in Sec. 10-5, n observations come from each

TABLE 10-28

	Estimate of
Column means	$\sigma^2 + n\sigma_I^2 + rn\sigma_c^2$
Row means	$\sigma^2 + n\sigma_I^2 + cn\sigma_r$
Interaction	$\sigma^2 + n\sigma_I$
Subtotal	
Within	σ^2
Total	

row and column category combination. Inspection of the estimate column indicates that, if $\sigma_I^2 = 0$ is rejected, further tests for σ_c^2 and σ_r^2 should be carried out with the "Interaction" mean square as the denominator. Estimation of σ_I^2, σ_c^2, σ_r^2, of the mean of row populations, etc., can be carried out in a manner similar to that shown for estimating σ_m^2. This will not be discussed here.

10-9. Various Topics Related to the Analysis of Variance

This section contains a discussion of several topics closely connected with the analysis-of-variance procedures introduced in this chapter. These topics are: interpretation of significant results obtained from analysis-of-variance procedures, some extensions of the analysis-of-variance models, and the use of a change of scale for the purpose of satisfying more nearly some of the assumptions made in the analysis.

The procedure outlined for testing hypotheses includes the agreement to say, "We reject the hypothesis" if a significant result is obtained. In testing for interaction it can be noted that some possible factors causing a significant result are:

1. There is no interaction, but we have obtained a value which we have declared significant. This will occur with chance equal to the level of significance when there is no interaction in the populations.
2. The two variables are interacting, and we have correctly recognized this fact.
3. An uncontrolled and unmeasured variable may be of sufficient importance to appear as an interaction effect.
4. The items in the subgroups are not randomly drawn.

We have emphasized particularly the first and second interpretation. One should be concerned about the third factor in any experiment, whether the model contains interaction effects or not. Some research workers always attempt to randomize the placing of the experimental units among the various categories so that any unnoticed extraneous variable is scattered randomly over the categories. Table A-1 can be used as an aid to randomization.

Supposedly the fourth item has no place here since it has been assumed at all times that the observations are randomly drawn. Unfortunately, however, these procedures are sometimes applied without allowance for the fact that the observations are on individuals selected in intact groups, e.g., classes of school children, family groups, or groups selected subjectively by experimenters.

Similar comments can be made in any of the analysis-of-variance problems about the occurrence of a significantly small F ratio. Although there are many possible causes for this result, one important cause may be nonrandom choice of individuals or groups.

The analysis of variance has sometimes been misused on measurements made on the same individuals over a period of time representing growth curves or on measurements on the same person recorded in different categories. Special care must be taken not to confuse the variance of repeated measurements on an individual and the variance of measurements made on different randomly selected individuals.

If the experiment is designed so that the observations are dependent, or, in the terminology of the next chapter, correlated, appropriate techniques of analysis should be used. Alternatively, the experimenter should attempt to choose a sample (design his experiment) in such a way that dependency is avoided. For example, if a study is to be made of weights of animals at 1 month, 6 months, and 12 months, a choice of different animals at each age level will avoid dependency. However, when different animals are chosen, less information is gained about individual growth patterns; so the experimenter may wish to use the same animals throughout the experiment but different techniques to allow for this dependency. Chapters 11 and 12 introduce some relatively simple alternative techniques.

We have presented here only an introduction to the topic of analysis of variance. The analysis extends readily to factorial designs where four or more variables of classification are included in the experiment. These cases are used frequently in agriculture, industry, psychology, etc. For example, an experiment involving five high schools, four grades in the high schools, two sexes of students, and three income categories for parents has four variables of classification. In this case there are four main effects, six two-category interactions, four three-category interactions, and one four-category interaction. A factorial design for this situation replicated three times would require 3 students from each of the $5 \times 4 \times 2 \times 3 = 120$ categories, or 360 students in all. The analysis may be undertaken to estimate, or to test hypotheses about, the main effects or any of the interaction effects.

A number of modifications of the factorial and of randomized-block experiments are available for situations where measurements are made only for a portion of the categories of each variable of classification. The Latin-square and the Greco-Latin-square designs are two examples of such designs, and there are many others. The reader wishing to study experimental designs further will find sources in the References (page 357).

Tests for Homogeneity of Variances. Since the test of the hypothesis $\mu_1 = \mu_2 = \cdots = \mu_k$ made in the analysis-of-variance F test assumes homogeneity of variances, we may wish to test the hypothesis

$$\sigma_1^2 = \sigma_2^2 = \cdots = \sigma_k^2$$

(see References, page 357).

Bartlett's Test. This test requires computation with natural logarithms, which may be found in Table A-14.

The hypothesis to be tested is that the variances of k normally distributed populations are equal. The samples are of size n_i, where $\Sigma n_i = N$. If there are several samples, we shall follow the procedure of using n_i as sample size rather than N_i. We denote the variance of the ith sample by s_i^2.

Let $M = (N - k) \ln s_p^2 - \Sigma[(n_i - 1) \ln s_i^2]$

$$s_p^2 = \frac{\Sigma(n_i - 1)s_i^2}{N - k}$$

$$A = \frac{1}{3(k-1)}\left[\sum\left(\frac{1}{n_i - 1}\right) - \frac{1}{N - k}\right]$$

$$\nu_1 = k - 1$$

$$\nu_2 = \frac{k+1}{A^2}$$

$$b = \frac{\nu_2}{1 - A + (2/\nu_2)}$$

Then the sampling distribution of $F = \dfrac{\nu_2 M}{\nu_1(b - M)}$ is approximately $F(\nu_1,\nu_2)$. Although this is an approximate formula, it gives sufficient accuracy for practical purposes for any size, n_i, samples. The values of ν_2 will usually not be an integer, and it may be necessary to interpolate in the F table. Good accuracy can be obtained by the method of interpolating on the reciprocals of the degrees of freedom as in the example below. Usually, however, the observed value will differ sufficiently from the table value so that interpolation is not necessary.

Suppose, for example, that we have four samples of sizes 3, 3, 3, 4 with variances 6.33, 1.33, 4.33, 4.33, respectively. Substituting these numbers, we obtain

$$\begin{aligned} M &= 9 \ln 4.11 - 2 \ln 6.33 - 2 \ln 1.33 - 2 \ln 4.33 - 3 \ln 4.33 \\ &= 9(1.413) - 2(1.846) - 2(0.284) - 2(1.466) - 3(1.466) \\ &= 1.127 \\ A &= \frac{1}{3 \times 3}\left(\frac{1}{2} + \frac{1}{2} + \frac{1}{2} + \frac{1}{3} - \frac{1}{9}\right) = .1913 \\ \nu_1 &= 3 \\ \nu_2 &= \frac{5}{(.1913)^2} = 136.6 \\ b &= \frac{136.6}{1 - .1913 + (2/136.6)} \\ &= 165.9 \end{aligned}$$

For $\alpha = .05$ we read

$$\begin{aligned} F(3,120) &= 2.68 \\ F(3,\infty) &= 2.60 \end{aligned}$$

Interpolating by means of reciprocals, proceed as follows:

Corresponding to $1/\infty = .0000$ we have 2.60.

Corresponding to $\frac{1}{120} = .0083$ we have 2.68.

We are interested in $1/136.6 = .0073$, which is $\frac{73}{83} = .88$ of the way between .0000 and .0083. We take a value .88 of the way between 2.60 and 2.68, or $2.60 + .88(.08) = 2.67$.

Thus if the observed F is larger than 2.67, we shall reject, at the 5 per cent level of significance, the hypothesis that the four populations have equal variances. The observed value is

$$F = \frac{136.6(1.127)}{3(165.9 - 1.127)} = .31$$

Since this value is less than 2.67, we accept the hypothesis. Note that the interpolation was not necessary since $F(3,136.6)$ is between 2.60 and 2.68 and that is sufficient information in this case.

Cochran's Test. One type of deviation from homogeneous variance which is serious in terms of invalidating the analysis-of-variance test for means occurs when one variance is very much larger than the remainder of the variances. The following test statistic is designed especially for this situation and is referred to as Cochran's test:

$$C = \frac{\text{largest } s_i^2}{\Sigma s_i^2}$$

The 95th and 99th percentiles of the sampling distribution of C are in Table A-17. They can be used for a test at the 5 per cent and 1 per cent levels of significance. The hypothesis of equal variances is rejected if the computed value of the above statistic exceeds the value in the table. Critical values are indicated only for the case where the sample variances have an equal number of degrees of freedom.

Estimation of Means from Analysis-of-variance Experiments. The confidence-interval estimate for the population mean μ for a sample of N observations is $\bar{X} \pm ks/\sqrt{N}$, where the value k is obtained from the t table corresponding to the degrees of freedom for s and the degree of confidence desired for the confidence interval. The analysis-of-variance computations include an estimate of the population σ^2 as the residual mean square or the within-groups mean square. This estimate may be used to compute confidence-interval estimates for the mean for any group in an analysis-of-variance experiment. For example, the 95 per cent confidence-interval estimate for the mean μ_{11} of the population corresponding to the first cell of Table 10-15 is computed as follows:

$$\bar{X}_{11\cdot} = \frac{4 + 7 + 5}{3} = 5.33$$

Residual mean square = 1.34, and $\sqrt{1.34} = 1.16$. The two percentiles of t are $t_{.025}(14) = -2.14$ and $t_{.975}(14) = 2.14$. The confidence-interval estimate is

$$5.33 - \frac{2.14(1.16)}{\sqrt{3}} < \mu_{11} < 5.33 + \frac{2.14(1.16)}{\sqrt{3}}$$

or

$$3.90 < \mu_{11} < 6.76$$

Equal Sample Sizes. The computations for the analysis of variance and the computations for the test for homogeneity of variances are simplified if all samples are of the same size. An additional reason for selecting samples of equal size is an expected improvement in our estimate of the variance of the difference of two means. To illustrate this effect, consider the denominator for the t test of difference between two means.

$$t = \frac{\bar{X}_1 - \bar{X}_2}{s_p\sqrt{(1/N_1) + (1/N_2)}}$$

If a total of 100 observations is made and in one case each group has 50 observations and in the other case one group has 95 and the other group 5, we obtain

$$t_1 = \frac{\bar{X}_1 - \bar{X}_2}{s_p\sqrt{\frac{1}{50} + \frac{1}{50}}} \qquad \text{or} \qquad t_2 = \frac{\bar{X}_1 - \bar{X}_2}{s_p\sqrt{\frac{1}{95} + \frac{1}{5}}}$$

Computing the square root in the denominator, we obtain

$$t_1 = \frac{\bar{X}_1 - \bar{X}_2}{s_p(.200)} \qquad \text{or} \qquad t_2 = \frac{\bar{X}_1 - \bar{X}_2}{s_p(.459)}$$

and see that equal sample sizes will give a much smaller denominator and thus a large t. Similar effects hold for the analysis of variance. Whether the samples are of equal size or not has no effect on the level of significance α, the chance of rejecting when true the hypothesis of equal means. However, in many cases of inequality of means we shall discover this inequality more frequently if the samples are of equal size. Also note that the equality of sample sizes gives a much shorter confidence interval for the difference in means.

Transformations. Certain assumptions about the distributions of the populations are necessary for most statistical procedures. Examples of these assumptions are (1) one or more populations are normally distributed, (2) two or more populations have equal variances, and (3) a two-variable analysis-of-variance model has no interaction (also assumed in the Latin-square design). It sometimes happens that an appropriate change of scale, e.g., using the square root or logarithm of the observations, will more nearly satisfy some of the assumptions. The exact change of scale is, in general, difficult to determine, and success in finding a good transformation depends in part on experience in the particular field of application. For example, it is often found that size measurements on plants and animals are approximately normally distributed if logarithms are used.

A large number of observations is usually required before any definite statement can be made about the appropriate transformation. Without prior information the experimenter has little chance of proving or disproving normality or of finding a normalizing transformation from samples as small as 10 or 20. The remainder of this section describes several procedures designed to improve scales.

Means of Several Observations. Since a mean is usually more nearly normally distributed than individual measurements, it is sometimes convenient to draw a series of small samples and record the means for use in the analysis in place of the single observations. An example was given in Sec. 6-9 for the case where σ was known. For the cases where σ is not known we may use the observed means with Table A-5 to estimate μ or with Table A-6*b* to estimate σ^2/n, where n is the size of each sample. We can then estimate σ^2 by multiplying the estimate of σ^2/n by n.

Square-root Transformation. If the sample means are approximately proportional to the variances of the respective samples (or the squares of the ranges), replacing each measurement by its square root will often result in homogeneous variances. This type of transformation is appropriate for data having the Poisson distribution discussed in Chaps. 13 and 20. In this case the transformation $\sqrt{X} + \sqrt{X+1}$ will approximately stabilize the variance at $\sigma^2 = 1$ if the mean of the original observations is greater than .8.

Logarithmic Transformation. If the means of the samples are proportional to the range or to the standard deviation of the respective samples, replacing each measurement by its logarithm will often result in the variances being more nearly equal. Actually it happens in many applications that the logarithmic transformation also tends to normalize the distribution. Graph paper is available with a logarithmic scale on one axis and a normal-probability scale on the other. This paper simplifies examination of data for normality of the transformed observations. An approximately straight cumulative-distribution polygon is an indication of normality of the transformed observations.

Arc Sine Transformation. If data are collected in the form of proportions, the variance of the observed results is $\sqrt{p(1-p)/N}$ as noted in Chap. 5. The arc sine transformation of the observed proportions produces an approximately constant variance unless $Np < .8$ or $N(1-p) < .8$. The transformation can be obtained by reference to Table A-28 for values of X and N. The tabled values are in radians, and the variance of the transformed measurements is approximately $1/(N + \frac{1}{2})$. The formula for the transformation is

$$\phi = \arcsin \sqrt{\frac{X}{(N+1)}} + \arcsin \sqrt{\frac{(X+1)}{(N+1)}}$$

In this case the transformed observations are also approximately normal. We may refer to Table A-4, using

$$z = \sqrt{N+1}[2 \arcsin \sqrt{(X+1)/(N+1)} - 2 \arcsin \sqrt{p}]$$

to give approximate confidence limits for p or to test a hypothesis $p = p_0$. The use of the arc sine transformation avoids the difficulty (encountered in Chaps. 6 and 7) that σ^2 is unknown if p is unknown.

Use of T Scores. In Chap. 5 we assigned normalized scores to the ranks of observations. It is noted again that this automatically forces the new scores to be approximately normally distributed. If the sample sizes are not greater than 20, Table A-8*b*(5) can be used to obtain normalized scores for the ranks of observations which differ slightly from T scores. These scores are the mean positions of ordered observations from a normal population with mean zero and unit variance.

GLOSSARY

analysis of variance
between means
homogeneity of variance
interaction
Latin square
mean square
randomized blocks
replication
residual
variable of classification
within groups

DISCUSSION QUESTIONS

1. State in your own words the assumptions about the population which are made in the use of the factorial experiment. Do you have any way to check these assumptions? Of what significance is it to an experimenter if the assumptions do not appear to be true?

2. Give examples of situations in fields of application where analysis of variance might be used.

3. Construct a 5 × 5 Latin square. Give an example showing the use of such a designed experiment.

4. Define each term in the Glossary.

5. If a Latin-square-designed experiment is used in agriculture and the rows and columns of data actually correspond to rows and columns of plots in a field, is it reasonable to assume that interaction is not present? Can you think of a possible cause of interaction in such an experiment?

6. What conclusions are made when you reject a hypothesis using the analysis-of-variance technique? When you accept a hypothesis?

7. If you reject a hypothesis using analysis of variance, what further analysis of the data can be made?

CLASS EXERCISES

1. For Class Exercise 1, Chap. 8, each student has computed the value of s_p^2 and the total sum of squares for an analysis-of-variance single-classification experiment with $k = 6$, $n = 10$, $N = 60$. Each student now computes the among-means variance s_M^2. Collect the values of s_p^2, for all the students, into a distribution, and verify that the mean s_p^2 is equal to σ^2, which is 1 for the populations sampled (Tables A-2 and A-23). Collect the values of s_M^2 into a distribution, and verify that the mean s_M^2 is $\sigma^2 + n\sigma_m^2$. Here $\mu_1 = \mu_2 = \mu_3 = 0$, $\mu_4 = \mu_5 = \mu_6 = 2$, $\bar{\mu} = 1$, $\sigma_m^2 = \frac{6}{5}$, and so the mean s_M^2 should be 13.

Form the quotient of s_M^2 and s_p^2 for each group, and collect the results for all the students into a distribution. Compare the 95th percentile of the observed distribution with $F_{.95}(5,54)$. Why is there a large discrepancy? Observe the frequency with which you reject the hypothesis of equal means for the six populations, at the 5 per cent level of significance.

2. Each student groups one sample of size $N = 10$ from Table A-2 with one sample of size $N = 10$ from Table A-23 (as recorded in the Exercise in Chap. 3). He then computes the values of s_p^2 and s_M^2 for each of his three groups ($k = 2, n = 10$), and the results of the class are collected into distributions of s_p^2 and of s_m^2. Verify, as in Exercise 1, whether the mean s_p^2 is equal to the population variance and whether the mean s_M^2 is equal to $\sigma^2 + n\sigma_m^2$.

Form the quotient of s_M^2 and s_p^2 for each group, and collect the results of all the students (three from each student) into a distribution. Compare the 95th percentile of the observed distribution with $F_{.95}(1,18)$. Why is there a large discrepancy? Observe the frequency with which you reject the hypothesis of equal means if actually $\mu_1 = 0$, $\mu_2 = 2$ (as is the case in this experiment).

3. Each student computes, on the three samples of size 10 each, drawn from Table A-2, the values of s_p^2 and s_M^2. Here $k = 3$, $n = 10$, $N = 30$. Collect the results, and verify that the mean s_p^2 and the mean s_M^2 are both equal to σ^2.

Form the quotient of s_M^2 and s_p^2 for each group, and collect these results into a distribution. Compare the 95th percentile of this observed distribution with $F_{.95}(2,27)$.

If there is a large number of cases in your experiment, you can expect fairly close agreement, otherwise only approximate agreement.

PROBLEMS

1. Use analysis-of-variance procedures to investigate Prob. 1 of Chap. 9. Note that $F(1,\text{df}) = t^2$ so that the analysis-of-variance test is equivalent to the two-sided t test when there are two categories.

2. The students in three classes in an elementary-statistics course obtained total scores as in the tabulation. Is there a significant difference in the scores received by students meeting at different times of day? State completely the hypothesis you are testing and your conclusions.

8 o'clock		10 o'clock		2 o'clock	
121	122	97	131	134	162
117	141	145	143	89	128
145	126	119	107	108	133
108	145	139	86	88	93
142	114	143	94	146	118
154	136	133	164	153	126
115	151	149	139	130	127
81	105	107	151	144	150
122	103	154	141	125	138
127	108	102	131	111	119
		108	65	87	142
		131	141		

3. Samples of 25 students each were taken from five schools and given an examination on current events. The mean scores for the five samples were $\bar{X}_{1\cdot} = 63$, $\bar{X}_{2\cdot} = 72$, $\bar{X}_{3\cdot} = 60$, $\bar{X}_{4\cdot} = 80$, $\bar{X}_{5\cdot} = 92$ with $s_p^2 = 26.01$. Give a set of interval estimates for all differences of pairs of means for the five schools such that we can be 95 per cent confident that all are correct.

4. The drained weight in ounces of frozen apricots was measured for various types of sirup and various concentrations of sirup. The original weights of the apricots were the same. Differences in drained weight would be attributable to differences in concentration or type of sirup. Analyze the data.

Concentration of sirup	Sirup composition			
	All sucrose	$\frac{2}{3}$ sucrose $\frac{1}{3}$ corn sirup	$\frac{1}{2}$ sucrose $\frac{1}{2}$ corn sirup	All corn sirup
30	28.80	28.21	29.28	29.12
40	29.12	28.64	29.12	30.24
50	29.76	30.40	29.12	28.32
65	30.56	29.44	28.96	29.60

5. In a study of the effect of the pollen parent on the protein content of corn a low-protein corn (ear parent) is pollinated with a high- and a low-protein strain. The measurement recorded is per cent protein. Two determinations were made from each ear and pollen parent. Analyze the data.

Ear	Pollen parent			
	High protein		Low protein	
1	11.44	11.18	11.22	11.00
2	10.12	9.78	9.54	9.42
3	10.59	10.64	9.98	10.08
4	11.55	11.39	10.67	10.87
5	9.90	9.85	10.06	10.21
6	12.29	12.45	12.10	11.89
7	10.88	11.30	11.26	10.83
8	9.57	9.74	9.44	9.61

6. Two fertilizers are used together in amounts of either 1 or 2 pounds per plot. A 2×2 factorial experiment replicated four times was carried out, with resulting yields given in the table. Analyze this completely randomized experiment at the 1 per cent level, examining all contrasts which seem of interest.

Amount of fertilizer 2		Amount of fertilizer 1: 1 lb	2 lb
	1 lb	17	13
		16	13
		15	14
		18	12
	2 lb	21	14
		20	16
		19	16
		18	14

7. Four fertilizers A, B, C, D were tested by arranging plants in a Latin-square design in a field. Thus rows and columns in the table are rows and columns in the field. The yields are recorded in the table. Analyze the data for evidence at the 5 per cent level that the mean yields are not equal for the four fertilizers. Comparisons can be made as in Sec. 10-6, using the four treatment means and the residual variance.

A 17	B 13	C 19	D 16
B 13	C 20	D 14	A 18
C 21	D 16	A 15	B 12
D 14	A 16	B 14	C 18

8. Each of the sets of observations is a random sample drawn from a normal population. Test for homogeneity of variances. Test for homogeneity of means by the analysis of variance. State the hypotheses and assumptions. Indicate how an

A	*B*	*C*	*D*
49	49	44	58
42	44	57	54
47	50	34	64
76	58	48	60
69	70	50	53
58			64
			52
			42

α error could be made, and give the consequences of such an error. Indicate how a β error could be made, and give the consequences of such an error.

9. The following experiment was designed to determine the relative merit of four different feeds in regard to the gain in weight of pigs. Analyze the data, comparing all pairs among the four feeds. Indicate how each of the two types of error might be made, and give the consequence of each error.

Twenty pigs are divided at random into four lots with five pigs in each. Each lot is given a different feed. The weight gain in pounds by each of the pigs for a fixed length of time is given in the table.

Feed *A*	Feed *B*	Feed *C*	Feed *D*
133	163	210	195
144	148	233	184
135	152	220	199
149	146	226	187
143	157	229	193

10. An agency wished to determine whether five makes of automobiles would average the same number of miles per gallon. A random sample of three cars of each make was taken from each of three cities, and each car had a test run with 1 gallon of gasoline. The table records the number of miles traveled.

a. Why were three cities used instead of just one city?

b. What populations are sampled from?

c. How would you go about getting such a random sample of three cars from a city?

d. What assumptions are made about the populations, and what hypotheses can be tested?

e. Perform the analysis of variance, and state fully your conclusions.

	Cities		
	Los Angeles	San Francisco	Portland
A	20.3, 19.8, 21.4	21.6, 22.4, 21.3	19.8, 18.6, 21.0
B	19.5, 18.6, 18.9	20.1, 19.9, 20.5	19.6, 18.3, 19.8
C	22.1, 23.0, 22.4	20.1, 21.0, 19.8	22.3, 22.0, 21.6
D	17.6, 18.3, 18.2	19.5, 19.2, 20.3	19.4, 18.5, 19.1
E	23.6, 24.5, 25.1	17.6, 18.3, 18.1	22.1, 24.3, 23.8

11. The table gives results of computations on the observations of the life of four brands of automobile tires used under five different road conditions. Four tires of each brand were used for each type of road. Complete the analysis of variance, stating hypotheses and conclusions. Explain the reason for including different road conditions in the experiment.

	Sum of squares
Tires	190.1
Roads	200.2
Subtotal	500.4
Total	804.6

CHAPTER 11

REGRESSION AND CORRELATION

A regression problem considers the frequency distributions of one variable when another is held fixed at each of several levels. A correlation problem considers the joint variation of two measurements, neither of which is restricted by the experimenter. Examples of regression problems can be found in the study of the yields of crops grown with different amounts of fertilizer, the length of life of certain animals exposed to different amounts of radiation, the hardness of plastics which are heat-treated for different periods of time. In these problems the variation in one measurement is studied for particular levels of the other variable selected by the experimenter. Examples of correlation problems are found in the study of the relationship between IQ and school grades, blood pressure and metabolism, height of cornstalk and yield, etc. In these examples both variables are observed as they naturally occur, neither variable being fixed at predetermined levels. For convenience in terminology the examples of the regression problem and the correlation problem treated in this chapter are stated in terms of the variables height and weight.

11-1. Regression

Suppose that we wish to make a study of the distribution of the weights of a population of men with relation to the heights of the men. We shall subdivide the population into groups of men of approximately equal height and examine the relationships between the distributions of weights in the various groups.

For any chosen height there is a distribution of weights. This distribution has a mean, the mean weight of all men who have this height, and a variance, the variance of weights of all men who have this height. We shall define the "regression of weight on height" as the mean of the distribution of weights of all men who have the given height.

In this usage the distribution of weights depends upon the particular height chosen, and we shall speak here of the weight as a dependent variable and the height as an independent variable.

It is convenient to introduce symbols, and we shall designate Y as the dependent measurement and X as the independent measurement. Corresponding to any man in the population, there is, then, a pair of measurements, X and Y. The mean of any distribution of weights Y for given height X will be denoted by $\mu_{y \cdot x}$ and the variance of this distribution by $\sigma_{y \cdot x}^2$. These are parameters. They are constant for any fixed height but may vary between distributions of weights for different heights. The mean of weights of all men, of all heights, will be denoted by μ_y and the variance of these weights by σ_y^2. We shall assume that $\sigma_{y \cdot x}^2$ is constant for all values of X.

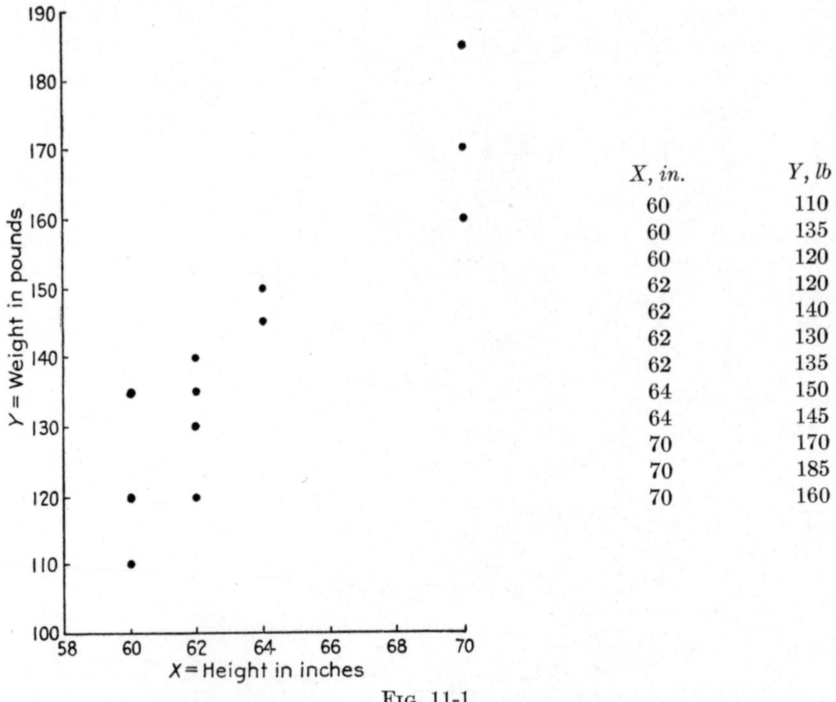

X, *in.*	Y, *lb*
60	110
60	135
60	120
62	120
62	140
62	130
62	135
64	150
64	145
70	170
70	185
70	160

Fig. 11-1

To study the distributions of weights, we shall select several heights and make several random observations of men having these heights. Suppose, for example, we decided to choose heights of $X = 60$, 62, 64, and 70 inches, and we made the observations in the tabulation. These observations have been *plotted* on the graph in Fig. 11-1. Each point represents one man, his weight being read on the vertical scale and his height being read on the horizontal scale. The graph with the points plotted is called a *scatter diagram*.

11-2. Linear Regression

In many important applications of regression theory the regression curve is a straight or approximately straight line for the range of X values under consideration. In a case of this sort we say there is *linear regression*.

We shall assume, for our examples, that the regression curve is a straight line. A test of this hypothesis using the observed data is given in Sec. 11-5.

If there is linear regression, we may write the formula for the mean Y when X is given as

$$\mu_{y \cdot x} = A + B(X - \bar{X}) \tag{1}$$

where A and B are parameters,* X is any given value (height for our example), and $\bar{X}$ is the mean of the chosen X values of the individuals in the sample. B is the slope of the line, i.e., the amount $\mu_{y \cdot x}$ changes when X changes by one unit.

11-3. Estimation of Parameters

The regression equation (1) is in terms of the population parameters. We shall use the data in a sample to estimate these parameters. The unbiased estimates of A and B, whose sampling distributions have minimum variance, are $\bar{Y}$ and b, where

$$b = \frac{\sum X_i Y_i - \dfrac{\Sigma X_i \Sigma Y_i}{N}}{\sum X_i^2 - \dfrac{(\Sigma X_i)^2}{N}} \tag{2}$$

If we let $\bar{Y}_x$ denote our estimate of the mean Y when X is given, we have

$$\bar{Y}_x = \bar{Y} + b(X - \bar{X}) \tag{3}$$

An unbiased estimate of $\sigma_{y \cdot x}{}^2$ is $s_{y \cdot x}{}^2$, where

$$s_{y \cdot x}{}^2 = \frac{1}{N-2} \sum \{Y_i - [\bar{Y} + b(X_i - \bar{X})]\}^2 \tag{4}$$

or the algebraically equivalent formula

$$s_{y \cdot x}{}^2 = \frac{N-1}{N-2} (s_y{}^2 - b^2 s_x{}^2) \tag{5}$$

where $s_x{}^2$ and $s_y{}^2$ are the variances of the observed X values and of the observed Y values, respectively. It can be seen from formula (4) that $s_{y \cdot x}{}^2$ is a mean-square deviation of sample points from the estimated

* These parameters, called *regression coefficients*, are frequently denoted in the literature by α and β. We do not use α and β since these symbols have been used for chances of error in testing hypotheses.

regression line. The value of $s_{y \cdot x}$ is often called the *standard error of estimate.*

For the example above we have computed

$$\begin{aligned} \Sigma X_i &= 766 & \bar{X} &= 63.83 \\ \Sigma Y_i &= 1{,}700 & \bar{Y} &= 141.67 \\ \Sigma X_i Y_i &= 109{,}380 \\ \Sigma X_i^2 &= 49{,}068 \\ \Sigma Y_i^2 &= 246{,}100 \end{aligned}$$

$$s_x^2 = \frac{49{,}068 - \dfrac{(766)^2}{12}}{11} = \frac{171.67}{11} = 15.61$$

$$s_y^2 = \frac{246{,}100 - \dfrac{(1{,}700)^2}{12}}{11} = \frac{246{,}100 - 240{,}833.3}{11} = \frac{5{,}266.7}{11} = 478.8$$

$$b = \frac{109{,}380 - \dfrac{766 \times 1{,}700}{12}}{171.67} = \frac{109{,}380 - 108{,}516.7}{171.67} = \frac{863.3}{171.67} = 5.029$$

$$s_{y \cdot x}^2 = \tfrac{11}{10}[478.8 - (5.029)^2(15.61)] = \tfrac{11}{10}(478.8 - 394.8) = 92.4$$

$$\bar{Y}_x = 141.67 + 5.029(X - 63.83)$$

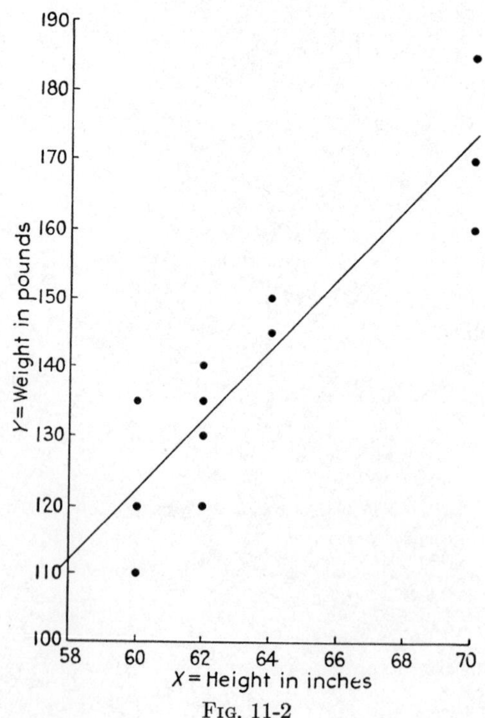

FIG. 11-2

Figure 11-2 shows the original data with this estimated regression line drawn.

Figure 11-3 shows the original data with the estimated regression line and indicates the vertical deviations of the observations from the line.

Least Squares. The line drawn by using Eq. (3) has the property that the sum of squares of vertical deviations of observations from this line is smaller than the corresponding sum of squares of deviations from any other line. This is called a *least-square* property.

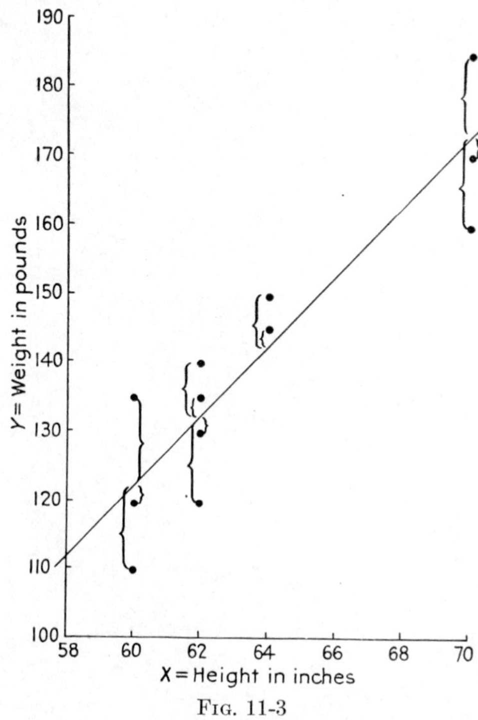

FIG. 11-3

The principle of least squares is frequently used as a justification for using Eq. (3) as a formula connecting X and Y values. This is basically a different principle from those developed here, and the principle of least squares is often used in problems unrelated to statistical inference. It happens that in many cases, as in this one, the least-square principle and the principle of having an efficient unbiased estimate lead to the same formulas.

11-4. Estimation and Tests in Normal Populations

In Sec. 11-3 we made no assumption about the distribution of Y for given X except that $\sigma_{y \cdot x}^2$ is constant for all X and that the regression was linear. *If it also happens that the distribution of Y for any given X is a normal distribution, then it is possible to indicate by confidence intervals estimates of A, B,* $\sigma_{y\cdot x}^2$, *and* $\mu_{y\cdot x}$.

If the above assumptions are satisfied, then:

The sampling distribution of $t = \dfrac{(\bar{Y} - A)\sqrt{N}}{s_{y\cdot x}}$ *is a t distribution with* $N - 2$ *degrees of freedom.*

The sampling distribution of $t = \dfrac{(b - B)s_x\sqrt{N-1}}{s_{y\cdot x}}$ *is a t distribution with* $N - 2$ *degrees of freedom.*

The sampling distribution of $\dfrac{s_{y\cdot x}^2}{\sigma_{y\cdot x}^2}$ *is a* χ^2/df *distribution with* $N - 2$ *degrees of freedom.*

These distributions may be used in the same manner as in Chaps. 6, 8, and 9 to give confidence limits for, or to test hypotheses about, A or B or $\sigma_{y\cdot x}^2$.

Thus $100(1 - \alpha)$ per cent confidence limits for A, B, and $\sigma_{y\cdot x}^2$ are

$$\bar{Y} + t_{\frac{1}{2}\alpha}\frac{s_{y\cdot x}}{\sqrt{N}} < A < \bar{Y} + t_{1-\frac{1}{2}\alpha}\frac{s_{y\cdot x}}{\sqrt{N}} \tag{6}$$

$$b + t_{\frac{1}{2}\alpha}\frac{s_{y\cdot x}}{s_x\sqrt{N-1}} < B < b + t_{1-\frac{1}{2}\alpha}\frac{s_{y\cdot x}}{s_x\sqrt{N-1}} \tag{7}$$

where the t values are from Table A-5 for $N - 2$ degrees of freedom, and

$$\frac{s_{y\cdot x}^2}{\chi^2_{1-\frac{1}{2}\alpha}/\text{df}} < \sigma_{y\cdot x}^2 < \frac{s_{y\cdot x}^2}{\chi_{\frac{1}{2}\alpha}^2/\text{df}} \tag{8}$$

where the χ^2/df percentiles are obtained from Table A-6*b* for $N - 2$ degrees of freedom. For our example above, 90 per cent confidence limits for these parameters are

$$141.67 - 1.81\frac{9.61}{3.46} < A < 141.67 + 1.81\frac{9.61}{3.46}$$

or

$$136.64 < A < 146.70$$

and for B

$$5.028 - 1.81\frac{9.61}{13.1} < B < 5.028 + 1.81\frac{9.61}{13.1}$$

or

$$3.70 < B < 6.35$$

Further

$$\frac{92.4}{1.83} < \sigma_{y\cdot x}^2 < \frac{92.4}{.394}$$

or

$$50.5 < \sigma_{y\cdot x}^2 < 235.$$

Estimation of $\mu_{y\cdot x}$. If the above assumptions hold, $100(1 - \alpha)$ per cent confidence limits for the mean of the Y values of all individuals having a particular X value are

$$\bar{Y}_x + t_{\frac{1}{2}\alpha} s_{y\cdot x} \sqrt{\frac{1}{N} + \frac{(X - \bar{X})^2}{(N-1)s_x^2}} < \mu_{y\cdot x} < \bar{Y}_x + t_{1-\frac{1}{2}\alpha} s_{y\cdot x} \sqrt{\frac{1}{N} + \frac{(X - \bar{X})^2}{(N-1)s_x^2}} \qquad (9)$$

where the t values are read from Table A-5 for $N - 2$ degrees of freedom. This is an estimate of the *mean Y only*, not an estimate of some individual's Y score from his X score.

In the example we have for $X = 65$, say,

$$\bar{Y}_{65} = 141.67 + 5.029(65 - 63.83) = 147.55$$

and 95 per cent confidence limits for $\mu_{y\cdot 65}$ are

$$147.55 - 2.23(9.61)\sqrt{\frac{1}{12} + \frac{(65 - 63.83)^2}{11(15.61)}} < \mu_{y\cdot 65} < 147.55 + 2.23(9.61)\sqrt{\frac{1}{12} + \frac{(65 - 63.83)^2}{11(15.61)}}$$

or $$147.55 - 21.4\sqrt{.0913} < \mu_{y\cdot 65} < 147.55 + 21.4\sqrt{.0913}$$

or $$141.09 < \mu_{y\cdot 65} < 154.01$$

We are 95 per cent confident that the mean weight of all individuals 65 inches tall is between 141.09 and 154.01. If we repeat this experiment with another sample, we should obtain another set of limits instead of 141.09 and 154.01. In the long run, 95 per cent of such intervals would cover $\mu_{y\cdot 65}$. This is the interpretation we use in our statements of degree of confidence. We do not know that $\mu_{y\cdot 65}$ is between 141.09 and 154.01, but we do give a level of our belief that it is between them.

Estimation of an Individual's Y Value. The interval (9) is an estimate of the mean Y for a particular group of individuals. The interval given below can be used to estimate (or predict) the Y value for a single observed X value. The confidence level is correct for a single prediction. The confidence level is not correct for repeated predictions using the same sample.

The $100(1 - \alpha)$ per cent confidence interval for an individual's Y score in terms of his X score is

$$\bar{Y}_x + t_{\frac{1}{2}\alpha} s_{y\cdot x} \sqrt{1 + \frac{1}{N} + \frac{(X - \bar{X})^2}{(N-1)s_x^2}} < Y < \bar{Y}_x + t_{1-\frac{1}{2}\alpha} s_{y\cdot x} \sqrt{1 + \frac{1}{N} + \frac{(X - \bar{X})^2}{(N-1)s_x^2}}$$

Tolerance Interval. A formula which gives an interval having chance γ of covering a proportion P of the population is

$$\bar{Y}_x \pm k s_{y \cdot x}$$

where $$k = z_{\frac{1}{2}(1+P)} \left(1 + \frac{1}{2N'} - \frac{2z^2_{\frac{1}{2}(1+P)} - 3}{24\,N'^2}\right) \sqrt{F_{1-\gamma}(\infty, N-2)}$$

and $$N' = \frac{1}{\dfrac{1}{N} + \dfrac{(X - \bar{X})^2}{(N-1)s_x^2}}$$

This is an approximate formula which is good when $N' \geq 2$ and $N \geq 3$. The derivation of the formula assumes that $\sigma_{y \cdot x}^2$ is constant, the regression of Y on X is linear in the range of X considered, and the distributions of Y are normal for each X.

Test for Independence. A hypothesis frequently tested in regression analysis is that a variable Y is independent of a variable X. One criterion of independence is that the mean Y is the same for each value of X, which, in the case of linear regression, means that $B = 0$. We shall test the hypothesis $B = 0$ and if this hypothesis is rejected say that there is sufficient reason to believe, at the specified level of significance, that Y is dependent upon X.

1. H: $B = 0$.
2. Choose α.
3. As a test statistic, use $t = \dfrac{(b - 0)s_x \sqrt{N-1}}{s_{y \cdot x}}$.
4. If the distribution of Y for each X is normal with the same variance and with the same mean ($\mu_{y \cdot x} = A$), then the sampling distribution of this statistic is a t distribution with $N - 2$ degrees of freedom.
5. Reject if $t < t_{\frac{1}{2}\alpha}(N - 2)$ or if $t > t_{1-\frac{1}{2}\alpha}(N - 2)$.
6. Perform the computations, and accept or reject the hypothesis.

For our numerical example the test proceeds as follows:

1. H: $B = 0$.
2. Choose $\alpha = .05$.
3. $t = \dfrac{(5.029)(13.1)}{9.61}$.
4. If the distribution of Y for each X is normal with the same variance and with the same mean, then the sampling distribution of this statistic is a t distribution with 10 degrees of freedom.
5. The critical region is t less than -2.23 and larger than $+2.23$.
6. Here $t = 6.9$, which is larger than 2.23, and so we have sufficient reason to say, at the 5 per cent level of significance, that Y is dependent on X.

11-5. Test for Linearity of Regression

To test the hypothesis of linearity of regression, we use an analysis-of-variance technique. Instead of the hypothesis $\mu_1 = \mu_2 = \cdots = \mu_k$, we test whether or not the mean for each group is located on a straight line. We shall compare the variance within groups with the variance of the deviations of the group means from the estimated regression line. The appropriate mean squares for the F ratio are obtained from Table 11-1.

The sum of squares of the deviations of the group-mean Y values from the estimated regression line is obtained by subtracting the "Regression" sum of squares from the "Total."

The test for linearity is the ratio of the mean square about regression to the mean square within groups, which, if the assumptions of Sec. 11-4 concerning normality are true and if the hypothesis is true, has an $F(k-2, N-k)$ sampling distribution. The analysis for this example is shown in Table 11-2. $F = 31.0/108.1 = .29$ is compared with $F_{.95}(2,8) = 4.46$ and declared not significant. Therefore we accept the hypothesis that the regression curve is a straight line.

TABLE 11-1

	Sum of squares	df	Mean square
Within groups	$\sum\sum Y_{ij}^2 - \sum \frac{T_{Yi+}^2}{n_i}$	$N-k$	
Regression	$b^2\left[\sum\sum X_{ij}^2 - \frac{(\Sigma\Sigma X_{ij})^2}{N}\right]$	1	
About regression	difference	$k-2$	
Total	$\sum \frac{T_{Yi+}^2}{n_i} - \frac{T_{Y++}^2}{N}$	$k-1$	

TABLE 11-2

	Sum of squares	df	Mean square
Within groups	864.6	8	108.1
Regression	4,340.0	1	
About regression	62.1	2	31.0
Total	4,402.1	3	

The sums of squares in Table 11-2 can be extracted from the previous computations but are indicated completely below for ease in reference.

$$\frac{T_{Y++}^2}{N} = 240{,}833.3$$

$$\sum \frac{T_{Yi+}^2}{n_i} = \frac{(365)^2}{3} + \frac{(525)^2}{4} + \frac{(295)^2}{2} + \frac{(515)^2}{3} = 245{,}235.41$$

$$\Sigma\Sigma Y_{ij}^2 = 246{,}100$$

$$\sum\sum Y_{ij}^2 - \frac{T_{Y++}^2}{N} = 5{,}266.7$$

$$\sum \left(\frac{T_{Yi+}^2}{n_i}\right) - \frac{T_{Y++}^2}{N} = 4{,}402.1$$

$$b^2 \left[\sum\sum X_{ij}^2 - \frac{(\Sigma\Sigma X_{ij})^2}{N}\right] = (5.028)(171.67) = 4{,}340.0$$

11-6. Extensions of Regression Problems

Extensions of the theory and applications of regression exist for two important types of problems. The first of these considers cases where the regression curve of Y on X is not a straight line, and the second considers cases where there are two or more independent (or fixed) variables and we are interested in the mean Y values of all individuals who have certain fixed values for the several independent variables.

An example of the first type of problem is one where we know that the regression curve of Y on X has for its equation

$$\mu_{y \cdot x} = A + BX + CX^2$$

Here A, B, and C are parameters whose values are to be estimated from the sample. Graphically this regression curve is a parabola.

An example of the second type is the case of a variable Y whose mean value is given in terms of the values of two other variables X and Z as

$$\mu_{y \cdot xz} = A + BX + CZ$$

Here A, B, and C are parameters to be estimated from the sample. The sample consists of N sets of three numbers each, i.e., one X, one Y, and one Z measurement on each individual in the sample. Graphically the regression is a plane in three dimensions.

We shall not give numerical examples or formulas to be used in estimating parameters for these extensions. Students applying statistics at a reasonably advanced level in almost any field of study will see or use regression applications of this type, and reference should be made to advanced statistics texts in subject-matter fields.

11-7. Correlation Problems

In a correlation problem we sample from a population, observing two measurements on each individual in the sample. This contrasts with a purely regression problem, where the sample is chosen with preassigned

X values. A large part of the classical study of this subject is based upon the assumption that the distribution of values (X,Y) is a "two-variable normal" distribution. In appearance this distribution surface is bell-shaped. The distribution of Y values for any fixed X is normal, and the distribution of X values for any fixed Y is also normal. The regression curve of Y on X and the regression curve of X on Y are both straight lines with *homoscedasticity* (constant variance) for both X and Y variables. The regression lines intersect at a point which has as its X coordinate μ_x, the mean of the X measurements of all individuals in the population, and as its Y coordinate μ_y, the mean of the Y values of all individuals in the population. Figure 11-4 illustrates such a distribution surface.

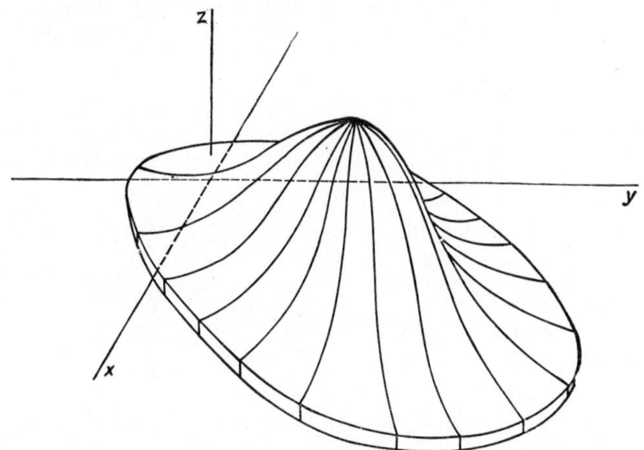

FIG. 11-4. Height-weight frequency distribution.

We shall write the equation of the regression line of Y on X in the form

$$\frac{\mu_{y \cdot x} - \mu_y}{\sigma_y} = \rho \frac{X - \mu_x}{\sigma_x} \tag{10}$$

Here, σ_y and σ_x are the standard deviations of all the Y and X measurements, respectively, in the population. ρ is defined as the population *correlation coefficient* and is equal to

$$\rho = \sqrt{BB'}$$

where B = regression coefficient from regression line of Y on X
B' = regression coefficient from regression line of X on Y

The equation of the regression line of X on Y is

$$\frac{\mu_{x \cdot y} - \mu_x}{\sigma_x} = \rho \frac{Y - \mu_y}{\sigma_y} \tag{11}$$

Equation (10) is satisfied by the values $X = \mu_x$ and $\mu_{y \cdot x} = \mu_y$, and the line goes through the point which has the mean X and the mean Y for its coordinates. Similarly the regression of X on Y goes through the same point. The lines coincide only if $\rho = \pm 1$.

The population values are estimated by sample values as follows: for μ_x use $\bar{X}$, for μ_y use $\bar{Y}$, for σ_x use s_x, for σ_y use s_y, for ρ use the sample correlation coefficient r defined by

$$r = b\frac{s_x}{s_y} \qquad \text{or} \qquad r = \sqrt{bb'}$$

where b is the estimate of B defined on page 191 and b' is the estimate of B' found by interchanging the X and Y values in the formula for b.

Figure 11-6 shows a scatter diagram with the two estimated regression lines drawn.

Equations (10) and (11) with the sample values substituted for the parameters are the same as those obtained by estimating the two regression lines separately by the methods of Sec. 11-3. One advantage of a correlation situation is that it allows us to estimate both equations from one sample. A serious disadvantage is the rare occurrence of populations which have bivariate normal distributions, i.e., populations having both the distribution of Y values for given X and the distribution of X values for given Y normal. Another disadvantage lies in the sampling procedure, which requires that neither variable be controlled.

Test for Independence. If the assumptions of normality are satisfied, it is possible to use the observed value of r to test for independence in the following way: If the two variables are independent, the regression curves are horizontal and vertical straight lines. This implies that the parameter ρ is equal to zero. If r, which is an estimate of ρ, is close to zero, we shall say that there is not sufficient reason to doubt the independence, while if r is far from zero, we shall reject the hypothesis that the two variables are independent. Table A-30a gives several percentiles of the sampling distribution of r under the assumption that X and Y have independent normal distributions. For example, if the observed r in a sample of 50 observations is larger than .279 or less than $-.279$, we should reject the hypothesis that $\rho = 0$ at the 5 per cent level of significance. For regression problems the hypothesis of $B = 0$ can be tested by the t test as illustrated in Sec. 11-4. This can also be done in correlation problems.

Confidence Interval for ρ. Table A-30a should be used only to test the hypothesis that $\rho = 0$ and should not be used to test either the hypothesis that ρ equals some number not zero or the hypothesis that two correlation coefficients are equal. For these hypotheses we can use the variable $\mathbf{z} = .5 \ln \frac{1+r}{1-r}$, which has a nearly normal sampling distribution with mean approximately $.5 \ln \frac{1+\rho}{1-\rho}$ and standard deviation approximately $1/\sqrt{N-3}$. In many practical problems it is more informative to deal with the regression coefficients in the manner previously studied. Values of $.5 \ln \frac{1+r}{1-r}$ are given in Table A-30*b*.

If a two-sided test with $\alpha = .05$ or if .95 confidence limits are desired, the chart in Table A-27 may be used in place of this approximation.

Example. Suppose for a sample of $N = 25$ observations we observe $r = .2$. To use the approximation, we refer to Table A-30*b* to find $z = .20273$. The standard deviation is $1/\sqrt{N-3} = 1/\sqrt{22} = .213$; so we may say with 95 per cent confidence that $.5 \ln \frac{1+\rho}{1-\rho}$ is between $.203 - 1.96(.213) = -.214$ and $.203 + 1.96(.213) = .620$. Using the table in reverse, we find corresponding to $-.214$ and $.620$ the limits $-.211$ and $.551$ for ρ. To solve the same problem by use of Table A-27, we enter the chart with $r = .2$ and read the heights of the two $N = 25$ curves above $r = .2$ on the horizontal scale as $\rho_1 = -.21$ and $\rho_2 = +.54$. These two numbers are 95 per cent confidence limits for the population parameter ρ and differ little from those obtained from the approximation. A test of any hypothetical value of ρ can be made by either method. In this example any hypothetical ρ between $-.21$ and $+.54$ would be accepted at the 5 per cent level of significance.

11-8. Computation Using a Frequency Table

Table 11-3 illustrates data arranged in a two-variable frequency table. This frequency table has heights recorded along the horizontal axis and

TABLE 11-3. HEIGHT-WEIGHT FREQUENCY DISTRIBUTION

Y variable (weight, lb)	*X* variable (height, in.)							
	60	62	64	66	68	70	72	74
230					1		1	3
220						4	4	3
210					5	1	2	1
200		2	1	3	9	1	7	1
190		1	3	8	16	3	5	
180		1	5	8	15	12	1	
170		2	8	18	26	8	1	
160			19	40	20	4		
150		5	15	26	9	2		
140	1	4	6	5	1			
130	2	3	1	1				
120	1	1						

weights on the vertical axis, and the frequencies of observations are recorded. The particular data correspond to the points on the scatter diagram in Fig. 11-5. It is customary to denote measurements along the horizontal axis as X and measurements along the vertical axis as Y. In correlation problems either variable may be considered as the independent variable. Figure 11-6 shows the same scatter diagram with the two estimated regression lines.

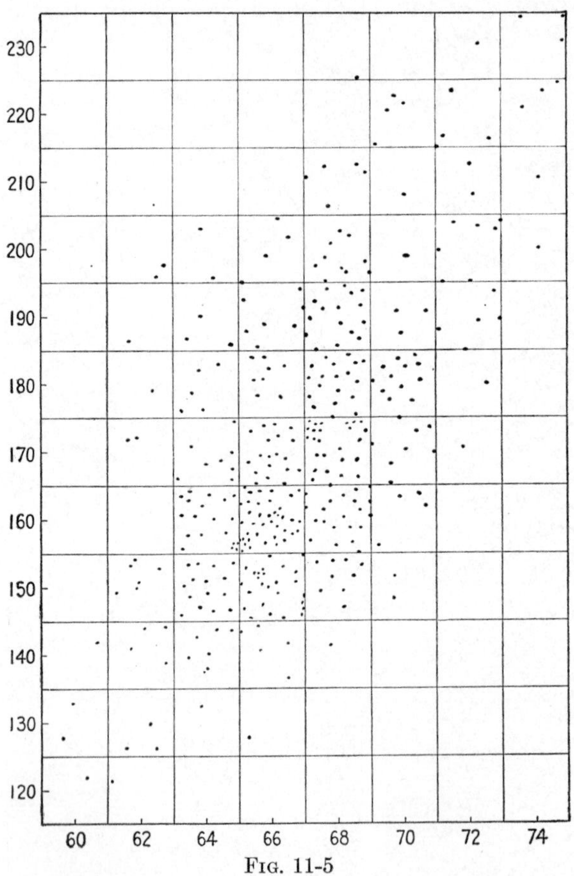

FIG. 11-5

Computations may be carried out in the manner illustrated in Table 11-4. The numbers in the column denoted by $Y\Sigma X$ are obtained by adding the X values in each row and multiplying by the Y for that row. Thus for the first row

$$\Sigma X = 68 + 72 + 3(74) = 362 \qquad \text{and} \qquad Y\Sigma X = 230 \times 362 = 83{,}260$$

The sum of these $Y\Sigma X$ is ΣXY, which is used in the computation of b and

r. As a check of this number we also find ΣY for each column and then $X\Sigma Y$. The sum of these terms also gives ΣXY.

If the mid-points for X are equally spaced and if the mid-points for Y are equally spaced, then the values of the mid-points for both X and Y may be replaced by the numbers 0, 1, 2, 3, ... The value of r obtained by using these coded numbers will be exactly the same as that

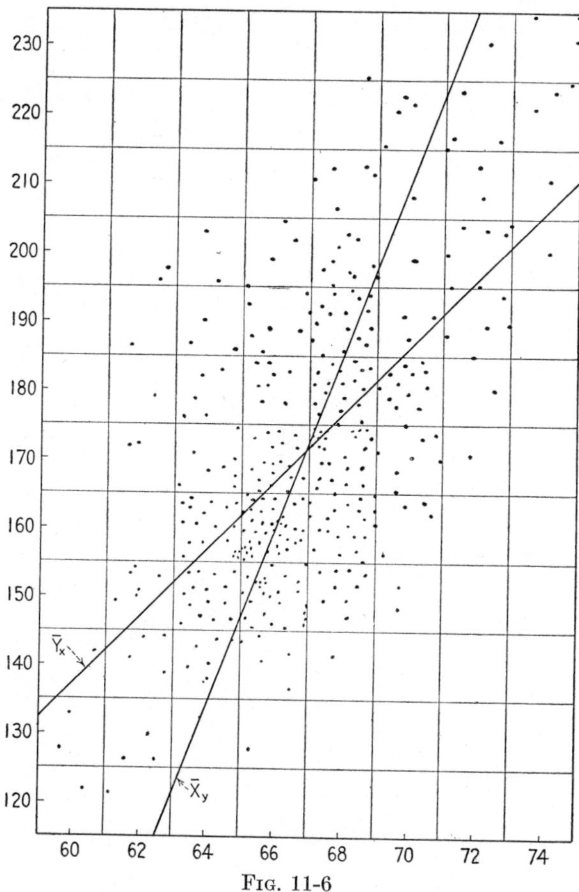

FIG. 11-6

found by using the actual values for the mid-points. The value of s_x found with the coded numbers must be multiplied by the length of the X interval, and similarly the coded s_y must be multiplied by the length of the Y interval. The coded b must be multiplied by the length of the Y class interval and divided by the length of the X class interval. Coding is especially valuable if lengthy computation must be carried out without the use of computing machines.

TABLE 11-4

Y \ X	60	62	64	66	68	70	72	74	f_y	ΣX_i	$Y\Sigma X$
230					1		1	3	5	362	83,260
220						4	4	3	11	790	173,800
210					5	1	2	1	9	628	131,880
200		2	1	3	9	1	7	1	24	1,646	329,200
190		1	3	8	16	3	5		36	2,440	463,600
180		1	5	8	15	12	1		42	2,842	511,560
170		2	8	18	26	8	1		63	4,224	718,080
160			19	40	20	4			83	5,496	879,360
150		5	15	26	9	2			57	3,738	560,700
140	1	4	6	5	1				17	1,090	152,600
130	2	3	1	1					7	436	56,680
120	1	1							2	122	14,640
f_x	4	19	58	109	102	35	21	8	356		4,075,360
ΣY	520	2,930	9,290	17,750	17,930	6,320	4,230	1,760			
$X\Sigma Y$	31,200	181,660	594,560	1,171,500	1,219,240	442,400	304,560	130,240	4,075,360		

Y	f_y	Yf_y	Y^2f_y
230	5	1,150	264,500
220	11	2,420	532,400
210	9	1,890	396,900
200	24	4,800	960,000
190	36	6,840	1,299,600
180	42	7,560	1,360,800
170	63	10,710	1,820,700
160	83	13,280	2,124,800
150	57	8,550	1,282,500
140	17	2,380	333,200
130	7	910	118,300
120	2	240	28,800
	356	60,730	10,522,500

X	f_x	Xf_x	X^2f_x
74	8	592	43,808
72	21	1,512	108,864
70	35	2,450	171,500
68	102	6,936	471,648
66	109	7,194	474,804
64	58	3,712	237,568
62	19	1,178	73,036
60	4	240	14,400
	356	23,814	1,595,628

$$\bar{Y} = \frac{60{,}730}{356} = 170.59 \qquad \bar{X} = \frac{23{,}814}{356} = 66.89$$

$$s_y^2 = \frac{10{,}522{,}500 - \dfrac{(60{,}730)^2}{356}}{355} = 457.9 \qquad s_x^2 = \frac{1{,}595{,}628 - \dfrac{(23{,}814)^2}{356}}{355} = \frac{2{,}632}{355} = 7.41$$

$$s_y = 21.40 \qquad s_x = 2.72$$

$$b = \frac{4{,}075{,}360 - \dfrac{23{,}814 \times 60{,}730}{356}}{2{,}632} = 4.913$$

$$s_{y \cdot x}^2 = \tfrac{355}{354}[457.9 - (4.913)^2(7.41)] = 280$$

$$r = \frac{(4.913)(2.72)}{21.40} = .624$$

GLOSSARY

correlation
homoscedasticity
independence
least squares
regression
scatter diagram
standard error of estimate

DISCUSSION QUESTIONS

1. What are some methods of graphically representing data for two variables?

2. Suppose a school class has an examination at the beginning and at the end of the school year. What is meant by "regression of final grades on beginning grades"? What is meant by "regression of beginning grades on final grades"? Which of these would be more useful in practice? Might these regressions coincide?

3. What "estimate" might be referred to in the term standard error of estimate? Is the standard error of estimate a parameter or a statistic?

4. What is the meaning of a point on a sample regression line?

5. Is the regression in the population always a straight line? If not, give an example of a population where it is not.

6. What assumptions are made about the population for the applications of the procedures in this chapter?

7. Describe a sampling experiment to illustrate correlation.

8. Explain the difference between regression and correlation problems. Can a correlation problem also be a regression problem? Can a regression problem also be a correlation problem?

9. Label the following examples as regression- or correlation-type problems. Discuss methods of obtaining a sample and procedures of analysis in each case. Explain the interpretation of possible results.

It is desired to study:

(*a*) The connection between IQ and weight of fifteen-year-old girls.

(*b*) The connection between the velocity of the Willamette River and its depth at various points.

(*c*) The connection between the amount of winter snow and the barley yield for some locality.

(*d*) The connection between tensile strength and hardness of aluminum.

(*e*) The connection between milk production and number of hours of light (either sunlight or artificial).

(*f*) The connection between the size of brains and success in life.

(*g*) The effect of an antihistamine drug upon length of time it takes to recover from colds.

(*h*) The effect upon the size of fish of dumping waste material from mills into a river.

(*i*) The relation between age and weight of trout.

(*j*) The relationship between a student's financial status and the amount of "dating."

(*k*) The connection between city size and amount of crime.

(*l*) The relationship between the degree of body consciousness of an individual and the elapsed time between hospital discharge and the recurrence of active tuberculosis.

PROBLEMS

1. It is believed that the mean yield of wheat per acre plotted against the number of pounds per acre of a nitrogen fertilizer would be approximately a straight line for the amount of fertilizer applied. A sample of 82 acres of wheat has been treated with varying amounts of fertilizer and the yields recorded. Find $\bar{X}$, $\bar{Y}$, s_x, s_y, b, $s_{y.x}$. Write the equation of the estimated regression line for yield on fertilizer. Test for linearity of regression.

Yield	Fertilizer					
	50	60	70	80	90	100
31–35				2	6	3
26–30			5	12	7	2
21–25		4	8	8	6	
16–20		2	7		1	
11–15	1	3				
6–10	3	1				
1–5	1					
Total.....	5	10	20	22	20	5

2. In the tabulation are quantities X, the body weight in kilograms, and Y, the blood volume in cubic centimeters, for goats.

X	Y	X	Y	X	Y	X	Y	X	Y
34	2,370	21	1,480	38	2,980	18	1,070	35	2,410
28	2,100	39	2,450	30	2,020	40	2,300	38	2,900
19	1,120	37	2,560	26	1,710	66	4,230	21	1,580
41	2,810	23	1,550	19	1,240	34	2,440	52	3,600
21	1,500	17	1,100	60	3,990	16	1,050	28	1,850
20	1,660	48	3,550	45	2,940	30	2,360	45	3,010

(*a*) Make a scatter diagram for the data.
(*b*) Find $\bar{X}$, $\bar{Y}$, s_x, s_y, r, $s_{y \cdot x}$, and the slopes of the two regression lines.
(*c*) Draw the estimated regression lines on the scatter diagram.
(*d*) Estimate the mean Y for $X = 50$. How close to the true mean Y for $X = 50$ can you state such an estimate to be with 95 per cent confidence?

3. Measurements were taken of the ability of rats to run a maze before (X) and after (Y) a stimulus. In a sample of 300 rats it was found that $\bar{X} = 16.0$, $\bar{Y} = 12.8$, $s_x^2 = 4.0$, $s_y^2 = 3.7$, $r = .4$.
(*a*) Draw the estimated regression line of Y on X.
(*b*) Estimate the mean Y for $X = 17.0$.
(*c*) What are 95 per cent confidence limits for this estimate?
(*d*) If a rat has $X = 17$, estimate by a 90 per cent interval his Y value.

4. The data on page 207 are measurements of students' ability, first by an IQ examination and second by an achievement test in a general science course. Let X be the result of the IQ test and Y the result of the achievement test. Make a scatter diagram to represent the observations. Collect the data into a frequency table, using intervals of 7 for the X measurements and intervals of 5 for the Y measurements. Use values of $X = 100$ and $Y = 50$ as mid-points of intervals. The interval corresponding to $X = 100$ extends from 96.5 to 103.5, and the interval for $Y = 50$ extends from 47.5 to 52.5, etc.

IQ	*Achievement*	*IQ*	*Achievement*
100	49	104	45
117	47	95	46
98	69	117	68
87	47	101	47
106	45	108	45
134	55	121	55
77	72	106	73
107	59	114	60
125	27	70	30
105	50	121	50
89	72	128	72
96	45	106	46
122	66	126	67
130	63	114	62
116	43	109	44
101	44	94	43
92	50	115	50
120	60	92	31
80	31	125	53
117	55	120	64
93	50	107	43
90	51	121	75
106	63	90	40
126	60	132	80
132	71	116	55
84	58	137	73
72	34	113	48
77	26	110	41
90	39	114	29
111	75	112	61
125	67	96	38
100	68	105	76
136	80	117	66
106	50	109	66
105	47	122	75
95	46	107	59
126	67	80	54
111	66	123	57
121	59	116	42
106	49	102	36
134	78	119	68
125	39	93	34
140	66	102	32
137	69	100	61
142	68	91	26
130	71	104	60
120	59	114	70
97	50	79	58
100	47	110	61
80	51	92	27

(a) Find $\bar{X}$, $\bar{Y}$, s_x, s_y, r and the slopes of the two estimated regression lines.

(b) Test the hypothesis: $\rho = 0$.

(c) Estimate $\mu_{y\cdot 90}$ and $\mu_{x\cdot 60}$ by 95 per cent confidence intervals.

5. The data in the table give X, blood hemoglobin in per cent of normal, and Y, red blood cells in millions per cubic millimeter, for dogs.

X	Y	X	Y	X	Y	X	Y	X	Y
93	7.3	94	6.7	112	7.5	96	7.8	110	7.7
96	6.5	96	6.7	81	6.4	99	7.5	61	4.6
108	7.7	111	8.6	102	6.6	100	7.2	96	6.6
86	5.4	104	7.5	92	6.8	93	7.4	101	6.8
92	6.7	84	7.2	94	7.8	118	8.4	79	6.3
80	5.1	80	6.5	80	6.4	98	7.0	109	7.5
96	7.0	70	5.8	90	6.6	62	6.0	101	6.9
117	8.5	92	7.4	111	7.8	86	6.7	100	7.5
95	7.8	94	6.8	98	6.3	98	7.5	80	6.0

(a) Make a scatter diagram for the data.

(b) Find $\bar{X}$, $\bar{Y}$, s_x, s_y, r, $s_{y\cdot x}$ and the slopes of the two regression lines.

(c) Plot the regression lines on the scatter diagram.

(d) Compute a tolerance interval which has chance .10 of covering 50 per cent of the population.

CHAPTER 12

ANALYSIS OF COVARIANCE

In the two-variable-of-classification problem treated in Chap. 10 by analysis-of-variance methods a test for the effect of one variable was made, separated from the effect of the second variable. The second variable was represented by several categories. If the second variable represents an actual measurement or score for each individual, we can again test for the effect of the first variable, separated from the effects of the second variable. The method of analysis to be presented is called the analysis of covariance. The second variable is often referred to as a "control" variable.

If we wish to compare the effects of different feeds on the weight of hogs, a measurement of the weight of each hog before the experiment would be valuable as a control. If we wish to say that food mixture A is the best, we should be able to state that the extra weight of the group fed by mixture A was not largely the result of the original weights. Even if the original weights are comparable, it is often impossible to have individuals in the experiment maintain equal amounts of intake of the particular diets. The related variable of total intake could be measured and taken into account in comparing the diets.

In an experiment designed to study the results of a program to increase the spelling ability of four classes of students we measure the spelling ability, Y, of each student at the end of the program and introduce the original spelling ability, X, for each student as a control variable. We may study the differences in the effectiveness for the four classes with the use of the Y variable, "controlled" or "adjusted" for the X variable.

The analysis-of-variance procedure for difference in means was based on the separation of a total sum of squares into several portions. If the mean square for means was significantly large, we rejected the hypothesis of equal means. The analysis-of-covariance procedure also leads to a test for difference in means by separation of a sum of squares into several portions. In this case we test for a difference in means of "residuals." The residuals are the differences of the actual observations and a regression quantity based on the associated second variable. The definition of the test procedure is developed in the following sections.

Most of this chapter deals with a single-variable-of-classification problem where we have samples from a fixed number of populations.

12-1. Statement of the Problem

For a single-variable-of-classification problem there are k populations. Random samples of sizes n_i are chosen from the respective populations. The sample from the ith population will be in the form (X_{i1}, Y_{i1}), (X_{i2}, Y_{i2}), . . . , (X_{in_i}, Y_{in_i}), where the first subscript indicates the population and the second subscript indicates the particular individual from that population. Data in this form are illustrated in Table 12-1 with $k = 3$, $n_1 = n_2 = n_3 = 4$, and a numerical example is given in Table 12-2. This section deals with the general principle behind the analysis, and later sections give the details of the numerical analysis.

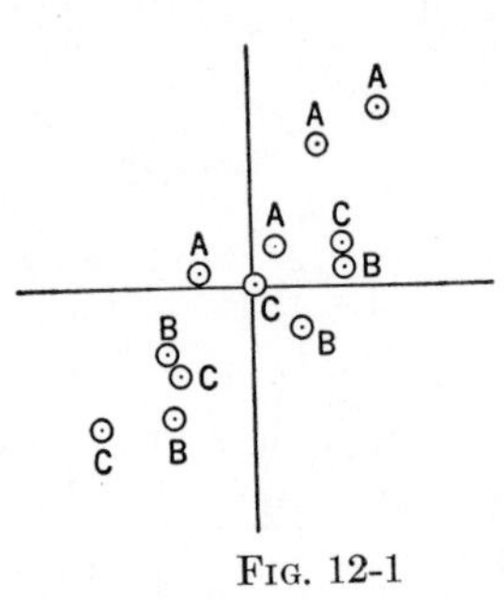

FIG. 12-1

Suppose the observations are plotted on X and Y coordinates about the grand mean. That is, we plot the deviations from $\bar{X}_{..}$ and $\bar{Y}_{..}$ as in Fig. 12-1, where the points representing the pairs of values (X,Y) in the first treatment are designated by A, those in the second by B, and those in the third by C. Using the methods of Chap. 11, we may compute the

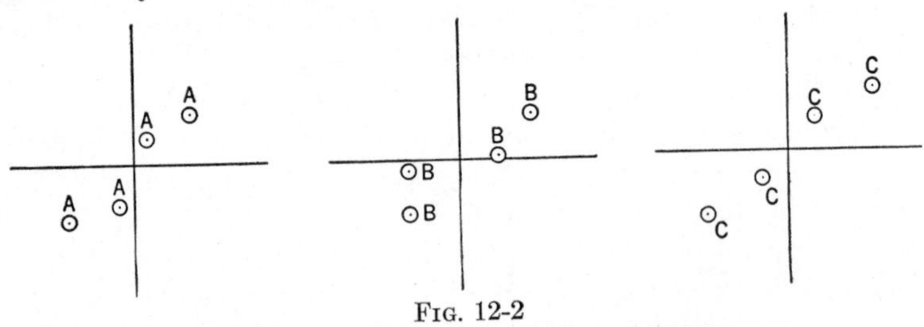

FIG. 12-2

regression line of Y on X for these points. Designate this regression coefficient by b_t and the variance of deviations from this regression line by $(s_{y \cdot x}^2)_t$, where t represents *total*. Differences between the samples as well as differences within each sample will affect the size of $(s_{y \cdot x}^2)_t$.

We next consider the three groups of values plotted about their own means (we plot deviations from $\bar{X}_{i.}$ and $\bar{Y}_{i.}$) as in Fig. 12-2 and then superimpose these figures into a single figure as in Fig. 12-3. We compute a regression line and variance about the regression line for the points as plotted in Fig. 12-3. Denote this *within* regression coefficient by b_w and the variance by $(s_{y \cdot x}^2)_w$.

A regression line gives the mean Y for different values of X. If in each of the three populations the regression lines have the same slope, then b_w

is an estimate of this slope and $(s_{y \cdot x}^2)_w$ is an estimate of the variance about the regression line in each of the populations.

We expect the variation about the regression line in Fig. 12-3 to be less than in Fig. 12-1 since the means were made to coincide. However, if the dispersion $(s_{y \cdot x}^2)_w$ for Fig. 12-3 is significantly smaller than the dispersion $(s_{y \cdot x}^2)_t$ for Fig. 12-1, we shall conclude that the procedure of bringing all the means together has had a significant effect on the data and state that there is a difference in the Y means not explained by the X measurements.

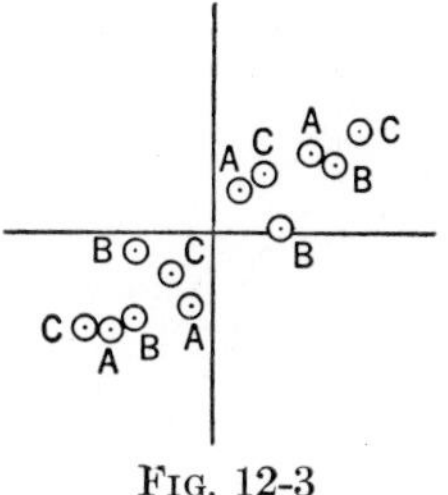

FIG. 12-3

Of course, it is possible that this significant reduction in sum of squares of deviations might occur if the X variable is not taken into account or if the regression coefficient is near zero, but in those cases this means only that the X variable is not important or that the differences in Y were so pronounced that this refinement in technique is not necessary.

TABLE 12-1

	Category								
	A		*B*		*C*				
	X_{11}	Y_{11}	X_{21}	Y_{21}	X_{31}	Y_{31}			
	X_{12}	Y_{12}	X_{22}	Y_{22}	X_{32}	Y_{32}			
	X_{13}	Y_{13}	X_{23}	Y_{23}	X_{33}	Y_{33}			
	X_{14}	Y_{14}	X_{24}	Y_{24}	X_{34}	Y_{34}			
Total	$T_{X_{1+}}$	$T_{Y_{1+}}$	$T_{X_{2+}}$	$T_{Y_{2+}}$	$T_{X_{3+}}$	$T_{Y_{3+}}$	$T_{X_{++}}$	$T_{Y_{++}}$	Grand total
Mean	$\bar{X}_{1\cdot}$	$\bar{Y}_{1\cdot}$	$\bar{X}_{2\cdot}$	$\bar{Y}_{2\cdot}$	$\bar{X}_{3\cdot}$	$\bar{Y}_{3\cdot}$	$\bar{X}_{\cdot\cdot}$	$\bar{Y}_{\cdot\cdot}$	Grand mean

12-2. Computation and Conclusion

First a relation for sums of products similar to that for sums of squares will be shown, then altered into computing form, and then the computing form for the dispersion about a regression line will be given. The expression for sums of products is

$$\sum_i \sum_j (X_{ij} - \bar{X}_{\cdot\cdot})(Y_{ij} - \bar{Y}_{\cdot\cdot})$$
$$= \sum_i \sum_j (X_{ij} - \bar{X}_{i\cdot})(Y_{ij} - \bar{Y}_{i\cdot}) + n \sum_i (\bar{X}_{i\cdot} - \bar{X}_{\cdot\cdot})(\bar{Y}_{i\cdot} - \bar{Y}_{\cdot\cdot})$$

where n is the number of observations in each of k groups. Any of these sums of products divided by their degrees of freedom is called a *covariance.*

1. The computing form for the quantity on the left, called the *total sum of products*, is

$$\sum\sum \mathbf{X}_{ij}\mathbf{Y}_{ij} - \frac{\mathbf{T}_{X_{++}}\mathbf{T}_{Y_{++}}}{\mathbf{nk}} \qquad \textbf{total sum of products}$$

2. The computing form for the first quantity on the right above, called the *within-groups sum of products*, is

$$\sum\sum \mathbf{X}_{ij}\mathbf{Y}_{ij} - \frac{\sum_i \mathbf{T}_{X_{i+}}\mathbf{T}_{Y_{i+}}}{\mathbf{n}} \qquad \textbf{within-groups sum of products}$$

3. The computing form for the second expression on the right above, called the *among-means*, or *among-groups, sum of products*, is

$$\frac{\sum_i \mathbf{T}_{X_{i+}}\mathbf{T}_{Y_{i+}}}{\mathbf{n}} - \frac{\mathbf{T}_{X_{++}}\mathbf{T}_{Y_{++}}}{\mathbf{nk}} \qquad \textbf{among-means sum of products}$$

The above computing forms can be verified algebraically in a manner similar to the derivation of the corresponding formulas for sums of squares. However, it can be seen from the computing forms that the first is the sum of the second and the third. Note that the computing forms for the sums of products are very similar to those for the sums of squares.

TABLE 12-2

	A		*B*		*C*			
	X	*Y*	*X*	*Y*	*X*	*Y*		
	3	10	4	12	1	6		
	2	8	3	12	2	5		
	1	8	3	10	3	8		
	2	11	5	13	1	7	$T_{X_{++}}$	$T_{Y_{++}}$
Total	8	37	15	47	7	26	30	110

The formulas shown thus far will be applied to the data in Table 12-2, and then the computations for dispersion about a regression line will be shown. The sums of products are

1. Total:

$$3(10) + 2(8) + \cdots + 1(7) - \frac{(30)(110)}{12} = 302 - 275 = 27$$

2. Among means:

$$\frac{8(37)}{4} + \frac{15(47)}{4} + \frac{7(26)}{4} - \frac{(30)(110)}{12} = 295.75 - 275 = 20.75$$

3. Within groups:

$$27 - 20.75 = 6.25$$

The computations for sums of squares on X and on Y are made as for the analysis of variance. The results are entered in Table 12-3, where

TABLE 12-3

	df	Σx^2	Σxy	Σy^2
Among means	2	9.5	20.75	55.17
Within groups	9	7.5	6.25	16.50
Total	11	17	27	71.67

$x = X - \bar{X}$ and $y = Y - \bar{Y}$. The computations on X and Y are given in Table 12-4. To find the sum of squares about a regression line, we

TABLE 12-4

	Σx^2	Σy^2
Total	$92 - \frac{(30)^2}{12} = 17$	$1{,}080 - \frac{(110)^2}{12} = 71.67$
Means	$\frac{338}{4} - \frac{(30)^2}{12} = 9.5$	$\frac{4{,}254}{4} - \frac{(110)^2}{12} = 55.17$
Within	$17 - 9.5 = 7.5$	$71.67 - 55.17 = 16.50$

compute the sum of squares of the residuals,

$$Y - \bar{Y}_X = Y - [\bar{Y} + b(X - \bar{X})]$$

since

$$\bar{Y}_X = \bar{Y} + b(X - \bar{X})$$

so that the sum of squares of residuals is

$$\Sigma(Y - \bar{Y}_X)^2 = \Sigma[Y - \bar{Y} - b(X - \bar{X})]^2$$

It will be more convenient to use $y = Y - \bar{Y}$ and $x = X - \bar{X}$. This relation then appears as follows:

$$\Sigma(Y - \bar{Y}_X)^2 = \Sigma(y - bx)^2 = \Sigma(y^2 - 2bxy + b^2x^2)$$
$$= \Sigma y^2 - 2b\Sigma xy + b^2\Sigma x^2$$

In this notation the slope b of the regression line is $b = (\Sigma xy/\Sigma x^2)$ and, substituting this into the above equation, we obtain

$$\sum (Y - \bar{Y}_X)^2 = \sum y^2 - 2\left(\frac{\Sigma xy}{\Sigma x^2}\right)\sum xy + \left(\frac{\Sigma xy}{\Sigma x^2}\right)^2 \sum x^2 = \sum y^2 - \frac{(\Sigma xy)^2}{\Sigma x^2}$$

The three summations in the final form of the above expression are given in Table 12-3. For the sum of squares about the regression line for "Total," we have then

$$71.67 - \frac{(27)^2}{17} = 28.79$$

and, for "Within groups,"

$$16.50 - \frac{(6.25)^2}{7.5} = 11.29$$

We now have estimates of the variances (dispersions) referred to at the beginning of this chapter—the sums of squares about the regression line with coefficient b_t and the line with coefficient b_w, 28.79 and 11.29, respectively. The dispersion about the line with coefficient b_t is the total dispersion of the Y about the grand mean $Y_{..}$, minus the variance due to the regression. Even though all samples are from the same population, the means will not be exactly equal. Therefore, this second value will always be less than the first. The reduction in sum of squares $28.79 - 11.29 = 17.50$ is attributable to the dispersion of the means. When all groups are from the same population the ratio of this last quantity (17.50) to the estimate of variance obtained from within groups (11.29) has as a sampling distribution the F distribution. The assumptions involved here will be discussed below. We can make a test of significance of difference in means with each measurement adjusted for measurement X. The complete computation can be indicated in an analysis-of-covariance table. Note that the use of an estimated regression coefficient to adjust our values used 1 degree of freedom, as does the use of an estimated value of the mean. The regression coefficients b_t and b_w were used for "Total" and for "Within," respectively, and therefore the degrees of freedom have been decreased by 1 in the last two lines of the table. y' is used to denote $Y - \bar{Y}_x$.

TABLE 12-5. ANALYSIS OF COVARIANCE

	df	Σx^2	Σxy	Σy^2	df	$\Sigma y'^2$	Mean square
Among means	2	9.5	20.75	55.17	2	17.50	8.75
Within groups	9	7.5	6.25	16.50	8	11.29	1.41
Total	11	17.0	27.00	71.67	10	28.79	

$$F = \frac{8.75}{1.41} = 6.2 \qquad F_{.95}(2,8) = 4.46$$

Here there is significance at the 5 per cent level for differences in means of the Y values among the groups after the Y values have been adjusted by the within-groups regression coefficient b_w. The test of significance of differences in the Y means not making use of the X values would give

$$F = \frac{55.17/2}{16.50/9} = \frac{27.58}{1.83} = 15.07 \qquad F_{.95}(2,9) = 4.26$$

The very large value for F obtained here can be accounted for by differences in the X values since when the Y values are adjusted for X the value of F is reduced to about the 5 per cent level.

To provide a more concrete example, suppose that the analysis of covariance in Table 12-5 reports the results of an experiment on three types of rations A, B, C. Four animals were given each ration, and X = food intake in pounds per day, Y = gain in ounces at the end of 1 week. The conclusions could be described as follows:

1. The three types of rations resulted in significantly different gains; $F = 15.07$, $F_{.95}(2,9) = 4.26$.

2. The three types of rations resulted in significantly different residual gains. The residual indicating a gain adjusted for the amount of food intake as given by the within-groups regression line

$$\bar{Y}_x = \bar{Y}_{i\cdot} + b_w(X - \bar{X}_{i\cdot})$$

For example, in group A the regression line is

$$\bar{Y}_x = \frac{37}{4} + \left(\frac{6.25}{7.5}\right)\left(X - \frac{8}{4}\right) = 9.25 + .833(X - 2)$$

and the first residual is $10 - [9.25 + .833(3 - 2)] = 10 - 10.083 = -.083$. The F ratio for this test is in Table 12-5; $F = 6.2$, $F_{.95}(2,8) = 4.46$. Therefore the residual gains are significantly different for the three rations. The F ratio for this test is smaller than for the test above.

It can be seen that in analyses of this type the first test could be significant and the second test not significant. We could then infer that the differences in weight gains for the different rations were largely due to the differences in food intake.

12-3. Hypothesis and Assumptions

The analysis-of-covariance test described above applies when it is known that the regression curves in the k populations are parallel straight lines. The hypothesis states that the parallel lines coincide, i.e., the populations have the same Y means when the same X is used for each population (Y means are equal after adjustment for X values). The population variances $\sigma_{y\cdot x}^2$ about the regression lines are assumed to be equal in each of the k populations. Tests of the hypothesis that the regression curve is a straight line and of the hypothesis that the regression lines are parallel are given in Sec. 12-5.

In order that the percentiles of the computed F statistic are as given in Table A-7 it is also assumed that within each population and for each X value the Y values are approximately normally distributed.

12-4. Extension to Other Problems

The analysis-of-covariance procedure has been extended in several ways:

1. The procedure can be developed for problems having several variables of classification, e.g., the two-way table with single or multiple observations as presented in Chap. 10, Analysis of Variance, and the Latin square.
2. The procedure can be developed for using several control variables to adjust the Y observations.
3. Curves other than straight lines may be used as regression curves.

The first extension is fairly straightforward; the second, however, involves multiple-regression methods.

12-5. Tests for the Validity of the Assumptions Underlying the Analysis of Covariance

In the analysis of variance for single variable of classification, we obtained two independent estimates of variance, (1) within groups, (2) among means. These were both estimates of the population σ^2 if the hypothesis is correct. In the analysis of covariance the population value for the variance about the regression line can be estimated in four independent ways. Comparisons of these estimates can be made to investigate departures from uniformity of various sorts. These estimates are obtained from sums of squares divided by their degrees of freedom. The four sums of squares will be denoted by S_1, S_2, S_3, S_4.

It will be convenient to denote the quantities in the covariance table by individual letters as in Table 12-6. The definitions of the quantities to

TABLE 12-6

	Σx^2	Σxy	Σy^2	$\Sigma y'^2$
Within each group (1)	C_{xx1}	C_{xy1}	C_{yy1}	C'_{yy1}
(2)	C_{xx2}	C_{xy2}	C_{yy2}	C'_{yy2}
.	.	.	.	.
.	.	.	.	.
.	.	.	.	.
(k)	C_{xxk}	C_{xyk}	C_{yyk}	C'_{yyk}
Among means	C_{xxm}	C_{xym}	C_{yym}	C'_{yym}
Within groups	C_{xxw}	C_{xyw}	C_{yyw}	C'_{yyw}
Total	C_{xxt}	C_{xyt}	C_{yyt}	C'_{yyt}

be computed are as follows:

C_{xx1}, C_{xx2}, etc., represent the computation $\Sigma X^2 - (\Sigma X)^2/n$ for the first, second, etc., groups. For example, for the data in Table 12-2, $C_{xx1} = 3^2 + 2^2 + 1^2 + 2^2 - 8^2/4 = 2.00$.

C_{xy1}, C_{xy2}, etc., represent the computation $\Sigma XY - (\Sigma X)(\Sigma Y)/n$ for the first, second, etc., groups. In the example,

$$C_{xy1} = 3(10) + 2(8) + 1(8) + 2(11) - \frac{8(37)}{4} = 2.00$$

C_{yy1}, C_{yy2}, etc., represent the computation $\Sigma Y^2 - (\Sigma Y)^2/n$ for the first, second, etc., groups. In the example,

$$C_{yy1} = 10^2 + 8^2 + 8^2 + 11^2 - \frac{(37)^2}{4} = 6.75$$

The quantities in the column headed $\Sigma y'^2$ are computed by the formula $\Sigma y^2 - (\Sigma xy)^2/\Sigma x^2$, using in every case the entries in the same line. For example, $C'_{yy1} = 6.75 - (2.00)^2/2.00 = 4.75$.

All entries in the last three lines are the same as entered in Table 12-5 except C'_{yym}, which is computed like the other C' quantities. For example, $C'_{yym} = 55.17 - (20.75)^2/9.5 = 9.85$. In the analysis-of-covariance table the quantity appearing in this position was computed as the difference $C'_{yyt} - C'_{yyw}$.

The completed table for the example of this chapter is given in Table

TABLE 12-7

	Σx^2	Σxy	Σy^2	$\Sigma y'^2$
Within each group (1)	2.00	2.00	6.75	4.75
(2)	2.75	2.75	4.75	2.00
(3)	2.75	1.50	5.00	4.18
Among means	9.50	20.75	55.17	9.85
Within groups	7.50	6.25	16.50	11.29
Total	17.00	27.00	71.67	28.79

12-7. The quantities S_1, S_2, S_3, S_4 are now defined as in Table 12-8 in terms of the C's. S_1 is the sum of squares within each group from the regression line in each group, totaled for all groups. S_2 measures the variation among regression coefficients of the different groups. S_3 is the sum of squares of deviations of the means from the regression line of the means. S_4 is the square of the difference between b_w and b_m multiplied by the appropriate factor to make it an estimate of variance. The quantities b_w and b_m are the regression coefficients obtained from the within and mean sums of squares, and $S_T = S_1 + S_2 + S_3 + S_4$.

For the example,

$$S_1 = 4.75 + 2.00 + 4.18 = 10.93$$
$$S_2 = 11.29 - 10.93 = .36$$
$$S_3 = 9.85$$
$$S_4 = 28.79 - 11.29 - 9.85 = 7.65$$
$$S_T = 28.79$$

These four estimates of variance can be used to investigate the various ways in which the relationship of X and Y may deviate more than would be expected by sampling fluctuation when the groups are all from the same normal population.

TABLE 12-8

Definition of S_i	df	Example	
		S_i	df
$S_1 = \Sigma C'_{yyi}$	$k(n-2)$	10.93	6
$S_2 = C'_{yyw} - S_1$	$k-1$	.36	2
$S_3 = C'_{yym}$	$k-2$	9.85	1
$S_4 = C'_{yyt} - C'_{yyw} - C'_{yym}$	1	7.65	1
$S_T = C'_{yyt}$	$nk-2$	28.79	10

1. As a test for difference in means as described earlier in this chapter:

$$F = \frac{\dfrac{S_3 + S_4}{k-1}}{\dfrac{S_1 + S_2}{k(n-1)-1}}$$

Example

$$F = \frac{17.50/2}{11.29/8} = 6.20$$

$$F_{.95}(2,8) = 4.46$$

2. As a test of whether one regression line can be used for all the observations:

$$F = \frac{\dfrac{S_2 + S_3 + S_4}{2(k-1)}}{\dfrac{S_1}{k(n-2)}}$$

Example

$$F = \frac{17.86/4}{10.93/6} = 2.45$$

$$F_{.95}(4,6) = 4.53$$

If this F ratio is significant, i.e., if a single regression line is not adequate, it may be of interest to see in what particular manner the data fail in this quality. These estimates can also be used for this purpose as follows:

(*a*) As a test of whether the slopes of the regression lines within the groups are the same:

$$F = \frac{\dfrac{S_2}{k-1}}{\dfrac{S_1}{k(n-2)}}$$

Example

$$F = \frac{.36/2}{10.93/6} = .10$$

$$F_{.95}(2,6) = 5.14$$

If the regression slopes within groups are not significantly different, we may use the estimates

(b) As a test of whether the regression for means is linear (assuming the slopes within the groups are the same):

$$F = \frac{\dfrac{S_3}{k-2}}{\dfrac{S_1 + S_2}{k(n-1) - 1}}$$

Example

$$F = \frac{9.85/1}{11.29/8} = 6.98$$

$$F_{.95}(1,8) = 5.32$$

If this is accepted, then the estimates may be used

(c) As a test of whether the regression coefficients b_w and b_m are the same (assuming that the regression slopes within groups are the same and that the regression for means is linear):

$$F = \frac{\dfrac{S_4}{1}}{\dfrac{S_1 + S_2}{k(n-1) - 1}}$$

Example

$$F = \frac{7.65/1}{11.29/8} = 5.42$$

$$F_{.95}(1,8) = 5.32$$

For the numerical example, the conclusions may be stated as follows: The first F ratio is the F ratio computed in Table 12-5, and the interpretation is given there. The second F ratio indicates that a single regression line may be used for all the observations. In this case the other F ratios need not be computed. The numerical results are given to illustrate their use.

GLOSSARY

"adjusted" values
covariance
regression of means
regression within groups

DISCUSSION QUESTIONS

1. State carefully what hypothesis is tested by the analysis-of-covariance technique. What assumptions are made before the F test is valid?

2. Could we fill in the $\Sigma y'^2$ for among means in the same manner as we did the other two rows? Why do we proceed as we do?

3. Define each term in the Glossary.

4. What advantage does the analysis of covariance have over the analysis of variance? Is it easier to take samples for the analysis of covariance than for the analysis of variance?

5. It is desired to compare the IQ's of the students in three schools. It is suspected that IQ is related to the student's grade point average (GPA). If samples of 12 students are taken from each school, should their IQ values be adjusted for their GPA by an analysis of covariance, or should an analysis of variance of their IQ's be performed directly?

6. Describe a sampling experiment to illustrate the technique of analysis of covariance.

7. Discuss the uses and advantages of analysis of covariance in an *experiment* and in a *survey*. Give several examples.

PROBLEMS

1. Complete the analysis of covariance in the table, comparing score Y on the final examination in a statistics course for three different classes. The variable X used to adjust this score is the GPA for each student. The data have been reduced for simplification to three classes of 16 students each.

Sum of squares for Y means	504
Total sum of squares for Y	13,813
Sum of squares for X means	.5864
Total sum of squares for X	8.296
Sum of products for means	17.19
Total sum of products	157.88

2. An experiment on gain in weight of rats resulted as shown in the table. X indicates the quantity of food and Y the gain in weight. Did the four rations produce different gains among the rats? Are the gains affected materially by quantity of food?

Group							
A		*B*		*C*		*D*	
X	*Y*	*X*	*Y*	*X*	*Y*	*X*	*Y*
96	98	109	64	179	71	127	72
108	102	125	86	132	84	100	54
94	102	85	51	163	71	151	109
128	108	82	72	143	62	116	93

CHAPTER 13

ENUMERATION STATISTICS

Previously we have dealt with measurements of certain variables. There are many problems where we are interested merely in counting the number of cases which fall in specified categories. For example, in tossing coins we count the number of heads in 20 tosses; in the study of genetics we count the number of progeny which inherit certain characteristics, e.g., hair color; in public-opinion polls we count the number of favorable votes in a sample; in acceptance sampling for quality control we count the number of defective items in a sample; in a study of performance we count the number passing or failing, etc. We frequently change a problem involving measurements to one where we count the number of occurrences by arbitrarily assigning certain measurements to each category. For example, we could measure the heights and count the number of cases between 60 inches and 65 inches, calling this the first category, etc. We do this, of course, in constructing any frequency table. The difference will be that we now forget the actual measurements and remember only the several categories and the number of observations falling into each.

One of our most useful tools will be a statistic called *chi square*, which, although different in form from that in Chap. 8, has a χ^2 distribution as given in Table A-6*a*. Other useful distributions are the binomial and Poisson distributions.

13-1. Chi Square

We shall suppose that there are k categories and that we have a random sample of N observations such that each observation must fall in one and only one category. We then count the *observed frequency* in each category and denote these frequencies by $f_1, f_2, \ldots, f_k$, where $\sum_{i=1}^{k} f_i = N$. We shall be interested in situations where there exists some *theoretical frequency* $F_1, F_2, \ldots, F_k$, for each category where $\sum_{i=1}^{k} F_i = N$, and we shall ask the question whether or not the observations disagree with the values

$F_1, F_2, \ldots, F_k$. That is, we wish to test the hypothesis that states the

TABLE 13-1

	Observed	Theoretical
1	f_1	F_1
2	f_2	F_2
.	.	.
.	.	.
.	.	.
k	f_k	F_k
Total.......	N	N

values of the theoretical frequencies. The statistic we shall use is

$$\chi^2 = \sum_{i=1}^{k} \frac{(f_i - F_i)^2}{F_i}$$

The sampling distribution of this χ^2 statistic is in approximately the form given in Table A-6*a*, i.e., a χ^2 distribution with $k - 1$ degrees of freedom. Thus, for example, if there are 10 categories, we have 9 degrees of freedom and the chance that χ^2 will be less than 3.33 is .05, the chance of χ^2 being less than 16.92 is .95, etc.

Notice that the total number of observations does not enter the χ^2 formula except as the total of all the f_i or the total of the F_i. In using the χ^2 table, reference is made only to the number of categories and not to the total number of observations. However, in order that the approximation of the distribution to that in Table A-6*a* be close, the sample size N must be sufficiently large so that none of the F_i's is less than 1 and not more than 20 per cent of the F_i's are less than 5.

The above discussion is an indication of the general nature of χ^2. Specialized examples will follow.

13-2. Single Classification

A single-classification problem is a problem where the theoretical proportion of cases in each category is specified in advance.

For example, in tossing a true coin we expect 50 per cent heads. The theoretical frequencies, therefore, in 140 tosses are 70 heads and 70 tails. If in 140 tosses we actually observe 60 heads and 80 tails, we compute

$$\chi^2 = \frac{(80 - 70)^2}{70} + \frac{(60 - 70)^2}{70} = \frac{100}{70} + \frac{100}{70} = 2.857$$

If the coin does have a 50 per cent chance of coming up heads, then χ^2 has (from Table A-6*a*, with 1 degree of freedom) a 99 per cent chance of being less than 6.63 and a 95 per cent chance of being less than 3.84. The observed value $\chi^2 = 2.857$ is not large enough to cause us to reject the hypothesis that the proportion of heads is .5, at the 5 per cent level of significance. It may be large enough to make us somewhat doubtful, and we might wish to toss the coin a greater number of times.

In the study of genetics it has been found that certain characteristics are inherited in a ratio 1:3. That is, in the long run, one-fourth of the progeny will have a given characteristic, and three-fourths will not. In an experiment in genetics, 1,981 fruit flies were found to have white eyes, while 7,712 flies had red eyes. If we wish to test the hypothesis that the ratio of the number of flies with white eyes to the number of flies with red eyes is 1:3, we have as theoretical frequencies one-fourth and three-fourths of the total, as in Table 13-2. This gives a χ^2 of

TABLE 13-2

	Observed	Theoretical
White	1,981	2,423.25
Red	7,712	7,269.75
	9,693	9,693.00

$$\frac{(1{,}981 - 2{,}423.25)^2}{2{,}423.25} + \frac{(7{,}712 - 7{,}269.75)^2}{7{,}269.75} = 107.6$$

This is much larger than any number in Table A-6*a* for 1 degree of freedom, and the theoretical ratio 1:3 would be rejected.

As another example from genetics we could consider the problem of crossing two types of peas. In one experiment Mendel counted the seeds of plants as shown in Table 13-3. The Mendelian theory of inheritance states that the frequencies should be in the ratios 9:3:3:1. That is, $\frac{9}{16}$ should be round and yellow, etc. The χ^2 statistic here has $4 - 1 = 3$ degrees of freedom. The theoretical frequency of round and yellow

TABLE 13-3

Description	Frequency		$f_i - F_i$	$(f_i - F_i)^2/F_i$
	Observed	Theoretical		
Round and yellow	315	312.75	2.25	.016
Wrinkled and yellow	101	104.25	−3 25	.101
Round and green	108	104.25	3.75	.135
Wrinkled and green	32	34.75	−2.75	.218
Total	556	556.00	......	.470

peas is $\frac{9}{16} \times 556 = 312.75$, $\frac{3}{16} \times 556 = 104.25$, etc. Here $\chi^2 = .470$; the 5 per cent critical value is 7.81, and so we do not have sufficient reason to reject the hypothesis.

13-3. Two-way Classification, Independence

In this type of problem the observations are classified by two characteristics. For example, hair and eye color might be the classifications and the observed results recorded as in Table 13-4. If the theoretical

TABLE 13-4

Eye color	Light hair	Dark hair	Total
Blue...............	32	12	44
Brown..............	14	22	36
Other..............	6	9	15
Total.............	52	43	95

frequencies for the six categories are given, the problem would be a one-variable-of-classification problem. The last example in Sec. 13-2 is not a two-way-classification problem because the four theoretical proportions have been stated.

We shall examine a method to test the hypothesis that the two characteristics are *independent*. Here the term independent has the same meaning as in Chap. 11, viz., the distribution of one characteristic should be the same regardless of the other characteristic. For example, if eye color and hair color are independent, then the proportion of the blue-eyed people having light-colored hair should be the same as the proportion of the brown-eyed people having light hair, etc. These theoretical proportions are in the population, not in the sample. Our procedure will be to examine the proportions in the sample and to determine whether or not they are significantly different. If they are significantly different, we shall reject the hypothesis that the two characteristics are independent, while if they are not significantly different, we say that the sample does not contradict the hypothesis.

The statistic we use to compare the proportions is a χ^2 statistic obtained in the following manner: First we record the number of observations that fall into each category. In Table 13-4 there are 32 people having blue eyes and light hair, etc. Next we look at each characteristic separately and record the total number of observations as before. Here there are 52 people with light hair, 43 with dark, 44 people with blue eyes, etc. We find theoretical frequencies by using these "marginal" totals. We note that 52 out of 95 people had light hair. If the characteristics are independent, we should expect to find the same proportion of light-haired people among those who have blue eyes. Since we observe 44 people with blue eyes, we should expect to find that $\frac{52}{95} \times 44 = 24.1$ of these people have light hair. Also, we should expect $\frac{43}{95} \times 44 = 19.9$ of them to have dark hair. These two numbers, of course, add to 44, and the second could have been found by subtracting the first from 44. Similarly, the theoretical frequency of people with brown eyes and light hair is $\frac{52}{95} \times 36 = 19.7$. Table 13-5 shows both the observed and the theoretical frequencies. The theoretical frequencies are asterisked. The χ^2 statistic is computed from the six categories in exactly the same fashion as before. The distribution of this statistic can be shown to be a χ^2 distribution, given in Table A-6*a*, with, if r denotes the number of rows and c the number of columns, $(r - 1)(c - 1)$ degrees of freedom. Thus in this example $(3 - 1)(2 - 1) = 2$ degrees of freedom. Here

TABLE 13-5

Eye color	Hair color		Total
	Light	Dark	
Blue	32 (24.1*)	12 (19.9*)	44
Brown	14 (19.7*)	22 (16.3*)	36
Other	6 (8.2*)	9 (6.8*)	15
Total	52	43	95

$$\chi^2 = \frac{(7.9)^2}{24.1} + \frac{(-7.9)^2}{19.9} + \frac{(-5.7)^2}{19.7} + \frac{(5.7)^2}{16.3} + \frac{(-2.2)^2}{8.2} + \frac{(2.2)^2}{6.8}$$
$$= 2.59 + 3.14 + 1.65 + 1.99 + .59 + .71 = 10.67$$

For 2 degrees of freedom $\chi_{.95}^2 = 5.99$. The hypothesis of independence is rejected at the 5 per cent level of significance. The χ^2 approximation will be adequate if the minimum theoretical frequency is 2 or if no more than 20 per cent of the theoretical frequencies are less than 5 with a minimum of 1.

Two-way-classification tables of this type are frequently called *contingency tables.* If the totals for rows (or columns) are specified in advance, the test is called a test of *homogeneity.* We are actually testing that the various columns (or rows) have the same proportions of individuals in the various categories. The procedure is exactly the same as in the test of independence.

Two-by-Two Tables. In general the test for independence can be carried out as above. In the case where there are only two rows and two columns the computing forms can be simplified. Also in the case of 1 degree of freedom, the approximation of the χ^2 distribution can be markedly improved by reducing the absolute value of each difference by

.5 before it is squared. In particular for a 2×2 table we can include this correction and simplify the χ^2 statistic to the formula below the table. The minimum theoretical frequency for the 2×2 table should not be less than 5.

Suppose we have two rows and two columns and have observed frequencies a, b, c, d, as in Table 13-6. Then the χ^2 statistic, corrected as

TABLE 13-6

	I	II	Total
1	a	b	$a + b$
2	c	d	$c + d$
Total.......	$a + c$	$b + d$	$a + b + c + d = N$

above, used in the test of independence can be written in the form

$$\chi^2 = \frac{(|ad - bc| - \frac{1}{2}N)^2 N}{(a + b)(a + c)(b + d)(c + d)}$$

This is somewhat easier to compute since only one division is necessary.

Example. Suppose that in a public-opinion survey answers to the questions

1. Do you drink beer?
2. Are you in favor of local option on the sale of liquor?

were as shown in the tabulation. For 1 degree of freedom $\chi_{.95}^2 = 3.84$,

Question 2	Question 1: Yes	No	Total
Yes..........	37	20	57
No...........	15	6	21
Total......	52	26	78

$$\chi^2 = \frac{(|222 - 300| - 39)^2 \times 78}{52 \times 26 \times 57 \times 21} = \frac{(78 - 39)^2 \times 78}{52 \times 26 \times 57 \times 21} = \frac{118{,}638}{1{,}618{,}344} = .073$$

and the hypothesis of independence is accepted, i.e., we do not have sufficient reason to say that opinion on local option is dependent on whether or not an individual drinks beer.

13-4. Test for Goodness of Fit

This term *goodness of fit* refers to the comparison of some observed sample distribution with a theoretical frequency distribution. Actually all the tests for which we are using χ^2 are problems of this type. In this section we shall make the comparison of a sample distribution with a normal distribution. That is, we shall test the hypothesis that the universe has a normal distribution. The general technique is the same for any theoretical distribution except for counting the degrees of freedom.

Suppose we have a sample of N observations which have mean $\bar{X}$ and variance s^2. The normal curve fitted to these data has the equation

$$Y = \frac{N}{s\sqrt{2\pi}} e^{-\frac{1}{2}\left(\frac{X-\bar{X}}{s}\right)^2}$$

Using Table A-4 and the techniques explained in Chap. 5, we can find the area under this curve between any two points. Corresponding to categories, we divide the range of the variable X into a number of intervals. The choice of intervals is arbitrary except that the theoretical frequency in each should be 1 or larger. The theoretical frequency is the area under the normal curve in the interval, while the observed frequency is the actual number of observations which fall in the interval. The χ^2 statistic is then computed in the same fashion as before. The number of degrees of freedom for this example is $k - 3$, where k is the number of categories. In general, in measuring the fit of any frequency curve the number of degrees of freedom decreases one for each parameter estimated from the sample. Here we estimated the mean and standard deviation and thus lost 2 degrees of freedom,

$$(k - 1) - 2 = k - 3$$

As an example, suppose we have a sample of 100 observations as shown in Table 13-7. Since the observed value of 1.99 is smaller than 9.49, we

TABLE 13-7

Midpoint	Frequencies	$\frac{X - \bar{X}}{s}$ at end points	Interval	Theoretical frequency	Observed frequency	$\frac{(f_i - F_i)^2}{F_i}$
145	8	+1.60	Above 140	5.5	8	1.14
135	9	+1.00	130–140	10.4	9	.19
125	16	+ .40	120–130	18.6	16	.36
115	23	− .20	110–120	23.5	23	.01
105	21	− .80	100–110	20.9	21	.00
95	15	−1.40	90–100	13.1	15	.29
85	8		Below 90	8.1	8	.00
	100			100.1	100	1.99

$\bar{X} = 113.3$ $\quad \chi_{.95}^2(4) = 9.49$
$s = 16.65$

accept, at the 5 per cent level of significance, the hypothesis that the distribution is normal.

13-5. Binomial Distribution, Proportion

In Chaps. 5 to 7 we have introduced dichotomous populations, i.e., populations in which a proportion p of the individuals have a certain characteristic and a proportion $1 - p$ of the individuals do not have it. We have seen that we could discuss this case as a special case of an arithmetic mean by assigning the score 1 to those individuals having the characteristic and the score 0 to the rest. For large samples we drew inferences under the assumption that the sampling distribution of the proportion $\bar{X}$ of the sample having the characteristic was normal. The following material discusses the problem more exactly for small samples.

As usual we assume that we have a random sample of N individuals from the population. The assumption of randomness is important, and the analysis depends on it. Although this statement has been made before, it is emphasized here because of the wide use of stratified and quota sampling designs in public-opinion polls and other samples of human populations. Frequently these designs produce more precise results than those obtained from random sampling, but their analysis is different from that presented here.

Note that p is a parameter. Since the use of p is widely accepted as the population proportion, we are using it instead of a Greek letter.

The best estimate of p is the proportion, say, $\bar{X} = X/N$, observed in the sample. Here X is the number in the sample having the characteristic, and N is the size of the sample. X/N is a statistic which can only have as its value one of the following sequence:

$$0, \frac{1}{N}, \frac{2}{N}, \frac{3}{N}, \ldots, \frac{N-1}{N}, 1$$

For random samples the sampling distribution of X/N is given by

$$\frac{1 \cdot 2 \cdot 3 \cdots (N-2)(N-1)N}{(1 \cdot 2 \cdot 3 \cdots X)[1 \cdot 2 \cdot 3 \cdots (N-X)]} p^X (1-p)^{N-X}$$

for $X = 0, 1, 2, 3, \ldots, N$. A distribution where the frequencies are given by this formula is called a *binomial distribution*. The formula

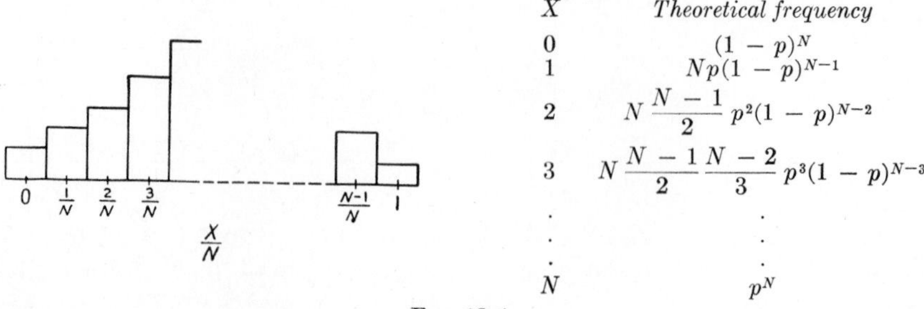

X	*Theoretical frequency*
0	$(1-p)^N$
1	$Np(1-p)^{N-1}$
2	$N\frac{N-1}{2}p^2(1-p)^{N-2}$
3	$N\frac{N-1}{2}\frac{N-2}{3}p^3(1-p)^{N-3}$
.	.
.	.
.	.
N	p^N

FIG. 13-1

indicates the chance, or relative frequency, of the statistic X/N appearing as a particular one of the values which it can take on. This is indicated in Fig. 13-1 in table and graphical form. The reasoning leading to this formula is mathematical in nature and is outlined in Chap. 20.

We have drawn a histogram here although actually the variable X/N can only be one of a discrete series of values. This somewhat inexact method of depicting the distribution is used so that we may continue to interpret the area as frequencies.

The computation involved in finding the values of these theoretical frequencies is rather formidable even for small values of N, while for large values of N it is prohibitive. Table A-29(a) lists values for sample sizes less than or equal to 10. As pointed out in Chap. 5, it can be shown that if Np and $N(1 - p)$ are fairly large, say, each larger than 5, the statistic $(\bar{X} - p)\Big/\sqrt{\dfrac{p(1-p)}{N}}$ has an approximately normal sampling distribution with zero mean and unit variance. A verification of this approximation can be shown by sampling experiments. The mean and variance of the observed $\bar{X}$ distribution should be approximately p and $\dfrac{p(1-p)}{N}$, and the cumulative should be approximately a straight line on normal-probability paper. (See, for example, the experiment described in Chap. 5.)

The chance of observing a value of $\bar{X}$ between $\bar{X} = a$ and $\bar{X} = b$ is approximately the area under the unit normal curve between

$$z = \frac{a - \dfrac{1}{2N} - p}{\sqrt{\dfrac{p(1-p)}{N}}} \qquad \text{and} \qquad z = \frac{b + \dfrac{1}{2N} - p}{\sqrt{\dfrac{p(1-p)}{N}}}$$

The term $1/2N$ is included so that the area under the continuous curve will better approximate the sum of the probabilities of $\bar{X}$ falling at the points $a, a + \dfrac{1}{N}, \cdots, b$. That is, we wish the entire area corresponding to the rectangles centered at these points.

For large samples, $[Np > 5$, and $N(1 - p) > 5]$, $100(1 - \alpha)$ per cent confidence limits for estimating p are

$$\frac{N}{N + z^2_{1-\frac{1}{2}\alpha}}\left[\bar{X} + \frac{z^2_{1-\frac{1}{2}\alpha}}{2N} \mp z_{1-\frac{1}{2}\alpha}\sqrt{\frac{\bar{X}(1-\bar{X})}{N} + \frac{z^2_{1-\frac{1}{2}\alpha}}{4N^2}}\right]$$

where $z_{1-\frac{1}{2}\alpha}$ is read from Table A-4. If N is very large, these limits are approximately

$$\bar{X} + z_{\frac{1}{2}\alpha}\sqrt{\frac{\bar{X}(1-\bar{X})}{N}} < p < \bar{X} + z_{1-\frac{1}{2}\alpha}\sqrt{\frac{\bar{X}(1-\bar{X})}{N}}$$

as given in Sec. 6-8.

Similarly for large samples we can test the hypothesis that p has some specified value, say, $p = p_0$, at any desired level of significance by comparing the value of

$$z = \frac{\bar{X} - p_0}{\sqrt{\frac{p_0(1 - p_0)}{N}}}$$

with values from Table A-4. If $z < z_{\frac{1}{2}\alpha}$ or if $z > z_{1-\frac{1}{2}\alpha}$, we should reject the hypothesis at the α level of significance.

In Table A-9 there are graphs giving confidence limits for p corresponding to the observed $\bar{X}$ for several different sample sizes. Four graphs are given for 80 per cent, 90 per cent, 95 per cent, 99 per cent confidence limits. The observed $\bar{X}$ is read on the horizontal scale, and values of p are read from the vertical. Various belt-shaped curves, two for each N, indicate the confidence interval. The confidence limits for p are read above the observed $\bar{X} = X/N$ as in Fig. 13-2 which show 80 per cent confidence limits for $N = 10$. Suppose that for 10 items $\bar{X} = .6$. The confidence limits are .35 and .82. For larger N the curves are closer together, and we obtain shorter confidence intervals.

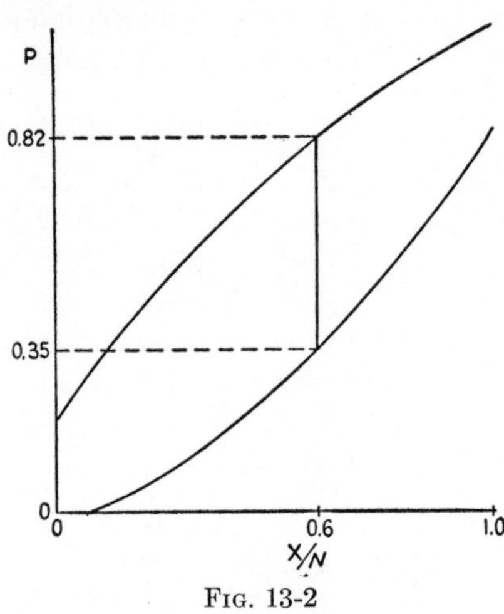

FIG. 13-2

We can test the hypothesis that $p = p_0$ at the α level of significance by observing whether or not p_0 is in the $100(1 - \alpha)$ per cent confidence interval corresponding to the observed $\bar{X}$. If it is, we accept the hypothesis $p = p_0$; if it is not, we reject the hypothesis.

Example 1. In a random sample of 100 articles, there were 40 having a certain characteristic. Find 90 per cent confidence limits for the proportion of the population having the characteristic. We use the 90 per cent graph for $N = 100$. Above $\bar{X} = \frac{40}{100} = .40$ we read the limits as .32 and .48. Thus we are 90 per cent confident that p is between .32 and .48.

Example 2. The binomial distribution can also be used to state the chance of rejecting at least one of N true statistical hypotheses tested independently at the α level of significance. The chance of rejecting exactly none is $(1 - \alpha)^N$, and the chance of rejecting at least one is $1 - (1 - \alpha)^N$. Values of $(1 - \alpha)^N$ can be read from Table A-29. We read from the table for $p = \alpha$ and $X = 0$. For example, if $N = 5$ independent tests are performed at the $\alpha = .01$ level of significance, we read in the table under $p = .01$, $N = 5$, $X = 0$ that $(1 - \alpha)^N = .9510$ and so if all hypotheses are true the chance of rejecting at least one is $1 - .9510 = .0490$.

Poisson Distribution. If N is large and Np is fairly small ($Np < 5$), the area under the normal curve will not be a good approximation to the area under the binomial-distribution histogram. In this case the value of

$$\frac{1 \cdot 2 \cdot 3 \cdots N}{(1 \cdot 2 \cdots X)[1 \cdot 2 \cdots (N - X)]} p^X (1 - p)^{N-X}$$

is given approximately by

$$e^{-Np} \frac{(Np)^X}{1 \cdot 2 \cdot 3 \cdots X} \qquad X = 0, 1, 2, 3, \cdots$$

A distribution where the frequencies are given by this formula is called a *Poisson distribution*. The only parameter in this formula is Np, which can be treated as a single quantity and is denoted by λ. Sometimes this value is known where N alone is not. It happens that both the mean and variance of this distribution are equal to λ.

Table A-15 gives values of the cumulative Poisson distribution for various values of λ and X. Values of λ are recorded on the left of the page, and values of X are across the top. The numbers in the table are the cumulated relative frequency (or probability) that values less than or equal to X will be observed. For example, if $\lambda = 1.2$, we read that 66.3 per cent of the time X will have the values 0 or 1, 87.9 per cent of the time X will have the values 0 or 1 or 2, etc. These tabled numbers are actually $\sum_{k=0}^{k=X} e^{-\lambda} \frac{\lambda^k}{1 \cdot 2 \cdot 3 \cdots k}$, and this formula could be used for computation.

Further material on the binomial and Poisson distributions can be found in Chap. 20.

Goodness of Fit. The general procedure of Sec. 13-4 using χ^2 can be used to compare any hypothetical distribution with an observed distribution. However, for the binomial and Poisson distributions a comparison of the variances of the observed and theoretical distributions is recommended as an alternative.

For the binomial we compute

$$\chi^2 = \frac{N\Sigma(\bar{X}_i - p)^2}{p(1 - p)}$$

if p is known. Here $\bar{X}_1, \bar{X}_2, \ldots, \bar{X}_n$ are the successive proportions observed, in samples of size N. This statistic has an approximate χ^2 distribution with n degrees of freedom when the hypothesis is correct.

If p is estimated by $\bar{X} = \Sigma \bar{X}_i/n$ and substituted in this formula for p, the degrees of freedom are $n - 1$.

In the Poisson case we compute

$$\chi^2 = \frac{\Sigma(X_i - \lambda)^2}{\lambda}$$

which analogously has an approximate χ^2 distribution with n degrees of freedom, or if $\bar{X} = \Sigma X_i/n$ obtained from the sample is substituted for λ in this formula, it has $n - 1$ degrees of freedom.

13-6. Difference in Proportions

Suppose we have two populations in which proportions p_1 and p_2, respectively, have some characteristic. We take random samples of size N_1 and N_2 from the populations and observe proportions $\bar{X}_1$ and $\bar{X}_2$. If N_1 and N_2 are large, say, such that N_1p_1, N_2p_2, $N_1(1 - p_1)$, $N_2(1 - p_2)$ are all larger than 5, we can estimate the difference between p_1 and p_2 by the following approximate confidence intervals:

$$\bar{X}_1 - \bar{X}_2 + z_{\frac{1}{2}\alpha}\sqrt{\frac{\bar{X}_1(1 - \bar{X}_1)}{N_1} + \frac{\bar{X}_2(1 - \bar{X}_2)}{N_2}} < p_1 - p_2 < \bar{X}_1 - \bar{X}_2 + z_{1-\frac{1}{2}\alpha}\sqrt{\frac{\bar{X}_1(1 - \bar{X}_1)}{N_1} + \frac{\bar{X}_2(1 - \bar{X}_2)}{N_2}}$$

If these limits cover zero, then there would be no reason to reject the hypothesis $p_1 = p_2$, at the 100α per cent level of significance. If they do not cover zero, we should reject the hypothesis.

Example. Suppose that in a survey of 400 people from one city 188 preferred a brand A soap to all others and in a sample of 500 people from another city 210 preferred the same product. Is there reason to doubt the hypothesis $p_1 = p_2$ at the 5 per cent level of significance?

$$\bar{X}_1 = \tfrac{188}{400} = .47 \qquad 1 - \bar{X}_1 = .53 \qquad \bar{X}_2 = \tfrac{210}{500} = .42 \qquad 1 - \bar{X}_2 = .58$$

The 95 per cent confidence limits are

$$.47 - .42 - 1.96\sqrt{\frac{(.47)(.53)}{400} + \frac{(.42)(.58)}{500}} < p_1 - p_2 < .47 - .42 + 1.96\sqrt{\frac{(.47)(.53)}{400} + \frac{(.42)(.58)}{500}}$$

or

$$.05 - .065 < p_1 - p_2 < .05 + .065$$

or

$$-.015 < p_1 - p_2 < .115$$

Since these limits cover zero, there is not sufficient reason to reject the hypothesis.

This analysis is equivalent to the χ^2 test of independence for the 2×2 table in Sec. 13-3 except that the correction factor has been omitted here.

Correlated Proportions. Consider data obtained as follows: A group of individuals are asked a question on public affairs which they are to answer yes or no. After a certain period of time or after a propaganda lecture they are asked the same question again. The data are recorded in the table. If we wished to test the hypothesis that the answers to the

		Before		
		Yes	No	Total
After	Yes.......	30	15	45
	No........	9	51	60
	Total......	39	66	105

second question are independent of the answers to the first, these data could be analyzed as a contingency table testing the hypothesis: the proportion of yes answers to the second question is the same for both those answering yes and those answering no to the first question. However, this analysis would not answer the question, which we state as: Is the passage of time or the propaganda lecture effective in changing the proportion saying yes? The proportion saying yes originally is $\frac{39}{105}$ and finally is $\frac{45}{105}$. This case of difference of proportions differs from the case discussed above since these proportions are not independent (both include the 30 individuals saying yes both times). The standard deviation of this difference can be estimated, using the notation of Table 13-6, by

$$\sqrt{\frac{b + c - (b - c)^2/N}{N(N - 1)}} = \sqrt{\frac{9 + 15 - (9 - 15)^2/105}{105 \times 104}} = .0466$$

An approximate 95 per cent confidence interval for increase in the population answering yes is $(\frac{45}{105} - \frac{39}{105}) \pm 1.96(.0466)$, giving the interval $-.0342$ to $.1484$.

A test of the null hypothesis of no change in opinion can also be made by testing the hypothesis that of those who changed their minds an equal number changed from yes to no and from no to yes. In this example we could test whether or not the observed binomial $\bar{X} = \frac{9}{21}$ is significantly different from $p = .50$ as in Sec. 13-5.

This test is in reality a test of symmetry and can be applied to tables with more than two categories. Suppose the data are recorded as in Table 13-8, where n_{ij} represents the observed frequency in the ith column and jth row. We wish to test the hypothesis that the population frequencies are the same in symmetrically located cells, i.e., that for all i's and j's the frequency in the ij cell is equal to the frequency in the ji cell.

TABLE 13-8

First classification

Second classification	1	2	⋯	k
1	n_{11}	n_{21}	⋯	n_{k1}
2	n_{12}	n_{22}	⋯	n_{k2}
.	.	.	⋯	.
.	.	.		.
.	.	.	⋯	.
k	n_{1k}	n_{2k}	⋯	n_{kk}

This hypothesis can be tested by computing the sum

$$\sum_{i<j} \frac{(n_{ij} - n_{ji})^2}{n_{ij} + n_{ji}}$$

When the hypothesis is true and the total frequency large, this statistic has, approximately, a χ^2 distribution with $k(k-1)/2$ degrees of freedom. The summation extends over all cells in the table where i is less than j.

13-7. Binomial-probability Paper

There is a type of graph paper, called binomial-probability paper, which frequently can be used in analyzing enumeration data. Figure 13-3 shows a sheet of this paper. The scales are marked off for observations, but the units of length change as the distance from the origin changes. Actually the distance from the origin is the square root of the coordinate. We shall give here only three examples of the use of this paper without details as to why it can be used in the stated manner.

A straight line through the origin passes through points whose coordinates are proportional. For example a line through the origin and (80,20) also passes through (160,40), (40,10), (20,5), etc. A line through the origin on this paper is called a split and is referred to in terms of the coordinates of the point where the line cuts the quarter circle marked on the graph. Note that these coordinates add up to 100. Thus the line on Fig. 13-3 is the 80:20 split.

A paired count refers to the numbers in the sample observed as having and as not having some characteristic. Thus, if 80 in a sample of $N = 100$ have a particular characteristic, we say the paired count is (80,20). A paired count is plotted as a right triangle, the vertex being plotted in the usual manner and then two sides extending one unit parallel to the horizontal and vertical axes, respectively. For example, (5,7) is plotted with (5,7) as the right-angle vertex and with (6,7), (5,8) as the other two vertices. If one or both of the coordinates is larger than 100, the addition of one will not show on the paper and the triangle appears as a short (one unit long) line or as a point.

The distances from any split to the two acute angles of a plotted point are called the *short distance* and the *long distance*, respectively. These distances can be interpreted by referring to the scale at the top of the paper marked "Full Scale—Individual Standard Errors." The units on this scale refer to a normal-probability scale, and thus a deviation of two full-scale units would be considered as just significant at the 5 per cent level for a two-sided test. The probabilities corresponding to the long and short distances form a *significance zone*, and test results are significant at some level between them. For example, a zone of (15%,0.1%) would not indicate significance at the 5 per cent level, while the zone (4%,0.1%)

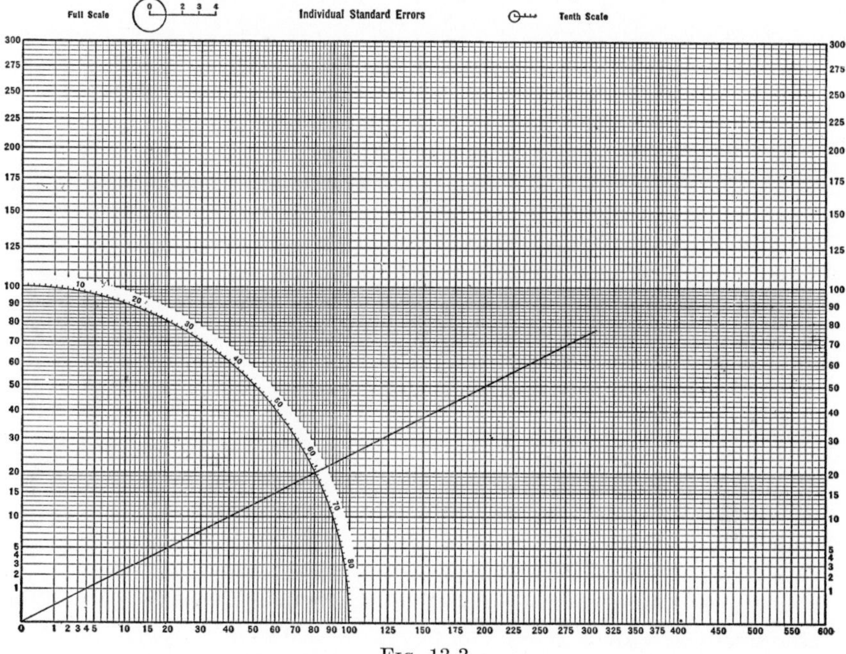

FIG. 13-3

would. The use of this zone instead of a single level considers the possible effect of another observation on our conclusion.

Example 1. Suppose we wish to test the hypothesis that 50 per cent of a population has some particular characteristic. If we observe that 40 out of a sample of 100 have the characteristic, is there reason to reject the hypothesis at the 5 per cent level of significance?

Answer. Draw the 50:50 split (corresponding to the theoretical proportions of 50:50). Plot the paired count (40,60), and measure the long and short distances to be 2.0 and 2.1 (see Fig. 13-4). This gives a significance zone of (4.6%,3.6%), and we thus have reason to doubt the 50: 50 hypothesis at the 5 per cent level of significance.

Example 2. Form 95 per cent confidence limits for the population proportion if we obtain 321 individuals having the characteristic out of a sample of 500.

Answer. Draw splits which would be accepted at the 5 per cent level of significance, i.e., within two full-scale units of (321,179). The proportions of these two splits are the desired limits, .60 and .69 for this problem.

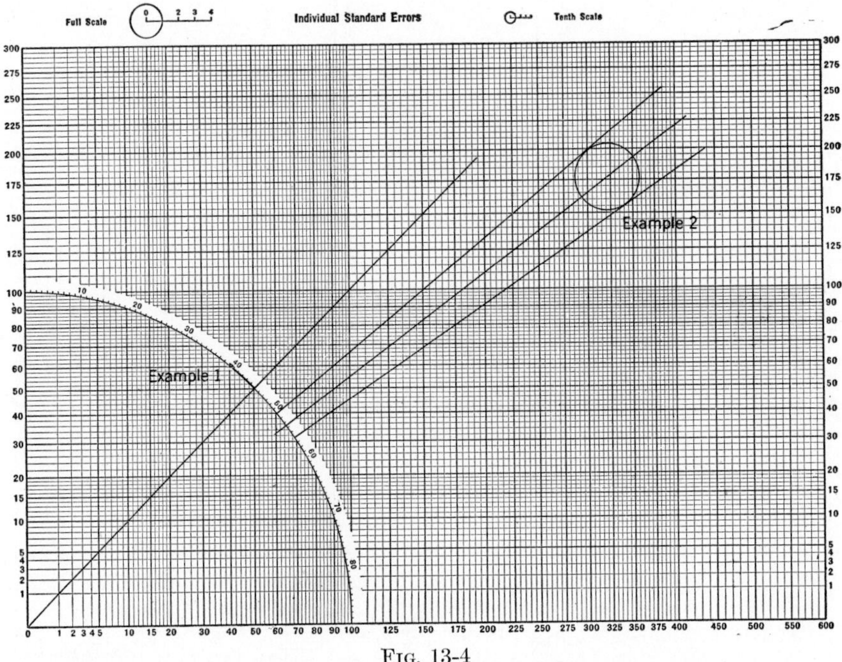

FIG. 13-4

Example 3. Suppose the proportion of a population having a certain characteristic is either .50 or .25. A two-sided test of the hypothesis $p = .50$ is made at the 5 per cent level of significance. How large a sample should be taken to have a .005 chance of rejecting this hypothesis if $p = .25$?

Answer. Draw the 50:50 split and two parallel lines 2 full-scale units on each side of it. Points inside these parallel lines are acceptable for the 50:50 hypothesis at the 5 per cent level. Draw the 25:75 split and two lines 2.6 full-scale units on either side of it. Points inside this band are acceptable for $p = .25$ at the 1 per cent level of significance. The inside lines intersect at (32,51), and it may be noted that, if a sample has size larger than $32 + 51 = 83$, then it is impossible to accept both $p = .50$ and $p = .25$ at the desired levels of significance and the test must therefore indicate which is to be accepted. In a practical case it may happen that both values would be rejected; i.e., we may reject both .50 and .25.

Two things should be emphasized. The paper provides a quick method of obtaining (approximately) the same numbers arrived at by the other techniques. Also, we have only touched the uses of this type of graph paper. Rough approximations to the results of t tests, analysis of variance, tolerance limits, two-sample tests, goodness-of-fit tests, etc., can

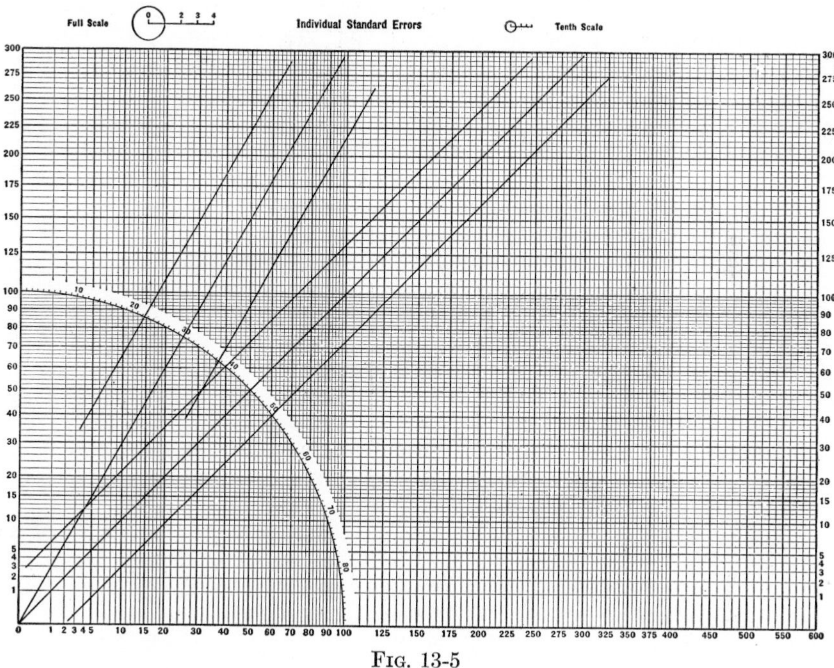

FIG. 13-5

also be read from the paper. For these and further applications see the References (page 358).

13-8. Control Chart for Percentages

Control charts may be constructed for proportions in a manner similar to the construction of charts for the mean and range given in Chap. 9. Suppose p is the proportion of the population having the characteristic. We have noted that the proportion $\bar{X}$ of a sample which has the characteristic has a sampling distribution which is approximately normal for large sample sizes. We stated the formula for the variance of $\bar{X}$ as $\sigma_{\bar{X}}^2 = \dfrac{p(1-p)}{N}$.

If some standard percentage p is given and we wish to construct control

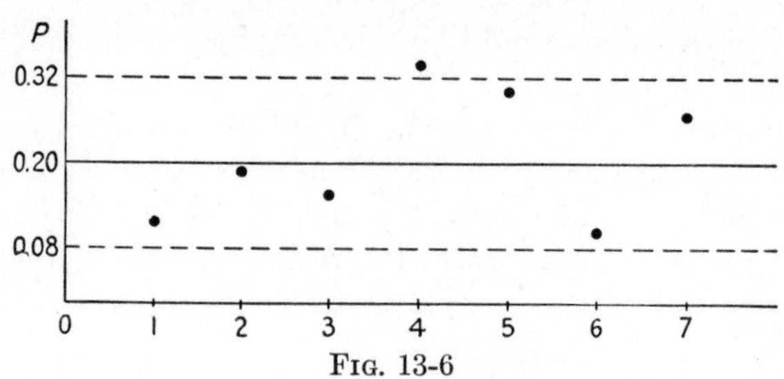

FIG. 13-6

lines, it is customary to draw lines $3\sqrt{\frac{p(1-p)}{N}}$ units above and below p. Figure 13-6 illustrates such control lines for $p = .2$, $N = 100$. Usually the data are recorded in tabular form as well as on a graph. Table 13-9

TABLE 13-9

Sample No.	Sample size	Observed
1	100	.12
2	100	.19
3	100	.16
4	100	.34
5	100	.30
6	100	.10
7	100	.27

records the data which are pictured on the graph in Fig. 13-6. In the first sample there were 12 items having the characteristic; thus $\bar{X} = \frac{12}{100} = .12$. The control limits are $.2 \pm 3\sqrt{\frac{(.2)(.8)}{100}}$ or $.2 \pm .12$.

If the sample size changes, the upper and lower control limits also change and they are frequently recorded as in Table 13-10. The factor $3\sqrt{p(1-p)}$ is constant for all N, and this can be divided by the various

TABLE 13-10

Sample No.	Sample size	Observed $\bar{X}$	$\frac{3\sqrt{.2(.8)}}{\sqrt{N}}$	Upper control limit	Lower control limit
1	250	.120	.076	.276	.124
2	320	.150	.067	.267	.133
3	450	.177	.057	.257	.143
4	175	.246	.091	.291	.109
5	1,840	.217	.028	.228	.172
6	200	.260	.085	.285	.115
7	900	.244	.040	.240	.160

$\sqrt{N}$. Again we use $p = .2$. Figure 13-7 shows the control lines and observations for the results in this table.

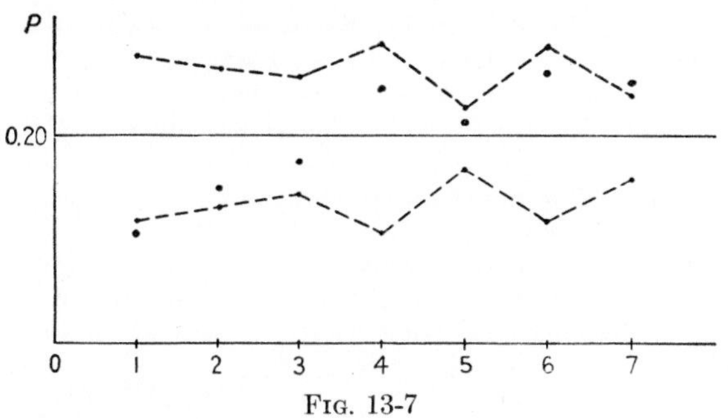

FIG. 13-7

GLOSSARY

binomial distribution
binomial-probability paper
chi-square distribution
chi-square statistic
contingency table
goodness of fit
homogeneity of proportions
Poisson distribution
proportion

DISCUSSION QUESTIONS

1. What is the difference between a χ^2 distribution and a χ^2/df distribution?

2. What is the difference between a single-classification and a two-way-classification experiment?

3. Is it always necessary to specify the hypothetical proportions to perform a χ^2 test?

4. What does *independence* mean?

5. Verify that for large samples a χ^2 test for a single-classification two-category table is exactly equivalent to the test using proportions (i.e., show that the critical regions coincide).

6. What connection is there between control charts and tests of hypotheses?

7. Define each term in the Glossary.

8. Has any assumption about the population been made before application of the χ^2 test in a single-classification experiment?

CLASS EXERCISES

1. For Class Exercise 1, Chap. 5, verify that the mean proportion of observed red beads is $\frac{2}{3}$ and that the variance of the proportion of observed red beads is

$$\frac{p(1-p)}{N} = .011$$

2. Draw samples of 25 beads from a box containing 200 red beads, 400 blue beads, and 400 white beads. Compute the value of χ^2 for each sample, and collect the observed values into a distribution. Compare the 95th percentile of the observed distribution with the theoretical value from Table A-6*a*.

3. In Class Exercise 3, Chap. 6, the number of 90 per cent confidence intervals for μ which actually covered μ were counted. Test the hypothesis that the theoretical proportion of intervals which cover μ is 90 per cent.

4. Work Exercise 3, using the data in Class Exercise 4, Chap. 6.

5. Work Exercise 3, using the data in Class Exercise 2, Chap. 9.

6. Draw samples of size 5 from a box of 500 white beads and 500 red beads, and verify that the frequencies of red beads in the samples are as given by the binomial-distribution formula (i.e., verify that 1 time out of 32 you get no red beads out of 5, etc.). After a number of samples have been drawn, test the agreement with the theoretical frequencies by a χ^2 test.

7. From a box of 100 red beads and 900 white beads draw samples of size 10, and observe the number of red beads in each sample. Test the hypothesis that the Poisson-distribution formula gives the frequencies with which various proportions of red beads occur in these samples.

8. From a two-category population draw samples of size 50. An example of such a population is a number of tags, some white and some colored, and each tag bearing a plus or a minus sign. Record the results of the sample in a table. Compute the

	+	−
White		
Colored		

χ^2 statistic to test for independence. Tabulate a number of χ^2 values found in this manner, compute the 95th percentile of the observed values, and compare it with $\chi_{.95}^2(1)$ in Table A-6*a*.

9. Suppose a variable takes on the values 0, 1, 2, 3, 4 with the frequencies shown in the tabulation. Each student draws 5 samples of 25 from the random-number

X	0	1	2	3	4
f	.1	.2	.4	.2	.1

table (Table A-1), assigning to the numbers drawn values X so that the frequencies in the tabulation hold in the population (e.g., assign to 0 the score 0, to 1 and 5 the score 1, to 2 and 6 and 7 and 8 the score 2, to 3 and 9 the score 3, and to 4 assign the score 4). Compute χ^2 for each experiment, and then collect the results into a single distribution of χ^2. Compare the 90th percentile of the observed distribution with $\chi_{.90}^2(4)$ from Table A-6*a*.

PROBLEMS

1. In an experiment in botany the results of crossing two hybrids of a species of flower gave observed frequencies of descriptive categories of 120, 48, 36, 13. Do these results disagree with theoretical frequencies which specify a 9:3:3:1 ratio?

2. Two hundred throws of a die resulted in the observations shown in the table.

No. of spots............	1	2	3	4	5	6
Frequency...............	30	27	29	31	40	43

Is this reason to believe that the die is not balanced correctly?

3. How many occurrences of heads in 100 throws of a coin would make you reject, at the 1 per cent level of significance, the hypothesis that it was a true coin?

4. In the Northern Division Basketball Conference for the 1948 season 40 games were played. Twenty-eight games were won by the team playing on its home floor. Is this a significant departure from the proportion to be expected if the team playing at home has no advantage or disadvantage and each team plays the same number of games at home and away from home? Each team plays the same number of games with each other team.

5. On page 40 there are two distributions of sample means, one for samples of size 10 and the other for samples of size 40. (*a*) Use χ^2 to test the hypothesis that the means for $N = 10$ are from a normal population. (*b*) Do the same for the means of 40 items.

6. Of the 400 winning numbers in a sweepstakes drawing, 176 were odd numbers and 224 were even numbers. Is this significantly different from 50:50?

7. A student newspaper polled 20 students and found that 14 of them favored a change from a term system to the semester plan. Read 90 per cent confidence limits for the proportion of students in the student body who favor this change.

8. Celery seed is treated chemically in an attempt to reduce the incidence of blight. Of 100 plants from treated seeds there were 20 which showed blight. Of 100 plants from untreated seeds 46 showed blight. Is this difference significant?

9. The data in the table record the number of calls and sales made by a life insurance salesman. Fill in the table, and draw a control chart showing control lines. Inspect this chart for significant changes in sale conditions. For p use the proportion of sales during the entire year.

Month	Calls	Sales	$\bar{X}$	$\frac{3\sqrt{p(1-p)}}{\sqrt{N}}$	Upper control limit	Lower control limit
January	95	7				
February	100	15				
March	110	14				
April	90	8				
May	97	12				
June	105	6				
July	100	7				
August	108	12				
September	120	15				
October	98	12				
November	100	17				
December	85	9				
Total						

10. The data in the table are the results of random samples of articles from five manufacturers. Indicate for each of the hypotheses tested the possible errors which could be made and the consequences of making each of them.

(*a*) Test the hypothesis that the defective rate of the product made by manufacturer *A* is 3 per cent. In case of rejection of the hypothesis, find the 95 per cent confidence interval for p.

(*b*) Test the hypothesis that the defective rates of the products made by the manufacturers A and B are the same. In case of rejection of the hypothesis, find a 99 per cent confidence interval for the difference between the two defective rates.

(c) Test the hypothesis that the defective rates of the products made by the five manufacturers are the same. In case of rejection of the hypothesis, what would you do next?

Manufacturer	Defective articles	Nondefective articles
A	41	259
B	15	301
C	21	401
D	13	304
E	19	405

11. An $\bar{X}$ chart with 95 per cent control limits was used in controlling the mean. Out of 500 points plotted on the chart, 14 points fell below the lower limit, and 16 points fell above the upper limit. Use the χ^2 test to determine whether or not this indicates that the population mean has been changing during the period when the chart was used.

12. The grade distribution of three instructors who taught the same course for a period of 2 years is given in the table. Did the instructors give significantly different percentages of the five grades?

	A	B	C	D	F
Smith.	21	39	128	19	23
Jones.	35	52	212	24	29
Brown.	15	42	178	20	17

13. A certain vitamin was thought to increase energy. In an experiment 100 men were given the vitamin. Also, as a control 100 men were given harmless sugar pills but told that they were being given the vitamin. Their reactions are given in the table. Analyze the data.

	Had more energy	Had less energy	No change
Control group.	20	10	70
Treated group.	36	8	56

14. Over a period of several years there had been an average of 12 accidents per year in a certain city. This year there were accidents in the 12 months as follows: 0, 0, 2, 2, 1, 1, 2, 0, 1, 0, 1, 2. Do these data agree with a theory that the number of accidents per month follows a Poisson distribution with $Np = 1$?

15. A manufacturer of brand A automobiles believed that his cars would last longer than those of certain competitors. A random sample of automobiles from a certain city showed the data given in the table. As constructed this experiment cannot prove or disprove the manufacturer's belief. Why not?

	Age of car		
	Over 10 years	5–10 years	Less than 5 years
A	33	127	256
B	42	205	409
C	10	55	100

Later another survey was made of cars manufactured exactly 10 years ago. The results are as in the second table. What do these figures prove? State carefully the populations sampled from and what interpretations can and cannot be made from the data.

	No. of years car ran without major overhaul					
	0–1	2–3	4–5	6–7	8–9	No overhaul yet
A	15	37	55	108	118	60
B	5	13	180	205	386	400
C	55	160	300	106	55	40

16. A man took a survey in the following fashion: He took a random sample of 100 names from a telephone book and interviewed those people. He found that 55 stated that they had voted in the last election and 37 stated that they had not voted and the remainder refused to answer or could not be contacted. What conclusions can he draw? From what population did he sample?

17. Analyze the tabulated data on the number of children in families. State assumptions, hypotheses, and conclusions.

Family income, dollars	No. of children			
	0	1	2	More than 2
Under 2,000	15	27	50	43
2,000–5,000	25	37	12	8
Over 5,000	8	13	9	10

CHAPTER 14

PROBABILITY OF ACCEPTING A FALSE HYPOTHESIS

We have dealt with various techniques for testing a hypothesis. If the hypothesis were true, the chance, or probability, of rejecting it was some preassigned number α. That is, the chances of rejecting true hypotheses have been controlled. Our method of testing any one hypothesis was not unique. It involved a choice of a test statistic and a choice of a critical region. While some of our choices seemed obvious, others did not. In this chapter we shall examine more carefully the advantages of some particular tests.

We also go more deeply into the problem of evaluating the chance, β, of failing to detect the falsity of a hypothesis. This topic deserves careful attention and thought, especially from those who must determine whether or not an experiment is to be performed. If it has already been decided to perform the experiment, it may be argued that the size of β is of interest but is not particularly vital. However, if an experimenter is interested in discovering a deviation from the hypothesis of a certain magnitude and if the time and money available give him, say, only a 15 per cent chance of recognizing such a difference if it is present, there seems little point in the experiment being performed. In such a case the research worker may wish to use his resources either on some less expensive problem or on one where he has more assurance of arriving at a correct conclusion.

14-1. Alternatives and Two Types of Error

A *test* of a statistical hypothesis consists in choosing a test statistic and selecting a critical region. When the hypothesis is true, the test specifies that the chance of rejecting the hypothesis is some preassigned level of significance α. It would be an error to reject the hypothesis when it is true, and this type of error is called an α error. If it happened that the hypothesis were not true, accepting it would be a mistake, and this type of error is called a β error. Of course, it is possible to make only one of these two errors in any problem, but there is no way to determine which error, if either, is likely to be made. Our method of testing has controlled the chance of making the α error. We shall examine the chance of accepting a hypothesis when it is false (β error).

Declaring a hypothesis false should imply that we have some idea of what alternative situations might exist. For example, if, for a normal distribution with $\sigma = 1$, we are testing the hypothesis that the mean $\mu = 5$, possible alternatives might be $\mu = 6$, $\mu = 3$, etc. In fact, alternatives might include any number, except 5, for the value of μ. If it happens that $\mu = 6$, then there is a certain probability of rejecting the hypothesis $\mu = 5$. If $\mu = 3$, there is some other probability of rejecting the hypothesis $\mu = 5$. *This probability of rejecting a hypothesis is called the power of the test.*

The power depends upon which alternative is actually true. In practice we do not know which alternative is true and are interested in the power of the test for several possible alternatives. If the hypothesis is not true, we would like the chance of rejecting it to be as large as possible and thus would like the power to be large. Suppose that the chance of rejecting a certain hypothesis when it is true is equal to α for two different tests. We would then use the test which is more powerful.

These two types of error are sometimes called producers' and consumers' risks. To illustrate this usage, suppose a hypothesis states that a batch of manufactured articles meets some standard and a statistical test is to be applied. The risk of rejecting a true hypothesis would be a producers' risk since if the hypothesis is rejected the articles are not sold and the producer takes an unjustified loss. On the other hand the chance of below-standard articles being accepted for sale is a chance of loss for the consumer.

14-2. Power Function for Testing the Hypothesis $\mu = \mu_0$

Choice of Critical Region. In the example above we had a normally distributed population with $\sigma = 1$ and tested the hypothesis $\mu = 5$. A random sample of N items is taken from the population, and the mean $\bar{X}$ of the sample is computed. The sampling distribution of the statistic $\bar{X}$ is known to be a normal distribution with the same mean as the mean of the population and with a standard deviation $\sigma_{\bar{X}}$ equal to $\sigma/\sqrt{N}$. Thus $\dfrac{\bar{X} - \mu}{\sigma/\sqrt{N}}$ has a normal distribution with zero mean and unit standard deviation, and the table of this probability distribution may be used to determine critical regions.

One test of the hypothesis $\mu = 5$ at the 5 per cent level of significance ($\alpha = .05$) would be to reject it if $\dfrac{\bar{X} - 5}{1/\sqrt{N}} > 1.645$. A second test would be to reject it if $\dfrac{\bar{X} - 5}{1/\sqrt{N}} < -1.645$. A third test would be to reject it if either $\dfrac{\bar{X} - 5}{1/\sqrt{N}} > 1.960$ or if $\dfrac{\bar{X} - 5}{1/\sqrt{N}} < -1.960$. If the hypothesis is true, any one of these three tests would reject it 5 per cent of the time. In each case, we have selected, using the sampling distribution of $\bar{X}$, regions where $\bar{X}$ would fall 5 per cent of the time by chance if $\mu = 5$. There are many other such regions, but these are perhaps three of the more useful.

Suppose we have a sample of 100 individuals ($N = 100$). Then the three critical regions can be described as follows:

(a) $\dfrac{\bar{X} - 5}{1/\sqrt{100}} > 1.645$ or $\bar{X} > 5 + .1645$ or $\underline{\bar{X} > 5.1645}$.

(b) $\dfrac{\bar{X} - 5}{1/\sqrt{100}} < -1.645$, or $\underline{\bar{X} < 4.8355}$.

(c) $\dfrac{\bar{X} - 5}{1/\sqrt{100}} < -1.960$, and $\dfrac{\bar{X} - 5}{1/\sqrt{100}} > 1.960$, or $\underline{\bar{X} > 5.1960}$, and $\underline{\bar{X} < 4.8040}$.

Figure 14-1 indicates the rejection regions for these three tests. Any one of these regions has 5 per cent of the area of a normal curve with mean 5 and $\sigma = (1/\sqrt{N}) = \frac{1}{10}$. Thus, if μ does equal 5, the probability of rejecting the hypothesis $\mu = 5$ is $\alpha = .05$ no matter which of the three tests we might decide to use. Let us find the power of each of these critical regions against certain alternatives.

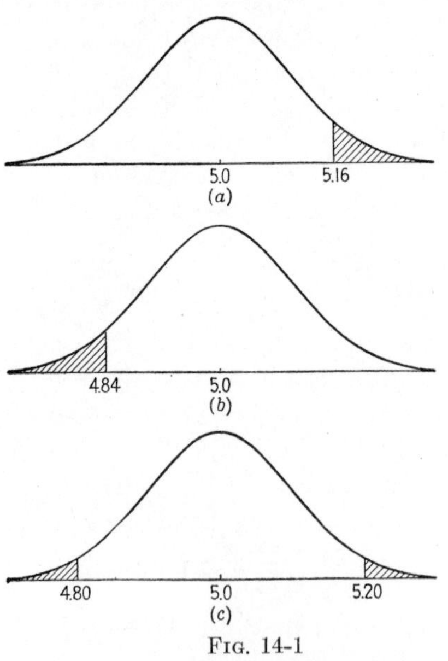

FIG. 14-1

First let us consider the operation of these tests in the event that the population mean μ is 5.2. Then the sampling distribution of $\dfrac{\bar{X} - 5.2}{1/\sqrt{100}}$ is a normal distribution with zero mean and unit standard deviation. We shall find the area under this curve corresponding to each of the three regions (a), (b), (c) above. These areas will be the chances of rejecting the hypothesis $\mu = 5$ if actually $\mu = 5.2$ corresponding to the three tests. To find these areas we find z scores for the end points of the critical regions.

(a) For $\bar{X} = 5.1645$, $z = \dfrac{5.1645 - 5.2}{1/\sqrt{100}} = -0.355$.

(b) For $\bar{X} = 4.8355$, $z = \dfrac{4.8355 - 5.2}{1/\sqrt{100}} = -3.645$.

(c) For $\bar{X} = 5.1960$, $z = \dfrac{5.1960 - 5.2}{1/\sqrt{100}} = -0.040$, and, for $\bar{X} = 4.8040$, $z = \dfrac{4.8040 - 5.2}{1/\sqrt{100}} = -3.960$.

The areas under the unit normal curve for these regions can be read from Table A-4 as:

(a) .639

(b) .000

(c) .516 + .000 = .516

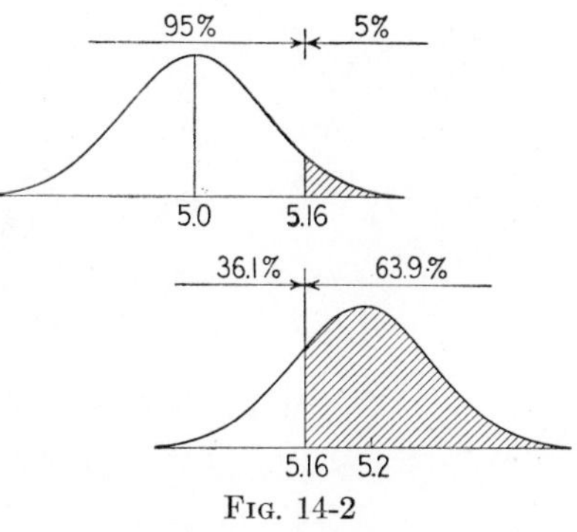

FIG. 14-2

If the true value of μ is 5.2, then, using critical region (a), we would have a chance .639 of rejecting the hypothesis $\mu = 5$. Using region (b), we would have a chance .000, while using region (c) the chance is .516. Thus, for this alternative $\mu = 5.2$ the region (a) is the most powerful of the three regions. Figure 14-2 illustrates the chance of falling in region (a) when $\mu = 5.0$ and when $\mu = 5.2$.

Figure 14-3 illustrates the chance of falling in region (b) when $\mu = 5.0$ and when $\mu = 5.2$.

Figure 14-4 illustrates the chance of falling in region (c) when $\mu = 5.0$ and when $\mu = 5.2$.

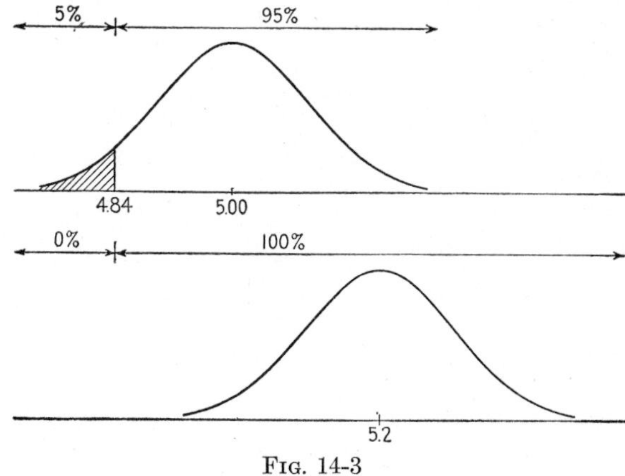

FIG. 14-3

Second let us consider the operation of these tests in the event that the population mean μ is 4.8. Then the sampling distribution of $\dfrac{\bar{X} - 4.8}{1/\sqrt{100}}$ is a normal distribution with zero mean and unit standard deviation.

We shall find the areas under this curve corresponding to the three regions (*a*), (*b*), (*c*). The end points of the intervals are:

(*a*) For $\bar{X} = 5.1645$, $z = \dfrac{5.1645 - 4.8}{1/\sqrt{100}} = 3.645.$

(*b*) For $\bar{X} = 4.8355$, $z = \dfrac{4.8355 - 4.8}{1/\sqrt{100}} = 0.355.$

(*c*) For $\bar{X} = 5.1960$, $z = 3.960$, and, for $\bar{X} = 4.8040$, $z = 0.040$.

The areas under the unit normal curve for these regions are:

(*a*) .000
(*b*) .639
(*c*) .516

Thus, if $\mu = 4.8$, using region (*a*) would give us no chance of rejecting the hypothesis $\mu = 5.0$, while (*b*) gives a chance of .639 and (*c*) a chance of .516. Region (*b*) is the most powerful of the three against the alternative $\mu = 4.8$.

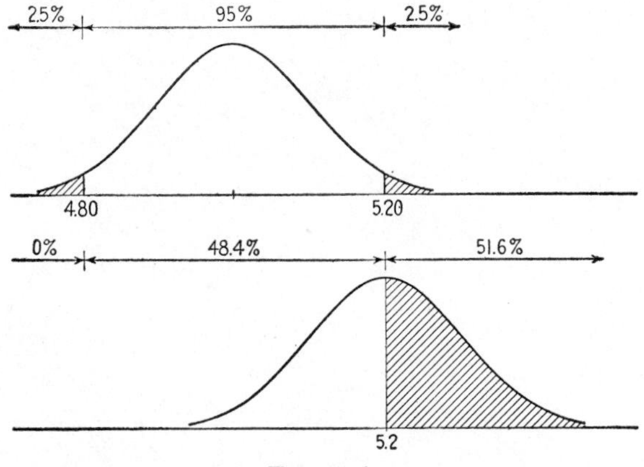

FIG. 14-4

The results above can be generalized by saying that region (*a*) is the best region if the true value of μ is greater than 5.0, while region (*b*) is the most powerful if the true value of μ is less than 5.0. Of course, if μ is less than 5.0, region (*a*) is very poor, and likewise if μ is greater than 5.0, region (*b*) is very poor. Region (*c*), while not as uniformly powerful as (*a*) or (*b*), guards against both alternatives. If we know, or are only worried about the possibility, that $\mu > 5.0$, then we would use region (*a*). Similarly we would use region (*b*) to test the hypothesis $\mu = 5.0$ against alternatives $\mu < 5.0$, while if we must consider the possibility of μ being either less than or greater than 5.0, we would use region (*c*).

We have computed the power for the three points $\mu = 4.8$, $\mu = 5.0$ (here the probability of rejecting is $\alpha = .05$), and $\mu = 5.2$. We have computed similar values of the power function for other values of μ, and these are shown by means of the three curves in Fig. 14-5. These curves correspond to a level of significance $\alpha = .05$. The hypothesis is now $\mu = \mu_0$, and the regions are now given in terms of μ_0 and σ.

The three critical regions are:

(a) $z = \dfrac{\bar{X} - \mu_0}{\sigma/\sqrt{N}}$, reject if $z > 1.645$.

(b) $z = \dfrac{\bar{X} - \mu_0}{\sigma/\sqrt{N}}$, reject if $z < -1.645$.

(c) $z = \dfrac{\bar{X} - \mu_0}{\sigma/\sqrt{N}}$, reject if $z < -1.960$ or if $z > +1.960$.

The alternative values of μ are read along the horizontal axis in units of $\sigma/\sqrt{N}$. The zero of the horizontal scale is $\mu = \mu_0$. Thus for the example above $\mu_0 = 5.0$, and the unit along the horizontal axis would be

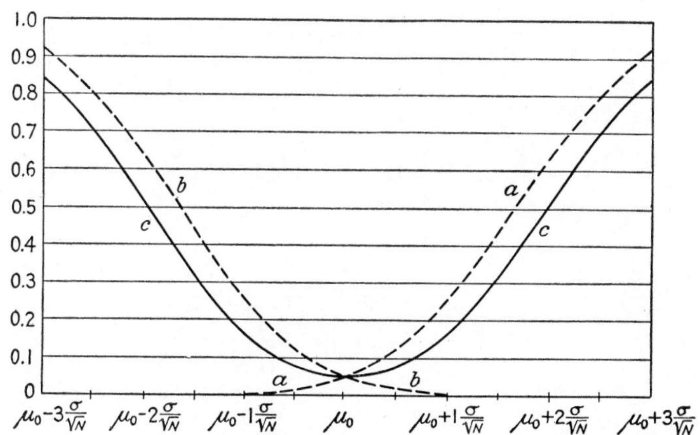

FIG. 14-5. Power functions for three tests of the hypothesis: $\mu = \mu_0$ in normal distribution, $\alpha = .05$. For $z = \dfrac{\bar{X} - \mu_0}{\sigma/\sqrt{N}}$ these tests are (a) Reject if $z > 1.645$, (b) Reject if $z < -1.645$, (c) Reject if $z > 1.96$ or if $z < -1.96$.

$(\sigma/\sqrt{N}) = 1/\sqrt{100} = .1$. An alternative of $\mu = 4.8$ would correspond to $(4.8 - 5.0)/.1 = -2.0$. Check on the graph to see that above -2.0 the heights of the three curves are, respectively, (a) .000, (b) .639, (c) .516, as we found before. Similarly above 2.0 the heights correspond to the numbers we obtained. In general the horizontal scale is read with the number $\dfrac{\mu - \mu_0}{\sigma/\sqrt{N}}$. Then the height of the curve in each case tells how frequently we would reject the hypothesis $\mu = \mu_0$ for various possible values of μ. We see that, using (a), the power is large if $\mu > \mu_0$ but very small if

$\mu < \mu_0$. The reverse is true for (*b*), while (*c*) is fairly powerful in either case.

Here we assumed a normal universe. However, the procedure is valid if the sample is large enough so that $\bar{X}$ can be assumed to have an approximately normal sampling distribution.

There are infinitely many possible regions such that $\alpha = .05$. It can be proved that (*a*) has a power curve higher than that for any other region if $\mu > \mu_0$, while (*b*) is more powerful than any other region if $\mu < \mu_0$.

If it is desired to have a test such that the power curve goes up on both sides of μ_0, then region (*c*) is the *best* region that can be found.

The figures in Table A-12*a* show power curves for one- and two-sided tests for several values of α. The deviation of the alternative mean μ from the hypothetical mean μ_0 in units of $\sigma/\sqrt{N}$ is

$$d = \frac{\mu - \mu_0}{\sigma/\sqrt{N}}$$

and is given on the horizontal axis. The power $1 - \beta$ is on the vertical axis. The values of $1 - \beta$ have been plotted on a normal-probability scale to straighten the curves. The power curves for the one-sided test are exactly straight.

Determination of Power. Thus far we have used the power curves merely to tell us which test would have the best chance of rejecting a false hypothesis. They can also be used to find the power of the adopted test against a *specified* alternative.

In the example above, the hypothesis was $\mu = 5.0$, and any of the regions gives a chance of .05 of rejecting this hypothesis if it is true. What is the chance of rejecting this hypothesis if $\mu = 5.1$? We read at

$$\frac{\mu - \mu_0}{\sigma/\sqrt{N}} = \frac{5.1 - 5.0}{1/\sqrt{100}} = 1.0$$

on the horizontal scale and the heights of the curves as (*a*) .26, (*b*) .004, (*c*) .170. If we used region (*a*) as a critical region, the chance of rejecting the hypothesis $\mu = 5.0$ if $\mu = 5.1$ is .26. Using region (*b*), the chance is .004. Using region (*c*), the chance is .170.

Sample Size. The curves can also be used to help in designing experiments by indicating how large a sample may be needed. For example, suppose we have a normal distribution with $\sigma = 1$ and we wish to test the hypothesis $\mu = 5.0$. We do not know whether the true μ is larger or smaller than 5.0, and so we shall use region (*c*) as a critical region. Suppose we wish to guard against accepting the hypothesis if μ is more than .3 unit larger or more than .3 unit smaller than 5.0 with power .80. That is, if $\mu \leq 4.7$ or if $\mu \geq 5.3$, we wish the chance of rejecting the hypothesis $\mu = 5.0$ to be at least .80. How large a sample is needed? We move across from .80 on the vertical scale until we reach the (c) curve. Below the intersection we read $2.8(\sigma/\sqrt{N})$ (approximately). We wish this to correspond to .3 unit, and so we have

$$.3 = 2.8\frac{\sigma}{\sqrt{N}} \text{ or } .3 = 2.8\frac{1}{\sqrt{N}} \text{ or } .3\sqrt{N} = 2.8 \text{ or } .09N = 7.84$$

and thus

$$N = \frac{7.84}{.09} = 87.1 \text{ or } 88$$

Two-sample Case. A method of testing the hypothesis that two populations have equal means, where the value of the common variance is known, is discussed in Sec. 9-3. We compute

$$z = \frac{\bar{X}_1 - \bar{X}_2}{\sigma\sqrt{\dfrac{1}{N_1} + \dfrac{1}{N_2}}}$$

and accept the hypothesis if the observed z is not significantly far from zero. The mean of the sampling distribution of $\bar{X}_1 - \bar{X}_2$ is equal to the difference in the means of the two populations, $\mu_1 - \mu_2$, and the hypothesis tested is $\mu_1 = \mu_2$ (that is, $\mu_1 - \mu_2 = 0$). If in fact the means are unequal and we use

$$d = \frac{\mu_1 - \mu_2}{\sigma\sqrt{\dfrac{1}{N_1} + \dfrac{1}{N_2}}}$$

the power curves are exactly the same as above and we may use Table A-12a. Suppose, for example, we take samples of sizes $N_1 = 20$, $N_2 = 20$ from two populations with $\sigma_1 = \sigma_2 = 10$ and prepare to test the hypothesis $\mu_1 = \mu_2$ at the 5 per cent level of significance. If in fact $\mu_1 - \mu_2 = 4$, that is, $d = 4/(10\sqrt{.10}) = 1.26$, we read from Table A-12a that $1 - \beta = .24$. The chance of not recognizing that these populations do not have equal means is $\beta = .76$.

Case Where σ Is Unknown. Suppose we have a normally distributed population with unknown mean μ and unknown variance σ^2. To test the hypothesis that $\mu = \mu_0$, we have used the statistic

$$t = \frac{\bar{X} - \mu_0}{s/\sqrt{N}}$$

which, if the hypothesis is true, has a t distribution with $N - 1$ degrees of freedom.

In this case the chance of rejecting μ_0 when in fact some alternative is true cannot be computed quite so simply as in the case of σ known. Two factors complicate the problem. First, the critical region, in terms of a number of standard deviations, depends on the number of degrees of freedom (e.g., for 10 degrees of freedom and $\alpha = .05$ we read from Table A-5 that $t = 2.23$ units is significant). For a large number of degrees of freedom $t = z$, and we find $z = 1.96$ units is significant. Second, the value of s in the denominator of t varies from one sample to another. For large samples, say, $N > 30$, these factors could be neglected with little error and the preceding results used. However, for smaller sample sizes or for more precise results for larger sample sizes the results are given in Table A-12*b*. The table gives the relationship among:

(*a*) $d = \dfrac{\mu - \mu_0}{\sigma/\sqrt{N}}$ for the one-sample case or

$$d = \frac{\mu_1 - \mu_2}{\sigma\sqrt{\dfrac{1}{N_1} + \dfrac{1}{N_2}}}$$ for the two-sample case.

(*b*) The level of significance, α.

(*c*) The degrees of freedom, df $= N - 1$, for the one-sample case and $N_1 + N_2 - 2$ for the two-sample case.

(*d*) The power of the test, $1 - \beta$.

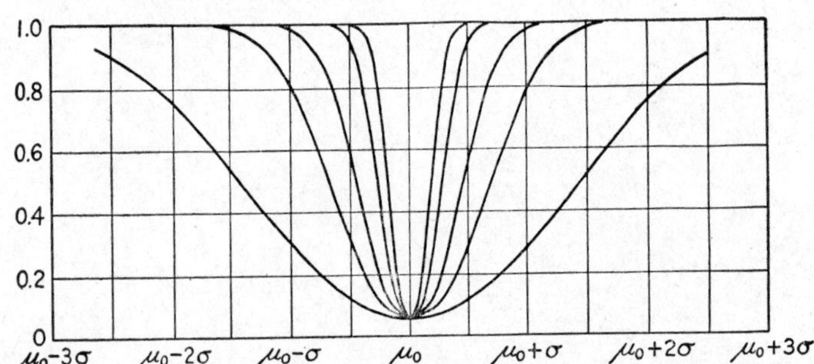

FIG. 14-6. Probability of rejecting hypothesis: $\mu = \mu_0$ using t test with critical region c. The five curves drawn, reading from the lowest curve to the highest, are for $N = 4$, 10, 20, 50, 100.

The values listed are for a one-sided test at the α level of significance or, if d is not near zero, for a two-sided test at the 2α level of significance.

For the two-sided test with $\alpha = .01$ or .05 the graphs in Table A-13 may be used with $\nu_1 = 1$, since a two-sided t test is equivalent to the analysis-of-variance test with 1 degree of freedom for the numerator. In fact, the values in the F table for $F(1,N - 1)$ are the squares of the values in the t table for $N - 1$ degrees of freedom.

Figure 14-6 shows power curves for $\alpha = .05$ for a two-sided test. The shape of the curves can be seen from this figure. The figures in Table A-12*a* have been plotted on a normal-probability scale and show only the portion for $\mu > \mu_0$.

An approximate formula for the numbers in the Table A-12*b* giving the value d for a test at the α level of significance with power $1 - \beta$ is

$$d = (z_{1-\alpha} + z_{1-\beta})[1 + 1.21(z_{1-\alpha} - 1.06)/\text{df}]$$

where $z_{1-\alpha}$ and $z_{1-\beta}$ are percentiles of the standard normal distribution in Table A-4. This formula gives accuracy within one-half of 1 per cent for the range of α and β considered in the table if df > 9. The values of $(z_{1-\alpha} + z_{1-\beta})$ are listed in the ∞ line in Table A-12*b* and are the values of d for the case where σ is known.

For example, consider a two-sided test of the hypothesis $\mu = 50$ with $\alpha = .10$ and $N = 25$. The critical region is $t < -2.06$ and $t > 2.06$, where $t = \dfrac{\bar{X} - 50}{\sqrt{s^2/25}}$. Suppose in fact that $\mu = 52$ and σ is approximately 10. Then we compute $d = \dfrac{52 - 50}{\sqrt{\frac{100}{25}}}$. In Table A-12*b* for $\alpha = .10$ (two-sided) we read across from df = 24 and find that $d = 1.0$ is between values for $1 - \beta = .2$ and $1 - \beta = .3$, showing that the chance of making the mistake of accepting $\mu = 50$ if in fact $\mu = 52$ is between 70 and 80 per cent.

Table A-12*c* lists the necessary sample size for a test to have power $1 - \beta$ against an alternative $d' = d/\sqrt{N} = (\mu - \mu_0)/\sigma$ in the single-sample case or $d' = d\sqrt{2/N} = (\mu_1 - \mu_2)/\sigma$ in the two-sample case with $N_1 = N_2 = N$. We see for the above example that to have 80 per cent power $(1 - \beta = .80)$ against an alternative $d' = (52 - 50)/10 = .2$ requires a sample of 156 individuals. If the sample size is to be fairly large, the approximate formula $N = [(z_{1-\alpha} + z_{1-\beta})/d']^2$ can be used, where as before the value of $(z_{1-\alpha} + z_{1-\beta})$ is read from the ∞ line of Table A-12*b*. In the above example we find $N = (2.487/.2)^2 = 154.6$, which is nearly equal to the value 156 obtained from the table.

Paired Data. In Sec. 9-4 is a discussion of a technique for collecting and analyzing data in pairs in order to compare two populations. The chance of accepting a hypothesis $\mu_1 - \mu_2 = 0$ using this design when the means are actually not equal can be read from Table A-12*b*, using $d = (\mu_1 - \mu_2)/\sqrt{(\sigma_1^2 + \sigma_2^2)/N}$ and df $= N - 1$, where N is the number of pairs of observations. For example, suppose we are testing the null hypothesis at the 5 per cent level of significance, using 20 pairs of observations. If in fact $\mu_1 - \mu_2 = 4$ and $\sigma_1 = \sigma_2 = 10$, $d = 4/\sqrt{10} = 1.26$ and in Table A-12*b* we see that, for df = 19, $d = 1.26$ corresponds approximately to $1 - \beta = .22$. The linear interpolation for this result can be performed as in the accompanying table. Values are interpolated for

	$1-\beta$ .2	(.22)	.3
16	1.19		1.53
df (19)	(1.18)	(1.26)	(1.52)
24	1.16		1.50

$$\frac{1.26 - 1.18}{1.52 - 1.18} = \frac{8}{34} = .2 \text{ (approximately)}$$

19 degrees of freedom for both $1 - \beta = .2$ and $1 - \beta = .3$, obtaining 1.18 and 1.52. It is then determined that 1.26 is about $\frac{2}{10}$ of the way between 1.18 and 1.52, and thus $1 - \beta$ is read $\frac{2}{10}$ of the way between $1 - \beta = .2$ and $1 - \beta = .3$, obtaining $1 - \beta = .22$.

Note that this example involves the same parameters and sample size as the preceding examples and that the paired design has a slightly smaller power $1 - \beta$. This shows that unnecessary pairing has increased our chance of making an error, due mainly to having $N - 1$ instead of $2N - 2$ degrees of freedom. The increase in this case is not great, .76 for σ known, to .77 for σ_1, σ_2 not known but equal, to .78 for paired data with $\sigma_1 = \sigma_2$.

This discussion applies only to the case where independent measurements are taken from two populations. It does not apply to the case where a pair of measurements are made on each individual since the first two tests are not appropriate. For the case of paired observations refer to Example 2 in Sec. 9-4. The appropriate d for the use of Table A-12*b* is

$$d = \frac{(\mu_1 - \mu_2)}{\sqrt{\dfrac{{\sigma_1}^2}{N_1} + \dfrac{{\sigma_2}^2}{N_2} - \dfrac{2\rho\sigma_1\sigma_2}{\sqrt{N_1N_2}}}}$$

where ρ is the correlation coefficient between the measurements.

14-3. Operating-characteristic Curves

Curves giving the chance of accepting a hypothesis are called *operating-characteristic curves* (OC curves). They are related to power curves in that the height of an operating-characteristic curve is 1 minus the height of the power curve for the same alternative. Figure 14-7 shows operating-characteristic curves for the three tests of the hypothesis that $\mu = \mu_0$ in a normal distribution (Sec. 14-2).

14-4. Power Function of Test for Proportions

In this section we shall examine the problem of testing the hypothesis that a given proportion p_0 of a population has some attribute. Alternatives will be that the true proportion p of the population having the attribute is some value other than p_0. Thus we shall test the hypothesis $p = p_0$.

It has been pointed out that if N is fairly large ($Np > 5$) the sampling distribution of the observed proportion $\bar{X}$ is approximately normal. In this case we can proceed as we did in Sec. 14-2 to test the hypothesis that the mean has a given value ($\mu = p_0$). Here $\sigma^2 = p(1 - p)$,

$$\sigma_{\bar{X}}^2 = \frac{p(1 - p)}{N}$$

For small values of N (or very small values of p) the sampling distribution of $\bar{X}$ differs considerably from normal, and the normal tables cannot be used. However, in many cases, the exact distributions have been evalu-

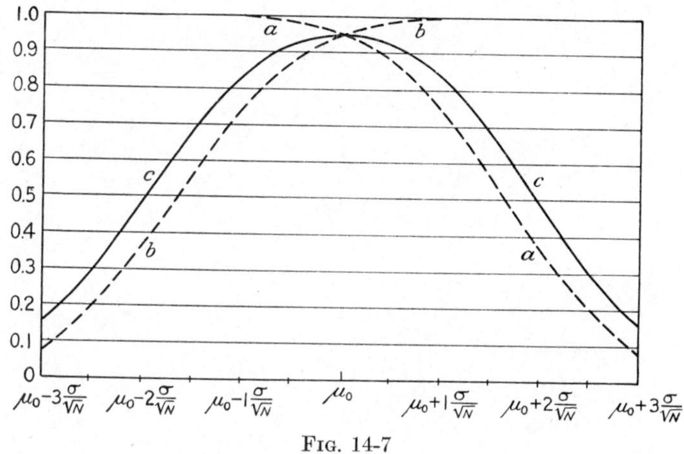

FIG. 14-7

ated. The following example discusses a case of the selection of a sample without replacement.

Example. Acceptance Sampling. Suppose we are to inspect batches of manufactured articles, each batch having K articles. Our inspection wili consist in choosing a random sample of n articles, inspecting them, and rejecting the entire batch if we find more than c defective articles among the n. The curves in Fig. 14-8 are the operating-characteristic curves for this procedure. Obviously there are many possible sets of numbers K, n, c, and a statistician would need to have either many such sets of curves or else the mathematical training needed to draw them.

These curves tell us how frequently we would accept batches having certain percentages of defective items. Thus in batches of 100 items the

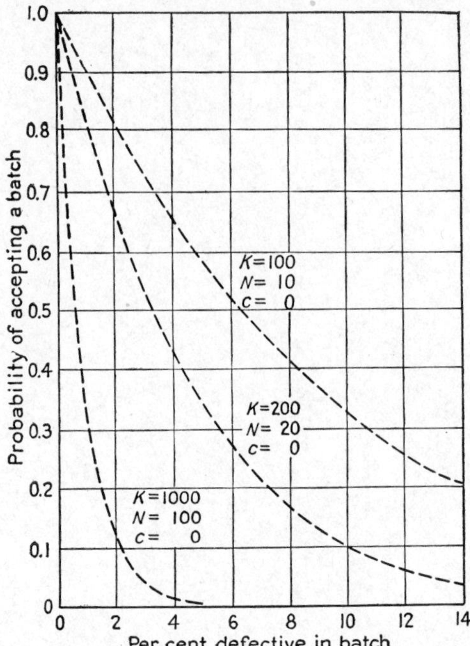

FIG. 14-8. Operating-characteristic curves; batch of size K; sample of size N.

inspection plan where we inspect 10 and reject if we observe 1 or more defective items will result in accepting batches having 2 per cent defectives 82 per cent of the time.

14-5. Power of the Analysis-of-variance Tests

The analysis-of-variance technique is used to compare means of several populations. It is assumed that each of the populations has a normal distribution with a common value σ^2 foı the variance. The means of the populations are $\mu_1, \ldots, \mu_k$, and the usual hypothesis to be tested is $\mu_1 = \mu_2 = \cdots = \mu_k$. Alternatives to this hypothesis would specify values for the $\mu_1, \ldots, \mu_k$ not all the same. We can measure the dispersion of the μ_i's by using the variance of these quantities,

$$\frac{\sum_{i=1}^{k} (\mu_i - \bar{\mu})^2}{k}$$

where $\bar{\mu} = \dfrac{\sum_{i=1}^{k} \mu_i}{k}$.

It is convenient to divide this quantity by σ^2/n, and call it ϕ^2.

$$\phi^2 = \frac{\dfrac{\sum_{i=1}^{k} (\mu_i - \bar{\mu})^2}{k}}{\dfrac{\sigma^2}{n}}$$

where n is the number of observations from each population.

This number ϕ^2 can be used to measure an alternative. The probability of rejecting the hypothesis $\mu_1 = \mu_2 = \cdots = \mu_k$ when actually they have specified unequal values can be obtained in terms of ϕ^2.

In Table A-13 are graphs giving the value of $1 - \beta$ on the vertical scale related to ϕ on the horizontal. The graphs are for two levels of significance, $\alpha = .01$ and $.05$, for eight values of ν_1, the number of degrees of freedom for the numerator, and several values of ν_2, the number of degrees of freedom in the denominator of the F ratio. Note that there is a different curve for each set of values ν_1, ν_2, and α. Consider the curve on the third page of Table A-13 for $\alpha = .05$, $\nu_1 = 3$, and $\nu_2 = 12$. This would be used, for example, in testing the hypothesis that four ($\nu_1 = 4 - 1 = 3$) populations have equal means using samples of size $n = 4$ from each population ($\nu_2 = 16 - 4 = 12$). Reading above $\phi = 2.0$, we see that the chance of recognizing that the four populations do not have equal means when actually $\phi^2 = 4$ is $1 - \beta = .82$. Thus the power of the test against any set of values $\mu_1, \mu_2, \mu_3, \mu_4$ giving $\phi^2 = 4$, is .82. The alternatives are in terms of ϕ^2 alone, not distinguishing among different sets of means which give the same value to ϕ^2. For example, the four population means could be 50, 50, 52, 52 or 50, 50, 50, 52.31 for $\sigma^2 = 1$ and give $\phi^2 = 4$.

Example 1. Suppose we are to test the hypothesis that the means of five populations are equal, using the analysis-of-variance technique at the 1 per cent level of significance. Suppose further that we know that σ^2 is approximately 100. We shall take three observations from each population. Our F ratio will have $\nu_1 = 5 - 1 = 4$ and $\nu_2 = 5(3) - 5 = 10$. We can read from the graph that we have a chance of .7 of detecting a $\phi = 2.34$ or $\phi^2 = 5.48$. Many different sets of $\mu_1, \ldots, \mu_5$ will give $\phi^2 = 5.48$. One approximate example is

$$\begin{aligned} \mu_1 &= \bar{\mu} - 27.00 \\ \mu_2 &= \bar{\mu} + 6.75 \\ \mu_3 &= \bar{\mu} + 6.75 \\ \mu_4 &= \bar{\mu} + 6.75 \\ \mu_5 &= \bar{\mu} + 6.75 \end{aligned} \qquad \phi^2 = \frac{\dfrac{(-27)^2 + 4(6.75)^2}{5}}{\dfrac{100}{3}} = 5.47$$

Here we would reject the hypothesis when such alternatives were true about 7 out of 10 times.

Example 2. A different problem which can be solved in a similar manner is as follows: Suppose μ_1, μ_2, μ_3 are 10 units larger than μ_4 and μ_5, μ_6, μ_7 are 10 units smaller than μ_4. Again we suppose a normal distribution with σ^2 known, say, $\sigma^2 = 100$. How many items should we take from each of the seven populations so that the analysis of variance with $\alpha = .05$ will have chance .7 of detecting this difference? Let n be the number taken from each population. The degrees of freedom for F are $\nu_1 = 6$ and $\nu_2 = 7n - 7$. We now compute ϕ^2.

$$\phi^2 = \frac{\dfrac{(-10)^2 3 + (10)^2 3}{7}}{\dfrac{100}{n}} = \frac{6}{7} n = .86n$$

Now we read from the $\alpha = .05$ graph for $\nu_1 = 6$ for $\nu_2 = 7n - 7$ corresponding to several values of n, each time comparing the tabled value with $.86n$ until approximate agreement is obtained. Reference was made to the graphs using $n = 2, 3, 4, 5$ and the results in the accompanying tabulation obtained. For $n = 2$ the tabular ϕ^2 is greater than $.86n$ and for $n = 3, 4, 5$ is less than $.86n$. This indicates a solution between $n = 2$ and $n = 3$. We conclude that three items should be taken from each population.

n	ν_2	$.86n$	From Table A-13	
			ϕ	ϕ^2
2	7	1.72	1.88	3.5
3	14	2.58	1.55	2.4
4	21	3.44	1.48	2.2
5	28	4.30	1.42	2.0

Two-way Classification. In dealing with a two-way classification (without replication) the procedure is the same except that ν_2 will not be $(n - 1)k$. Instead it will be $\nu_2 = (n - 1)(k - 1)$ (k columns and n rows). ϕ^2 is computed from the same formulas as above, and the examples are exactly the same except for entering the table with a different ν_2.

It is also possible to use the analysis-of-variance procedure to test for differences in row means, in which case $\nu_1 = n - 1$, $\nu_2 = (n - 1)(k - 1)$, and

$$\phi^2 = \frac{\dfrac{\sum_{i=1}^{n} (\mu_i' - \bar{\mu}')^2}{n}}{\dfrac{\sigma^2}{k}}$$

where the μ_i' are the population means for rows and

$$\bar{\mu}' = \frac{\sum_{i=1}^{n} \mu_i'}{n}$$

Latin Square. In the case of a Latin-square design where there are n rows, n columns, and n treatments, each treatment occurs once and only once in every row and column. Here $\nu_1 = n - 1$, $\nu_2 = (n - 1)(n - 2)$.

For example, suppose we have designed a Latin-square experiment to test the effects of five drugs on 25 mice. We shall have $\nu_1 = 5 - 1 = 4$, $\nu_2 = (5 - 1)(5 - 2) = 12$, and refer to the table for $\alpha = .05$, $\beta = .3$ to find $\phi = 1.69$. Thus differences in treatment means which result in $\phi = 1.69$ will be detected by the F test 7 times out of 10 with level of significance .05.

GLOSSARY

acceptance sampling	hypothesis
alternative	operating-characteristic (OC) curve
α error	power function
β error	test

DISCUSSION QUESTIONS

1. What are the two types of error? Why can only one of these errors be made in a particular problem?

2. What is the power of a test?

3. How can there be different tests of the same hypothesis? Will different tests of the same hypothesis have the same power? Can they have the same level of significance?

4. In what way is a test useful if you do not have any information about its power function? What additional information does the power function give?

5. What is the effect on the power function of increasing the sample size?

6. Which is more useful—a power curve or an operating-characteristic curve?

7. Define each term in the Glossary.

8. Explain first in your own words and second by means of an example the use and interpretation of each of the graphs in this chapter.

9. In what way does a power curve help you to design an experiment? In what way is it dangerous to ignore the power function? Can you give a practical example where you are not particularly interested in the power of a test?

CLASS EXERCISES

1. Suppose you wish to test the hypothesis that a population is normally distributed with zero mean and unit variance. As a test you agree to reject if $\bar{X} > 1.96/\sqrt{10}$. From the samples of size 10 drawn from Table A-23 estimate the chance of rejecting this hypothesis if actually the mean is 2. Using this result, test the hypothesis that the chance of rejecting is that given by the graphs in the text.

2. Put 4 red beads and 96 white beads in a box, and take samples of size $N = 10$ without replacement (i.e., take all 10 at once, record the number of red beads, and then replace the 10). From a number of such trials test the hypothesis that the value in Fig. 14-8 is correct.

Repeat this experiment with 10 red beads and 90 white beads.

Repeat this experiment with 14 red beads and 86 white beads.

3. In Class Exercise 1, Chap. 10, an estimate was obtained of the chance a particular false hypothesis would be detected by an analysis-of-variance-designed experiment. Compare the observed result with that in Table A-13.

Make the same comparison for Class Exercise 2, Chap. 10.

PROBLEMS

1. The power curves drawn in Fig. 14-5 were for the 5 per cent level of significance. Draw the similar curves for the same hypothesis for the 1 per cent level of significance.

2. In a normal distribution $\sigma = 5.0$. It is desired to test the hypothesis $\mu = 12$ with $\alpha = .05$. With a sample of 64 cases what is the chance of rejecting the hypothesis if $\mu = 14$? If $\mu = 9$? How large a sample (instead of 64) should be used if it is desired to have a chance of .60 of rejecting the hypothesis if $\mu \geq 14$ or if $\mu \leq 10$? Be careful here to use region (*c*).

3. In testing the hypothesis $\mu = 50$ in a normal distribution how frequently would you accept the hypothesis if the true mean is $.5\sigma$ above 50? ($\alpha = .05$, $N = 10$.)

4. We wish to test the hypothesis that $\mu = 50$, and we know σ is between 3 and 8. At the 5 per cent level of significance how large a sample must be taken so that the probability of rejecting $\mu = 50$ is at least .80 if μ is more than three units away from 50?

5. If we wish to select a school for a special experiment, and wish to be at least 90 per cent sure of accepting a school for the purpose if the mean IQ of its students is 105 or above, and wish to be at least 90 per cent sure of rejecting the school for the purpose if the mean IQ is 100 or less, how large a sample is needed? (Assume $\sigma = 16$.)

6. A two-sided t test is used to test at the 5 per cent level of significance that the mean height of a population is 66.0 inches. A random sample of 10 individuals is taken. Using 3 inches as an approximate value of σ, find the chance that the hypothesis will be rejected if the sample is taken from a population of mean height 67.0 inches. Of mean height 64.5 inches.

7. Two groups of 20 animals each are to be compared. If the standard deviations of the two populations are taken to be 10 pounds each, what is the chance that a t test at the 1 per cent level of significance will recognize a difference of 1 pound in the two means?

8. A one-sided t test of the hypothesis that the means of two populations are equal is to be performed at the 5 per cent level of significance on 20 pairs of individuals, one member of each pair from each population. If the standard deviations of the populations are taken to be 10 and 20 pounds, respectively, what is the chance that the t test will detect a difference of 5 pounds in the population means?

9. Suppose, in a Latin-square experiment for testing for differences in five means, one mean is actually six units larger than the other four. It is known that σ^2 is approximately 1.7. What chance would the F test have of rejecting at the 5 per cent level of significance the hypothesis that all means are equal?

10. Four schools are to be compared on the basis of the amount of knowledge the students have of current affairs. A standardized test is given to random samples of 20 students at each school. It is desired to test the hypothesis, at the 5 per cent level of significance, that the mean knowledge of current affairs, as measured by this test, is the same for all four schools. Past experience with the test has indicated that σ^2 is approximately 100. What chance would the analysis of variance have of detecting the fact that two of the school means are 10 units higher than the other two?

11. Suppose we have a single-variable-of-classification experiment with five categories and n items in each category. We wish to test the hypothesis that row means are equal at the 5 per cent level of significance. Suppose the standard deviation σ is thought to be about 10 per cent of $\bar{\mu}$. Suppose that four means are equal and the other is 10 per cent higher than the four. How large a sample is needed to have a chance of .7 of detecting this difference?

CHAPTER 15

MACROSTATISTICS

This chapter deals with those procedures of analysis which are particularly suited for the statistical treatment of very large samples. By a very large sample we shall usually mean $N > 100$, and in many cases we shall have in mind samples with several hundreds or thousands of observations.

15-1. Sorting and Tabulating Machines

The statistical treatment of large numbers of observations is often tedious unless the operations of sorting and counting can be made automatic. The treatment of census data involving millions of observations was adapted to automatic equipment about fifty years ago. The procedure used then and modified in various ways since is that of registering data on cards by punching holes in the cards in various positions. By means of the positions of the holes in the cards the machines can automatically sort and count the cards. These machines have been adopted by a large number of universities and business firms and are frequently used primarily for accounting, but they are sufficiently versatile so that they can be used for a variety of statistical applications. The International Business Machines equipment is widely used and is described here. The basic machines to be described are the punch, verifier, sorter, tabulator, reproducer, and collator.

The *punch* automatically punches a rectangular hole in successive columns of the card as the information to be recorded is "typed" on the keyboard. The *card* has 80 columns in which data can be recorded and 12 positions in each column. A single hole is punched in each column to indicate a number, and a combination of two holes is punched for letters of the alphabet. Several columns can be used to record numbers of several digits. The cards feed automatically into the machine and are advanced and stacked automatically, so that the operator records the data on the cards as fast as the keys are depressed. An efficient operator can punch and verify (automatically on another machine) several hundred cards per hour. The punches are checked for accuracy in a *verifier*, where another operator "repunches" the cards. The machine indicates discrepancies automatically.

The *sorter* can be set to "look at" a single column on each of a large stack of cards and separate into 12 different stacks of cards the original stack according to which position is punched in that column. The sorter "looks at" the card by holding a wire brush which electrically controls gates to the 12 "pockets." The cards pass under this brush, and a contact is made between the brush and a roller beneath at a varying time depending on the position punched. The sorter is usually equipped with a set of counters which tally the number of cards having each position punched without the necessity of having the cards go into the separate pockets. The sorter "leafs" through the stack of cards at the rate of 450 to 600 cards per minute.

The *tabulator* performs the functions of printing and addition. Any information punched on the cards can be printed. The printing operation is performed by a set of 88 type bars which print a whole line at a time and will print about 100 lines per minute. The tabulator can add several different sequences of numbers at the same time up to 80 digits capacity. These totals are printed automatically at intervals which can be determined by the cards themselves. The tabulator can perform a large number of specialized operations, many of which can be controlled by the cards or the numbers recorded on the cards as they pass automatically through the machine. For example, the tabulator can cause these totals to be punched in other cards in a *reproducer* attached electrically to the tabulator.

The *reproducer*, besides receiving information from the tabulator, can reproduce punches from one set of cards into another set. Certain columns can be selected for reproduction and can be reproduced into any of the columns of the new set. The reproducer can automatically verify the reproducing it is performing.

The *collator* can leaf through two packs of cards, selecting from one pack cards which have information called for on successive cards of the second pack. This machine can be used to select subsets (samples) from a pack of cards and can be used to interleaf these selected cards back into order later.

Various other machines perform specialized operations. The operations to be discussed in this chapter rely mainly on the use of a sorter for very large numbers of observations. Data may be placed on cards for analysis by the methods to be discussed here, but very frequently the observations have been made and entered on punched cards for other purposes. In engineering, routine recording of measurements on produced items is frequently maintained. Information on production and sales is regularly recorded in this fashion. The employees' time cards and information cards often contain a large amount of information. Police and hospital records are often available on punched cards. Punched cards are also used by labor unions, universities, and state bureaus. Most departments of the Federal government record data in this manner. These files of cards are usually available for special researches.

These comments on computing machinery are intended only as an introduction indicating some of the effects the machines may have on statistical procedures. No attempt is made to describe the wide variety of electronic computing machinery.

15-2. Statistical Efficiency

The estimates $\bar{X}$, s^2, and r for the mean, variance, and correlation coefficient, respectively, are efficient in the sense that we obtain the maximum amount of information from the sample. More precisely, these estimates have a smaller variance than any other estimates when our observations are from a normal population. A statistic which has a variance smaller than any other estimate of the same population parameter is called an *efficient* estimate. This is *statistical efficiency.* The relative efficiency of another estimate can be measured by dividing its variance into the variance of the efficient estimate. This quotient is called the efficiency E of the estimate. The efficiency of all estimates other than efficient estimates will then be less than 1. Note that, if we have an estimate of the population mean which is 50 per cent efficient, then the ratio of the variances is .50. Therefore, the variance of the sampling distribution of the other estimate is twice as large as the variance of the sampling distribution of $\bar{X}$. We know that the variance of $\bar{X}$ is σ^2/N; therefore, the variance of the other estimate is $2\sigma^2/N$. Suppose we take a sample of N_2 items and compute a less efficient estimate of the population mean. How large is N_1 for using $\bar{X}$ so that these estimates have the same precision? We have stated that in this example

$$\frac{\sigma^2}{N_1} = \frac{2\sigma^2}{N_2}$$

Solving this equation for N_1, we obtain $N_1 = \frac{1}{2}N_2$. We see then that we can obtain the same precision as from $\bar{X}$ if we use sample sizes twice as large and use an estimate with relative efficiency .50. If sufficient information is available and there are rapid means of examining the information, a more precise estimate may be obtained in a short time with the use of an "inefficient" statistic. The various other estimates introduced will have an advantage either in time or in effort. It is sometimes necessary to obtain estimates in a very short time. We should then use the most efficient estimate which can be obtained in the allowed time, even if it is not the estimate of greatest efficiency. It will be seen that many of these inefficient statistics allow considerable economy in obtaining the necessary measurements since in many cases only a certain few of the sample selected will actually be measured. The procedures of this chapter may be found useful when it is desired to make a preliminary exploration of large bodies of data to discover those particular aspects which may warrant further more precise analysis.

15-3. Estimates of Central Value

In symmetric populations the *median* is an estimate of μ, the population mean.

If a sampling distribution of the median were constructed by repeated samplings from a normal population with variance σ^2, we would find that the variance of this sampling distribution is $1.57\sigma^2/N$ for the large samples assumed in this chapter. For the estimation of the mean, then, the efficiency of the median P_{50} is .637.

$$E_{P_{50}} = \frac{\sigma^2/N}{1.57\sigma^2/N} = .637$$

On the average we can obtain the same precision from a median of 200 items as from an $\bar{X}$ based on 127 items. $200(.637) = 127.4$.

We can obtain higher efficiencies from the mean of several percentile values. If we wished to pick the two percentile values whose mean would give the highest efficiency possible, we could construct the sampling distributions of each suggested combination and pick that pair whose sampling distribution has the smallest dispersion. This investigation can be made mathematically, and the result here is $(P_{28.6} + P_{71.4})/2$. There is slight change in efficiency from $(P_{25} + P_{75})/2$. The latter is easier to remember and will be suggested for use here. The efficiency is .808. The efficiency can, of course, be increased by obtaining more percentile values. The efficiencies in Table A-8*a*(1) are for the percentile estimates obtained from the mean of the indicated percentiles. It might be stated that 93 per cent of the available information for estimating the mean is obtained by noting five percentile values.

Let us assume that the data are recorded on 560 cards. The percentiles can be found rapidly by arranging the cards in order of increasing magnitude of the observations and then, if the mean is to be estimated by four percentiles, letting $\frac{560}{8} = 70$ cards run through a sorter, observing the value on the 70th card, letting another 140 cards run through, etc. The mean of these four values is then computed. It should be noted that it is not necessary to record or even read the information on any but 4 of the 560 cards.

15-4. Estimates of Dispersion

The dispersion can also be estimated by percentiles. The estimate $P_{93} - P_{07}$ mentioned earlier is the particular percentile difference which is the most efficient if only two values are used. The efficiency of this estimate is .65. A third percentile value is of little use in estimating dispersion. The four percentiles which are the most efficient are P_{03}, P_{15}, P_{85}, P_{97}. Here we compute $P_{97} + P_{85} - P_{15} - P_{03}$. Using these four values, the efficiency is increased to .80. Other results in addition to these are contained in Table A-8*a*(2).

The values for the coefficients in the percentile estimates for the standard deviation [Table A-8*a*(2)] are obtained from the normal distribution. For example, the difference between P_{07} and P_{93} for a normal distribution is from $\mu - 1.476\sigma$ to $\mu + 1.476\sigma$ as read from Table A-4. This difference is 2.952σ. The coefficient $.3388 = 1/2.952$. We divide our estimate of 2.952σ by 2.952 (or multiply by .3388) to obtain an estimate of σ. The coefficient for the second estimate is $.1714 = 1/5.834$, where 5.834 is obtained as for the first estimate, $2(1.881) + 2(1.036)$.

The efficiencies of the estimates of the standard deviation are obtained by comparing these estimates with an estimate obtained from the sample variance. For the large sample sizes considered here, we can state as we did for estimates of the mean that equal precision is available from an estimate which is 50 per cent efficient by examining a sample twice as large. For example, if we consider a sample of 300 items and compute the percentile estimate of σ based on four percentiles, we see that equivalent precision could be obtained from the computation of s^2 for a sample of $300(.80) = 240$ observations.

An example of the use of this procedure is as follows: Suppose the percentiles of a distribution of values are

P	X	
97	45.2	
85	39.2	84.4
15	25.0	
03	18.6	43.6
		40.8

We add P_{97} and P_{85} and subtract the sum of P_{15} and P_{03}. The estimate of σ is $(40.8)(.1714) = 6.99$.

For estimation of the mean we obtain high efficiencies by finding percentiles which are near the center. For estimating the standard deviation the best percentiles are closer to the end of the distribution. We are often interested in estimating both the mean and standard deviation. Percentile values which can be used for estimating both, and the efficiencies for the estimation of each, are given in Table A-8*a*(3). These values are not the best for each but are a compromise, giving fairly high efficiencies for both the mean and standard deviation and using percentiles easy to remember. The values of K are the multipliers for the estimate of σ.

As an example of the use of these values, suppose that a stack of 572 cards is arranged in order on a certain observation. If we wish to use six percentiles to estimate the mean and standard deviation, we note, from Table A-8*a*(3), percentages 05, 15, 40, 60, 85, 95. We multiply each by 572 and obtain 29, 86, 229, 343, 486, 543. We find the value of the observation on card 29, on card 86, etc. We add these and divide by 6 to obtain an estimate of the mean μ. We add the last three and subtract the first three and multiply by K (in this case .1704) to obtain our estimate of σ. These estimates are of the same precision in sampling from a normal population as an $\bar{X}$ obtained from a sample of $572(.89) = 509$ items and an s obtained from a sample of $572(.80) = 458$ items.

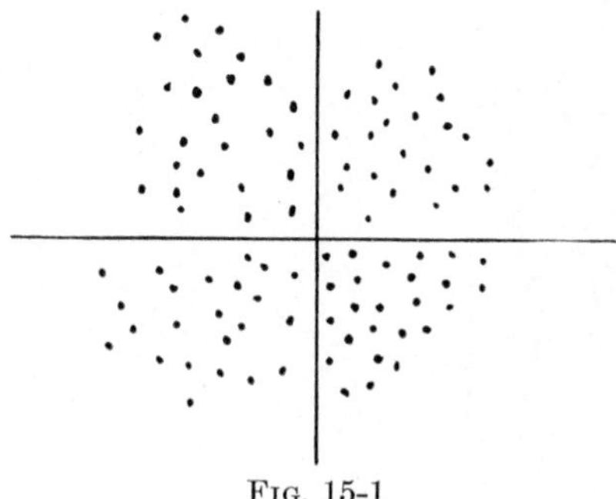

FIG. 15-1

The *mean deviation* from the mean and the mean deviation from the median have been used for many years. They are computed by finding the mean of the absolute deviations from the mean or median. To estimate σ, the mean deviation for large samples must be multiplied by $\sqrt{\pi/2} = 1.253$. The efficiency of the mean deviation for large samples is .88. It will not be investigated further here since we can obtain a more efficient estimate from eight percentile values.

15-5. Estimates of Correlation

Suppose there is a linear relationship between two variables and a number of observations are made on those variables. Let us plot the results on a graph and observe, if there is a positive relationship, that by dividing the data in half with a horizontal line and then in half by a vertical line there will be more observations in the upper right and lower left quadrants. There will be more in the upper left and lower right if there is an inverse relationship.

If we designate by n_1, n_2, n_3, n_4 the number of points in each quadrant (for example, see Fig. 15-1),

n_2	n_1
n_3	n_4

we first compute

$$\frac{n_1 + n_3}{n_1 + n_2 + n_3 + n_4} \quad \text{or} \quad \frac{n_2 + n_4}{n_1 + n_2 + n_3 + n_4}$$

whichever is larger, and refer to Fig. 15-2. Enter Fig. 15-2 at the bottom; read up to the curve marked $\lambda = .50$ and left to the scale marked "Estimate of ρ." The correlation is positive if the first ratio is used and negative if the second is used. The curve for $\lambda = .50$ is used since the vertical line divides the observations into two equal groups.

The use of the graph for obtaining the estimate of ρ avoids the need of substitution in a formula. If the observations are from a normal bivariate population, this estimate of ρ, called *tetrachoric r*, has efficiency of .40 as compared with the efficient estimate r.

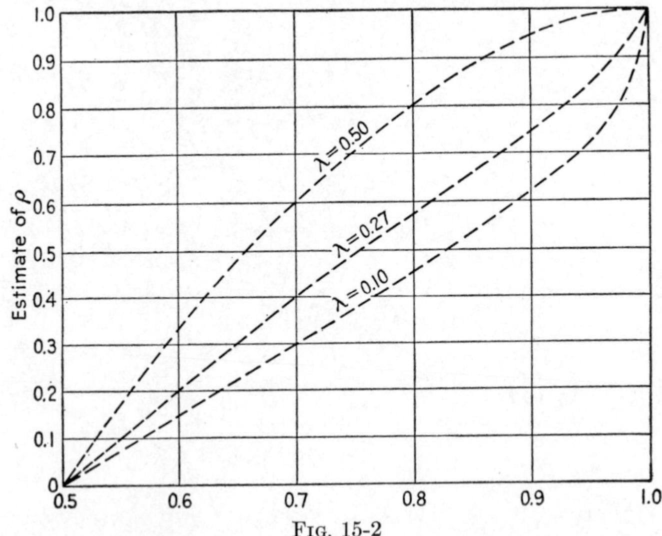

FIG. 15-2

The efficiency of this estimate is low, and the following procedure, which is little more difficult, will be presented since its efficiency is .52. It should be stated that these efficiencies are computed under the assumption that $\rho = 0$. In order to maintain precision, it may be more efficient in time and effort to analyze a sample approximately twice the size by this less efficient method.

The modified procedure is as follows, where the measurements we investigate for correlation are X and Y:

1. Retain the observations whose X is among the top or bottom 27 per cent; discard the remainder.

2. Separate each of these groups into upper and lower halves with respect to the Y value.

Estimate ρ as before except that the line $\lambda = .27$ will be used in place of the line $\lambda = .50$. Any value of λ from zero to .50 may be used, but the estimate of highest efficiency is obtained by using $\lambda = .27$. If the observations are plotted on a graph, this estimate can be obtained by drawing lines as indicated in Fig. 15-3 and counting the dots in the four

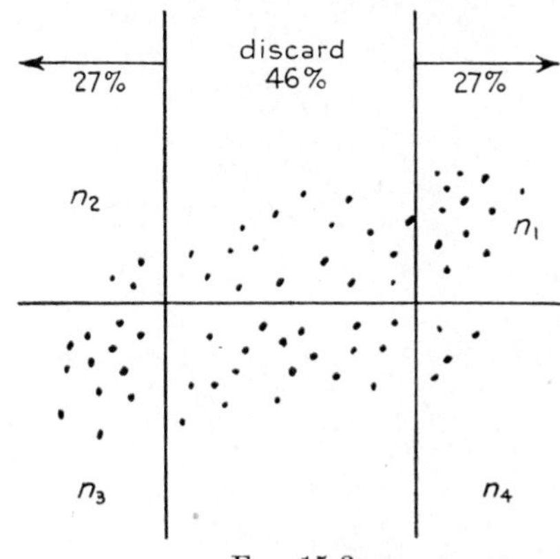

FIG. 15-3

corner sections. If the observations are punched on cards, it is not necessary to record the values of any of the observations, but merely to count cards as indicated below. We can use the counting sorter as follows:

1. Sort the cards into order on the X value.

2. Retain only those cards whose X observations are in the upper and lower 27 per cent.

3. Sort the retained cards into order on the Y value.

4. Retain only the half with larger Y values.

5. Sort the remaining cards on X again. The number of cards in the last group which were in the upper 27 per cent after the first sort is n_1; the remaining number in this last group is n_2. Note that $n_1 = n_3$ and $n_2 = n_4$, and we can estimate ρ as before.

Discussion of Percentile Estimate. It has been proposed that the percentile estimates presented in this chapter are superior to the efficient estimates in that they are affected little by a small percentage of very extreme values. If these extreme values are more numerous or more extreme than would be expected by sampling from a normal population, there may be reason to prefer these percentile estimates. However, the principal reason for the presentation of these methods is the considerable saving in time and effort gained by the use of these estimates. Percentile estimates are particularly useful in situations where it is not difficult to arrange objects in order of size but is difficult actually to measure the objects. For example, if a percentile estimate of the standard deviation is used, the actual measurement of only 8 objects in a sample of 300 objects will give equivalent precision to the actual measurement of $300(.90) = 270$ objects.

GLOSSARY

machines:
- collator
- punch
- reproducer
- sorter
- tabulator
- verifier

percentile estimates
statistical efficiency
tetrachoric r

DISCUSSION QUESTIONS

1. Define the terms in the Glossary.

2. Give an example of a situation in which the observations may easily be ordered before the actual measurements are made.

3. Describe a procedure for selecting random samples from a population recorded on cards by using random numbers which are punched on cards.

4. Describe a sampling experiment for estimating the efficiency of the estimate of ρ obtained by the procedure described on page 268, with $\lambda = .10$.

CLASS EXERCISE

Use two adjacent columns in Table A-2 as pairs of uncorrelated observations. For samples of size 50 compute tetrachoric r, using the population median in place of the sample median. This can easily be done from Table A-2, which has median zero, since n_1 is the number of pairs with both signs positive and n_3 is the number of pairs of items with both signs negative. Collect the results into a distribution. From the variance of this distribution and the variance of the correlation coefficient $1/(N - 1)$, estimate the efficiency of the substitute method.

PROBLEMS

1. If percentiles 07 and 93 of a distribution of data give the values -27 and 58, what is an estimate of the standard deviation? What is the efficiency of that estimate? Can the mean be estimated from these values?

2. The selection of percentiles 17, 50, 83 from a large body of data yields the values 127, 136, 147. Estimate the mean and state the efficiency of the estimate.

3. Suppose percentiles were run off from a distribution of 3,000 items as in the tabulation. If you were asked to compute estimates of the mean using only four of these values, which would you use? Compute your estimate of the mean. Compute in a similar manner an estimate of the standard deviation based on two items. If you were asked to estimate both the mean and standard deviation from the same four values, which would you select? Compute estimates of the mean and standard deviation from these values.

P	X	P	X
95	150	45	97
90	139	40	91
85	130	35	88
80	126	30	84
75	120	25	80
70	116	20	75
65	112	15	69
60	107	10	62
55	104	05	50
50	100		

How would you use all 19 percentiles to estimate μ? How could you use all 19 percentiles to estimate σ? Find the multipliers to make the estimate of σ unbiased.

4. In estimating correlation by the method of counting the number of measurements in the four quadrants of the data picked as lying in the end 27 per cent regions,

150	50
50	150

the values were as in the tabulation. Estimate the coefficient of correlation, and state the efficiency of your estimate.

CHAPTER 16

MICROSTATISTICS

In this chapter we shall investigate various statistics computed on samples of size $N \leq 20$, from a normal population. With the assumption of normality the statements "The mean is more efficient than the median" and "The sample standard deviation s is more efficient than the range" are true. These statements may be false for samples from nonnormal populations. When we use the material in this chapter, we presuppose we may assume that the population distribution is normal.

The observations will be arranged in order of size and labeled X_1, X_2, . . . , X_N. Thus X_1 is the smallest of the N observations, X_2 is the second smallest, etc. When arranged in this way the observations are called *order statistics*.

It is not difficult to obtain approximate verification of the various results presented in this chapter by using random normal numbers from Table A-2. One can form a number of samples of fixed size, compute one or all of the estimates discussed for each sample, and collect the results for comparison with the tabled values. This procedure was carried out in detail for the median and range in Chap. 6.

16-1. Estimates of Central Value

Three alternate estimates of central value will be considered.

The *median* of an odd number of observations is the observation with an equal number of observations on either side. The median of an even number of observations is the mean of the two middle values. For this definition of median and for samples of similar size the efficiency of the median is higher for the even sample sizes than for odd sample sizes. For larger sample sizes the efficiency levels off and approaches .637. Here as in previous chapters the efficiency of the median is the ratio of the variances of the sampling distributions of the mean and the median. The variance and the efficiency of the median are listed in Table A-8*b*(4).

The *midrange*, $M_r = (X_1 + X_N)/2$, is the mean of the largest and smallest observations and estimates the mean of the population. The efficiencies relative to the sample mean are shown in Table A-8*b*(4). It is probably not advisable to use the midrange for samples of more than five observations since for larger sample sizes its efficiency drops below that of the median.

In Chap. 15 it was noted that in large samples the most efficient estimate to be obtained from two observations is the mean of $P_{28.6}$ and $P_{71.4}$. Except for very small samples the median and midrange are computed from observations which are not near these percentiles; so we may expect that two observations may be selected whose mean is more efficient. Table A-8*b*(4) indicates for each sample size the best choice of two observations for estimating the mean of a normal population. For example, in a sample of size $N = 10$, the statistic $(X_3 + X_8)/2$ is more efficient than $(X_1 + X_{10})/2$ or $(X_4 + X_7)/2$ or any other such estimate based on two observations.

Table 16-1 illustrates the computation of these statistics on seven observations ($N = 7$) from a normal population arranged in order of size, $X_1 = 0.676$, $X_2 = 1.113$, etc. The data were taken from Table A-23 which are observations from a normal population with $\mu = 2$ and $\sigma = 1$.

TABLE 16-1

Statistic	Formula	Computation	Result
Mean	$\Sigma X_i/N$	13.668/7	1.953
Midrange	$\frac{1}{2}(X_1 + X_7)$	(0.676 + 3.445)/2	2.060
Median	X_4	1.847	1.847
Mean best two	$\frac{1}{2}(X_3 + X_5)$	(1.707 + 2.167)/2	1.937

Observations: 0.676, 1.113, 1.707, 1.847, 2.167, 2.713, 3.445.

16-2. Estimates of Dispersion

The range is frequently used as a measure of dispersion for a very small number of observations. The range is the difference between the largest and smallest observations, $X_N - X_1 = w$. We noted in Chap. 6 that the range is a biased estimate of σ. By multiplying the computed range by the coefficient in Table A-8*b*(1), we obtain an unbiased estimate of σ.

The *mean deviation* can be used to estimate σ. It is easy to compute for small samples if the deviations are taken from the median. Table A-8*b*(2) indicates the computation of the sum of these deviations. The multiplier to convert this sum to an unbiased estimate of σ and the efficiency of this estimate are also included. Instead of computing the mean of the differences indicated in the column headed "Computation," that factor has been included in the multiplier to simplify computation.

The efficiencies of the range and mean deviation are less than for estimates simpler to compute than the mean deviation. For sample sizes from 5 to 10 these estimates use the difference of the sum of the two largest values and the sum of the two smallest values. For larger sample sizes three or four of the largest and smallest values are used. Table A-8*b*(3) indicates the values to use in computing an estimate of σ which will give the highest efficiency for an estimate of this type. The coefficient is such that this statistic will give an unbiased estimate of σ.

Best Linear Estimate of σ. The estimation of σ by a linear function of the observations requires the use of different coefficients for the different observations if it is to be the best estimate in the sense of being the most efficient unbiased linear estimate. For samples of size 2 or 3 this estimate is the same as above. However, beginning with samples of size 4 a greater efficiency is obtained by computing the estimates as given in Table A-8*b*(6). The efficiency of each of these estimates is also indicated.

The computation of the estimates of dispersion given in this section is illustrated in Table 16-2 for the same data used in Table 16-1.

TABLE 16-2

Statistic	Computation	Est. of σ
Range	.370(3.445 − 0.676)	1.025
Mean deviation	.2031(3.445 + 2.713 + 2.167 − 1.707 − 1.113 − 0.676)	0.981
Modified linear est.	.2370(3.445 + 2.713 − 1.113 − 0.676)	1.035
Best linear est.	.2778(3.445 − 0.676) + .1351(2.713 − 1.113) + .0625(2.167 − 1.707)	1.014

For this particular sample the "Best linear estimate" actually was the closest to μ of the four statistics, but for other samples it may not be the closest. The higher efficiency for the "Best linear estimate" indicates that with all possible samples the values of this statistic will vary less (have a smaller standard deviation) than the values of the other statistics.

16-3. Substitute *t* Ratio

The inefficient estimates given in the previous sections can be combined to form ratios similar to the *t* ratio $\dfrac{\bar{X} - \mu}{s/\sqrt{N}}$.

Mean over Range. If the arithmetic mean is retained in the numerator and s in the denominator is replaced by the estimate $K_1 w$ obtained from the range w, we could form the ratio $\dfrac{\bar{X} - \mu}{K_1 w/\sqrt{N}}$ and use this statistic to test hypotheses about μ. It is simpler to compute $\tau_1 = (\bar{X} - \mu)/w$. Percentiles of the sampling distribution of τ_1 are given in Table A-8*c*(1) for sample sizes up to 20. The percentiles at the top of the table are the upper percentage points. The lower percentage points are obtained by entering the foot of the table and prefixing the tabulated value with a minus sign. Since the range has high efficiency for small sample sizes, it can be expected that τ_1 will have high efficiency as a substitute for t.

The ranges may be used in a substitute for the t ratio for differences between means. Percentiles for the statistic $\tau_d = \dfrac{\bar{X}_1 - \bar{X}_2}{\frac{1}{2}(w_1 + w_2)}$ are given in Table A-8c(2) for samples of equal size up to 20.

Midrange over Range. Using the midrange as an estimate of μ and the range as an estimate of σ has an advantage as both are computed from the same two observations. This substitute t ratio is $\tau_2 = (M_r - \mu)/w$. It should be noted that the efficiency of the midrange decreases rapidly for sample sizes greater than 5. The efficiency of the midrange, however, is larger than that of the median for the smaller sample sizes. A comparison of the power function for this test with the power function for the t test for smaller sample sizes shows that an additional observation will compensate for the loss in performance of this statistic in samples up to size 8 at the 1 per cent level of significance and in samples up to size 6 at the 5 per cent level of significance. For larger sample sizes the loss in performance is greater. Percentiles of the distribution of τ_2 are given in Table A-8c(3) for samples of size 10 or less.

16-4. Substitute F Ratio

The ratio of two ranges can be used as substitute for the ratio of two variances. Although it is somewhat less efficient for normal populations, it may be advisable to use such a substitute if the time available is seriously limited. Several percentiles for the distribution of the ratio of two ranges are given in Table A-8d for respective sample sizes N_1 and N_2 less than or equal to 10. The hypothesis $\sigma_1 = \sigma_2$ is rejected if w_1/w_2 is significantly large or small. For example, if two samples of sizes $N_1 = N_2 = 5$ are used to test the hypothesis $\sigma_1 = \sigma_2$ at the 5 per cent level of significance, we may use the critical region $w_1/w_2 < .32$ and $w_1/w_2 > 3.2$. For the one-sided test $\sigma_1 \leq \sigma_2$ the 5 per cent critical region is $w_1/w_2 > 2.6$.

16-5. Processing Data for Extreme Values

Sometimes a statistical criterion is desired which will indicate whether or not the largest or smallest observation is significantly far removed from the main body of the data. Such extreme observations, or *outliers*, may occur because of *gross errors*, or *blunders*, or may be from a population other than the population from which the rest of the data come, or may result from the fact that the population under investigation contains a certain proportion of extreme cases and our sample happens to include one. Of course, individual observations of any of the three types above may occur in the main body of the sample and not be recognized by statistical techniques which test the extreme observations in the sample.

As an example of a possible gross error, consider the results of weighing an object four times. The four observations are 20.1, 20.0, 20.1, 19.1. It seems likely that the observation 19.1 is an incorrect reading or gross error.

An anthropologist may wish to decide whether a particular skeleton belongs to the same population as the remainder of a group of skeletons. We have an example of populations which contain a group of extreme measurements in income studies where a small portion of the population has very high incomes. In the first two examples the research worker may wish to eliminate extreme values from his sample before making statistical inferences about the populations. However, in the third example we may wish to treat an individual with high income in the sample as representative of the population on equal terms with any other member of the sample.

A statistic which can be used to detect outliers in either direction (too large or too small) is w/σ, the range divided by the population σ if it is known, or $q = w/s$ if σ is not known. Percentiles of the sampling distribution of w/σ are given in Table A-8*b*(1), and percentiles for $q = w/s$ are given in Table A-18. In either case, if a significantly large value is observed, we view this as evidence that the most extreme observation is from a different population. The tables of percentiles for both statistics are based on the assumption that the observations come from a normally distributed population.

An alternative set of test statistics and several percentiles of their sampling distributions are given in Table A-8*e*. These r ratios compare the distance of one end observation from its neighbors with the range of all, or all but one or two, of the observations. For example, for the four observations ordered by size 326, 177, 176, 157, Table A-8*e* indicates the use of $r_{10} = \dfrac{X_2 - X_1}{X_4 - X_1} = \dfrac{177 - 326}{157 - 326} = .882$, and since this is greater than the 95th percentile .765, we reject at the 5 per cent level the hypothesis that the observation 326 is from the same population as the other observations. Note that X_1 in Table A-8*e* can be either the largest or the smallest observation in the sample. Also X_i may be individual observations or the means of equal-size samples. The percentiles in Table A-8*e* are based on the assumption that the observations are from a normal population.

In place of tagging an individual observation from another population, we may be concerned with estimating the parameters of the basic distribution free from these contaminating effects. How might we process the data so that our estimates will come closer to the mean and standard deviation of this basic distribution? If very little is known about the distribution from which the extraneous observations may come, about the best one can do is to "tag" observations and remove them from estimates of μ and σ. If even a moderate amount is known about the distribution of extreme values in the population, rules can be stated for samples of size less than 20 which minimize the effects on the estimates of μ and σ of any outliers which may be present. Such rules are given in Table 16-3 and are used as follows:

Decide from past experience or from knowledge of the measuring apparatus whether the outliers are causing light, medium, or heavy effects on the samples. The table gives examples to indicate what is meant by these rough categories. The column α indicates the percentiles of the r distributions to be used in tagging outliers. The ratios are used repeatedly until no additional observations can be tagged. The mean and standard deviation are then estimated from the remaining observations as recommended in the table, i.e., the mean by $\bar{X}$ or the median and the standard deviation by the range or the sample standard deviation.

TABLE 16-3. RULES FOR ESTIMATION IN THE PRESENCE OF OUTLIERS

Degree	Examples	α	$N \leq 10$		$10 < N < 20$	
			Mean	s.d.	Mean	s.d.
Light.....	Up to {10% obs. shifted 1σ; 5% obs. shifted 2σ; 1% obs. shifted 10σ}	.05	$\bar{X}$	Range	$\bar{X}$	s
Medium..	Up to {30% obs. shifted 1σ; 10% obs. shifted 3σ; 5% obs. shifted 9σ}	.10	$\bar{X}$	Range	Median	s
Heavy....	Over amounts for medium	.20	Median	Range	Median	s

Example. Suppose samples of size 5 are taken and it is expected that about 10 per cent of the observations will be shifted by three to four standard deviations. This falls in the medium classification which prescribes $\alpha = .10$ and estimation with $\bar{X}$ and the range for sample sizes under 10. The observations recorded in order of size are: $X_1 = 23.2$, $X_2 = 23.4$, $X_3 = 23.5$, $X_4 = 24.1$, $X_5 = 25.5$. We note by inspection that $X_1 = 23.2$ would not be rejected. To test $X_5 = 25.5$, we compute

$$r_{10} = \frac{25.5 - 24.1}{25.5 - 23.2} = \frac{1.4}{2.3} = .609 \qquad (r_{10})_{.90} = .557$$

Therefore X_5 is rejected. We now proceed with $N = 4$ and test X_4 by computing

$$r_{10} = \frac{24.1 - 23.5}{24.1 - 23.2} = \frac{.6}{.9} = .667 \qquad (r_{10})_{.90} = .679$$

Therefore X_4 is not rejected. We estimate μ with

$$\bar{X} = \frac{(23.2 + 23.4 + 23.5 + 24.1)}{4} = 23.55$$

and estimate σ by $.486w = .486(24.4 - 23.2) = .44$. The use of a large value of α will discover more outliers when they are present but, of course, will make the estimates of μ and σ less precise if the samples do not contain outliers. This loss of precision is, however, small and usually is very small compared with the reduction in precision in the estimates if even occasional extreme values are not removed.

16-6. Discussion of Inefficient Statistics for Small Samples

The choice of one of the procedures discussed in this chapter will often depend on which estimate is the easiest or quickest to compute in a particular situation, and, of course, the substitution of the method will also depend on the relative efficiency of the substitute method. The less efficient statistics may be quite adequate for the following purposes:

1. For *preliminary*, or *pilot*, *studies* which are based on very few observations from which rough estimates of population parameters are made for use in the principal study to follow.

2. For *rapid computation*, perhaps performed by slide rule or by mental calculation for use in surveying a large number of data in search of portions of the data which may require more precise or extensive analysis.

3. For *simple computation* where the test is to be made by an individual who does not have the time to perform and check computations. The simpler computation will in general introduce fewer errors due to the computation itself.

In connection with the third point the authors have conducted classroom sampling experiments where both s and the range are computed for small samples where the efficiency of the range is high. The computed values were collected into distributions for the comparison of the variances, i.e., to investigate the efficiency of the range as an estimate of σ. When these values are collected into distributions before the students have checked and corrected their computations, more often than not the variance of the estimate obtained from the range is smaller than the variance of the distribution of s values.

GLOSSARY

extreme values
linear estimate
substitute F ratio
substitute t ratio

DISCUSSION QUESTIONS

1. State why the critical value for $N = 2$ for τ_1 is equal to the critical value for $N = 2$ for τ_2.

2. Describe a situation where it might be advantageous to use one of the statistics of this chapter.

3. Discuss the comparative frequencies with which the confidence intervals using t and those using τ_1 cover the population mean.

CLASS EXERCISE

Each student computes the following statistics, if not already computed, for the six samples of 10 observations each used in previous class exercises:

(*a*) Median
(*b*) Midrange
(*c*) Range
(*d*) Mean deviation
(*e*) τ_1
(*f*) τ_2
(*g*) τ_d (for pairs of samples)

Estimate from distributions of the above statistics (*a*) the efficiencies of the median and midrange as estimates of the population mean by comparison with sample mean, (*b*) the efficiencies of the range and mean deviation as estimates of the population σ by comparison with the sample standard deviation s.

Compare the performance of τ_1, τ_2, τ_d as substitutes for t by comparing the lengths of confidence intervals from these substitutes with the lengths of confidence intervals obtained by using t.

If distributions of the sample means, sample standard deviations, and t values both for single samples and for pairs of samples have not been constructed previously, they should be prepared for comparison with the distributions described above.

PROBLEMS

1. Analyze Example 3 in Sec. 9-3, using τ_d.

2. Analyze the data of Example 2 in Sec. 9-3, using the ratio of ranges to test for difference in dispersion.

3. Analyze Prob. 1 of Chap. 9, using τ_d.

4. Analyze Prob. 4 of Chap. 9, using τ_1 and using τ_2.

5. Analyze Prob. 7 of Chap. 9, using τ_1 and using τ_2.

6. Given the following measurements on per cent Na_2O in soda ash: 40.32, 40.37, 40.27, 40.35, 40.30. Determine 90 per cent confidence limits for the population mean μ, using (*a*) $\bar{X}$ and s, (*b*) $\bar{X}$ and w, (*c*) midrange and w.

7. Use the methods of this chapter to analyze Prob. 2, Chap. 17. In particular, consider the ninth pair for rejection.

CHAPTER 17

NONPARAMETRIC STATISTICS

In previous chapters we have usually assumed that the population had some known form. Frequently we assumed a normal distribution, and we estimated, or tested hypotheses about, the means and variances. Recent advances in statistics have been in the direction of attempts to find test statistics which would compare distributions without specifying the form of the distributions. Since the comparison is between distributions and not between parameters, the procedures are frequently called *nonparametric statistics*. Probably the most widely used nonparametric technique is the χ^2 test for independence and goodness of fit. In this chapter we shall consider certain other nonparametric techniques.

17-1. The Sign Test

In experimental investigations, it is often desired to compare two materials or treatments under various sets of conditions. Pairs of observations (one observation for each of the two materials or treatments) are obtained for each of the separate sets of conditions. For example, in comparing the yield of two hybrid lines of corn, A and B, one might have a few results from each of several experiments carried out under widely varying conditions. The experiments may have been performed on different soil types, with different fertilizers, and in different years with consequent variations in seasonal effects such as rainfall, temperature, amount of sunshine, etc. It is supposed that both hybrids appeared equally often in each block of each experiment so that the observed yields occur in pairs (one yield for each line) produced under quite similar conditions.

The above example illustrates the circumstances under which the sign test is most useful, viz.:

1. There are pairs of observations on two things being compared.
2. Each of the two observations of a given pair was made under similar conditions.
3. The different pairs were observed under different conditions.

This last condition generally makes the t test invalid, since this would usually mean the differences have different variances. If this were not the case (i.e., if all the pairs of observations were comparable), the t test would ordinarily be employed unless there were other reasons, for example, obvious nonnormality, for not using it.

Even when the t test is the appropriate technique, the sign test may be used because of its extreme simplicity. One merely counts the number of positive and negative differences and refers to a table of significance values. Frequently the question of significance may be settled at once by the sign test without any need for calculations.

It should be pointed out that, strictly speaking, the methods of this section are applicable only to the case in which no ties in paired comparisons occur. In practice, however, even when ties would not occur if measurements were sufficiently precise, ties do occur because measurements are often made only to the nearest unit or tenth of a unit, for example. Such ties should be excluded.

Finally, it is assumed that the differences between paired observations are independent, i.e., that the outcome of one pair of observations is in no way influenced by the outcome of any other pair.

Procedure. Let A and B represent two materials or treatments to be compared. Let X and Y represent measurements made on A and B. Let the number of pairs of observations be N. The N pairs of observations and their differences may be denoted by

$$(X_1,Y_1),\ (X_2,Y_2),\ \ldots\ ,\ (X_N,Y_N)$$

and

$$X_1 - Y_1,\ X_2 - Y_2,\ \ldots\ ,\ X_N - Y_N$$

The sign test is based on the signs of these differences. The letter r will be used to denote the number of times the less frequent sign occurs. If some of the differences are zero, they will be excluded and the sample size reduced.

As an example of the type of data for which the sign test is appropriate, we may consider the data in Table 17-1 giving the yields of two hybrid lines of corn obtained from several different experiments. In this example $N = 28$, and $r = 7$.

The null hypothesis here is that each difference has a probability distribution (which need not be the same for all differences) with median equal to zero. This null hypothesis will be true, for instance, if each difference is symmetrically distributed about a mean of zero, although such symmetry is not necessary. We shall reject the null hypothesis when the numbers of positive and negative signs differ significantly from equality.

Table A-10a gives the critical values of r for 1, 5, 10, 25 per cent levels of significance. A value of r less than or equal to the tabled value is significant at the given per cent level.

Table A-10b gives percentiles for the sampling distribution of the number of plus signs when the hypothesis is true. This is the binomial distribution with $p = \frac{1}{2}$. In general there are no values of r which correspond exactly to the usual levels of significance, for example, $\alpha = .05$ or $\alpha = .01$. However, we can find levels of significance close to any desired level if the sample size is fairly large. In the example in Table 17-1, where $N = 28$, we find from Table A-10*b* that a one-sided test of the hypothesis that the population consists of 50 per cent or more plus signs can be made at the $\alpha = .044$ level by rejecting if 9 or fewer *plus* signs are observed in the sample. Similarly a one-sided test of the hypothesis that the population consists of 50 per cent or fewer plus signs can be made at the $\alpha = .044$ level by rejecting if 9 or fewer *minus* signs (i.e., more than 18 plus signs)

TABLE 17-1. YIELDS OF TWO HYBRID LINES OF CORN

Experiment No.	Yield of		Sign of $X - Y$	Experiment No.	Yield of		Sign of $X - Y$
	A	B			A	B	
1	47.8	46.1	+	4	40.8	41.3	−
	48.6	50.1	−		39.8	40.8	−
	47.6	48.2	−		42.2	42.0	+
	43.0	48.6	−		41.4	42.5	−
	42.1	43.4	−				
	41.0	42.9	−	5	38.9	39.1	−
					39.0	39.4	−
2	28.9	38.6	−		37.5	37.3	+
	29.0	31.1	−				
	27.4	28.0	−	6	36.8	37.5	−
	28.1	27.5	+		35.9	37.3	−
	28.0	28.7	−		33.6	34.0	−
	28.3	28.8	−				
	26.4	26.3	+	7	39.2	40.1	−
	26.8	26.1	+		39.1	42.6	−
3	33.3	32.4	+				
	30.6	31.7	−				

are observed in the sample. A two-sided test at the $\alpha = 2(.044) = .088$ level of significance can be made by rejecting the hypothesis if 9 or fewer plus signs or if 9 or fewer minus signs are observed in the sample. This two-sided test criterion designates the critical region as values of r less than or equal to 9. If the data in Table 17-1 are used to test the two-sided hypothesis, we shall reject the hypothesis at the $\alpha = .088$ level since there are only $r = 7$ plus signs in the sample.

For small samples it is often impossible to find a critical region of a given size. For example, if we desire a two-sided test at the $\alpha = .10$ level using $N = 12$ observations, we see in Table A-10*b* that the closest choices are $\alpha = 2(.019) = .038$ (rejecting if $r \leq 2$) and $\alpha = 2(.073) = .146$ (rejecting if $r \leq 3$). Even if the hypothesis of the population having 50 per cent plus and 50 per cent minus signs is true, a sample of size 4 or even one of size 5 will have more than a 5 per cent chance of having all signs alike. Four signs alike in a sample of size 4 will occur with a chance .125 and five signs alike in a sample of size 5 will occur with chance .0625 if the hypothesis is true. Therefore it is necessary to have at least six pairs of observations if any value of r is to cause rejection of the hypothesis at the 5 per cent level of significance.

Power Function and Sample Size. Just as with any statistical test, the power of the sign test to recognize cases where the hypothesis is not true improves when a larger sample size is used. The probability of

TABLE 17-2. MINIMUM VALUES OF N NECESSARY TO FIND SIGNIFICANT DIFFERENCES 95 PER CENT OF THE TIME FOR VARIOUS TRUE PROPORTIONS ON THE HYPOTHESIS THAT $p = .50$

p	N			
	$\alpha = 1\%$	5%	10%	25%
.45(.55)	1,777*	1,297*	1,080*	780*
.40(.60)	442*	327	267*	193*
.35(.65)	193*	143	118*	86
.30(.70)	106*	79	67	47
.25(.75)	66	49	42	32
.20(.80)	44	35	28	21
.15(.85)	32	23	18	14
.10(.90)	24	17	13	11
.05(.95)	15	12	11	6

The asterisked values are approximate. The maximum error is about 5.

rejecting the hypothesis can be given for alternatives which specify that some proportion p of the distribution of the differences are plus and a proportion $1 - p$ are negative. The hypothesis states that 50 per cent ($p = .50$) are plus and 50 per cent minus. Table 17-2 gives the minimum sample size needed so that there will be a probability of at least .95 of rejecting the hypothesis $p \doteq .50$ when p is actually the value given in the left-hand column.

For example, Table 17-2 shows that if the signs are actually distributed 45:55, then one must take samples of 1,080 pairs in order to give significance 95 per cent of the time at the 10 per cent level; i.e., if a large number of samples of 1,080 each were drawn from a 45:55 distribution, then 95 per cent of those samples could be expected to indicate a significant departure (at the 10 per cent level) from a 50:50 distribution.

Of course, in practice one would not do any testing if he knew in advance the expected distribution of signs (that it was 45:55, for example). The practical significance of Table 17-2 is of the following nature: In comparing two materials one is interested in determining whether they are of about equal or of different value. Before the investigation is begun, a decision must be made as to how different the materials must be in order to be classed as different. Expressed in another way, how large a difference may be tolerated in the statement "The two materials are of about equal value"? This decision together with Table 17-2 determines the sample size. If one is interested in detecting a difference so small that the signs may be distributed 45:55, he must be prepared to take a very large sample. If, however, one is interested only in detecting larger differences (for example, differences represented by a 70:30 distribution of signs), a smaller size sample will suffice.

Modifications of the Sign Test. If the same type or unit of measurement is made for every pair, i.e., if the measurements are comparable for all pairs of observations, then the sign test can be used to answer questions of the following kind:

1. Is material A better than B by P per cent?
2. Is material A better than B by Q units?

The first question would be tested by increasing the measurement on B by P per cent and comparing the results with the measurements on A. Thus, let

$$(X_1,Y_1),\ (X_2,Y_2),\ (X_3,Y_3),\ \ldots,\ (X_N,Y_N)$$

be pairs of measurements on A and B, and suppose one wished to test the hypothesis that the measurements X on A were 5 per cent higher than the measurements Y on B. The sign test would simply be applied to the signs of the differences

$$X_1 - 1.05Y_1,\ X_2 - 1.05Y_2,\ X_3 - 1.05Y_3,\ \ldots,\ X_N - 1.05Y_N$$

In the case of the second question the sign test would be applied to the differences

$$X_1 - (Y_1 + Q), X_2 - (Y_2 + Q), X_3 - (Y_3 + Q),\ \ldots,\ X_N - (Y_N + Q)$$

In either case, if the resulting distribution of signs is not significantly different from 50:50, the data are not inconsistent with a positive answer to the question. Usually there will be a range of values of P (or Q) which will produce a nonsignificant distribution of signs. If one determines such a range, using the 5 per cent level of significance, for example, then the range will be a 95 per cent confidence interval for P (or Q).

In some cases when the same unit of measurement is not used, it may still be possible to frame questions of the above kind, or it may be possible to change the scales of measurement so that such questions would be meaningful.

The efficiency of the sign test compared with the t test when the observations are from normal populations can be assessed by finding the sample size N_t for which a t test will have the same power as a sign test based on a sample of size N. The ratio $100N_t/N$ is called the *power efficiency* of the sign test relative to the t test. For the sign test the power efficiency decreases (1) with increasing α, (2) with increasing sample size, and (3) with increasing difference in the population means. Table 17-3 contains power efficiencies for the sign test when used for two normal populations with means μ_1 and μ_2, and with equal variances σ^2. The quantity δ in the table is the difference in population means divided by the standard

TABLE 17-3. POWER EFFICIENCY OF SIGN TEST FOR NORMAL POPULATIONS

N	α	δ				
		Near 0	.5	1.0	1.5	2.0
5	.0625	96	96	95	93	91
10	.0020	94	92	90	87	84
10	.0215	85	84	82	80	77
10	.1094	77	76	74	72	
20	.0118	76	75	73	70	
20	.0414	73	72	70	68	
20	.1153	70	69	67	65	
∞	α	63.7				

deviation of a difference of two observations, that is, $\delta = |\mu_1 - \mu_2|/\sqrt{2}\sigma$. It can be seen from this table that the sign test used with a sample of size $N = 20$ at the $\alpha = .0414$ level of significance has approximately the same power as a t test used with a sample of size $N_t = .70N = 14$. If $|\mu_1 - \mu_2|/\sqrt{2}\sigma$ is small and N is large, the t test needs approximately 64 per cent as many observations to have the same power as the sign test.

17-2. Extensions of the Sign Test

Table A-26 lists the level of significance for some of the values in the sign test and includes a number of additional tests for other significance levels.

The sign test can be described as follows: Suppose, for example, we arrange a sample of four differences in order of size, $d_1 < d_2 < d_3 < d_4$, and agree to reject the hypothesis $\mu = 0$ if d_4 is less than 0. Table A-26 gives the level of significance (chance of d_4 being less than zero if the hypothesis is true) as $\alpha = 6.2$ per cent. If we agree to reject if either $d_4 < 0$ or $d_1 > 0$, then $\alpha = 12.5$ per cent. Similarly, if we wish to compare X_i and $Y_i + \mu_0$, as indicated in the previous section, we might reject the hypothesis $\mu_x - \mu_y = \mu_0$ if the largest of the differences $X_i - Y_i$ in a sample of four pairs is less than μ_0. Table A-26 gives $\alpha = 6.2$ per cent for this test.

The additional tests included in Table A-26 are based on slightly different assumptions from those used for the sign test. The assumptions are such that the tests are valid if based on N observations independently drawn from N symmetrical populations each having the same median μ.

As an example of the use of Table A-26, consider the following six observations arranged in order of size,

$$-2.5,\ -1.5,\ -1.3,\ 0.1,\ 0.3,\ 0.8$$

and test the hypothesis $\mu = .5$ at the 9.4 per cent level of significance. We see from Table A-26 that we are to compute,

$$\text{Maximum of } .3 \text{ and } \tfrac{1}{2}(.1 + .8) \text{ is } .45$$
$$\text{Minimum of } -1.5 \text{ and } \tfrac{1}{2}(-2.5 - 1.3) \text{ is } -1.9$$

and if either the first of these is less than .5 or the second is greater than .5, we reject the hypothesis. Since $.45 < .5$, we reject the hypothesis $\mu = .5$ at the 9.4 per cent level of significance.

Power efficiencies for the tests in Table A-26 (which include several cases of the sign test) would be similar to those given in Table 17-3 for the sign test.

The Signed Rank Test. Another similar modification of the sign test is the Wilcoxon signed rank test. This is used to test the hypothesis that a median of a group of observations (or differences of pairs of observations) is equal to some specified value, say, μ_0. The signed rank statistic T is computed as follows:

1. Subtract μ_0 from each observation.
2. Rank the resulting differences in order of size, disregarding sign.
3. Restore the sign of the original difference to the corresponding rank.
4. Obtain T, the sum of the positive ranks.

Table A-19 lists percentiles of the sampling distribution of the T statistic.

An example of the use of this statistic to test the hypothesis that the median of a population is $\mu_0 = 2$ is given in Table 17-4. A sample of size 8 was chosen from the population. From Table A-19 we see that to have a level of significance close to .05 we could use for a critical region values of T less than or equal to 4 and values of T greater than or equal to 32. The level of significance for this critical region is $\alpha = 2(.027) = .054$. The data in Table 17-4 are not evidence at the .054 level that the hypothesis is incorrect.

TABLE 17-4

X	$X - \mu_0$	Rank $\lvert X - \mu_0 \rvert$	Signed rank	
2.55	.55	3		3
4.62	2.62	8		8
2.93	.93	4		4
2.46	.46	2		2
1.95	− .05	1	−1	
4.55	2.55	7		7
3.11	1.11	6		6
0.90	−1.10	5	−5	
				30 = T

17-3. Runs

In the previous sections on the sign test we compared the total number of positive differences observed with the total number of negative differences observed. It is reasonable also to ask whether the positive differences are scattered in a fairly random manner among the negative ones when the observations are in the order observed, i.e., in order of time. For example, if we observed the sequence +, +, +, +, −, −, −, −, −, we might want to consider it as different from the sequence −, +, −, +, −, +, −, +, −. Each of the sequences has four positive differences and five negative differences. However, in the first case the positive differences all occurred together. Any set of differences having the same sign which occur in a row we shall call a *run*. We shall understand that a run includes as many elements as possible, and thus the sequence −, +, +, +, − has three runs, two having a single negative and one having three positives. The sequence +, +, +, +, −, −, −, −, − has two runs, one of length four and one of length five. The sequence of n differences may have only one run (all positive or all negative) and may have as many as n runs if the signs alternate. We may wish to reject the hypothesis of random arrangement of plus and minus signs if there are too few or too many runs.

Runs can be used to test whether or not two random samples come from populations having the same frequency distribution. We arrange the observations of the two samples together in one series according to size. We then count the number of runs of items from each of the samples. If there are fewer runs than would be expected by chance if both populations are the same, we reject the hypothesis that the two populations have the same distribution.

The theory of runs may also be used to test the hypothesis that observations have been drawn at random from a single population. To do this, find the median of the sample, and denote observations below the median by a minus sign $(-)$ and observations above the median by a plus sign $(+)$. If the number of runs of plus and minus signs is larger or smaller than might be expected by chance, we reject the hypothesis.

Let N_1 be the number of occurrences of one type (positive differences, observations below median, etc.) and N_2 be the number of occurrences of the other type (negative differences, observations above median, etc.). Let u equal the total number of runs among the $N_1 + N_2$ observations. Table A-11 gives the sampling distribution of u for values of N_1 and N_2 less than or equal to 10 and a number of percentiles of the distributions for larger sample sizes.

Example 1. Suppose a manufacturing process is turning out steel rods and the diameters of the rods are measured. In the first 40 measured there is a total of 16 runs above and below the median. Let us test the hypothesis that the machinery is turning out rods whose diameters vary randomly. Here $N_1 = N_2 = 20$ (since there are one-half of the observations above the median and one-half below the median). The observed number 16 is not less than or equal to $u_{.025} = 14$ and is not greater than or equal to $u_{.975} = 27$, and so there is not sufficient evidence to reject the hypothesis at the 5 per cent level of significance.

Example 2. Suppose 10 plots of wheat are treated with type A fertilizer and 10 plots are treated with type B fertilizer. The yields are recorded in the tabulation. These are arranged in order of size, with the

A	26.3	28.6	25.4	29.2	27.6	25.6	26.4	27.7	28.2	29.0
B	28.5	30.0	28.8	25.3	28.4	26.5	27.2	29.3	26.2	27.5

observations in sample A underscored:

25.3, $\underline{25.4}$, $\underline{25.6}$, 26.2, $\underline{26.3}$, $\underline{26.4}$, 26.5, 27.2, 27.5, $\underline{27.6}$, $\underline{27.7}$, $\underline{28.2}$, 28.4, 28.5, $\underline{28.6}$, 28.8, $\underline{29.0}$, $\underline{29.2}$, 29.3, 30.0

There are 11 runs, which, for $N_1 = N_2 = 10$, corresponds to the 58.6 percentile of the distribution of u. Since this is between 2.5 and 97.5, there is no reason to reject at the 5 per cent level of significance the hypothesis that the two populations have the same distribution. Of course it is unlikely that anyone would be interested in rejecting the hypothesis of no difference in fertilizers if there were too many runs. In this case too many runs would indicate a lack of randomness in the selection of the sample. Therefore in this example we might use a one-sided test, rejecting only if the percentile rank of the observed u were less than .05, that is, 6 or fewer runs.

Normal Approximation. If N_1 and N_2 are both larger than 10, the cumulative sampling distribution of u can be approximated from the normal tables with $z = \dfrac{u - \mu_u + \frac{1}{2}}{\sigma_u}$, where

$$\mu_u = \frac{2N_1N_2}{N_1 + N_2} + 1 \qquad \sigma_u{}^2 = \frac{2N_1N_2(2N_1N_2 - N_1 - N_2)}{(N_1 + N_2)^2(N_1 + N_2 - 1)}$$

In Example 2 above, $N_1 = N_2 = 10$, $\mu_u = 11$, and $\sigma_u = \sqrt{4.73} = 2.17$. The observed value of $u = 11$ gives a z score of $.5/2.17 = .23$, or approximately the 59th percentile.

17-4. The Rank-sum Test

In Example 2 of Sec. 17-3 we counted the number of runs in the arrangement of 20 observations, 10 from each of two populations. Another statistic which may be used to compare the two samples is the *rank-sum* statistic T' defined as follows: Arrange the two samples together in order of size, and assign rank scores to the individual observations, score 1 to the smallest, score 2 to the second smallest, etc. Then T' is the sum of ranks of the observations in the smaller of the two samples. If the samples are of the same size, we may choose either sample. Note that if T' is the sum of the N_1 ranks, for samples of sizes N_1 and N_2, respectively, then T' can be as small as $1 + 2 + 3 + \cdots + N_1 = N_1(N_1 + 1)/2$ or as large as $N_1(2N_2 + N_1 + 1)/2$.

In Table A-20 we have recorded some of the percentiles of the sampling distribution of T' in the case where the two samples are from populations having identical distributions. We reject the hypothesis that we have random samples from identically distributed populations if T' is significantly large or significantly small.

For example, if $N_1 = N_2 = 10$, we see in Table A-20 that the chance of T' being less than or equal to 79 is .026 and the chance of T' being greater than or equal to 134 is .026. Thus values of $T' \leq 79$ and $T' \geq 134$ form a 5.2 per cent critical region for the above hypothesis. In Example 2 of Sec. 17-3 the ranks of the A sample are 2, 3, 5, 6, 10, 11, 12, 15, 17, 18, and so $T' = 99$; and since this is not in the critical region, we accept the hypothesis that we have random samples from identically distributed populations.

In the case of ties replace the observation by the mean of the ranks for which it is tied.

Normal Approximation. For N_1 and N_2 both larger than 10 we use the fact that the sampling distribution of T' is approximately normal with mean and variance as follows,

$$\mu_{T'} = \frac{N_1(N_1 + N_2 + 1)}{2} \qquad \sigma_{T'}{}^2 = \frac{N_1 N_2(N_1 + N_2 + 1)}{12}$$

and obtain the approximate chance that T' will be less than or equal to T'_0 by finding the area to the left of $z = (T'_0 - \mu_{T'} + \frac{1}{2})/\sigma_{T'}$ from Table A-4. For the example above with $N_1 = N_2 = 10$ this approximation gives $\mu_{T'} = 105$ and $\sigma_{T'} = \sqrt{175} = 13.2$. The observed value of $T' = 99$ gives a z score of $z = -5.5/13.2 = -.42$, and this, if compared with $z_{.025} = -1.96$ and $z_{.975} = 1.96$, is seen to be not significant at the 5 per cent level. Since the exact distribution of T' is given for $N_1 = N_2 = 10$, we can compare the normal approximation with the exact chance of T' being less than or equal to 99. The exact chance is .342. The normal approximation read from Table A-4 for $z = -.42$ gives the approximate chance .337. Also note that for $T'_0 = 79$, $z = (79 - 105 + \frac{1}{2})/13.2 = 1.93$, which gives the approximate chance .027 corresponding to the exact chance .026.

The rank-sum test requires approximately 5 per cent more observations than a t test to provide the same power as a t test for shifts in means of two normally distributed populations. For nonnormal populations the rank-sum test may be more powerful than the t test. In some cases the rank-sum test requires only 80 per cent as many observations for equal power. It should be noted that for nonnormal populations Table A-5 does not apply to the distribution of t, whereas the distribution of T' in Table A-20 may be used whether or not the populations are normal.

Rank-sum Test for Several Samples. Ranks can be used to test the hypothesis that k samples of sizes $n_1, n_2, \ldots, n_k$ are randomly drawn from k identically distributed populations. We arrange the $N = \Sigma n_i$ observations together in order of size and assign ranks as was done for the two-sample rank-sum test. Let R_i be the sum of ranks of the ith sample, and let

$$H = \frac{12}{N(N+1)} \sum \frac{R_i^2}{n_i} - 3(N+1)$$

If the hypothesis is true and the n_i's are not small, the sampling distribution of the statistic H is approximately χ^2 with $k - 1$ degrees of freedom. If all n_i's are greater than 5, the 95th and 99th percentiles in Table A-6a are reasonably accurate. In the case of ties replace the observation by the mean of the ranks for which it is tied. The statistic H is essentially the variance of the sample rank sums R_i. If a significantly large value of H is observed, the hypothesis is rejected.

17-5. Estimation of a Cumulative Frequency Distribution

Frequently in the earlier chapters of the book we attempted to estimate a distribution by sampling. We did this several times to approximate a sampling distribution. It is possible to predict, by means of confidence intervals, how close the cumulative distribution of a sample can be expected to be to the cumulative distribution of the population. The procedure is as follows:

Draw a cumulative-percentage histogram for observations in the sample (dotted line in Fig. 17-1). Above and below this histogram draw two parallel polygons at a distance $100d_\alpha$. The width of a band giving confidence $(1 - \alpha)$ for the statement "The cumulative frequency distribution

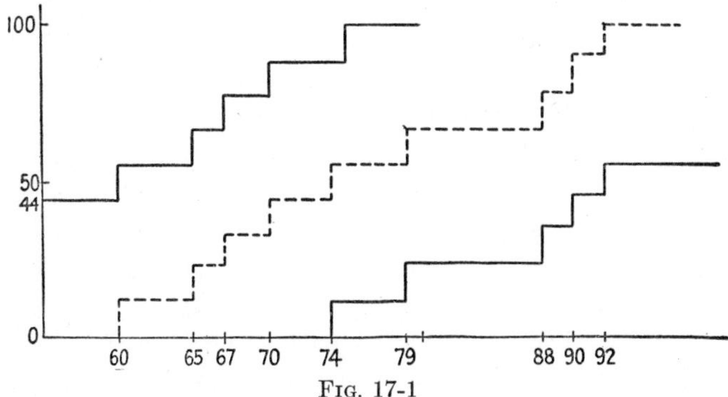

FIG. 17-1

of the population is in this band" is $200d_\alpha$. Values of d_α can be read from Table A-21. The sample size is on the left, and five levels of confidence are referred to at the top. For example, if $N = 50$ and we wish to be 90 per cent confident that the band covers the population cumulative distribution, then the band should be of width $2(.17) = .34$, or 34 percentage points.

Actually Table A-21 is a table of percentiles of the frequency distribution of the maximum deviation of a sample cumulative distribution from the population cumulative distribution. Thus in 90 per cent of samples of size 50 the maximum deviation of the sample distribution from the population distribution will be less than .17.

Example. Suppose the observations of a sample of size $N = 9$ are

$$88, 92, 65, 74, 67, 79, 90, 70, 60$$

For $1 - \alpha = .95$ and for $N = 9$, Table A-21 gives

$$100d_\alpha = 44$$

(between $N = 5$ and $N = 10$). Figure 17-1 shows the observed distribution by dotted lines and the confidence band, 44 percentage points above and below the observed distribution, by solid lines. We are 95 per cent confident that the population cumulative distribution is entirely inside this band.

Determination of Sample Size. Table A-21 can also be used to determine the required sample size to be 95 per cent confident of containing the population cumulative distribution within some interval of given width. Suppose, for example, that we wish to be 95 per cent sure of containing the distribution within an interval of width 5 percentage points. Here $d_\alpha = .05/2$. Thus $(1.36/\sqrt{N}) = .025$, or

$$N = \left(\frac{1.36}{.025}\right)^2 = (54.4)^2 = 2{,}960$$

To be 99 per cent confident, the sample must be of size

$$N = \left(\frac{1.63}{.025}\right)^2 = 4{,}251$$

To be 99 per cent confident of the sample distribution being within 1 percentage point of the population distribution, we would need a sample of size $N = (1.63/.01)^2 = 26{,}569$.

The above procedure can also be used as a test for goodness of fit. If we have a hypothetical cumulative curve that is completely inside the 95 per cent confidence strip for the sample drawn, we would accept the hypothetical curve at the 5 per cent level of significance. Similarly, if the hypothetical curve is outside the strip at one or more points, we would reject this curve as describing the population.

A similar procedure can be used to test the hypothesis that two samples are from populations having the same distribution. If the maximum vertical difference between the two sample cumulative histograms is greater than $136 \sqrt{(1/N_1) + (1/N_2)}$, we would reject the hypothesis at the 5 per cent level of significance.

No complete investigation has been made of the power function of these tests. However, preliminary investigations indicate that in many examples it is as good as or better than corresponding χ^2 tests.

17-6. Chebyshev's Inequality

The following inequality is not strictly nonparametric since it does involve μ and σ^2. However, it is distribution-free in the sense that it holds for any distribution.

This inequality states that the amount of area under any distribution curve which is farther away from the mean than k standard deviation units is less than $1/k^2$. Thus, for example, there is always less than

$(\frac{1}{2})^2 = .25$ unit of area farther than 2 standard deviations from the mean. In case the form of the distribution is known, more exact statements can be made. In a normal distribution there is approximately .045 unit of area farther than 2 standard deviations from the mean.

For symmetrical distributions with a single mode the maximum area farther than $k\sigma$ from the mean is $(2/3k)^2$.

Law of Large Numbers. Chebyshev's inequality can be applied to the sampling distribution of the mean. This distribution has standard deviation $\sigma/\sqrt{N}$. Therefore the chance that a sample mean from any distribution having variance σ^2 will fall farther than $k\sigma/\sqrt{N}$ from the population mean is less than $1/k^2$. By letting $d = (k\sigma/\sqrt{N})$ we can say that the chance of the sample mean falling farther than d units from the population mean is less than σ^2/d^2N.

If N is increased, this maximum chance approaches zero. This result is called the *law of large numbers.*

Example. How large should N be so that we can be 95 per cent sure that $\bar{X}$ will not fall farther than $\sigma/2$ from the mean? Here $d = .5\sigma$, and the chance that $\bar{X}$ is farther than $\sigma/2$ from the mean is less than

$$\frac{\sigma^2}{.25\sigma^2N} = \frac{1}{.25N}$$

This should be equal to .05, and so we set $(1/.25N) = .05$ and obtain

$$N = \frac{1}{(.25)(.05)} = 80$$

Thus the sample size should be at least 80.

17-7. Nonparametric Tolerance Limits

A method for constructing intervals which had a specified chance of covering a certain proportion of a normal population was given in Chap. 9. Such intervals were called tolerance intervals. It is possible to form tolerance intervals which are valid for any population. Generally they are somewhat less sensitive (longer) than those for a particular distribution, and it is usually necessary to take larger samples in order to obtain the same precision.

Table 17-5 gives the sample size required for a certain chance that a given proportion of the population will be between the smallest and the largest observations of the sample. For example, if the sample is of size $N = 47$, then there is a 95 per cent chance that 90 per cent of the observations in the population will be between the two extremes of the sample. Curves giving various chances of covering various proportions of the population are available (see References, page 358).

TABLE 17-5. SAMPLE SIZES FOR TOLERANCE LIMITS

Chance of covering stated proportion	Proportion of population to be contained between extreme values of a sample			
	.50	.90	.95	.99
.90	7	38	79	410
.95	8	47	97	490
.99	11	66	135	690

17-8. Confidence Limits for the Median

A confidence interval for the median of the population can be obtained immediately from the observations arranged in order of magnitude. No assumption is necessary about the population except that the observations are on a continuous variable. We arrange the observations in order $X_1 < X_2 < \cdots < X_N$ and state that the population median is between two of these observations. For example, for a sample of size 20 we might state that the median is between X_1 and X_{20} or between X_2 and X_{19}, etc. As we progress toward the central values of the sample, we are less confident that our statement is true. Table A-25 gives the largest values of k such that we have confidence more than .95 (or more than .99) that the population median is between X_k and X_{N+1-k}. The values of α listed are the exact chances of the statement being false. For example, if $N = 20$, we see from Table A-25 that the sixth and fifteenth observations are confidence limits of more than 95 per cent confidence for the population median. For $N = 40$ we can be 99.4 per cent confident that the median is between the 12th and 29th observations and 96.2 per cent confident that the median is between the 14th and 27th observations.

17-9. Rank Correlation

Suppose we have a sample of individuals and we make two measurements on each. We have then N pairs of observations (X_1,Y_1), (X_2,Y_2), . . . , (X_N,Y_N). We shall arrange the observed X values in order of size and assign a rank to each value. The largest value is assigned a rank of 1, the second largest a rank of 2, etc. We shall then do the same for the Y values. Next we subtract each (X_i) rank from its paired (Y_i) rank, and denote the difference by d_i. The statistic $r_s = 1 - \dfrac{6(\Sigma d_i^2)}{N(N^2-1)}$ is called the *rank-correlation coefficient*. It can be used to test the hypothesis that the two variables X and Y are independent. It has the advantage that no assumptions are made about the distributions of X or Y. r_s is similar to the correlation coefficient in that its values range from -1 to

$+1$. A value of $+1$ indicates perfect agreement, while a value of -1 indicates exactly opposite ranking. Table A-30c gives the distribution of Σd_i^2 for samples of size less than or equal to 10. These values are such that Σd_i^2 computed for a sample drawn from a population of independent variables X and Y will equal or exceed the tabulated value with chance as given in the table. For values of N larger than those tabulated the significance values of r_s for $\alpha = .025$ may be read from the curves of Table A-27 ($\rho = 0$) or from Table A-30a.

The tables may be used for two-sided tests. For example, if we agree to reject the hypothesis of independence whenever r_s is greater than .506 or less than $-.506$ in a sample of 12 observations, we are making a test at the 10 per cent level of significance.

In comparing rankings we are frequently interested in a one-sided test, rejecting the hypothesis of independence only when there is sufficiently close agreement in the rankings. For example, suppose two judges rank seven contestants in a beauty contest as in Table 17-6. We do not reject the hypothesis of independence in the ranking at the 5 per cent level of significance since $\Sigma d_i^2 = 20$ is not less than 18, the tabular value corresponding to the .055 level of significance.

TABLE 17-6

Contestant	First judge	Second judge	d_i
A	2	3	-1
B	1	4	-3
C	4	2	2
D	5	5	0
E	3	1	2
F	7	6	1
G	6	7	-1

$$\Sigma d_i^2 = 20 \qquad r_s = 1 - \frac{6 \times 20}{7 \times 48} = .643$$

17-10. Median Tests

The tests to be described in this section are particularly useful in situations where percentiles of a group of observations can be determined easily. In fact, if relative dimensions can be assigned, we may even avoid the actual measurement of more than a few of the individuals.

Median Test for Two Samples. The number of cases in two samples, of sizes N_1 and N_2, falling above and below the median of the combined $N = N_1 + N_2$ observations can be used to test the hypothesis that the samples are randomly drawn from two identically distributed populations. For example, Table 17-7 gives the results of two samples of sizes

$N_1 = N_2 = 15$ with the number of individuals falling above and below the median for each sample. The table is analyzed as a contingency table (Sec. 13-3), and the hypothesis is rejected if the observed χ^2 is larger than the critical value read from Table A-6*a* for 1 degree of freedom. For this example the value of χ^2 corrected for continuity is

$$\chi^2 = \frac{(|6^2 - 9^2| - 15)^2 \times 30}{15 \times 15 \times 15 \times 15} = .53$$

The critical region for $\alpha = .05$ is $\chi^2 > 3.84$; so we have no reason to reject the hypothesis at this level.

TABLE 17-7

	Sample No.		Total
	I	II	
Above median..........	6	9	15
Below median..........	9	6	15
	15	15	30

$\chi^2 = .53$
$\chi_{.95}^2$ (1 df) $= 3.84$

Median Test for *k* Samples. The hypothesis that k samples are randomly drawn from populations having identical distributions can be tested in a manner similar to that of the preceding section. For this case the data are arranged in a table showing the numbers of each sample above and below the median of the combined set. The table is then analyzed as a contingency table obtaining a χ^2 statistic having $k - 1$ degrees of freedom. The hypothesis is rejected if the observed χ^2 is significantly large.

Extension of the Median Test. The median test may be extended by using any fixed number of percentiles of the grouped data instead of the median only. The numbers in each sample falling between those percentiles are recorded in a table, and the data are then analyzed as a contingency table. The hypothesis that the k samples are randomly drawn from populations having identical distributions is rejected if the observed χ^2 is significantly large. For this problem the number of degrees of freedom is $(k - 1)(r - 1)$, where r is the number of categories used. For example, Table 17-8 records for three ($k = 3$) samples of size 20 each the number of observations above P_{75}, between P_{50} and P_{75}, between P_{25} and P_{50}, and below P_{25}. The χ^2 statistic has $2 \times 3 = 6$ df. The theoretical frequencies for the analysis of this example are all equal to $15 \times 20/60 = 5$.

TABLE 17-8

	Sample No.			Total
	I	II	III	
Above P_{75}	5	7	3	15
Between P_{50} and P_{75}	3	3	9	15
Between P_{25} and P_{50}	4	7	4	15
Below P_{25}	8	3	4	15
Total	20	20	20	60

The value of χ^2 is

$$\chi^2 = \frac{(5-5)^2}{5} + \frac{(7-5)^2}{5} + \cdots + \frac{(4-5)^2}{5} = \frac{52}{5} = 10.4$$

which, since $\chi^2_{.95}(6) = 11.07$, is not cause for rejection of the hypothesis at the 5 per cent level of significance.

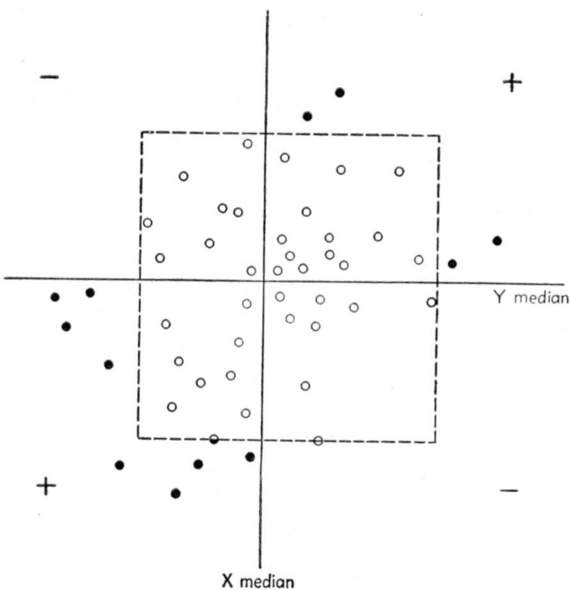

FIG. 17-2. Scatter diagram of 50 tests.

17-11. Corner Test for Association

The technique described in this section uses a very easily computed nonparametric statistic to test the hypothesis that two continuous variables are independent. It is especially useful if the data are plotted on a scatter diagram as in Fig. 17-2 or if the data can be easily ranked.

Figure 17-2 shows a scatter diagram of scores X and Y made by $N = 50$ people on two types of aptitude tests. The corner test statistic S is obtained as follows: Label the quadrants with plus and minus signs as in the figure. Locate the median values of X and Y. Starting at the extreme right and moving toward the center, count the number of points encountered before a point is found across the Y median, and give this total the sign of the quadrant the extreme points occur in. In the figure this is $+2$. Proceed similarly from the top, left, and bottom, obtaining $+2$, $+5$, and $4\frac{1}{2}$. (Note that the point at the lower left is counted twice and that the $\frac{1}{2}$ comes from a tie.) The statistic S then is the sum of these four numbers.

$$S = 2 + 2 + 5 + 4\tfrac{1}{2} = 13\tfrac{1}{2}$$

Table A-30*d* gives the sampling distribution of S in the case where X and Y are independent. We see that $S = 13\frac{1}{2}$ is a significant departure from independence at the $\alpha = .05$ level of significance.

If the sample size N is odd, the two median points can be replaced by a single point having for its coordinates the nonmedian values of the two. For example, if the individual (5,7) is median for X (i.e., median X value equals 5) and (12,6) is median for Y, these points are replaced by (12,7). The test may then be applied to the sample thus reduced by one observation.

17-12. Tests of Randomness

In the test and estimation techniques we have discussed, the method of drawing the sample from the population was in most cases specified to be random. If some characteristic of the population is known, the sample may be checked for the corresponding characteristic in order to test the hypothesis that it was randomly drawn. Actually a test of any hypothesis can be considered to be a test of randomness if the hypothesis is known to be correct. However, most of the test techniques were designed for specific types of discrepancies between the sample and the population rather than tests for a general lack of randomness.

The control chart is a widely used technique for examining a series of observations to determine whether or not it could be considered to be a random series. In particular it is effective in detecting extreme values. Other techniques are given below.

Example 1. If a population of people is known to contain 45 per cent men and 55 per cent women, then the proportion $\bar{X}$ of men in a sample can be used to test the hypothesis that the sample was drawn at random. Either the binomial distribution or its normal approximation with $z = (\bar{X} - .45)/\sqrt{.45(.55)/N}$ is used and the hypothesis rejected if z is very large, either positive or negative. In this case it may also be considered reasonable to reject the hypothesis if z is close to zero since, it may be argued, the agreement is so close that it would occur rarely in a random sample.

Example 2. If items are being manufactured in sequence, the number of runs above and below the median can be used to test for randomness, as discussed in Sec. 17-3.

Example 3. If observations are chosen in a sequence $X_1, X_2, \ldots, X_N$, the *mean-square successive difference*

$$\eta = \frac{\sum_{i=1}^{N-1} (X_{i+1} - X_i)^2}{\Sigma(X_i - \bar{X})^2}$$

can be used to test for randomness. If N is moderately large, say, N greater than 20, and the population is normal, then

$$z = \left(1 - \frac{\eta}{2}\right) \Big/ \sqrt{\frac{N - 2}{(N - 1)(N + 1)}}$$

is approximately normally distributed with zero mean and unit standard deviation. Long trends are associated with high positive values of z and short oscillations with high negative values.

17-13. Remarks on Nonparametric Methods

This section presents a brief discussion of the questions: When should nonparametric tests be used instead of the more classical tests? If a nonparametric test is to be used, which one should be used? For example, when should the sign test be used as an alternative to the t test, or when should the H statistic be used as an alternative to the one variable analysis of variance? As alternatives to the t test for two samples, when should one use the rank sum statistic, and when should one use the median test?

If the basic assumptions on the population are incorrect, any inferences based on these assumptions are of dubious validity. Specifically the numbers read from the percentile tables for these statistics will not provide the appropriate level of significance in testing hypotheses or the appropriate level of confidence in estimation. It is difficult to say how much the levels change if the assumptions are not met. However, for a moderate departure from normality, the t and F tables are sufficiently close for most practical purposes. If it is believed that the assumptions are not satisfied even moderately well, the levels of significance and confidence will be better satisfied using nonparametric methods.

The level of significance for a nonparametric method is not affected by the population distribution. Therefore the experimenter can be sure that he knows the chance of rejecting the null hypothesis when it is true. However, we know that some tests are better than others in detecting certain false hypotheses. If the necessary assumptions are correct, the classical tests are in most cases the most powerful tests and are to be preferred. Some comparisons of classical and nonparametric tests have been made in cases where the classical methods are known to be best. Some of these were noted previously. For example, for normal populations the sign test requires 4 to 50 per cent more observations than the t test, and the rank sum test requires approximately 5 per cent more observations than the t test to be equally powerful. Of course these figures apply only if the populations are normal. The comparison for nonnormal populations may even be reversed.

Comparisons among the various nonparametric tests have been made for samples of several sizes from two normal populations in an attempt to assess their relative efficiency. Some results for samples of size 5 are given in Table 17-9 for the case where the normal populations have equal variances and a difference in means $\delta = |\mu_1 - \mu_2|/\sigma$. The power efficiencies are relative to the t test.

TABLE 17-9. POWER EFFICIENCY OF SEVERAL NONPARAMETRIC TESTS FOR $\alpha = .025$ AND $N_1 = N_2 = 5$

Test	δ				
	Near 0	1.0	2.0	3.0	4.0
Rank sum	.96	.95	.93	.91	.89
Maximum absolute deviation	.81	.80	.78	.76	.74
Median	.70	.70	.71	.73	.73

Further comparisons for samples of size 10 and 20 have been made by sampling experiments. The tests listed in order of their observed power to reject the hypothesis $\delta = 0$ for samples of size 5, 10, and 20 are (1) rank sum, (2) maximum absolute deviation, (3) median, (4) run. The power of the rank-sum test is little less than the power of t. The power efficiency of the run test is less than .50. The rank-sum test is almost completely insensitive to differences in standard deviations of two normal populations with the same mean. The median test is insensitive to changes in standard deviation. The maximum absolute deviation has some power against this alternative, but not so much as the run test, which has close to 50 per cent power efficiency compared with the F test in detecting differences in standard deviations.

The various nonparametric statistics may be used to estimate parameters. As noted, the sign-test statistic may be used to estimate the population median. Distribution-free estimation can also be based on the material of Secs. 17-5, 17-7, and 17-8.

Additional comments on the use of nonparametric methods are:

1. In some cases nonparametric methods of analysis permit an easier method of collecting data. For example, no actual measurements are needed to use the sign test since we need to know only whether one observation is "better" or "worse" than another.

2. Nonparametric statistics for small samples are usually easier to compute and apply than the classical techniques.

3. In some cases data may be collected from several populations about which very little is assumed. It may be possible to use a nonparametric method of analysis.

4. Sometimes the data occur naturally in the form of ranks. We may use the nonparametric methods directly and are not required to make assumptions about the population distribution.

5. The classical methods may be easier to apply in some cases since it may be laborious to rank data for large samples unless automatic sorting machinery can be used.

6. If the form of the distribution of the population is known to agree with the assumptions of the classical methods or can be made to agree by means of transformations, the nonparametric test may be wasteful of information.

7. Some tests detect differences in population means but not other differences. For example, the rank-sum tests and t tests are designed to detect shifts in means but not in variances. Similarly an F test for variances will detect a difference in variances but is ineffectual in discovering differences in means.

8. In any problem the cost of collecting and analyzing data must be considered in the choice of a statistical method. Different amounts of effort or cost are required to collect data in the appropriate form for different techniques of analysis.

GLOSSARY

Chebyshev's inequality
confidence limits for
 cumulative-distribution functions
law of large numbers
nonparametric inference
rank correlation
runs
sign test
tolerance limits

DISCUSSION QUESTIONS

1. What situations favor the use of the sign test instead of a t test?

2. What concept is considered in the study of runs which is not considered in a sign test or in a t test?

3. What concept is considered in the use of a t test which is not considered in the sign test or in a run test?

4. Describe favorable and unfavorable aspects in the application of Chebyshev's inequality.

5. In what type of situation is rank correlation a better measure than the correlation coefficient?

6. Define each term in the Glossary.

7. How many samples would be needed to have a 99 per cent confidence belt for the cumulative distribution of $\bar{X}$ which would be 1 percentage point wide? .1 percentage point wide?

8. What is the difference between confidence limits and tolerance limits?

CLASS EXERCISES

1. For each of the samples of size $N = 10$ drawn from Table A-2 count the number of runs of elements above and below the median. Collect the results, and test the hypothesis that the values in Table A-11 are correct.

2. Make up some distributions of 10 items, and verify that Chebyshev's inequality holds for each. These distributions are to be considered as populations and the variance computed by dividing by 10.

3. Take a shuffled deck of playing cards, count the number of runs of red and black cards, and decide on this basis whether or not you think the pack of cards was thoroughly shuffled.

4. Draw on a sheet of tracing paper a cumulative-percentage normal curve with mean zero and unit variance. Above and below this curve draw two parallel curves, one 41 percentage points above and the other 41 percentage points below the original curve.

From a normal population having $\mu = 0$, $\sigma = 1$ draw a sample of $N = 10$ observations. Draw the cumulative histogram of this sample, and see whether or not it falls in the strip. This can be done easily by drawing the histogram on graph paper and superimposing the curves. Each student should repeat this 10 times, and the total number of samples which have histograms completely in the strip should be counted. Approximately 95 per cent of the histograms should be entirely within the strip.

The normal numbers (Table A-2)) can be used as a population, or a population of numbered tags can be used.

As an alternative exercise the uniform population may be used instead of a normal population. In a uniform distribution every number should have an equal chance of being chosen in the sample. Samples can be drawn from a table of random numbers (Table A-1), or a population of tags can be constructed as described for set 6 in Table A-22.

5. In samples of size 10 the chance of including 66 per cent of the population between X_1 and X_{10} is .90 (obtained from the graphs noted in the References, page 358). From the samples drawn in Class Exercise 4 count the number of cases where X_1 and X_{10} include 66 per cent of the area under the normal curve.

PROBLEMS

1. In the manufacture of automobile gears the data in the tabulation were obtained for the daily number defective for a production of 100 parts per day. Are the number of runs above or below the median significant at the 5 per cent level?

22	25	15	26	31	22	17	26
23	20	28	32	43	18	16	36
21	16	29	26	18	24	28	42
17	14	26	33	26	24	32	36
38	26	25	30	21	16	18	34

2. Use the sign test to analyze the data in the table giving the gains of 10 pairs of rats, half of which received their protein from raw peanuts, while the other half received their protein from roasted peanuts. Test to see whether or not roasting the peanuts had any effect on their protein value. Compare the results with the results of a t test, and explain the difference.

Raw......	61	60	56	63	56	63	59	56	44	61
Roasted...	55	54	47	59	51	61	57	54	62	58

3. If it is known that a distribution is symmetrical and has only one mode, how large a sample is needed so that the chance of $\bar{X}$ being within $\sigma/10$ of the population mean μ is at least .99? Do this by two methods, one using Chebyshev's inequality and the other assuming the distribution of $\bar{X}$ is normal.

4. The arrangement of diseased and healthy plants in a row of strawberries is

H H D H H H H H D H D D D H H H H H H H H H

Does this arrangement throw doubt upon the random arrangement of diseased plants among healthy?

5. A teataster claims that he can distinguish between two brands of tea by taste. In an experiment he correctly identified the brands 14 times out of 20 trials in the following order,

$$+ + - - + + + + + + - - - + + + + + + -$$

where + stands for a correct identification. Analyze the data by using the sign test and also by using the theory of runs.

6. A board of judges at a county fair ranked a group of 10 pigs. A 4-H club member also ranked the 10 pigs. The results were as in the table. Is there a lack of independence in these rankings?

Judges............	9	4	3	7	2	1	5	8	10	6
4-H member........	7	6	4	9	2	3	8	5	10	1

7. Analyze the data in Prob. 2, using the signed-rank test.

8. Analyze the data in Prob. 9 of Chap. 10, using the H statistic.

9. Analyze the data in Prob. 2 of Chap. 10, using the extension of the median test, dividing the data into four equal parts as in the example in Sec. 17-10.

10. Analyze the data in Example 3 of Sec. 9–3 using the rank-sum test.

CHAPTER 18

SEQUENTIAL ANALYSIS

If in testing a hypothesis we wish to decide in advance what risks we are willing to take of rejecting a true hypothesis or of accepting a particular false hypothesis, our sample size is determined. This assumes, however, that we are going to take a sample of this size no matter what results we obtain from our first few observations. It would seem reasonable to request a procedure which will not require more observations than are necessary to make a decision. *Sequential analysis* is a procedure which leads to a statistical inference and in which the number of observations to be made is not determined before the experiment is begun. The procedure indicates when sufficient observations have been gathered to make our decisions with the risks we have chosen. On the average, fewer observations will be required by this procedure, and its use will not increase the risks α and β. For some problems only half the number of observations will be required on the average for the sequential procedure as compared with the number required if the sample size is fixed in advance.

18-1. Sequential Test

This procedure of testing a hypothesis can be characterized as follows: Observations are taken one at a time. After every observation we decide to do one of the following three things:

1. Accept the hypothesis.
2. Reject the hypothesis.
3. Make an additional observation.

In order to determine which one of these three possible actions to take, we must determine the critical region for each sample size. To do this we compute p_{0m}, the probability that the m observations collected thus far would occur if our hypothesis H_0 were true, and p_{1m}, the probability that these observations would occur if some alternative statement H_1 were true. To find p_{0m}, we assume that sampling is from the population stated in H_0 and compute the probability that such a result would occur. Similarly, to find p_{1m}, we assume that sampling is from the population stated in H_1 and again compute the probability that such a result would occur.

When p_{0m} is much larger than p_{1m}, we shall accept H_0; when p_{1m} is much larger than p_{0m}, we shall accept H_1. If there is not much difference between p_{1m} and p_{0m}, we shall take another observation. We shall compare the two by the use of the ratio p_{1m}/p_{0m}. It can be shown mathematically that, for the given risks α of rejecting H_0 when it is true and β of accepting H_0 when H_1 is true, the characterization of the sequential test may be written:

1. If $\dfrac{p_{1m}}{p_{0m}} \leq \dfrac{\beta}{1 - \alpha}$, accept H_0.
2. If $\dfrac{p_{1m}}{p_{0m}} \geq \dfrac{1 - \beta}{\alpha}$, accept H_1.
3. If $\dfrac{\beta}{1 - \alpha} < \dfrac{p_{1m}}{p_{0m}} < \dfrac{1 - \beta}{\alpha}$, take another observation.

This continues until either condition 1 or condition 2 is satisfied.

The mathematical development of these inequalities involves certain approximations, but an experimenter following the above procedure can be sure that the sum of the risks α and β will not be increased and the increase in the number of observations caused by a possible decrease in these risks will be slight (e.g., a maximum of 3 when 30 observations are required and 5 when 100 are required when $\alpha = \beta = .05$).

18-2. Test for Proportion

The procedure to be developed here is applicable to any problem concerning a test of proportion. Such types of problems were discussed in Chaps. 7, 13, and 14. The sequential test will be illustrated by an application to acceptance inspection of a large lot of items, each of which is either good or bad. Suppose we wish to reject the lot only 1 per cent of the time if the proportion of defective parts is .10 and accept the lot only 5 per cent of the time if the proportion of defectives is .20. Of course this also implies that if the proportion were less than .10 we would be rejecting even less frequently than 1 per cent of the time and if the proportion were greater than .20 we would be accepting less frequently than 5 per cent.

$$H_0:\ p = p_0 = .10$$
$$H_1:\ p = p_1 = .20$$
$$\alpha = 1\%$$
$$\beta = 5\%$$

Suppose we select items at random from the entire lot. If we assume that p_1 is the proportion of defectives in the whole lot, the probability that we get, say, d_m defectives and g_m good items in some particular order among the first m observations is

$$p_{1m} = p_1{}^{d_m}(1 - p_1)^{g_m} \qquad (d_m + g_m = m)$$

If p_0 is the proportion of defectives in the lot, the probability that we get d_m defectives and g_m good items among the first m observations is

$$p_{0m} = p_0^{d_m}(1 - p_0)^{g_m}$$

For example, if we obtain one good, one bad, and one good item for the first three observations, then, under the assumption that p_1 is the proportion of times we shall get a defective, the probability of this result is

$$(1 - p_1)p_1(1 - p_1) = p_1^1(1 - p_1)^2$$

and if the assumed proportion is p_0, the probability is

$$(1 - p_0)p_0(1 - p_0) = p_0^1(1 - p_0)^2$$

The ratio p_{1m}/p_{0m} after obtaining one good observation is

$$\frac{1 - p_1}{1 - p_0} = \frac{1 - .2}{1 - .1} = .889$$

and after obtaining one good and one bad is

$$\frac{(1 - p_1)p_1}{(1 - p_0)p_0} = \frac{.8}{.9}\frac{.2}{.1} = 1.778$$

and after obtaining one good, one bad, and one good is

$$\frac{p_1^1(1 - p_1)^2}{p_0^1(1 - p_0)^2} = \left(\frac{p_1}{p_0}\right)^1\left(\frac{1 - p_1}{1 - p_0}\right)^2 = \left(\frac{.2}{.1}\right)\left(\frac{.8}{.9}\right)^2 = 1.58$$

Successive observations will continue to change this value, and if it at any time exceeds $\dfrac{1 - \beta}{\alpha} = \dfrac{1 - .05}{.01} = 95$ or is less than

$$\frac{\beta}{1 - \alpha} = \frac{.05}{.99} = .0505$$

we shall stop sampling and accept H_1 or $H_0 (p = .2$ or $p = .1)$ as indicating the proportion of items defective. We would then reject or accept the lot.

The quantities actually observed are the number of defective and good parts. The ratio

$$\frac{p_{1m}}{p_{0m}} = \left(\frac{p_1}{p_0}\right)^{d_m}\left(\frac{1 - p_1}{1 - p_0}\right)^{g_m}$$

can be transformed along with the values $(1 - \beta)/\alpha$ and $\beta/(1 - \alpha)$ to natural logarithms.

$$\ln\frac{p_{1m}}{p_{0m}} = d_m \ln\frac{p_1}{p_0} + g_m \ln\frac{1 - p_1}{1 - p_0}$$

The critical values may be obtained by setting

$$d_m \ln \frac{p_1}{p_0} + g_m \ln \frac{1-p_1}{1-p_0} = \ln \frac{1-\beta}{\alpha}$$

and

$$d_m \ln \frac{p_1}{p_0} + g_m \ln \frac{1-p_1}{1-p_0} = \ln \frac{\beta}{1-\alpha}$$

For our problem we write

$$d_m \ln \frac{.2}{.1} + g_m \ln \frac{.8}{.9} = \ln 95$$

and

$$d_m \ln \frac{.2}{.1} + g_m \ln \frac{.8}{.9} = \ln .0505$$

Substituting the values of the logarithms obtained from Table A-14, we obtain

$$0.693d_m - 0.118g_m = 4.554$$
$$0.693d_m - 0.118g_m = -2.986$$

These equations can be represented by lines on a graph. To draw a line, we find two points and draw the line through them. Actually for check purposes we shall determine three points.

For $g_m = 0$, $d_m = 6.57$ for the first line, and $d_m = -4.31$ for the second.
For $g_m = 20$, $d_m = 9.98$ for the first line, and $d_m = -.77$ for the second.
For $g_m = 40$, $d_m = 13.38$ for the first line, and $d_m = 2.50$ for the second.

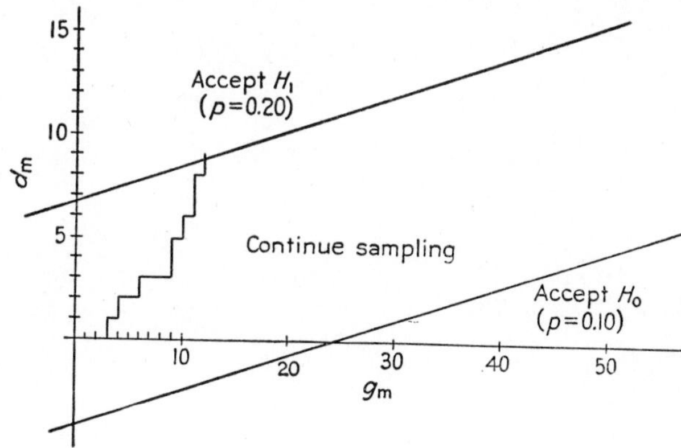

FIG. 18-1

The chart in Fig. 18-1 can be constructed in advance so that the data can be rapidly recorded as they are observed. The result of each observation can then be recorded easily by a line drawn one unit to the right if the item is good and a line drawn one unit up if the item is defective.

Suppose we represent by d the defective item and by g the good items and obtain the following results, which are placed on the graph:

$$g\,g\,g\,d\,g\,d\,g\,g\,d\,g\,g\,g\,d\,d\,g\,d\,g\,d\,d\,g\,d$$

The sampling is stopped at this point and the lot rejected.

Operating Characteristic (OC). We have defined an operating-characteristic (OC) function as the function which gives the probability that the lot will be accepted when p is the proportion of defectives in the whole lot. For this test we know four values and can sketch the curve roughly.

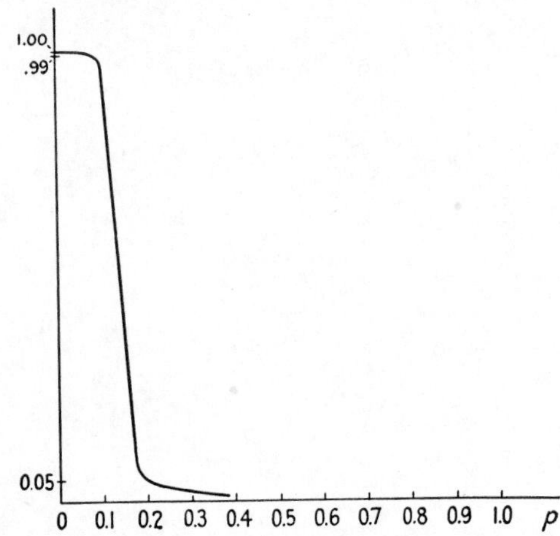

FIG. 18-2. Operating-characteristic curve.

An additional point between p_0 and p_1 can be plotted for the proportion

$$p' = \frac{\ln \dfrac{1 - p_1}{1 - p_0}}{\ln \dfrac{1 - p_1}{1 - p_0} - \ln \dfrac{p_1}{p_0}}$$

The height at that point is

$$\frac{\ln \dfrac{1 - \beta}{\alpha}}{\ln \dfrac{1 - \beta}{\alpha} - \ln \dfrac{\beta}{1 - \alpha}}$$

Of course, if the true proportion defective is less than .10, then the lot will be accepted more than 99 per cent of the time and lots that have more than a .20 proportion defective will be accepted less than 5 per cent of the time.

p	OC function
0	1
$p_0 = .1$	$1 - \alpha = .99$
$p' = .146$	.604
$p_1 = .2$	$\beta = .05$
1	0

Average Sample Number (ASN). It is easy to see that if the proportion of defectives is much less than p_0 or much greater than p_1 the sampling will terminate earlier than if the proportion is close to or between p_0 and p_1. If all the items are defective, we can see from our chart for recording observations that the sampling will stop with 7 observations. If all items are good, it will stop with 26 items. The average number of observations necessary for other proportions can be determined mathematically.

A curve adequate for most purposes can be drawn from five points. The numerical results in the following expressions were obtained by substituting the quantities $p_0 = .10$, $p_1 = .20$, $\alpha = 1$ per cent, and $\beta = 5$ per cent. If the true proportion is p_0, the average sample number is

$$\frac{(1-\alpha)\ln\dfrac{\beta}{1-\alpha} + \alpha\ln\dfrac{1-\beta}{\alpha}}{p_0\ln\dfrac{p_1}{p_0} + (1-p_0)\ln\dfrac{1-p_1}{1-p_0}} = \frac{.99(-2.986) + .01(4.554)}{.10(0.693) + .90(-0.118)} = 79$$

and at p_1 it is

$$\frac{\beta\ln\dfrac{\beta}{1-\alpha} + (1-\beta)\ln\dfrac{1-\beta}{\alpha}}{p_1\ln\dfrac{p_1}{p_0} + (1-p_1)\ln\dfrac{1-p_1}{1-p_0}} = \frac{.05(-2.986) + .95(4.554)}{.20(0.693) + .80(-0.118)} = 95$$

The formula for the number of observations when all items obtained are defective is

$$\frac{\ln\dfrac{1-\beta}{\alpha}}{\ln\dfrac{p_1}{p_0}} = 7$$

and for none defective is

$$\frac{\ln\dfrac{\beta}{1-\alpha}}{\ln\dfrac{1-p_1}{1-p_0}} = 26$$

It is also possible to obtain the ASN which occurs for the proportion p'

between p_0 and p_1. The formula for this ASN is

$$\frac{\ln \dfrac{\beta}{1-\alpha} \ln \dfrac{1-\beta}{\alpha}}{\ln \dfrac{p_1}{p_0} \ln \dfrac{1-p_1}{1-p_0}} = \frac{(4.554)(-2.986)}{(0.693)(-0.118)} = 167$$

The maximum value for the ASN curve occurs for a point which is generally very near p'.

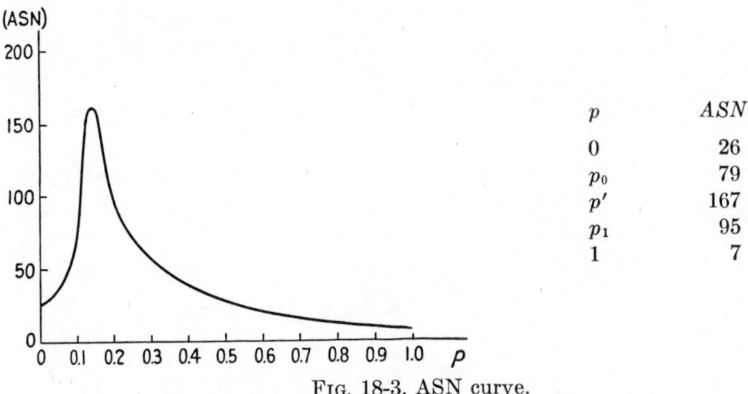

p	ASN
0	26
p_0	79
p'	167
p_1	95
1	7

FIG. 18-3. ASN curve.

Observations in Groups. If we wish to make several observations at a time and then record results as above, the effect on the sequential procedure is an increase in the ASN by an amount up to the number of items in each group. For example, if we examine 5 at a time, the ASN is increased not more than 5.

18-3. Test of Hypothesis on Means

A test of the hypothesis H_0: $\mu = \mu_0$ against the alternative H_1: $\mu = \mu_1$ will be developed for measurements from a *normal* population. For example, if yarn has been given an additional treatment to increase breaking strength, we would wish to investigate whether we should reject the hypothesis of $\mu = \mu_0$ (standard breaking strength) in favor of a larger value μ_1. As another example, assume a change has been made in the teaching process. We may wish to see whether we should reject the hypothesis $\mu = \mu_0$ (previous performance level) in favor of $\mu = \mu_1$ (some higher performance level).

The test procedure is developed in the same manner as the test on proportions. The measurements on the successive items put to test are $X_1, X_2, X_3, \ldots$. The ratio of the probability that we would get X_1 if $\mu = \mu_1$ to the probability that we would get X_1 if $\mu = \mu_0$ is

$$\frac{\dfrac{1}{\sqrt{2\pi}\,\sigma} e^{-\frac{1}{2\sigma^2}(X_1-\mu_1)^2}}{\dfrac{1}{\sqrt{2\pi}\,\sigma} e^{-\frac{1}{2\sigma^2}(X_1-\mu_0)^2}} = e^{-\frac{1}{2\sigma^2}(X_1-\mu_1)^2+\frac{1}{2\sigma^2}(X_1-\mu_0)^2}$$

$$= e^{-\frac{1}{2\sigma^2}(X_1^2-2X_1\mu_1+\mu_1^2-X_1^2+2X_1\mu_0-\mu_0^2)}$$

$$= e^{\frac{\mu_1-\mu_0}{\sigma^2}X_1+\frac{\mu_0^2-\mu_1^2}{2\sigma^2}} = R_{X_1}$$

The probability ratio for X_2 is the same except that X_2 appears in place of X_1.

$$\frac{p_{1m}}{p_{0m}} = R_{X_1} \cdot R_{X_2} \cdot R_{X_3} \cdot \cdot \cdot R_{X_m}$$

Using logarithms as before, we see that sampling will continue as long as

$$\ln \frac{\beta}{1-\alpha} < \ln \frac{p_{1m}}{p_{0m}} < \ln \frac{1-\beta}{\alpha}$$

i.e., as long as

$$\ln \frac{\beta}{1-\alpha} < \ln R_{X_1} + \ln R_{X_2} + \cdot \cdot \cdot + \ln R_{X_m} < \ln \frac{1-\beta}{\alpha}$$

Now notice that

$$\ln R_{X_1} = \ln e^{\frac{\mu_1-\mu_0}{\sigma^2}X_1+\frac{\mu_0^2-\mu_1^2}{2\sigma^2}}$$

which by the definition of natural logarithms gives

$$\ln R_{X_1} = \frac{\mu_1-\mu_0}{\sigma^2} X_1 + \frac{\mu_0^2-\mu_1^2}{2\sigma^2}$$

and
$$\sum \ln R_{X_i} = \frac{\mu_1-\mu_0}{\sigma^2} \sum X_i + \frac{\mu_0^2-\mu_1^2}{2\sigma^2} m$$

If we set this expression equal first to $\ln \frac{\beta}{1-\alpha}$ and then to $\ln \frac{1-\beta}{\alpha}$, we can obtain the critical lines for our test.

To illustrate this procedure, consider the problem of determining the passing or failure of students by a sequence of examination problems or projects which are of approximately equal difficulty and on which students in the past have obtained scores which for each student are normally distributed with $\sigma = 10$. Suppose an average of 60 points is a passing mark and we wish to have a chance of only 1 per cent of passing a student whose examinations are from a population with mean 50 and a chance of only 1 per cent of failing a student whose examinations are from a population with mean 70. Let us determine a chart or table for recording scores and see whether the plan is feasible in terms of the average number of problems or projects required to reach a decision. Here, we have

$$\mu_0 = 50 \qquad \alpha = 1\% \qquad \sigma = 10$$
$$\mu_1 = 70 \qquad \beta = 1\%$$

Substituting these values in the expression obtained above, we obtain

$$\frac{20}{(10)^2} \sum X_i + \frac{(50)^2 - (70)^2}{2(10)^2} m = \ln \frac{\beta}{1 - \alpha}$$
$$\frac{20}{(10)^2} \sum X_i + \frac{(50)^2 - (70)^2}{2(10)^2} m = \ln \frac{1 - \beta}{\alpha}$$

and, reducing,

$$.2\Sigma X_i - 12m = +4.595$$
$$.2\Sigma X_i - 12m = -4.595$$

The solution for ΣX_i is

$$\Sigma X_i = 60m + 23$$
$$\Sigma X_i = 60m - 23$$

We can draw a graph as before or form a table stating the critical values. These can be easily obtained by substituting in succession $m = 1, 2, 3, \ldots$ in the two equations just above. In most cases the table of values of ΣX will be more useful since it will often be difficult to plot the points

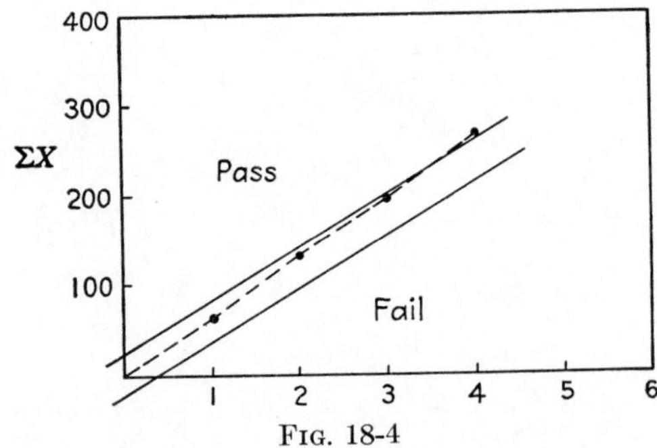

FIG. 18-4

on the graph with sufficient precision to determine whether or not it is between the lines. A student's successive scores on examinations of 60, 75, 65, 70 leading to a decision of passing are plotted on the graph and inserted in Table 18-1.

The operating-characteristic curve for this test is very similar to that drawn for the test on proportions. It is difficult to obtain specific values, but it is, of course, true that individuals with true mean above 70 will be failed less than 1 per cent of the time and those with true mean scores below 50 will be passed less than 1 per cent of the time by this procedure.

TABLE 18-1

No. of tests, m	Pass score	X	ΣX	Fail score
1	83	60	60	37
2	143	75	135	97
3	203	65	200	157
4	263	70	270	217
5	323		Pass	277
6	383			337
7	443			397

The columns headed X and ΣX indicate the recording of any particular set of scores.

Average Sample Number (ASN). The number of tests we can expect to make before a decision is reached is available for the true situations $\mu = \mu_0$, $\mu = \mu_1$, and $\mu = \dfrac{\mu_0 + \mu_1}{2}$. We designate the intercepts of the two lines in our graph by h_0 and h_1.

$$h_0 = \frac{\sigma^2}{\mu_1 - \mu_0} \ln \frac{1-\beta}{\alpha} \qquad h_1 = \frac{\sigma^2}{\mu_1 - \mu_0} \ln \frac{\beta}{1-\alpha}$$

For $\mu = \mu_0$ the ASN is

$$2\frac{h_1 + (1-\alpha)(h_0 - h_1)}{\mu_0 - \mu_1}$$

For $\mu = \mu_1$ the ASN is

$$2\frac{h_1 + \beta(h_0 - h_1)}{\mu_1 - \mu_0}$$

For $\mu = \dfrac{\mu_0 + \mu_1}{2}$ we obtain ASN $= -\dfrac{h_0 h_1}{\sigma^2}$. For our example, $h_0 = -23$, $h_1 = 23$, $\mu_0 = 50$, $\mu_1 = 70$, $\sigma = 10$, and we obtain 2.25 for the ASN at

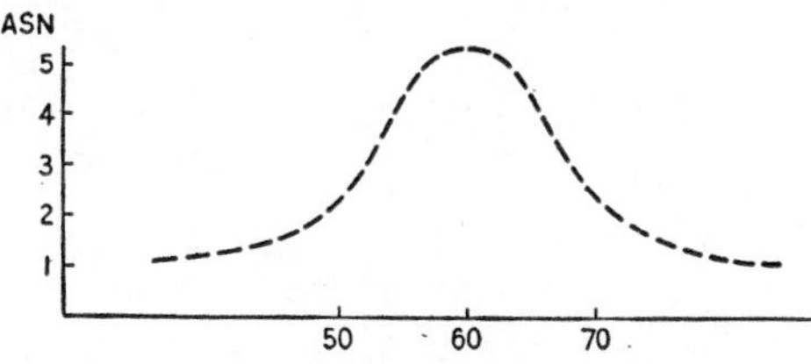

FIG. 18-5. ASN curve.

μ_0 and μ_1 and 5.3 for the ASN at $(\mu_0 + \mu_1)/2$. If we had solved by the procedures of Chap. 14 for the number of examinations required if given all at once, we would find the required number to be 5.4 or 6. The graph (Fig. 18-5), of course, does not drop below 1 at either end.

18-4. Test for Standard Deviation

Suppose we wish to investigate the effect on variability in breaking strength of a material when produced on machinery which operates at a greater rate of speed than formerly. Or suppose we investigate whether the variability in length of time rats can withstand a loud noise is greater for unrelated or related white rats. We shall test the hypothesis H_0: $\sigma^2 = \sigma_0^2$ against the alternative H_1: $\sigma^2 = \sigma_1^2$.

We shall assume that the observations are normally distributed. For the sequential test to be presented in this section it is necessary to know the mean value μ. The probability-ratio inequality for X_1 is given first. A second observation will be taken if

$$\frac{\beta}{1-\alpha} < \frac{\sigma_0}{\sigma_1} e^{-\frac{1}{2\sigma_1^2}(X_1-\mu)^2+\frac{1}{2\sigma_0^2}(X_1-\mu)^2} < \frac{1-\beta}{\alpha}$$

The central portion of the above inequality is obtained from the probability ratio

$$\frac{p_{11}}{p_{01}} = \frac{\dfrac{1}{\sqrt{2\pi}\,\sigma_1} e^{-\frac{1}{2\sigma_1^2}(X_1-\mu)^2}}{\dfrac{1}{\sqrt{2\pi}\,\sigma_0} e^{-\frac{1}{2\sigma_0^2}(X_1-\mu)^2}}$$

Taking logarithms in the above inequality, we obtain

$$\ln\frac{\beta}{1-\alpha} < \ln\frac{\sigma_0}{\sigma_1} + \frac{1}{2}(X_1-\mu)^2\left(\frac{1}{\sigma_0^2} - \frac{1}{\sigma_1^2}\right) < \ln\frac{1-\beta}{\alpha}$$

The successive ratios for X_2, X_3, . . . will have the same form and will be multiplied into the probability ratio above or added into the central portion where the logarithms have been taken, so that we obtain after m observations the following inequality, which determines whether sampling should continue:

$$\ln\frac{\beta}{1-\alpha} < m\ln\frac{\sigma_0}{\sigma_1} + \frac{1}{2}\left(\frac{1}{\sigma_0^2} - \frac{1}{\sigma_1^2}\right)\sum(X_i-\mu)^2 < \ln\frac{1-\beta}{\alpha}$$

As before, we set the central portion of this inequality equal to the two extremes and obtain the critical lines,

$$\sum(X_i-\mu)^2 = 2\frac{\ln\dfrac{\beta}{1-\alpha}}{\dfrac{1}{\sigma_0^2} - \dfrac{1}{\sigma_1^2}} + m\frac{2\ln\dfrac{\sigma_1}{\sigma_0}}{\dfrac{1}{\sigma_0^2} - \dfrac{1}{\sigma_1^2}}$$

$$\sum(X_i-\mu)^2 = 2\frac{\ln\dfrac{1-\beta}{\alpha}}{\dfrac{1}{\sigma_0^2} - \dfrac{1}{\sigma_1^2}} + m\frac{2\ln\dfrac{\sigma_1}{\sigma_0}}{\dfrac{1}{\sigma_0^2} - \dfrac{1}{\sigma_1^2}}$$

These can be written as

$$\Sigma(X_i - \mu)^2 = h_0 + mD$$
$$\Sigma(X_i - \mu)^2 = h_1 + mD$$

where $h_0 = 2\dfrac{\ln \dfrac{\beta}{1-\alpha}}{\dfrac{1}{\sigma_0^2} - \dfrac{1}{\sigma_1^2}}$

$$h_1 = 2\frac{\ln \dfrac{1-\beta}{\alpha}}{\dfrac{1}{\sigma_0^2} - \dfrac{1}{\sigma_1^2}}$$

$$D = \frac{\ln \dfrac{\sigma_1^2}{\sigma_0^2}}{\dfrac{1}{\sigma_0^2} - \dfrac{1}{\sigma_1^2}}$$

Testing now proceeds in the same fashion as with the sequential test for means.

We can write the ASN when H_0 is true as

$$\frac{(1-\alpha)h_0 + \alpha h_1}{\sigma_0^2 - D}$$

and when H_1 is true as

$$\frac{\beta h_0 + (1-\beta)h_1}{\sigma_0^2 - D}$$

The largest ASN occurs when σ^2 is larger than σ_0^2 and smaller than σ_1^2. The ASN for $\sigma^2 = D$ which lies between σ_0^2 and σ_1^2 is

$$\frac{-h_0 h_1}{2D^2}$$

Mean Unknown. If μ is not known, the same sequential table or graph may be used by computing at each stage $\Sigma(X_i - \bar{X})^2$ in place of $\Sigma(X_i - \mu)^2$ and comparing with the acceptance and rejection values for $m - 1$. This is a correct procedure but is perhaps less useful than the preceding tests presented since the value of $\bar{X}$ will also change after every observation, thus increasing the amount of computation necessary.

18-5. Discussion of Sequential Tests

The sequential tests presented, if applicable, can be very useful in reducing the amount of experimentation required for making a decision. However, in some cases it would not be efficient to make the observations one at a time or even in groups of 10 or 20 so that the sequential procedure would lose much of its advantage.

The test for means assumes that σ is known. Sequential procedures exist for testing the mean μ when σ is not known but are not so simple to use as those presented in this chapter and are therefore not given.

The sequential procedures as presented in this chapter are for one-sided alternatives, the proportion p_0 against an alternative p_1, the mean μ_0 against an alternative μ_1, the variance σ_0^2 against an alternative σ_1^2. Particularly in the case of the mean μ we are often interested in testing with two-sided alternatives, the mean μ against alternatives $\mu_0 \pm d$, that is, we wish to reject μ_0 for significant deviations in either direction. Sequential procedures for testing this hypothesis have been developed but are not given here.

GLOSSARY

average sample number
operating-characteristic curve
probability ratio
sequential test

DISCUSSION QUESTIONS

1. Discuss the change in the positions of the lines and the change in the method of recording necessary if the sequential procedure for testing for average proportion were set up in terms of the number of defective items and the total number tested in place of the number of defective and number of good items.

2. Explain why the graph in Fig. 18-5 does not drop below 1 at either end.

3. Describe the computations it is necessary to perform after each observation if the test for variance is made when μ is not known. What is the minimum number of observations which must be made in using this sequential procedure before it is possible to make a decision?

4. What is the minimum number of observations it is necessary to make in order to make a decision in testing for mean as described in Sec. 18-3?

CLASS EXERCISES

1. Construct a chart for recording observations for testing $p_0 = .5$ against $p_1 = .9$ with $\alpha = 5$ per cent and $\beta = 5$ per cent. Sketch the operating-characteristic function for this test. Sketch the ASN curve for this test, and determine experimentally the number of observations necessary to reach a decision when the true proportion is .50. This can be done by drawing red and white beads from a box or by tossing a coin. Having two colors of beads, one color could represent "good" items, and the other color could represent "bad" items. Draw beads one at a time, replacing each before the next is drawn. Record the number of beads drawn before a decision to accept or reject is reached. If the members of a class each determine several such results, a distribution of the required number can be formed and the mean obtained from this distribution.

2. Construct a table for the sequential test for $\mu_0 = -.5$ against the alternative $\mu_1 = +.5$ with $\sigma = 1$ and $\alpha = 5$ per cent and $\beta = 5$ per cent. Using the random normal numbers in Table A-2, sample from that population until a decision is reached, and record whether μ_0 or μ_1 is accepted and the number of observations required to reach a decision. Each student performs this experiment 10 times, and the results are collected. Compare the results with those to be expected theoretically, that is, μ_0 accepted as frequently as μ_1 and the average sample size 8.67. Note that the true mean is neither μ_0 nor μ_1.

PROBLEMS

1. Recompute the sequential test on means given in this chapter.

(*a*) With $\sigma = 20$, $\alpha = \beta = 5$ per cent.

(*b*) With $\sigma = 20$, $\alpha = \beta = 1$ per cent.

Note the changes in the positions of the lines and the change in the average sample size for $\mu = \dfrac{\mu_1 + \mu_2}{2}$.

2. For $\alpha = \beta = 5$ per cent, construct a table of acceptance and rejection values for a sequential test for H_0: $\sigma = 10$ against H_1: $\sigma = 15$. Find the average sample size corresponding to $\sigma^2 = D$.

3. Prepare a sheet of graph paper for the inspector, who is testing a batch of fuses so that he may record his tests of these fuses and reject batches of fuses only 1 per cent of the time if there are 4 per cent defectives and accept batches of fuses only 5 per cent of the time if there are 8 per cent defectives.

4. The following data were drawn one observation at a time in the order recorded. d denotes a defective item, and g denotes a good item. The experiment was performed to test the hypothesis that the proportion p of defective items in the population was .1, H: $p = .1$, with $\alpha = .05$, and so that if $p = .3$ the chance of rejecting is .90 ($\beta = .10$). Assuming that $\bar{X}$ is approximately normal and using the techniques of Chaps. 13 and 14 with $\alpha = .05$, is $\beta = .10$? Using these techniques, do you accept or reject H: $p = .1$? Analyze the data using sequential analysis, and see whether or not you would accept or reject before you had used the entire sample.

g g d g d g g g d d   g g g g g d g g g g   g g g d g g g g d g

CHAPTER 19

SENSITIVITY EXPERIMENTS

Experimental investigations often deal with continuous variables which cannot be measured in practice. For example, in testing the sensitivity of explosives to shock, a common procedure is to drop a weight on specimens of the same explosive mixture from various heights. There are heights at which some specimens will explode and others will not, and it is assumed that those which do not explode would have exploded were the weight dropped from a sufficiently greater height. It is supposed, therefore, that there is a critical height associated with each specimen and that the specimen will explode when the weight is dropped from a greater height and will not explode when the weight is dropped from a lesser height. The population of specimens is thus characterized by a continuous variable—the critical height—which cannot be measured. All one can do is select some height arbitrarily and determine whether the critical height for a given specimen is less than or greater than the selected height.

This situation arises in many fields of research. Thus, in testing insecticides, a critical dose is associated with each insect, but one cannot measure it. He can only try some dose and observe whether or not the insect is killed, i.e., observe whether the critical dose for the insect is less than or greater than the chosen dose. The same difficulty arises in pharmaceutical research dealing with germicides, anesthetics, and other drugs; in testing strength of materials; in psychophysical research dealing with threshold stimuli; and in several areas of biological and medical research.

In true sensitivity experiments it is not possible to make more than one observation on a given specimen. Once a test has been made, the specimen is altered (the explosive is packed; the insect is weakened) so that a bona fide result cannot be obtained from a second test. The common procedure in experiments of this kind is to divide the sample of specimens into several groups (usually but not necessarily of the same size) and to test one group at a chosen level, a second group at a second level, etc. The data consist of the numbers affected and not affected at each level. A simple method of analyzing such data (variously called *sensitivity data, all-or-none data, quantal responses*) is available if the particular method of obtaining data described in this chapter is used to obtain data.

If no special method is used for obtaining the data, i.e., if a certain number of tests are made at various levels of intensity, a rough analysis of the data may be made graphically. The graphical analysis is accomplished by plotting on normal-probability paper the percentage affected at each level, drawing a straight line which passes as close as possible to these points, and estimating the mean and standard deviation from this line. The mean is estimated by observing the point at which the line crosses the 50 per cent line. The standard deviation can be estimated by observing the points where the line crosses the 5 per cent and 95 per cent lines and dividing the distance between those points by $2(1.645) = 3.29$, the distance between P_{05} and P_{95} for the normal distribution. Computing procedures exist (see References, page 358) for obtaining the line which fits best, but they are fairly complex and will not be presented here.

If the data are obtained in a variety of special ways, the analysis is very much simplified and in many cases results in an increased precision for a given number of observations. The special method described in the next section is the best method available if it is desired to obtain general information about the whole distribution, i.e., estimate both the mean and standard deviation. Other special procedures are designed for estimating one particular percentile, for example, P_{10} or P_{90}, or are designed to minimize the number of reactions or the dependence on normality.

19-1. The "Up-and-down" Method

This technique for obtaining sensitivity data has been developed and used in explosives research. The method may be employed in any sensitivity experiment, but we shall discuss it in terms of explosives to avoid general terminology.

The technique is to choose some initial height h_0 and a succession of heights $h_1, h_2, h_3, \ldots$ above h_0 together with a succession $h_{-1}, h_{-2}, h_{-3}, \ldots$ below h_0. The first specimen is tested by dropping the weight from height h_0. If the first specimen explodes, the second specimen will be tested at h_{-1}; otherwise the second specimen will be tested at h_1. In general, any specimen will be tested at the level immediately below or immediately above the level of the previous test according as there was or was not an explosion on the previous test. The result of such an experiment might be portrayed as in Fig. 19-1, where the x's represent explosions and the o's nonexplosions. The first test is on the left at the highest level; this was a success (explosion), and so the second test was made at the next lower level and was also a success; the third test was therefore made at the level below that of the second; and since it was a failure, the fourth test was made at the level above that of the third test.

The primary advantage of this method is that it automatically concentrates testing near the mean. We shall see later that this increases the accuracy with which the mean can be estimated. In other words, for a given accuracy the up-and-down method will require fewer tests than the ordinary method of testing groups of equal size at preassigned heights. The saving in the number of observations may be of the order of 30 to 40 per cent.

Normalized height	Record of a sample of 60 tests	Freq.	
		x's	*o*'s
2.0	*x*	1	
1.7	*x x x x x x x x x x*	10	
1.4	*o x o x x x x x o o x o x x x o x x x o x x o x x o x*	18	9
1.1	*o x o o o o o o o o o o o o o o o o o x o*	2	18
.8	*o o*		2

FIG. 19-1

The method has one obvious disadvantage in certain kinds of experiments because it requires that each specimen be tested separately. This is not important in explosives experiments because each test must be made separately anyway. But in tests of insecticides, for example, a large group of insects can sometimes be treated as easily as a single one, and in large experiments of this kind any advantage of the up-and-down method might well be outweighed by this requirement of single tests. Even here, if expensive laboratory animals were being used, the advantage in economy of tests might offset the trouble of making single tests. Also, several sequences of tests may be run simultaneously and the results combined.

19-2. Conditions on the Experiment

The statistical analysis of data obtained can be quite simple, provided that the experiment satisfies certain conditions. Less restrictive conditions must be fulfilled for any analysis to be possible. These will be discussed here, and the actual analysis will be given in the following section.

In the first place, the analysis requires that the variate under analysis be normally distributed. In practice, the variate of interest to the research worker can rarely be considered to be normally distributed. It is therefore necessary that the natural variate be transformed to one which does have the normal distribution. This is readily done provided that the research worker has enough experience and data on his material to be able to specify rather accurately the shape of his distribution function. It is often the case in dosage-mortality experiments and in experiments on explosives that the logarithm of the dosage concentration or of the height is reasonably normally distributed. But in other areas of research, and sometimes in these areas, other transformations are more appropriate.

If one has no idea of the shape of his distribution function, then the data of the experiment itself must be used to provide this information. The common procedure here is to compute the percentage affected at each level and plot these percentages on arithmetic-probability paper against various functions of the variate in question. Usually one can soon discover what sort of function will force the percentages to lie sensibly along a straight line. There are, of course, infinitely many functions to choose from; the chosen function should be as simple as possible consistent with whatever knowledge is available concerning the nature of the material at hand.

We have already mentioned that the up-and-down method is particularly effective for estimating the mean. It is not a good method for estimating small or large percentage points (for example, the height at which 99 per cent of specimens explode) unless normality of the distribution is assured. In fact, no method which uses the normal distribution can be relied on to estimate extreme percentage points because such estimates depend critically on the assumption of normality. In most experimental research, it is possible to find simple transformations which make the variate essentially normal in the region of the mean, but to make it normal in the tails is quite another matter. Nothing short of an extensive exploration of the distribution, involving perhaps thousands of observations, will suffice in that case.

The information obtained by the up-and-down method is approximately equivalent to that which would be obtained with a sample only half as large if the minimum exploding height could be measured. This fact should be kept in mind in planning the size of the experiment.

A further condition is necessary if the statistical analysis is to be simple. One must be able to estimate roughly in advance the standard deviation of the normally distributed transformed variate. The interval between testing levels should be approximately equal to the standard deviation. This condition is not severe since it will be well enough satisfied if the interval actually used is less than twice the standard deviation. Furthermore, research workers who repeatedly perform these experiments on essentially similar materials can usually make very good preliminary estimates. This is the case in explosives research or biological assay, for example. This circumstance (of repeated experiments) is precisely the one in which a simple analysis is most desirable.

19-3. Statistical Analysis

The simple method of analysis given in this chapter is applicable only when all the conditions described in the preceding section are fulfilled.

The more complex analysis required when the levels are not equally spaced or when the distance between levels exceeds twice the standard deviation will not be included here.

We again revert to the explosives experiment in describing the method. Suppose it is known for the given type of explosive that the logarithms of the critical heights are normally distributed. Letting h represent the height, $y = \ln h$ will then be the normally distributed variate. We shall call y the normalized height and represent the mean and variance of its distribution by μ and σ^2. The experiment is performed by choosing an initial height for the first test, say, h_0. This should be chosen near the anticipated mean. The other testing levels are determined so that the values of the normalized height y are equally spaced. If d is the preliminary estimate of σ, and if $y_0 = \ln h_0$, then the actual testing heights are obtained by putting $\ln h = y_0 \pm d,\ y_0 \pm 2d,\ y_0 \pm 3d, \ldots$ and solving for h. The heights will then be so spaced that the transformed variate is equally spaced with spacing equal to its anticipated standard deviation. All computations are in terms of y.

In any experiment the total number of successes will be approximately equal to the total number of failures. In fact, the number of failures at any level cannot differ by more than 1 from the number of successes at the next higher level. For estimating μ and σ only the successes or only the failures are used, depending on which has the smaller total. In the example shown in Fig. 19-1 there are fewer failures than successes, and so the failures would be used. We shall let N denote the smaller total and let $n_0, n_1, n_2, \ldots, n_k$ denote the frequencies at each level for this less frequent event, where n_0 corresponds to the lowest level and n_k the highest level on which the event occurs. We have then $\Sigma n_i = N$.

The estimates of μ and σ are based on the sum and sum of squares of the y values using the observed frequencies n_i. But since the y values are equally spaced, these values are more easily computed in terms of the two sums of coded scores

$$A = \sum_{i=0}^{k} i n_i$$

$$B = \sum_{i=0}^{k} i^2 n_i$$

In this notation, the estimate of μ, say, $\bar{X}$, is

$$\bar{X} = y' + d\left(\frac{A}{N} \pm \frac{1}{2}\right) \tag{1}$$

where y' is the normalized height corresponding to the lowest level on which the less frequent event occurs. The plus sign is used when the analysis is based on the zeros, and the minus sign when it is based on the x's for data recorded as in Fig. 19-1, with x indicating that the next test is to be made at the next lower level and a zero indicating that the next test is to be made at the next higher level.

For this type of data the quantity

$$s = 1.620d\left(\frac{NB - A^2}{N^2} + .029\right) \tag{2}$$

is an estimate of the population σ. This is a curious estimate in that, while it is a linear function of $(NB - A^2)/N^2$, it gives the estimate of the standard deviation, not the square of the standard deviation. The formula is an approximate one which is quite accurate when $(NB - A^2)/N^2$ is larger than 0.3 but which breaks down rapidly when $(NB - A^2)/N^2$ becomes less than 0.3. In the latter instance the formula cannot be used.

TABLE 19-1

i	n_i	in_i	i^2n_i
2	9	18	36
1	18	18	18
0	2	0	0
	29	36	54

The example of Fig. 19-1 will illustrate the use of the formulas. Here the y values used were 2, 1.7, 1.4, 1.1, .8, the level of the first test y_0 being 2, and d being 0.3. Among the 60 tests there were 31 explosions and 29 failures; hence the latter are used to estimate the parameters. The failures appear on three levels (.8, 1.1, 1.4) with frequencies $n_0 = 2$, $n_1 = 18$, $n_2 = 9$. We have then $N = 29$, $A = 36$, $B = 54$, so that the mean is

$$\bar{X} = 0.8 + 0.3(\tfrac{36}{29} + \tfrac{1}{2}) = 1.32$$

and the standard deviation is

$$s = (1.620)(0.3)(\tfrac{270}{841} + .029) = .17$$

An alternative and approximately equivalent estimate of μ is the mean of all heights at which tests are made, excluding the first height but including the height at which a test would be made if one additional test were made at the end of the sequence. For this example, this definition gives $\bar{X} = 1.33$. The sample was actually drawn from a normal population with $\mu = 1.3$ and $\sigma = .2$, using Table A-2 of random normal deviates. Each value X read from the table was first substituted into the formula $y = .2X + 1.3$. The mean and standard deviation of the 60 observations were 1.312 and .158 so that it was a fairly representative sample.

Percentage points would be estimated by $\bar{X} + z_\alpha s$, where z_α is chosen from tables of the normal deviate to give the desired percentage. Thus, in the example, P_{05} is estimated by $1.32 - (1.645)(.17) = 1.04$. If the y values are thought of as natural logarithms of actual heights in feet in an explosives experiment, the antilogarithms of estimated percentage points would be estimates of the corresponding points for the distribution of h. Thus the median (not mean) value of h can be estimated by antiln $1.32 = 3.74$ feet, the 5 per cent height by antiln $1.04 = 2.83$ feet. The antilogarithm of s does not estimate the standard deviation for h, however, and any computation which involves the standard deviation (estimates of percentage points, confidence limits) must be done in terms of the normalized height, and only the final result transformed to actual heights.

19-4. Confidence Intervals

Ordinarily the standard deviation of a sample mean $\bar{X}$ is given by $\sigma_{\bar{X}} = \sigma/\sqrt{N}$, where σ is the population standard deviation and N the sample size. In the present case because of the manner of obtaining the data this expression must be multiplied by a factor which we shall call G, so that the formula for the standard error of the mean is

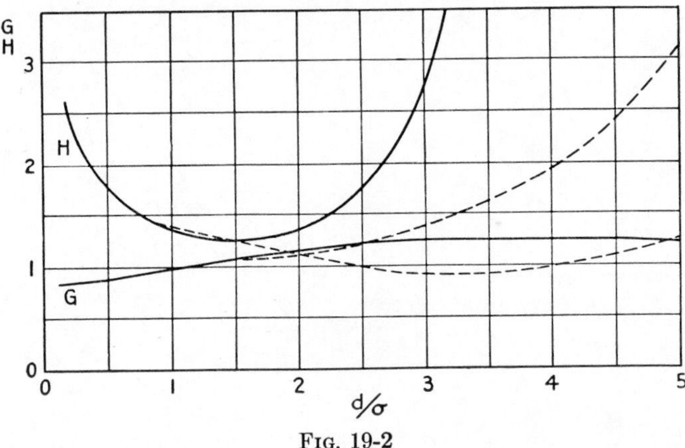

Fig. 19-2

$$\sigma_{\bar{X}} = \frac{G\sigma}{\sqrt{N}} \tag{3}$$

and G depends on the ratio d/σ and on the position of the mean relative to the testing levels. G is plotted in Fig. 19-2 as a function of d/σ. The position of the mean relative to the testing levels does not affect G unless the interval d is large; the solid branch of the curve gives the value of G when the mean falls on one of the testing levels, while the dashed branch gives the value when the mean falls midway between two levels. Curves for other positions of the mean would fall between the two branches.

In practice σ is not known, and s must be used in (3) to obtain an estimate, say, $s_{\bar{X}}$, of $\sigma_{\bar{X}}$. In the illustrative example with $s = .17$, we have $d/s = 1.8$ so that G is about 1.12. The estimate of $\sigma_{\bar{X}}$ is therefore

$$s_{\bar{X}} = \frac{(.17)(1.12)}{\sqrt{29}} = .035$$

A confidence interval for μ may now be estimated by $\bar{X} \pm z_\alpha s_{\bar{X}}$. Thus a 95 per cent confidence interval is

$$1.32 \pm (1.96)(.035) \qquad \text{or} \qquad 1.25 \text{ to } 1.39$$

For moderate values of N, it might be more accurate to use t values in place of z_α, but it is likely that this is a minor matter relative to the error caused by the approximations already used. Again assuming the confidence interval refers to the logarithm of an actual height, it gives rise to an asymmetric 95 per cent confidence interval (3.5 to 4.0 feet) for the median height.

The standard error of the sample standard deviation, say, σ_s, is estimated in the same manner as the standard error of the mean. We shall write

$$\sigma_s = \frac{H\sigma}{\sqrt{N}} \tag{4}$$

H is plotted in Fig. 19-2, where the solid branch gives the value of H when the mean falls on a level, while the dashed branch gives the value when the mean is midway between two levels. When d/σ is less than 2, there will be little error introduced by interpolating linearly between the two branches for other positions of the mean. Thus, if the mean falls $d/4$ from a testing level, one may use the value of G midway between the two branches. For the illustrative example with $d/s = 1.8$, we find H to be about 1.24 so that the estimate of σ_s is

$$s_s = \frac{(1.24)(.17)}{\sqrt{29}} = .039$$

The estimate s_s would be used to estimate the standard error of a percentage point $\bar{X} + z_\alpha s$; the estimate would be $\sqrt{s_{\bar{X}}^2 + z_\alpha^2 s_s^2}$. Thus, in the example, a 95 per cent confidence interval for the 5 per cent point would be estimated by

$$1.04 \pm (1.96)\sqrt{(.035)^2 + (1.645)^2(.039)^2} \qquad \text{or} \qquad .88 \text{ to } 1.20$$

We should mention again that the estimation of small or large percentage points depends strongly on the assumption of normality in the tails. It can easily happen that a relatively small error in this assumption may far outweigh the sampling error indicated by the confidence interval, especially in the case of very extreme percentages, say, 1 or 0.1 per cent.

19-5. Choice of Testing Interval

The curves in Fig. 19-2 have been extended beyond $d = 2\sigma$ in order to show what happens to the measures of precision for larger intervals. Curve G shows that the precision of the mean steadily decreases as d increases. The two branches of H show that there is an optimum spacing for estimating the standard deviation depending on the position of the mean relative to the testing levels. Since the mean is usually unknown, this information is of little practical value.

Curve G indicates that the interval should be quite small for maximum precision in the mean, but in practice this is not true for several reasons. In the first place, the curves are for expected values and essentially assume infinite sample sizes, and in fact very large samples are required to get good estimates of the mean for a very small interval. The estimate may be biased appreciably toward the initial testing level unless the sample is very large. Second, a small interval may cause one to waste observations unless a good choice for the initial level is made. If a poor choice is made, many observations must be spent getting from the level to the region of the mean. And finally, since σ is usually unknown, the precision of the mean must actually be measured by s, and the accuracy of s becomes poor for very small intervals as shown by curve H.

All these considerations indicate that the interval should be within the range of about 0.5σ to 2σ, and experiments with the method support this conclusion.

GLOSSARY

critical height or dose
sensitivity
"up-and-down" method

DISCUSSION QUESTIONS

1. Describe an experiment involving materials or subjects where the observations are all-or-none, or quantal, responses. In what way is the material or subject altered so that repeated tests may not be made on the same individual even though no reaction or response occurs?

2. Discuss the reason for the curves in Fig. 19-2 branching into two curves when d/σ becomes large.

3. If the observations are such that the logarithms of the observations are normally distributed, the graphical solution discussed at the beginning of this chapter may be effected by using logarithmic-probability paper. Logarithmic-probability paper differs from normal-probability paper in that the scale of measurements is marked so that in effect the logarithms of the measurements are plotted. Discuss how the estimates of the mean and standard deviation may be obtained from this paper.

CLASS EXERCISE

Each student makes a record of 50 tests, using as observations the random normal numbers in Table A-2 by taking the heights −3, −2, −1, 0, 1, 2, 3 as various levels and recording an x if the number is below the level considered at the moment and o if it is above. Change level as indicated by the up-and-down method. Compute $\bar{X}$, s, P_{05}, and P_{95}. Collect the results into frequency distributions, and compare the results with those to be expected theoretically.

PROBLEMS

1. The tabulated data were obtained by the up-and-down technique.

y																																										
3.3																																										
3.2									x																																	
3.1						x		o		x		x		x		x		x		x		x														x		x		x		
3.0	x				o		o				o		o		o		o		o		o		x		x						x		x		o		o		o		x	
2.9		x		o																				o		x		x		o		o		o								o
2.8			o																								o		o													
2.7																																										

Analyze the data by the techniques discussed in this chapter as follows:
(*a*) Estimate the mean.
(*b*) Estimate the standard deviation.
(*c*) Give 95 per cent confidence limits for the mean.
(*d*) Give 90 per cent confidence limits for P_{20}.
(*e*) If the y values are natural logarithms of dosages of a poisonous drug, estimate the dosage which kills 20 per cent of the individuals. Estimate, by a 95 per cent confidence interval, the dosage which kills 50 per cent of the individuals.

CHAPTER 20

PROBABILITY

The concept of probability may be discussed in a general way as a theory based on an equally likely set of events, or as relative frequencies, or as a subjective determination of fair odds.

Equally Likely. In an intuitive sense "probability" is usually related to a set of events which are *equally likely*. For example, if we select one person from a *well-mixed* group of 50 people, we may consider any of the 50 people to be equally likely to be chosen. If we draw a card from a *well-shuffled* deck of ordinary playing cards, we expect to have an equal chance of selecting any particular one of the 52 cards in the deck. In drawing a ball from a box containing seven *well-mixed* balls, we expect that any one of the balls is equally likely to be chosen—just as likely to be chosen as any other. A comparable situation may occur when people are chosen for a public-opinion poll or when a few items are selected for harvesting to estimate the total yield.

Relative Frequency. We may think of probability as the relative frequency of particular events in a very long sequence of trials. In tossing a coin, for example, we generally expect heads or tails to be equally likely. This is based on the fact that a coin has two sides and, when a fair (or true) coin is tossed repeatedly, it will fall heads with approximately the same frequency as it will fall tails. However, a *particular* coin in a long series of tosses may come up heads considerably less often than tails so that heads and tails would not be equally likely. Therefore we may think of the probability of a particular coin falling heads as the ratio of the number of heads occurring to the total number of tosses in a sequence of tosses. Similarly we may define the probability of a particular item being defective among a group of manufactured articles as the ratio of the number of defectives to the total number of articles manufactured, or the probability of an explosion occurring when a bomb is dropped as the ratio of the number of explosions to the total number of bombs. We can connect this concept of repeated trials to the equally likely concept by considering a long sequence of draws from a deck of cards (replacing the card drawn each time and reshuffling the deck), or a long sequence of draws from a box of balls (replacing and remixing each time).

Subjective Probability. A third reference to probability may be described as *subjective.* A man may feel that enough is known about a situation to enable him to assess the "odds" that some hypothesis might be true. He may indicate the extent of his belief that an event will occur or that a particular hypothesis is true by stating the odds he would call a fair bet. That is, 1:10 odds indicate a different level of belief or information about a situation from 1:2 odds. Odds of 1:10 indicate an assessment of probability as $\frac{1}{11}$, and odds of 1:2 indicate $\frac{1}{3}$. For example, a gambler may feel that today is his lucky day and be willing to bet on odds different from those he would accept under other circumstances. Even though no bet is involved, the degree of belief in a hypothesis may be indicated, for example, by the statement that the odds against life on the moon are 1:1,000,000. Presumably the odds would change with the addition of any further knowledge about the moon.

This last concept is not interpreted on a frequency basis, and of course the theorems derived from a relative-frequency or equally-likely basis should not be used in this case.

We shall approach probability from the first viewpoint discussed above, taking a finite set of equally likely possibilities, writing down the relationships which seem reasonable, and then formalizing the theory by stating these "reasonable" results as axioms or as theorems which follow from the axioms.

20-1. Two-way Frequency Table

Suppose we have a box containing 100 balls of the following description:

10 red balls marked with the digit 1
20 red balls marked with the digit 2
10 red balls marked with the digit 3
20 white balls marked with the digit 1
10 white balls marked with the digit 2
30 white balls marked with the digit 3

A tabular presentation of the composition of the box of balls is given in Table 20-1.

Instead of *color* and *number* describing a ball we can consider examples such as a person classified according to *sex* and *hair color* or manufactured parts classified according to *quality* and *type of process*. For test animals we could consider one classification *infected-uninfected* and the other classification *inoculated-uninoculated*.

Now, returning to the example of 100 balls described above, we shall agree to consider that, if a ball is drawn from the box, each ball is equally likely to be chosen. Further we shall interpret the fraction $\frac{1}{100}$ as the probability of choosing any particular ball which may be specified. Since there are a number of balls which have the same description, 10 which are red and marked 3, 40 which are red, 30 marked 2, etc., we shall define the probability of drawing a red ball marked 3 to be $\frac{10}{100}$, the probability of drawing a red ball to be $\frac{40}{100}$, the probability of drawing a ball marked 2 to be $\frac{30}{100}$, etc. That is, the probability of choosing one of these 100 equally likely balls having a certain characteristic will be defined as the number of balls in the group having the characteristic divided by the total number of balls in the box.

TABLE 20-1. TWO-WAY FREQUENCY TABLE

Color	Marking			Total for each color
	1	2	3	
Red	10	20	10	40
White	20	10	30	60
Total for each marking	30	30	40	100 Total No. of balls

We shall use the notation $P(A)$ to represent the probability that an object drawn will have characteristic A. We shall also interpret A as the "event" of drawing an object having a certain characteristic. In this notation

$P(\text{red ball marked } 2) = \frac{20}{100}$
$P(\text{red ball}) = P(\text{red ball marked either } 1, 2, \text{ or } 3) = \frac{40}{100}$
$P(\text{red ball marked 2 or white ball marked } 3) = \frac{50}{100}$
Etc.

The conditions of the drawing are often added to the above notation and of course must be stated if there is any doubt or if we wish to specify different conditions. For example we may wish to write the $P(\text{red ball})$ of the above example as:

$$P(\text{red ball} \mid \text{set of 100 equally likely balls of which 40 are red}) = \frac{40}{100}$$

The conditions of the drawing are stated following the vertical bar |, which is often read "given." If a drawing is to be made from some part of the originally specified group of objects, this condition should always be stated. Thus,

$$P(\text{red ball} \mid \text{ball is marked } 1) = \frac{10}{30}$$

which is obtained by following the same rules for computing a probability, i.e., by computing the ratio of the number of objects having the characteristic to the total number of balls available for the drawing. In this context this probability is referred to as a *conditional probability*. Another example is:

$$P(\text{ball marked } 2 \mid \text{white ball}) = \frac{10}{60}$$

In dealing either with two possible events or with two descriptive characteristics we find it very useful to consider the use of the words *and* and *or* in the following statements:

1. The first event *and* the second event both occur.
2. One event *or* the other event occurs.

Thus we speak of a ball being red *and* marked 1, or a ball marked 1 *or* marked 2, or a ball being red *or* marked 1. Note that the word *or* is used in the sense of including *either or both.* From Table 20-1 we see that we can write

$$P(\text{red } \textit{and} \text{ marked } 1) = \tfrac{10}{100}$$
$$P(\text{marked } 1 \textit{ or } 2) = (30 + 30)/100$$

Care must be taken in computing probabilities of the type $P(A \textit{ or } B)$ to avoid counting any ball more than once. For example, we write

$$P(\text{red } \textit{or} \text{ marked } 1) = (10 + 20 + 10 + 20)/100 = \tfrac{60}{100}$$

or we can actually count some of the balls twice and then subtract to correct the total as follows:

$$P(\text{red } \textit{or} \text{ marked } 1) = (40 + 30 - 10)/100 = \tfrac{60}{100}$$

The marginal total for red is 40, and the marginal total for balls marked 1 is 30. The sum of these two marginal totals will include in both cases the 10 red balls marked 1. This can be restated as

$$\begin{aligned} P(\text{red } \textit{or} \text{ marked } 1) &= \tfrac{40}{100} + \tfrac{30}{100} - \tfrac{10}{100} \\ &= P(\text{red}) + P(\text{marked } 1) - P(\text{red } \textit{and} \text{ marked } 1) \end{aligned}$$

Some further concepts which are useful are *complementary, exhaustive, independent,* and *exclusive.*

In the above example a ball is either red or white, and we refer to drawing a red ball as complementary to drawing a white ball. The event complementary to drawing a ball marked 1 is drawing a ball marked either 2 or 3.

An exhaustive set of events includes every event which could possibly happen. In our example drawing a red ball and drawing a white ball are two events which include every possibility. The probability that some event of a set of exhaustive events will occur is 1.

If the conditional probability of event A given another event B is equal to the probability of A without that condition, then events A and B are called independent. The condition for independence can be stated with the symbols

$$P(A|B) = P(A)$$

In our example $P(\text{red} \mid \text{marked } 1) = \tfrac{10}{30}$, which is not equal to $P(\text{red}) = \tfrac{40}{100}$; so these events are *dependent.*

Exclusive events cannot occur simultaneously, e.g., a single ball cannot be both red and white; so red and white are exclusive characteristics.

20-2. Axioms and Theorems of Probability

Table 20-1 can be generalized by introducing letters for the frequencies as in Table 20-2. Using this notation, we can write

TABLE 20-2

Color	Marking			Total for each color
	1	2	3	
Red.......	n_{11}	n_{12}	n_{13}	$n_{11} + n_{12} + n_{13}$
White.....	n_{21}	n_{22}	n_{23}	$n_{21} + n_{22} + n_{23}$
Total for each marking	$n_{11} + n_{21}$	$n_{12} + n_{22}$	$n_{13} + n_{23}$	$n_{11} + n_{12} + n_{13} + n_{21} + n_{22} + n_{23} = N$

$$P(\text{marked } 1) = \frac{n_{11} + n_{21}}{N}$$

$$P(\text{red} \mid \text{marked } 1) = \frac{n_{11}}{n_{11} + n_{21}}$$

$$\begin{aligned} P(\text{red } \textit{and} \text{ marked } 1) &= \frac{n_{11}}{N} = \frac{n_{11} + n_{21}}{N} \cdot \frac{n_{11}}{n_{11} + n_{21}} \\ &= P(\text{marked } 1) \cdot P(\text{red} \mid \text{marked } 1) \\ P(\text{red } \textit{or} \text{ marked } 1) &= \frac{(n_{11} + n_{12} + n_{13}) + (n_{11} + n_{21}) - n_{11}}{N} \\ &= P(\text{red}) + P(\text{marked } 1) - P(\text{red } \textit{and} \text{ marked } 1) \end{aligned}$$

Similar formulas may be written down for the white balls and for the balls marked 2 and 3.

In general we may note from this table that if A and B are two events we always have the following relationships among the probabilities:

1. $0 \leq P(A) \leq 1$.
2. $P(A \textit{ and } B) = P(A) \cdot P(B|A) = P(B) \cdot P(A|B)$.
3. $P(A \textit{ or } B) = P(A) + P(B) - P(A \textit{ and } B)$.

In order not to overcomplicate the presentation, we shall consider these three relationships as axioms for our probability calculations. The second and third relationships may be derived as theorems from a more extensive foundation. If the possible events are not assumed to be equally likely as was assumed in the tables above, a more elaborate development would be necessary.

Various theorems may be deduced from the above axioms. For example, using $A_1, A_2, \ldots, A_k$ to represent events, we have the following:

THEOREM 1. Two events:

$$P(A_1 \textit{ or } A_2) = P(A_1) + P(A_2) - P(A_1 \textit{ and } A_2)$$

Three events:

$$\begin{aligned} P(A_1 \textit{ or } A_2 \textit{ or } A_3) = {} & P(A_1) + P(A_2) + P(A_3) - P(A_1 \textit{ and } A_2) \\ & - P(A_1 \textit{ and } A_3) - P(A_2 \textit{ and } A_3) \\ & + P(A_1 \textit{ and } A_2 \textit{ and } A_3) \end{aligned}$$

Four events:

$$\begin{aligned} P(A_1 \textit{ or } A_2 \textit{ or } A_3 \textit{ or } A_4) = {} & P(A_1) + P(A_2) + P(A_3) + P(A_4) \\ & - P(A_1 \textit{ and } A_2) - P(A_1 \textit{ and } A_3) - P(A_1 \textit{ and } A_4) \\ & - P(A_2 \textit{ and } A_3) - P(A_2 \textit{ and } A_4) - P(A_3 \textit{ and } A_4) \\ & + P(A_1 \textit{ and } A_2 \textit{ and } A_3) + P(A_1 \textit{ and } A_3 \textit{ and } A_4) \\ & + P(A_1 \textit{ and } A_2 \textit{ and } A_4) + P(A_2 \textit{ and } A_3 \textit{ and } A_4) \\ & - P(A_1 \textit{ and } A_2 \textit{ and } A_3 \textit{ and } A_4) \end{aligned}$$

Similar relationships hold for more than four events.

THEOREM 2. If A_1 and A_2 are mutually exclusive, that is,

$$P(A_1 \textit{ and } A_2) = 0$$

then $P(A_1 \textit{ or } A_2) = P(A_1) + P(A_2)$. This is merely a special case of Theorem 1.

THEOREM 3. If $P(A_1|A_2) = P(A_1)$ and $P(A_1) \neq 0$, then

$$P(A_2|A_1) = P(A_2)$$

This follows directly from axiom 2.

DEFINITION. If $P(A_1 \textit{ or } A_2 \textit{ or } \cdots \textit{ or } A_k) = 1$, then $A_1, A_2, \ldots, A_k$ are an exhaustive set of events.

DEFINITION. If A_1 represents the occurrence of an event and $\tilde{A}_1$ (read "A tilde") represents the nonoccurrence of the same event, then A_1 and $\tilde{A}_1$ are called complementary events. It follows, of course, that

$$P(A_1) + P(\tilde{A}_1) = 1$$

20-3. Counting Techniques: Permutations and Combinations

The consideration of probability problems will often require the enumeration of the possible ways events can occur. This section will present several methods to aid in this enumeration.

DEFINITION. If N is a positive integer, the product

$$1 \cdot 2 \cdot 3 \cdot \cdots \cdot (N - 1) \cdot N$$

is defined by the symbol $N!$ and is read "N factorial." It will be convenient to define $0!$ to be 1.

DEFINITION. $0! = 1$.

THEOREM 1. The number of different ways N distinct objects can be arranged in line is $N!$. An arrangement of N objects in a line is called a permutation of the N objects. The total number of permutations, then, of N objects is $N!$

THEOREM 2. The number of ways of selecting and arranging r objects taken from N distinct objects is $P(N,r) = \dfrac{N!}{(N-r)!}$.

DEFINITION. The total number of possible selections of r objects from N distinct objects is called the number of combinations of N objects taken r at a time and will be denoted by $C(N,r)$. Other notations used are $\binom{N}{r}$ or ${}_NC_r$ or ${}^NC_r$.

THEOREM 3. $C(N,r) = \dfrac{N!}{r!(N-r)!}$.

THEOREM 4. $C(N,r) = C(N,N-r)$.

THEOREM 5. $C(N,N) = C(N,0) = 1$.

DEFINITION. If $r < 0$, or if $r > N$, $C(N,r) = 0$.

THEOREM 6. $(a+b)^N = \sum_{r=0}^{N} C(N,r)a^{N-r}b^r = C(N,0)a^N + C(N,1)a^{N-1}b$
$+ C(N-2,2)a^{N-2}b^2 + \cdots + C(N,N-1)ab^{N-1}$
$+ C(N,N)b^N$.

The values of $C(N,r)$ are often called binomial coefficients since they occur as coefficients in the relationship shown in Theorem 6. Values of $C(N,r)$ for $N \leq 10$ are given in Table A-29b.

THEOREM 7. $\sum_{r=0}^{N} C(N,r) = 2^N$.

The use of the above axioms, theorems, and definitions will be illustrated by several examples.

Example 1. We have a box of 50 light bulbs, of which 5 are defective. What is the probability, or chance, of finding exactly 2 defective bulbs in a sample of 4 chosen from the box? We consider any one of the $C(50,4)$ possible samples as being equally likely and define the probability as:

$$P(\text{exactly 2 defectives in sample of 4} \mid \text{box of 50 with 5 defectives}) = \frac{\text{Number of possible samples of 4 bulbs with 2 defectives}}{C(50,4)}$$

To count the possible samples having 2 defectives, we note that the 2 defectives must come from the 5 defectives in the box [this can be done in $C(5,2)$ ways] and the 2 nondefectives from the 45 nondefectives in the box [this can be done in $C(45,2)$ ways].

Note that the number of ways two independent events can occur together is the product of the numbers of ways each event can occur separately. Similarly note that the number of ways that some one of several exclusive events can occur is the sum of the number of ways each can occur. In this case the two events which must occur are the selection of 2 light bulbs from the 5 which are defective and the selection of 2 light bulbs from the 45 which are not defective. Thus we can select a sample of 4 having 2 defectives in a number of ways equal to the product $C(5,2) \cdot C(45,2)$, and the desired probability is

$$\frac{C(5,2) \cdot C(45,2)}{C(50,4)} = \frac{\left(\frac{5!}{2!3!}\right)\left(\frac{45!}{2!43!}\right)}{\left(\frac{50!}{4!46!}\right)} = \frac{5 \cdot 4}{2} \cdot \frac{45 \cdot 44}{2} \cdot \frac{4 \cdot 3 \cdot 2 \cdot 1}{50 \cdot 49 \cdot 48 \cdot 47} = .0430$$

In a similar manner we can compute the probabilities of no defectives, of exactly 1 defective, of exactly 3 defectives, of exactly 4 defectives in a sample of 4. The results are displayed in Table 20-3. The notation $f(x)$ and $F(x)$ in the column headings is used later in this chapter.

TABLE 20-3. PROBABILITY OF x DEFECTIVES IN A SAMPLE OF 4 FROM A BOX CONTAINING 45 GOOD AND 5 DEFECTIVE ITEMS

The total of $P(x$ defectives) for all the values of x is 1.0.

Measurement x	Frequency $P(x \text{ defectives}) = f(x)$	Cumulative frequency $P(x \text{ or fewer defectives}) = F(x)$
4	$\frac{C(5,4)C(45,0)}{C(50,4)} = .00002$	1.00000
3	$\frac{C(5,3)C(45,1)}{C(50,4)} = .00195$	.99998
2	$\frac{C(5,2)C(45,2)}{C(50,4)} = .04299$	.99803
1	$\frac{C(5,1)C(45,3)}{C(50,4)} = .30808$	.95504
0	$\frac{C(5,0)C(45,4)}{C(50,4)} = .64696$	.64696
Total..........	1.0	

The above discussion is *mathematical* in nature in that we are given complete information about the population sampled, that is, 50 items of which 5 are defective. A *statistical* question occurs when we do not know how many of the 50 items are defective but wish to infer from the sample the proportion defective in the population. For example, as in Chap. 7, we could use a rule of behavior (decision rule) which will declare the proportion of defectives in the population too high if any of the 5 in the sample are defective. If this occurs, we may decide to inspect all 50 items. From Table 20-3 we see that 64.7 per cent of the boxes containing 5 defectives would not be examined further if this decision rule were followed.

PROBLEMS

1. A man before buying a batch of 100 fuses tests 4. If the batch contains 10 defective fuses, what is the probability that the buyer will find none in the sample? That the buyer will find 4 defective fuses in the sample? *Ans.* $C(90,4)/C(100,4)$; $C(10,4)/C(100,4)$.

2. An aircraft factory plans to purchase small parts in batches of 40. The factory will inspect 3 from each batch. If a batch has 2 defectives, what is the probability that exactly 1 defective will be found in the sample? That no defectives will be found? Exactly 2 defectives will be found? Two or fewer defectives will be found? *Ans.* $C(2,1) \cdot C(38,2)/C(40,3)$, etc.

3. A shipment of electrical switches is packed in boxes of 100 each. A box is inspected by examining 20 switches and rejecting the box if any of the 20 switches is defective. What is the probability of rejecting a box containing 2 defectives? *Ans.* 0.362.

4. An experiment is conducted in which A looks at 5 cards (marked 1, 2, 3, 4, 5), concentrating on 2 particular cards, and B attempts to "read his mind" and to name the 2 cards. If actually B has no talent for mind reading, what is the probability that he will guess the 2 cards correctly? *Ans.* 0.1.

5. In Fig. 14-8 curves are drawn for the probability that a sample of size N from a batch of K items with a certain number of defectives present will contain no defectives. For example, if $K = 100$, $N = 10$, with 2 per cent defectives (2 defectives among 100), then the probability

$$P(\text{zero defectives in a sample of 10}) = \frac{C(98,10)}{C(100,10)} = \frac{98!}{10!88!}\,\frac{10!90!}{100!} = \frac{90 \cdot 89}{100 \cdot 99} = .809$$

which agrees with the curve in Fig. 14-8. Verify the point on the curve for $K = 200$, $N = 20$, above 2 per cent defective. Given a sample of $N = 10$ for a batch of $K = 100$ items having 0, 2, 4, 6, 8, or 10 per cent defectives, compute the probabilities $P(\text{zero } or \text{ 1 defective})$ for each case and draw an operating-characteristic curve comparable with those in Fig. 14-8. Compare this curve and the corresponding curve of Fig. 14-8 to decide which of the following two rules of behavior seems better: (*a*) Reject the batch if the sample contains 1 or more defectives, or (*b*) reject the batch if the sample contains 2 or more defectives.

Example 2. Suppose that an animal with a particular disease has a 40 per cent chance of recovering if treated with a certain drug (and, of course, a 60 per cent chance of not recovering). One interpretation of this statement is: If all of a very large number of animals with the disease were treated with the drug, 40 per cent of the animals would recover and we state a probability of 40 per cent due to our "random choice" of an animal from this large number of animals. The interpretation of this example is the same as in Example 1, except that the number of items from which the sample is chosen is very large or infinite. An alternative interpretation is: There is a 40 per cent chance of recovery for any animal when given the drug; i.e., the probability of recovery is inherent in the animal itself rather than representing the chance of selection of an animal which will recover when given the drug. This second interpretation is analogous to the occurrence of heads in the toss of a coin where the chance of heads is 40 per cent.

Suppose we desire the answer to the question: What is the probability that exactly 2 out of 5 treated animals will recover? We take .4 as the probability of recovery of the animal chosen first, take .4 as the probability of recovery of the animal chosen second (i.e., it is independent of the first choice as in tossing coins), and so on. The probability of recovery of any one of the 5 animals is .4 (independent of the recovery or non-recovery of the other choices).

We shall now attack the problem with a procedure useful for a wide variety of probability problems. We write the event of 2 recoveries resulting when 5 animals are treated as a series of exclusive events as follows:

"2 recoveries out of 5 treated" is the same as

"Animals 1 *and* 2 recover *and* animals 3, 4, 5 do not recover"
or "Animals 1 *and* 3 recover *and* animals 2, 4, 5 do not recover"
or "Animals 1 *and* 4 recover *and* animals 2, 3, 5 do not recover"
or "Animals 1 *and* 5 recover *and* animals 2, 3, 4 do not recover"
or "Animals 2 *and* 3 recover *and* animals 1, 4, 5 do not recover"
or "Animals 2 *and* 4 recover *and* animals 1, 3, 5 do not recover"
or "Animals 2 *and* 5 recover *and* animals 1, 3, 4 do not recover"
or "Animals 3 *and* 4 recover *and* animals 1, 2, 5 do not recover"
or "Animals 3 *and* 5 recover *and* animals 1, 2, 4 do not recover"
or "Animals 4 *and* 5 recover *and* animals 1, 2, 3 do not recover"

There are $C(5,2)$ exclusive events combined in the either/or statements listed above, and the probability of the combined event is the sum of the probabilities of the individual events. Since the chances for recovery for individual animals are independent, the probability that the first and second animals recover and the remaining 3 do not is

$$P(\text{1st recovers}) \cdot P(\text{2d recovers}) \cdot P(\text{3d does not recover}) \cdot P(\text{4th does not recover}) \cdot P(\text{5th does not recover}) = (.4)(.4)(.6)(.6)(.6) = (.4)^2(.6)^3$$

The chance of any of the $C(5,2) = 10$ events listed above will be the same since the only change in writing down the probability is an interchange in the order in which the factors are written. Therefore we have

$$P(\text{exactly 2 recover from 5}) = C(5,2)(.4)^2(.6)^3 = .3456$$

Similarly we can compute the probability of exactly 3 recoveries out of 5, etc. These results are presented in Table 20-4.

TABLE 20-4. PROBABILITY OF EXACTLY x RECOVERIES OUT OF 5 INDEPENDENT TRIALS WHERE THE CHANCE OF ANY INDIVIDUAL RECOVERING IS .4

x	P(exactly x recoveries) $= f(x)$	P(x or fewer recoveries) $= F(x)$
5	$C(5,5)(.4)^5 = .01024$	1.00000
4	$C(5,4)(.4)^4(.6) = .07680$	.98976
3	$C(5,3)(.4)^3(.6)^2 = .23040$	.91296
2	$C(5,2)(.4)^2(.6)^3 = .34560$	.68256
1	$C(5,1)(.4)(.6)^4 = .25920$	.33696
0	$C(5,0)(.6)^5 = .07776$	.07776

Again the above discussion is mathematical. The statistical question would occur here if we wished to estimate the chance of recovery of diseased animals from the observations made on 5 animals.

PROBLEMS

6. A process yields ball bearings of which, in the long run, 5 per cent are defective. What is the probability that in a run of 10 ball bearings there would be no defectives, 1 defective, . . . , 10 defectives? *Ans.* $(.95)^{10}$; $10(.05)(.95)^9$; . . . ; $(.05)^{10}$.

7. Ten per cent of people contracting a certain disease do not recover. What is the probability that all of 3 people contracting the disease do not recover? If a new drug is given to 20 people with the disease and all recover, can we conclude that the drug is effective? As an aid in making a decision, compute the probability that the observed result would occur if the drug had no effect at all. *Ans.* .001; P(all recover in 20 cases | proportion is .9) $= (.9)^{20} = .1216$.

8. If we assume that boy and girl births are equally likely, compute the probability that exactly 40 out of 100 babies born will be boys. *Ans.* $C(100,40) \cdot (.5)^{100} = .0108$.

9. Under the same assumption as in Prob. 8 how frequently will families of 5 children (no multiple births) have (*a*) no girls, (*b*) 1 girl, (*c*) 2 girls, (*d*) 3 girls, (*e*) 4 girls, (*f*) 5 girls? *Ans.* $(.5)^5$; $5(.5)^5$; $10(.5)^5$; $10(.5)^5$; $5(.5)^5$; $(.5)^5$.

Note that if actual observation disagrees too markedly from the assumptions used in computing the probabilities we may be forced to discard such assumptions. The probability that a baby will be a boy may actually differ from $\frac{1}{2}$. Furthermore the probability that a baby will be a boy may be different for different families and even at different times for the same family.

10. Assume that a man walking along a north-south street tosses a coin at each corner to decide whether to go north or south. What is the probability that in walking 10 blocks he is again at his starting point? *Ans.* The man must go a total of 5 blocks north and 5 blocks south; therefore the problem is equivalent to the probability of exactly 5 heads in tossing a true coin, namely, $C(10,5)(.5)^{10}$.

Note that Prob. 10 may also be worded in terms of the motion of a particle, where the change of direction is caused by collision in place of the coin toss. The probability of a change in direction will be the probability of a collision. The more practical problem of the motion of a particle in three dimensions involves more mathematics.

11. Actuarial tables indicate that, in a large group of 10-year-old children, 85 per cent will survive for 40 years. What is the probability that, of 3 children each age 10, exactly 1 will survive 40 years? *Ans.* $C(3,2)(.15)^2(.85)^1$.

Example 3. Y claims that he can tell whether or not there is water in a closed container by holding a forked stick above the container. To test his talent, it is suggested that the following experiment be performed: Six sets of 3 containers each are presented to Y. One container of each set of 3 is filled with water, the other 2 are empty, and Y is so informed. He attempts to choose the one container in each set which is filled with water. If he has no talent, he has a chance of $\frac{1}{3}$ of correctly choosing the container with water in any one set, independently of his other choices. If he has some ability, he should do better than by guessing. In other words, he would have an independent chance greater than $\frac{1}{3}$ of correctly choosing the container with water in any 1 set of 3 containers. If one specifies the chance, p, of Y correctly choosing the container with water, this example is the same as Example 2 and we can compute the probability of his picking exactly x correctly in 6 trials as in that example. The results of this computation are given in Table 20-5 for four values of p.

TABLE 20-5. PROBABILITY OF CORRECTLY PICKING EXACTLY x CONTAINERS OF WATER IN 6 TRIALS WITH CONSTANT PROBABILITY OF SUCCESS, p, IN EACH TRIAL

For example, $P(4 \text{ correct choices in 6 trials with } p = \frac{1}{3}) = C(6,4)(\frac{1}{3})^4(\frac{2}{3})^2 = .0823$.

x	$p = \frac{1}{3}$	$p = \frac{1}{2}$	$p = \frac{4}{5}$	$p = 1$
6	.0014	.0156	.2621	1
5	.0165	.0938	.3932	0
4	.0823	.2344	.2458	0
3	.2195	.3125	.0819	0
2	.3292	.2344	.0154	0
1	.2634	.0938	.0015	0
0	.0878	.0156	.0001	0

A possible assessment of the ability of Y may be made by agreeing to say there is evidence that he has some ability if he is correct in 5 or more of the 6 trials. If he is guessing, we would then have probability of concluding he has some ability (when he actually possesses no unusual ability) equal to $.0179 = .0014 + .0165$. Drawing an inference about his talent from a sample of his work is a *statistical* problem. As in Chaps. 7 and 14 the probability of our concluding Y has some talent when he actually has none is called the *level of significance* of the experiment.

The $P(5 \text{ *or* } 6 \text{ correct choices in 6 trials})$ is graphed in Fig. 20-1. This curve is a power curve for the test of Y's ability. The height of the curve gives the probability that we will decide to say, "Y is not guessing" if actually he has probability p of selecting the right container. If he has a 50 per cent chance of being correct, there is a probability of .11 that we will conclude that he is not guessing; if he has an 80 per cent chance, there is a probability of .66 that we will conclude that he is not guessing. The curve in Fig. 20-1 is the power curve of the test of the hypothesis H: $p = \frac{1}{3}$, where the critical region of the test is $x = 5, 6$.

It should be noted that other experiments could be designed to test Y. For example, the containers could be presented 2 at a time instead of 3 at a time or they could be presented singly, with a coin tossed to determine whether or not each container was empty. The specific way the data are

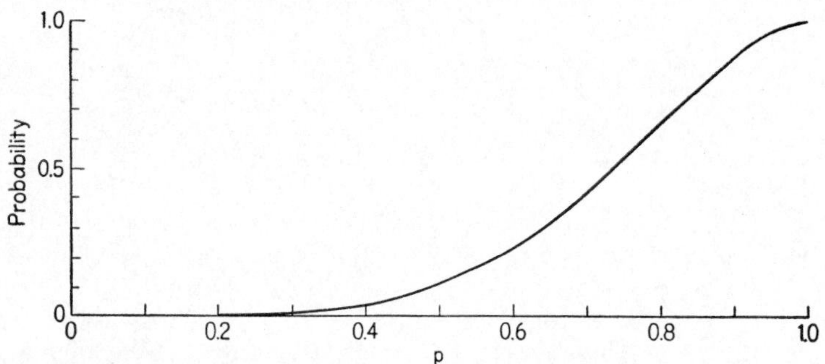

FIG. 20-1. Probability of Y having five or six correct choices out of six trials with probability, p, for each trial.

collected is referred to as the *design of the experiment*, the statement concerning the population (for example, $p = \frac{1}{3}$ to specify that Y is guessing) is called a *statistical hypothesis*, and the rule which indicates the experimenter's procedure (e.g., reject the hypothesis if 5 or 6 successes result) is a *statistical test* of the hypothesis.

PROBLEMS

12. Consider the results of Example 3 for an experiment which requires Y to choose between 2 containers, 1 empty and 1 with water, for 6 trials. Find the resulting level of significance if the critical region is, as before, 5 or 6 correct.

13. An experiment is performed as follows: A cuts a well-shuffled deck of playing cards (52 cards; 26 red and 26 black) and observes the color of the cut card. As in Prob. 4, B attempts to read his mind and writes down red or black. The cards are then reshuffled, and the trial is repeated. If B has no talent and is guessing, what is the probability that in 10 such trials he will call 8 correctly? At least 8 correctly? *Ans.* $C(10,8)(\frac{1}{2})^{10}$; $C(10,8)(\frac{1}{2})^{10} + C(10,9)(\frac{1}{2})^{10} + C(10,10)(\frac{1}{2})^{10} = .0547$.

14. Suppose in the last problem B has sufficient ability to enable him to recognize the correct color 80 per cent of the time. What is the probability that he will call at least 8 out of 10 correctly?

Ans. $C(10,8)(.2)^2(.8)^8 + C(10,9)(.2)(.8)^9 + C(10,10)(.8)^{10} = .6778$.

15. In recording the performance of B in Prob. 13 we may record the number of red cards called correctly and the number of black cards called correctly as in the accompanying table. Assume that B has no talent, and verify that the probability of obtaining exactly the recorded results is

P(6 red of which 4 are called correctly *and* 4 black all called incorrectly)

$$= C(10,6)(\tfrac{1}{2})^{10} \cdot C(6,4)(\tfrac{1}{2})^{6} \cdot C(4,4)(\tfrac{1}{2})^{4}$$

$$= \frac{10!}{6!4!}\frac{6!}{4!2!}\left(\frac{1}{2}\right)^{20} = .0030$$

Note that this is not the same as the probability that B calls exactly 4 correctly independently of whether the correct cards are red or black. This latter probability is $C(10,4)(\tfrac{1}{2})^{10} = .2051$.

	Correct	Incorrect	
Red	4	2	6
Black	0	4	4
	4	6	10

Example 4. Yellow guinea pigs crossed with yellow produce yellow guinea pigs, and white crossed with white produce white. Yellow guinea pigs crossed with white always produce cream-colored offspring. Cream guinea pigs when crossed produce in the long run 25 per cent yellow offspring, 50 per cent cream offspring, and 25 per cent white offspring. This type of inheritance may be explained with the use of the genetic formulas AA, Aa, aa, which represent yellow, cream, and white, respectively. When two animals are crossed, the offspring receive one factor represented by A or a from each parent. Therefore, if both parents are AA, all offspring will be AA, and if both parents are aa, all offspring will be aa.

If both parents are Aa, then their offspring may be AA, Aa, or aa. Since the cream guinea pigs are of the type Aa, all three types will result and we can compute the probabilities as follows, assuming that either factor has an equal chance of being transmitted by each parent:

P(offspring AA) = P(receiving A from father *and* A from mother)

$$= (\tfrac{1}{2})(\tfrac{1}{2}) = .25$$

P(offspring Aa) = P(receiving A from father *and* a from mother *or* receiving a from father *and* A from mother) $= (\tfrac{1}{2})(\tfrac{1}{2}) + (\tfrac{1}{2})(\tfrac{1}{2}) = .50$

P(offspring aa) = P(receiving a from father *and* a from mother)

$$= (\tfrac{1}{2})(\tfrac{1}{2}) = .25$$

Using the above assumptions and reasoning, we can compute various probabilities. In a group of 10 offspring from type Aa parents the probability of exactly 3 being cream is $C(10,3)(.50)^{10}$. The probability of exactly 4 being yellow is $C(10,4)(.25)^4(.75)^6$. The probability of exactly 3 being cream and exactly 4 being yellow is $C(10,3)(.50)^{10} \cdot C(7,4)(.50)^4(.50)^3$.

If one parent is AA and the other Aa, the probability that an offspring is AA is .50 and that an offspring is Aa is .50. Thus the probability that exactly 4 of 10 offspring from such parents are Aa is $C(10,4)(\tfrac{1}{2})^{10}$.

PROBLEMS

16. For a cross of two cream guinea pigs compute the probability that all of 3 offspring will be yellow; that 5 offspring will consist of 3 yellow and 2 cream; that all of 5 offspring will be cream; that 5 offspring will consist of 2 yellow, 2 cream, and 1 white. For a cross of cream guinea pigs with yellow compute the probabilities of the same results as above. *Ans.* $(.25)^3$, $10(.5)^8$, $(.5)^5$, $30(.5)^8$; $(.5)^3$, $10(.5)^5$, $(.5)^5$, 0.

17. The factor A is called dominant and the factor a is called recessive if individuals of type Aa have the same observable characteristic as AA, but this differs from those of type aa. Mendel observed that in crossing pea plants from a tall race (no dwarfness in their ancestry so far as he knew) with plants from a dwarf race all the resulting plants were tall. He now crossed these resulting plants (hybrids) with each other and observed that about $\frac{3}{4}$ were tall and about $\frac{1}{4}$ were dwarf. Explain in a manner similar to that of Example 4 the occurrence of these proportions.

18. For the cross of the hybrids of Prob. 17, compute the probability that of four offspring two will be tall and two dwarf. *Ans.* $6(.75)^2(.25)^2$.

Example 5. We plan to plant varieties A and B of corn on pairs of equal-size plots at six localities in the state. Since any pair of plots at the six places has uniform environmental conditions, we may suppose that the probability is $\frac{1}{2}$ that type A will produce a larger yield than type B at any one location if the varieties are equal in yield. When the yield of type A exceeds that of type B at any location we record a plus, and otherwise a minus. We suppose that the probability of a tie is zero. We can now compute the probabilities: P(zero plus values), P(1 plus value), P(2 plus values), etc. In fact a similar computation was done in Example 3. The results are given in Table 20-6.

TABLE 20-6. PROBABILITY OF x PLUS VALUES AND $6 - x$ MINUS VALUES IN SIX INDEPENDENT TRIALS EACH HAVING PROBABILITY $\frac{1}{2}$

For example, $P(\text{1 plus value}) = C(6,1)(\frac{1}{2})^6 = .093750$

x	$6 - x$	Probability	r
6	0	.015625	0
5	1	.093750	1
4	2	.234375	2
3	3	.312500	3
2	4	.234375	2
1	5	.093750	1
0	6	.015625	0

This situation will be recognized as that described in Sec. 17-1, in which the sign test is used. There we denoted by r the number of times the less frequent sign occurs. From Table 20-6 for $N = 6$ we can read possible values of r with the probabilities as recorded in Table 20-7.

Note that Table 20-7 contains the complete list of cumulative probabilities P(r or less) for $N = 6$. Therefore we cannot find a value of r to

TABLE 20-7. VALUES OF THE SMALLEST NUMBER OF PLUS OR MINUS SIGNS WITH THE PROBABILITIES FOR EACH

r	$P(r) = f(r)$	$P(r \text{ or less}) = F(r)$
3	.31250	1.00000
2	.46875	.68750
1	.18750	.21875
0	.03125	.03125

correspond to any arbitrarily chosen value of $P(r \text{ or less})$ unless the probability is listed. We can, however, state for the arbitrarily chosen value .01 that no integer r satisfies the relationship $P(r \text{ or less}) \leq .01$. The number $r = 0$ can be used as the largest integer for .05 and .10 since $P(0 \text{ or less}) \leq .05$ and $P(0 \text{ or less}) \leq .10$. The number $r = 1$ is the largest integer having the property that $P(r \text{ or less}) \leq .25$.

PROBLEMS

19. Suppose we planned to plant the two varieties of corn of Example 5 in 10 locations instead of 6. Write down the distribution of x as in Table 20-6, and verify the entries in Table A-10 for $N = 10$.

20. The distribution in Table 20-7 was constructed for r, the number of times the less frequent sign occurs. Consider x, the number of plus signs, and determine the largest x which satisfies the relationship $P(x \text{ or less}) \leq .01, .05, .10, .25$, for $N = 6$. *Ans.* None, 0, 1, 2.

21. The median M of a population is defined as that M for which $P(x \leq M) = \frac{1}{2}$. If the population is sufficiently large that this probability remains equal to $\frac{1}{2}$ as successive observations are taken from this population or if each of the observations is returned to the population before another is taken, we may use the same probability that each successive observation is less than the median. Compute the probability that of 10 observations the second largest observation will lie on one side of the median and the second smallest will lie on the other side. (*Hint:* This will occur unless there are exactly 0, 1, 9, or 10 observations smaller than the median.) Find the probability that the largest and the smallest observations will be on opposite sides of the median. *Ans.* .9790, .9981, which agree with the values .021 and .002, which can be read from Table A-25.

Example 6. Suppose for data of the type described in Example 5 we write the plus and minus signs in the order observed and compute for the given number of plus and minus signs the probability of any single arrangement. For example, if there are three plus and three minus signs, the possible arrangements are given in Table 20-8. Following each arrangement is a number u, which is the number of runs of plus and minus signs in that sequence. If we take each arrangement as equally likely, we can compute the probability for any value of u as in Table 20-9.

The total number of arrangements is the number of ways three of the six places can be chosen for the three plus signs, namely $C(6,3)$. In

TABLE 20-8. ALL POSSIBLE ARRANGEMENTS OF THREE PLUS AND THREE MINUS SIGNS

+ + + − − − 2	+ − + − + − 6	− + + + − − 3	− + − − + + 4
+ + − + − − 4	+ − + − − + 5	− + + − + − 5	− − + + + − 3
+ + − − + − 4	+ − − + + − 4	− + + − − + 4	− − + + − + 4
+ + − − − + 3	+ − − + − + 5	− + − + + − 5	− − + − + + 4
+ − + + − − 4	+ − − − + + 3	− + − + − + 6	− − − + + + 2

TABLE 20-9. NUMBER OF RUNS WITH THEIR PROBABILITIES IN ARRANGING THREE PLUS SIGNS AND THREE MINUS SIGNS AT RANDOM

u	$P(u) = f(u)$	$P(u \text{ or less}) = F(u)$
6	$\frac{2}{20}$	1.0
5	$\frac{4}{20}$	.9
4	$\frac{8}{20}$	.7
3	$\frac{4}{20}$	.3
2	$\frac{2}{20}$	.1

general, if there are N_1 plus signs and N_2 minus signs, then there are $C(N_1 + N_2, N_1)$ possible arrangements. It is more difficult to count the arrangements where u has a specified value. It has been shown that if u is even the number of arrangements is

$$2C(N_1 - 1, \tfrac{1}{2}u - 1) \cdot C(N_2 - 1, \tfrac{1}{2}u - 1)$$

and if u is odd the number of arrangements is

$$C(N_1 - 1, \tfrac{1}{2}u - \tfrac{1}{2}) \cdot C(N_2 - 1, \tfrac{1}{2}u - \tfrac{3}{2}) + C(N_1 - 1, \tfrac{1}{2}u - \tfrac{3}{2}) \cdot C(N_2 - 1, \tfrac{1}{2}u - \tfrac{1}{2})$$

Agreement of these formulas with the distribution computed in Table 20-9 can be shown by setting $N_1 = N_2 = 3$. For example, for $u = 2$ the number of arrangements is $2C(2,0) = 2$, and for $u = 3$ the number of arrangements is $C(2,1)C(2,0) + C(2,0)C(2,1) = 2 + 2 = 4$, etc.

The application of this theory is given in Sec. 17-3, where the use of Table A-11 is described.

It should be noted that we are computing the probability that a certain number of runs results when we are given N_1 and N_2. For some problems we may wish to allow N_1 and N_2 to vary also, i.e., to allow the number as well as the arrangement of plus and minus values to be a chance variable. This will lead to different probabilities, and Table A-11 will not be appropriate. For example, if we toss a coin three times, the probability that there are exactly two runs ($u = 2$) is the probability that one of the following exclusive sequences of heads and tails occurs: HHT, THH, TTH, HTT. Since the probability of any one of the sequences is $\frac{1}{8}$, the probability that two runs will occur is .5.

$$\begin{aligned} P(\text{two runs}) &= P(\text{HHT } or \text{ THH } or \text{ TTH } or \text{ HTT}) \\ &= P(\text{HHT}) + P(\text{THH}) + P(\text{TTH}) + P(\text{HTT}) \\ &= \tfrac{1}{8} + \tfrac{1}{8} + \tfrac{1}{8} + \tfrac{1}{8} = \tfrac{1}{2} \end{aligned}$$

PROBLEMS

22. Write down all possible arrangements of $N_1 = 4$ plus and $N_2 = 3$ minus signs, and verify the counting formulas in this case. Write down in a table the probabilities of 2, 3, 4, 5, 6, 7 runs.

23. Suppose there is a 50 per cent chance for a plus sign to occur and a 50 per cent chance for a minus sign to occur in each of four trials. What is the probability that 1 run will result; 2 runs; 3 runs; 4 runs? What is the probability that 2 runs will result if we know that 2 plus and 2 minus signs will result? *Ans.* $\frac{2}{16}, \frac{6}{16}, \frac{6}{16}, \frac{2}{16}; \frac{2}{6}$.

Example 7. Suppose we denote by x_1, x_2, x_3 and y_1, y_2, y_3 the yields of three plots of each of two varieties of corn. When the yields of the six plots are known, they are arranged in order of size and ranks are assigned: 1 to the largest, 2 to the next largest, and so on, to 6 for the smallest. Let T' be the sum of the ranks assigned to x_1, x_2, x_3, the yields of the first variety. The sum of all six ranks is 21; therefore the sum of the ranks assigned to y_1, y_2, y_3 will be 21 minus the sum assigned to the first variety. If the varieties are equally good as measured by yield, we shall consider any of the 20 possible arrangements of the ranks of the plot yields as equally likely. Table 20-10 lists the possible arrangements with the

TABLE 20-10. POSSIBLE ARRANGEMENTS OF THREE x AND THREE y VALUES WITH THE SUM OF THE RANKS OF THE x VALUES

xxxyyy	6	*xyxyxy*	9	*xyyxyx*	11	*yyxxxy*	12
xxyxyy	7	*yxxxyy*	9	*yxxyyx*	11	*yxyyxx*	13
xxyyxy	8	*xyxyyx*	10	*yxyxxy*	11	*yyxxyx*	13
xyxxyy	8	*xyyxxy*	10	*yxyxyx*	12	*yyxyxx*	14
xxyyyx	9	*yxxyxy*	10	*xyyyxx*	12	*yyyxxx*	15

TABLE 20-11. DISTRIBUTION OF T' FOR TWO SAMPLES OF THREE OBSERVATIONS EACH

T'	$P(T')$	$P(T'$ or less)
15	.05	1.00
14	.05	.95
13	.10	.90
12	.15	.80
11	.15	.65
10	.15	.50
9	.15	.35
8	.10	.20
7	.05	.10
6	.05	.05

corresponding values of T', and Table 20-11 gives the distribution of T'. The statistic T' is called the *rank-sum* statistic. Table A-20 gives the complete distributions of the rank-sum statistic T' for two samples of size N_1 and N_2, respectively, from the same population for all sample sizes less than or equal to 10 and a normal approximation for larger sample sizes.

PROBLEM

24. Write down all possible arrangements of three x and four y values, and verify the distribution of T' as given for $N_1 = 3$ and $N_2 = 4$ in Table A-20.

20-4. Discrete Frequency Distributions

The examples in the preceding section show the recording of various probabilities in a frequency (probability) table. Tables 20-3 to 20-7, 20-9, 20-11 contain particular examples in which are given the values x of the observable variable and the chance $f(x)$ that these values occur. The notation for a general table of this sort is given in Table 20-12. For a given x, $f(x)$ gives the probability that x will occur, $F(x)$ gives the probability that x or any smaller x occurs. In symbols

$$P(x) = f(x)$$
$$P(x \text{ or less}) = F(x)$$

The group of individual probabilities $f(x)$ is referred to as a *density distribution* (or "frequency function" or "elementary probability law"). The group of cumulative probabilities $F(x)$ is referred to as a *cumulative distribution* or sometimes by the single word *distribution*. A variable

TABLE 20-12. GENERAL NOTATION FOR A FREQUENCY AND CUMULATIVE DISTRIBUTION

x	$f(x)$	$F(x)$
.	.	.
.	.	.
.	.	.
3	$f(3)$	$f(0) + f(1) + f(2) + f(3)$
2	$f(2)$	$f(0) + f(1) + f(2)$
1	$f(1)$	$f(0) + f(1)$
0	$f(0)$	$f(0)$

which has associated with it a distribution given either in the density or in the cumulative form is called a *random variable* (or sometimes a *stochastic variable*). In Table 20-12 the random variable x takes on the values 0, 1, 2, 3, . . . with probabilities as given by the corresponding $f(0)$, $f(1)$, $f(2)$, $f(3)$, ... In Table 20-12 the random variable is illustrated as taking on only these values, but in any specific problem other values may occur. For example, the distribution given in Table 20-4 is for a random variable x which takes on the values 0, 1, 2, 3, 4, 5. If we consider the random variable representing the proportion of recoveries it will take on the values 0, 0.2, 0.4, 0.6, 0.8, 1.0.

The density function is never negative and the sum of all probabilities is equal to unity.

Since the cumulative distribution gives the probability that the random variable is equal to, or less than, a particular value, it will usually be used only where the random variable has an obvious ranking such as size, age, or number, and not for random variables which represent categories such as color, sex, variety, etc.

Distribution functions may be represented by tables as in the previous examples. In many cases, however, it is possible and convenient to write the density and cumulative distributions in the form of an equation. When a distribution can be presented in formula form, we can often find formulas for the mean and for the variance also. Formulas will be presented for the distributions which were developed in Examples 1 and 2.

If as in Example 1 we have a box containing K objects of which d are defective, the probability of exactly x defectives in a sample of N can be written

$$f(x) = \frac{C(d,x)C(K-d,N-x)}{C(K,N)}$$

for $x = 0, 1, \ldots, s$, where s is the smaller of N and d. The probability of x or fewer defectives can be written

$$F(x) = \frac{\sum_{i=0}^{x} C(d,i)C(K-d,N-i)}{C(K,N)}$$

For example, from Table 20-3 the probability of one or fewer defectives is represented by

$$\begin{aligned} F(1) &= \frac{\sum_{i=0}^{1} C(5,i) \cdot C(45,4-i)}{C(50,4)} \\ &= \frac{C(5,0) \cdot C(45,4)}{C(50,4)} + \frac{C(5,1) \cdot C(45,3)}{C(50,4)} \\ &= .64696 + .30808 = .95504 \end{aligned}$$

This distribution is called a *hypergeometric distribution*. The variable here is discrete (as it is in every case so far in this chapter), taking on values 0, 1, 2, . . . , s, and the distribution depends on three parameters, K, d, N. However, when this distribution is used in a problem of statistical inference, d is usually the only unknown parameter, since K, the total size of the population, and N, the size of the sample, would be known.

If as in Example 2 there are repeated independent trials with constant probability p of success, the probability of exactly x successes in N trials can be written

$$f(x) = C(N,x)p^x(1 - p)^{N-x}$$

for $x = 0, 1, \ldots, N$, and the probability of x or fewer successes in N trials is

$$F(x) = \sum_{i=0}^{x} C(N,i)p^i(1 - p)^{N-i}$$

This distribution is called a *binomial distribution*. The random variable is discrete, taking on the values $0, 1, \ldots, N$. The distribution depends on two parameters, p and N. The sample size N is usually known, with p the only unknown parameter.

There are, of course, many discrete density distributions which can be expressed in formula form. In addition to the hypergeometric and binomial distributions discussed above the Poisson distribution to be presented in Sec. 20-5 is among the most useful. In general a discrete density distribution is zero except at a countable number of points. In the examples described above the points where $f(x)$ is not zero are finite in number. The Poisson distribution to be described later has an infinite number of points where $f(x)$ is not zero.

PROBLEMS

25. Which of the following functions are density distributions?

(*a*) $f(x) = 0$ except $f(0) = .4$ and $f(1) = .6$.

(*b*) $f(x) = e^{-x}/3$ for $x = 0, 1, 2$; $f(3) = \frac{2}{3} - \frac{1}{3e} - \frac{1}{3e^2}$; $f(x) = 0$ for other values of x.

(*c*) $f(x) = 0$ except $f(0) = p^3$, $f(1) = 3p^2(1 - p)$, $f(2) = 3p(1 - p)^2$,

$$f(3) = (1 - p)^3.$$

26. Write down formulas for $f(x)$ and $F(x)$ in the following instances, specifying the values of x for which the formula applies:

(*a*) x is the number of defectives in a sample of 20 chosen from a batch of 200 articles of which 5 per cent are defective.

(*b*) x is the number of baby boys in a series of 30 births, assuming the chance for a boy at each birth is 50 per cent.

(*c*) x is the number of heads in 12 tosses of a "fair" coin.

(*d*) x is the number of shots among 50 fired which hit the center of a target, assuming that in the long run the frequency of such successes is 10 per cent.

(*e*) x is the number of patients in a group of 35 recovering from a disease, if the long-run frequency of recovery is 75 per cent.

We noted in Chaps. 2 and 3 that we could describe a distribution in part by computing such measurements as the arithmetic mean μ, the variance σ^2, the standard deviation σ, the various percentiles, etc. This can be done for the probability distributions which we are now studying. Thus from Tables 20-3 and 20-4 reproduced below in Table 20-13 we compute μ and σ^2. Note that since the entire population is present we divide by N in computing σ^2. The values of $f(x)$ correspond to f_i/N in the formulas for μ and σ^2; so

$$\mu = \Sigma x_i f(x_i) \qquad \text{and} \qquad \sigma^2 = \Sigma(x_i - \mu)^2 f(x_i) = \Sigma x_i^2 f(x_i) - \mu^2$$

As noted above, in cases where $f(x)$ is given by formula, the values of μ and σ^2 can also be given by formula, sometimes by a fairly simple formula. As an example, consider the binomial distribution. The computation is arranged in Table 20-14. To avoid extra difficulty in computing σ^2, we

TABLE 20-13. COMPUTATION OF μ AND σ^2 FOR EXAMPLES OF THE HYPERGEOMETRIC AND BINOMIAL DISTRIBUTIONS OF TABLES 20-3 AND 20-4

From Table 20-4

x	$f(x)$	$xf(x)$	$x^2f(x)$
5	.01024	.05120	.25600
4	.07680	.30720	1.22880
3	.23040	.69120	2.07360
2	.34560	.69120	1.38240
1	.25920	.25920	.25920
0	.07776	0	0
	1.00000	2.00000	5.20000

$\mu = 2.00000$
$\sigma^2 = 5.20000 - (2.00000)^2$
$= 1.2$
$\sigma = 1.09544$

From Table 20-3

x	$f(x)$	$xf(x)$	$x^2f(x)$
4	.00002	.00008	.00032
3	.00195	.00585	.01755
2	.04299	.08598	.17196
1	.30808	.30808	.30808
0	.64696	0	0
	1.00000	.39999	.49791

$\mu = .39999$
$\sigma^2 = .49791 - (.39999)^2$
$= .33791$
$\sigma = .58130$

shall use a trick as follows: Since $x^2 = x(x - 1) + x$, it follows that $\Sigma x^2 f(x) = \Sigma x(x - 1)f(x) + \Sigma xf(x)$. We shall obtain $\Sigma x^2 f(x)$ in this indirect way. The trick allows cancellation of the factors x and $x - 1$ in the numerator with two factors of $x!$ to give $(x - 2)!$ in the denominator. From Table 20-14 we find $\Sigma xf(x) = np$ and $\Sigma x(x - 1)f(x) = n(n - 1)p^2$, so that $\Sigma x^2 f(x) = n(n - 1)p^2 + np$. We can now compute $\mu = np$ and $\sigma^2 = n(n - 1)p^2 + np - (np)^2 = np(1 - p)$. Table 20-13 shows the numerical computation of the mean and variance of the binomial distribution of Table 20-4. For that example $N = 5$ and $p = .4$ so that the formulas give $\mu = 5(.4) = 2$ and $\sigma^2 = 5(.4)(.6) = 1.2$, which, of course, agrees with the numerical computation.

The final formulas obtained for the mean and variance of the binomial turned out to be quite simple. The algebraic derivation of these values would have been much more difficult, however, without the use of the trick of writing $x^2 = x(x - 1) + x$. Finding the mean and variance of any distribution given as a formula is a mathematical problem which is sometimes quite easy and sometimes of considerable difficulty.

TABLE 20-14. COMPUTATION OF MEAN AND VARIANCE FOR BINOMIAL DISTRIBUTION

x	$f(x)$	$xf(x)$	$x(x-1)f(x)$
N	p^N	Np^N	$N(N-1)p^N$
$N-1$	$Np^{N-1}(1-p)$	$N(N-1)p^{N-1}(1-p)$	$N(N-1)(N-2)p^{N-1}(1-p)$
.	.	.	.
.	.	.	.
.	.	.	.
3	$\frac{N(N-1)(N-2)}{1 \times 2 \times 3} p^3(1-p)^{N-3}$	$\frac{N(N-1)(N-2)}{1 \times 2} p^3(1-p)^{N-3}$	$\frac{N(N-1)(N-2)}{1} p^3(1-p)^{N-3}$
2	$\frac{N(N-1)}{1 \times 2} p^2(1-p)^{N-2}$	$\frac{N(N-1)}{1} p^2(1-p)^{N-2}$	$N(N-1)p^2(1-p)^{N-2}$
1	$Np(1-p)^{N-1}$	$Np(1-p)^{N-1}$	0
0	$(1-p)^N$	0	0

The sum of the $f(x)$ column is obtained directly from Theorem 6 to be 1.0.

The sum of the $xf(x)$ column is obtained by factoring out Np from each term and then noting that the terms remaining are the same as those in the $f(x)$ column, except that N is replaced by $N - 1$, and therefore, using Theorem 6, the column sum is

$$Np[p + (1 - p)]^{N-1} = Np$$

The sum of the $x(x - 1)f(x)$ column is obtained by factoring out $N(N - 1)p^2$ from each term and noting that the terms remaining are the same as in the $f(x)$ column, except that N is replaced by $N - 2$, and therefore, using Theorem 6, the column sum is

$$N(N - 1)p^2[p + (1 - p)]^{N-2} = N(N - 1)p^2$$

Referring again to the binomial distribution, let us consider the random variable in the form of the proportion of successes

$$\frac{x}{N} = 0, \frac{1}{N}, \frac{2}{N}, \frac{3}{N}, \ldots, \frac{N-1}{N}, 1$$

in place of $x = 0, 1, 2, 3, \ldots, N - 1, N$. This change would result in the distribution having mean $\mu = Np/N = p$ and variance

$$\sigma^2 = \frac{Np(1-p)}{N^2} = \frac{p(1-p)}{N}$$

These results can, of course, be obtained directly by the use of the rule that dividing each observation in a distribution by a constant divides the mean by that constant and divides the variance by the square of that constant.

Formulas can also be computed for the mean and variance of the hypergeometric distribution with somewhat more difficulty. They are

$$\mu = \frac{Nd}{K} \qquad \sigma^2 = \frac{Nd}{K}\left(1 - \frac{d}{K}\right)\left(\frac{K-N}{K-1}\right)$$

The numerical computation in Table 20-13 with the distribution from Table 20-3 is for $K = 50$, $d = 5$, $N = 4$ (thus $s = 4$); therefore, we find

$$\mu = \frac{4 \times 5}{50} = .4 \qquad \text{and} \qquad \sigma^2 = 4\left(\frac{5}{50}\right)\left(\frac{45}{50}\right)\left(\frac{46}{49}\right) = .33796$$

These agree with the numerical computation except for rounding errors caused by recording the probabilities to five places only.

Formulas for the mean and variance of the rank-sum statistic T' and the run statistic u are given in Chap. 17.

PROBLEMS

27. Compute the mean and variance of the distribution in Table 20-9. Compare the results with those given by the formulas for the mean and variance given in Sec. 17-3. (*Note.* $N_1 = N_2 = 3$.)

28. Compute the mean and variance of the distribution in Table 20-6, and compare the results with those given by the formulas for the binomial.

29. Compute the mean and variance of the distribution in Table 20-11. Compare the results with those given by the formulas for the mean and variance in Sec. 17-4.

20-5. The Poisson Distribution

The Poisson distribution has very wide application. It arises from two different approaches, which we now discuss.

The Poisson Distribution as a Limit of the Binomial Distribution. Consider the following modifications in the way the binomial distribution may be written:

$$\begin{aligned} f(x) &= C(N,x)p^x(1-p)^{N-x} \qquad x = 0, 1, 2, \ldots, N \\ &= \frac{N!}{x!(N-x)!}p^x(1-p)^{N-x} \\ &= N(N-1)(N-2)\cdots(N-x+1)\frac{p^x(1-p)^{N-x}}{x!} \end{aligned}$$

Let $p = \lambda/N$ (i.e., define $\lambda = Np$). We then have

$$f(x) = \frac{N}{N}\frac{N-1}{N}\frac{N-2}{N}\cdots\frac{N-x+1}{N}\frac{\lambda^x(1-\lambda/N)^N(1-\lambda/N)^{-x}}{x!}$$

For large N and for fixed small values of x the terms

$$\frac{N}{N}, \frac{N-1}{N}, \ldots, \frac{N-x+1}{N}, \left(1-\frac{\lambda}{N}\right)^{-x}$$

are all close to unity; so $f(x)$ is approximately

$$f(x) \doteq \frac{\lambda^x}{x!}\left(1-\frac{\lambda}{N}\right)^N$$

where we have used the dot over the equal sign to represent "approximately equal." It can be shown that the value of $(1 - \lambda/N)^N$ can be approximated as a power of e, where e is the limit as N becomes infinite of $(1 + 1/N)^N \doteq 2.7183 \cdots$. For our problem the factor $(1 - \lambda/N)^N$ is approximated by $e^{-\lambda}$; so

$$f(x) \doteq \frac{\lambda^x}{x!} e^{-\lambda} \qquad x = 0, 1, 2, \ldots$$

This formula, defined for zero and all positive integral values x, is called the Poisson distribution. It will give approximately the same probabilities as the binomial distribution if N is large and Np is fairly small ($Np < 5$ is the requirement usually stated).

The cumulative Poisson distribution is given for several values of λ in Table A-15.

One computation will be presented to indicate how closely the Poisson distribution approximates the binomial distribution. The binomial with $N = 40$ and $p = .02$ is

$$f(x) = C(40,x)(.02)^x(.98)^{40-x}$$

The approximating Poisson distribution has $\lambda = Np = .8$. Individual probabilities can be computed from the binomial formula and, for the Poisson distribution, can be read from Table A-15 in the Appendix. Table 20-15 lists these probabilities for comparison.

TABLE 20-15. COMPARISON OF THE BINOMIAL PROBABILITIES FOR $N = 40$, $p = .02$ AND THE POISSON PROBABILITIES FOR $\lambda = .8$

x	$C(40,x)(.02)^x(.98)^{40-x}$	$\frac{(.8)^x e^{-.8}}{x!}$
5 or over	.001	.001
4	.007	.008
3	.037	.038
2	.145	.144
1	.364	.360
0	.446	.449
	1.000	1.000

The Poisson Distribution Derived from a Set of Axioms. The Poisson distribution is derived above as an approximation to the binomial distribution for a certain range of values for N and p. The binomial distribution was originally derived to describe probabilities for a fixed number of independent trials having a constant probability of success. The Poisson distribution also can be shown to arise from a different axiomatic approach.

We consider a fixed unit of time, T (perhaps a second, day, or week), in which certain events may occur. We shall assume that events occur independently and that for short periods of time Δt the probability of one event occurring is proportional to the length of time Δt, that is, is equal to $c\,\Delta t/T$, where c is constant during the time period T. We shall assume that the probability of two or more events occurring in Δt is so small that it may be neglected. With these assumptions it can be shown, using tools studied in the calculus, that

$$P_x(t) = \frac{\lambda^x e^{-\lambda}}{x!} \qquad \lambda = \frac{ct}{T}$$

i.e., the probability that x events occur before time t is given by the Poisson distribution.

If we are observing real events and the conditions under which they are being observed seem to correspond to the above assumption, i.e., the events are reasonably independent and the probability that an event occurs is proportional to the length of the time interval, then the frequency of observed events may follow the Poisson distribution. It should be noted that, although the problem was stated in terms of time intervals, it would be just as reasonable to use units of length, area, or volume.

The assumptions leading to the Poisson distribution may apply in the following situations:

1. Let x be the number of telephone calls originated in an exchange between, say, 3 and $3 + t$ o'clock. We have noted in the past that calls are originated at the rate of 120 per hour between 2 and 4 o'clock. If we then use $120/60 = 2$ per minute as our value of c/T, we would obtain $P_x(t) = (2t)^x e^{-2t}/x!$ as the probability of $x = 0, 1, 2\ 3, \ldots$ calls per t minutes.

2. Let x be the number of boxes of cereal sold on Monday in a grocery store. Here $\frac{c}{T}$ is the average number sold on Monday, and t is 1.

3. Let x be the number of tire failures per week for a fleet of delivery trucks.

4. Let x be the number of atoms disintegrating per second in a certain quantity of radioactive material.

5. Let x be the number of defects in the enamel of manufactured pans.

6. Let x be the number of typing errors per page.

7. Let x be the number of electrons emitted by a heated cathode in a given time interval.

8. Let x be the number of molecules of a gas which are in a subregion v of a container of volume V. This is an example for the limiting case of the binomial $C(n,x)(v/V)^x(1 - v/V)^{n-x}$ for n very large.

Formulas for the mean and variance of the Poisson distribution are

$$\mu = \lambda \quad \text{and} \quad \sigma^2 = \lambda$$

These results can be obtained by setting $\lambda = Np$ in the formulas for the mean and variance of the binomial and considering N to be very large. We see that the mean is equal to the variance for the Poisson distribution.

20-6. Continuous Density Functions

In the preceding examples we have considered only discrete distributions, the random variable taking on only a countable number of possible values. Following are examples where the random variable can take on any one of a continuous range of values.

Example 1. Suppose a pointer is spun on a pivot and the angle the pointer makes with a prechosen direction is measured when it comes to rest. We may wish to consider that any angle between 0 and 360° is equally likely to occur. Therefore the probability that the observed angle θ is between two particular angles, say, a and b, is equal to a quantity proportional to the difference $b - a$. Since θ must be between 0 and 360°, we say $P(a \leq \theta \leq b) = (b - a)/360$, where, of course, a and b are both between 0 and 360 and a is less than b. We could express the same result by defining a density function $f(\theta) = \frac{1}{360}$ and obtain the probability as the area under the density function $f(\theta)$ between a and b. The graph of the density function is drawn in Fig. 20-3.

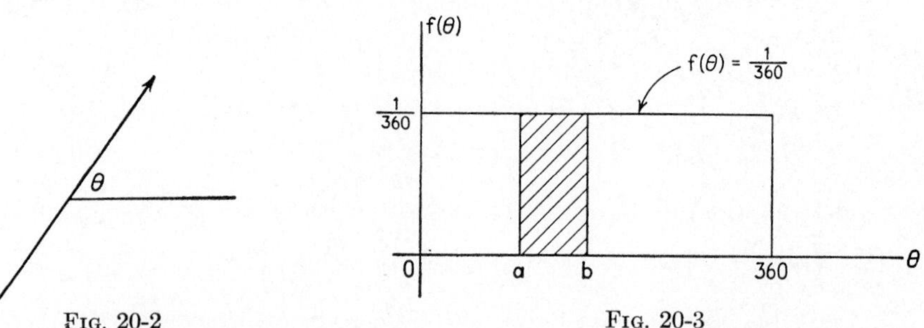

FIG. 20-2

FIG. 20-3

The density function of this example is called a *uniform*, or *rectangular*, distribution. To represent equal probabilities for all values of x ranging from d to $d + r$, we can set $f(x) = 1/r$, for $d \leq x \leq d + r$. The mean and variance for this distribution are

$$\mu = d + \frac{r}{2} \quad \text{and} \quad \sigma^2 = \frac{r^2}{12}$$

Example 2. Suppose in shooting at a target the lateral errors from the aiming point are such that all hit within 6 inches of the aiming point and the numbers missing the center by x inches decrease in proportion to x. (This assumption is not very realistic but should serve as an example.) We suppose the density function to be $f(x) = \frac{1}{3}(1 - x/6)$. The density function is graphed in Fig. 20-4. The probability that the lateral error will be less than t inches is the area of the shaded portion of Fig. 20-4.

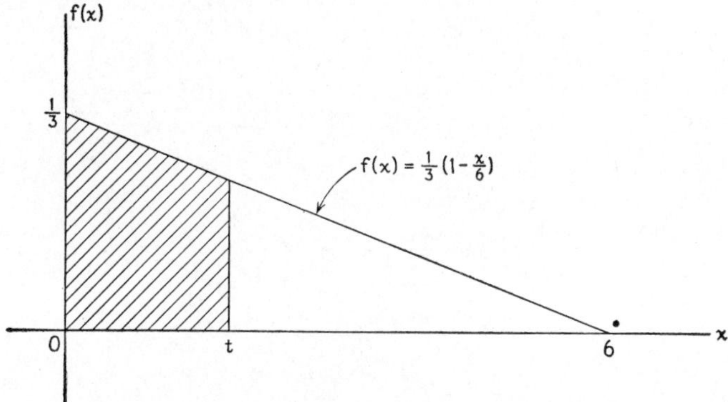

FIG. 20-4

In general we can state that a density function is nonnegative for all values of the variable which are possible, since this function is used to represent probabilities, and further that the total area under the density function is equal to 1, since we wish the total probability to be 1. In fact any continuous function which is nonnegative and which has unit total area can be called a continuous density function. These requirements are the same as those stated for the discrete distribution functions except that area replaces the sum of individual probabilities.

20-7. Expectation

Let x be a random variable with density function $f(x)$. The mean of the distribution for discrete variables is $\Sigma x f(x)$. For either the discrete or the continuous case the mean is called the *expected value of x*.

It should be noted that the expected value of x is the arithmetic mean and, of course, is "typical" only in this sense. The probability that a value of x will be less than the expected value is equal to $\frac{1}{2}$ only for very special types of distributions. Also the expected value is the most probable value only for certain types of distributions.

In gambling games the expected value of a win is sometimes referred to as a "fair" amount to pay to play the game. This is correct in the sense that if one plays the game over a long period of time, paying that amount, the amounts he may win or lose will average out. However, many people are willing to pay more than the expected winning to play for stakes which are very high. For example, suppose a lottery has

1,000,000 tickets at \$1 per ticket with a first prize of \$100,000 and three prizes of \$50,000 each. A person buying one ticket has expected winnings of

$$100{,}000\left(\frac{1}{1{,}000{,}000}\right) + (50{,}000)\left(\frac{3}{1{,}000{,}000}\right) + 0\left(\frac{999{,}996}{1{,}000{,}000}\right) = .25$$

and so a fair price would be 25 cents. Many people, however, are willing to pay \$1 for tickets to such a lottery. The explanation has been advanced that for these people the loss of \$1 is of small consequence but the gain of \$100,000 or even \$50,000 is such a fortune that they are willing to play, even against such odds. In other words, each dollar does not have the same value. The value will depend on whether it is the first, second, one thousandth, one millionth.

GLOSSARY

combinations
conditional probability
equally likely
expectation
hypergeometric
independent events
permutations
random variable
stochastic variable
uniform distribution

REFERENCES

In this text, Chaps. 1 to 7 are devoted to a discussion of elementary concepts of descriptive statistics, sampling and inference. The student will find additional information on these subjects in the following references arranged by subject orientation:

Agriculture: Ostle (99).

Bacteriology: Stearman (111).

Business and social science: Sprowls (109).

Economics and business: Croxton and Cowden (25), Sprowls (109).

Education: Walker (119), Walker and Lev (120).

Engineering: Grant (53).

General: Moroney (82), Wilks (129), Wallis and Roberts (122).

Psychology: Adams (1).

Public health and medicine: Hill (58).

Sampling techniques and attendant problems: Cochran, Mosteller, and Tukey (22).

Sociology: Cohen (24).

The material on confidence intervals and the power of tests of hypotheses is based on the work of Neyman and Pearson, which is described in Neyman (93) and Neyman and Pearson (90).

Chapters 8 to 12 are largely devoted to an introduction to the classical statistical procedures which assume sampling from normal populations. More detailed discussions of analysis of variance and design of experiments are given in the following references, most of which include discussions of regression theory with extensions to several variables and to the nonlinear case:

Agriculture and biology: Cochran and Cox (19), Fisher (47), (49), Goulden (52), Ostle (99), and Snedecor (108).

Chemistry and industry: Bennett and Franklin (4), Brownlee (11), Youden (133).

Education and psychology: Edwards (37), Jackson (59), Johnson (62), Lindquist (69), Walker and Lev (120).

Survey theory: Cantril (13), Cochran (21), Hanson, Hurwitz, and Madow (55), Yates (131).

Theory of analysis of variance: Anderson and Bancroft (2), Kempthorne (63).

Further information on various topics may be found in the following references:

Chapter 10

Theory and application of variance components: Crump (26), (27).

Pooling of sums of squares: Paull (100).

Use of transformations to normalize data and stabilize the variance: Bartlett (3), Cochran (18).

Test of largest variance over sum of variances: Cochran (17).

Comparison of several variances: Box (9), (10).

Table of Latin squares: Fisher and Yates (48).

Simultaneous estimation of several parameters (contrasts): Tukey (114), Scheffé (106).

Chapter 13

Discussion of the χ^2 test for enumeration data: Cochran (23).

Binomial distribution and elementary probability: David (29), Wilks (129).

Use of binomial-probability paper: Mosteller and Tukey (85).

Applications of acceptance sampling and quality-control charts in engineering: Bowker and Goode (8), Grant (53).

Chapter 14

Discussion of corrections to the level of significance in using the χ^2 test for goodness of fit of a normal distribution is given by Chernoff and Lehmann (15).

Chapters 15, 16

Systematic statistics, inefficient statistics, percentiles: Dixon (33), Godwin (51), Noether (95).

Ratio of ranges: Link (70).

Chapter 17

Nonparametric methods in psychology: Moses (83).

Nonparametric tolerance limits (graphs): Murphy (86).

Use of ranks in the analysis of variance: Kruskal and Wallis (65).

Rank correlations: Kendall (64).

Rank-sum test: Festinger (45), Mann and Whitney (74), Wilcoxon (128).

Chapter 18

General theory of sequential analysis: Wald (116).

Applications of sequential analysis: Eisenhart, Hastay, and Wallis (41), Grant (53), Statistical Research Group (110).

Chapter 19

Up-and-down method for sensitivity data: Dixon and Mood (35). See also Brownlee, Hodges, and Rosenblatt (12).

Other analyses of sensitivity data: Bliss (6), Finney (46).

Tables

General statistical tables: Fisher and Yates (48), Hald (54), *Biometrika Tables* (104).

Tables of the power of the analysis-of-variance tests: Lehmer (66), Tang (113), Neyman and Tokarska (t-test) (91). Useful computing formulas for powers for small sample sizes are given by Nicholson (94).

Tables of the binomial distribution: (57), (89), and Romig (105).

Extensive table of normal distribution: National Bureau of Standards (88).

Tables of the Poisson distribution: Molina (79).

1. Adams, J. K., *Basic Statistical Concepts.* McGraw-Hill Book Company, Inc.. New York, 1955.
2. Anderson, R. L., Bancroft, T. A., *Statistical Theory in Research.* McGraw-Hill Book Company, Inc., New York, 1952.
3. Bartlett, M. S., "The use of transformations," *Biometrics*, vol. 3 (1947), p. 39.

4. Bennett, C. A., Franklin, N. L., *Statistical Analysis in Chemistry and the Chemical Industry.* John Wiley & Sons, Inc., New York, 1954.
5. Birnbaum, Z. W., "Numerical tabulation of the distribution of Kolmogorov's statistic for finite sample size," *Journal of the American Statistical Association*, vol. 47 (1952), p. 425.
6. Bliss, C. I., "The calculation of the dosage-mortality curve," *Annals of Applied Biology*, vol. 22 (1935), p. 134.
7. Bliss, C. I., "A chart of the chi-square distribution," *Journal of the American Statistical Association*, vol. 39 (1944), p. 246.
8. Bowker, A. H., Goode, H. P., *Sampling Inspection by Variables.* McGraw-Hill Book Company, Inc., New York, 1952.
9. Box, G. E. P., "A general distribution theory for a class of likelihood criteria," *Biometrika*, vol. 36 (1949), p. 317.
10. Box, G. E. P., "Non-normality and tests on variances," *Biometrika*, vol. 40 (1953), p. 318.
11. Brownlee, K. A., *Industrial Experimentation.* Chemical Publishing Co., New York, 1949.
12. Brownlee, K. A., Hodges, J. L., Rosenblatt, M., "The up-and-down method with small samples," *Journal of the American Statistical Association*, vol. 48 (1953), p. 262.
13. Cantril, H., *Gauging Public Opinion.* Princeton University Press, Princeton, N.J., 1944.
14. Chapin, F. S., *Experimental Designs in Sociological Research.* Harper & Brothers, New York, 1947.
15. Chernoff, H., Lehmann, E. L., "The use of maximum likelihood estimates in χ^2 tests for goodness of fit," *Annals of Mathematical Statistics*, vol. 25 (1954), p. 579.
16. Clopper, C. J., Pearson, E. S., "The use of confidence or fiducial limits illustrated in the case of the binomial," *Biometrika*, vol. 26 (1934), p. 404.
17. Cochran, W. G., "The distribution of the largest of a set of estimated variances as a fraction of their total," *Annals of Eugenics*, vol. 11 (1941), p. 47.
18. Cochran, W. G., "Some consequences when the assumptions for the analysis of variance are not satisfied," *Biometrics*, vol. 3 (1947), p. 22.
19. Cochran, W. G., Cox, G. M., *Experimental Designs.* John Wiley & Sons, Inc., New York, 1950.
20. Cochran, W. G., "Modern methods in the sampling of human populations," *American Journal of Public Health*, vol. 41 (1951), p. 647.
21. Cochran, W. G., *Sampling Techniques.* John Wiley & Sons, Inc., New York, 1953.
22. Cochran, W. G., Mosteller, F., Tukey, J. W., *Statistical Problems of the Kinsey Report.* The American Statistical Association, Washington, 1954.
23. Cochran, W. G., "Some methods for strengthening the common chi-square tests," *Biometrics*, vol. 10 (1954), p. 417.
24. Cohen, L., *Statistical Methods for Social Scientists.* Prentice-Hall, Inc., New York, 1954.
25. Croxton, F. E., Cowden, D. J., *Applied General Statistics*, 2d ed. Prentice-Hall, Inc., New York, 1955.
26. Crump, S. L., "The estimation of variance components in analysis of variance," *Biometrics*, vol. 2 (1946), p. 7.
27. Crump, S. L., "The present status of variance component analysis," *Biometrics*, vol. 7 (1951), p. 1.
28. David, F. N., *Tables of the Correlation Coefficient.* Cambridge University Press, New York, 1938.

29. David, F. N., *Probability Theory for Statistical Methods.* Cambridge University Press, New York, 1949.

30. David, F. N., *Tables of the Ordinates and Probability Integral of the Distribution of the Correlation Coefficient in Small Samples.* The Biometrika Office, London.

31. Deming, W., "A brief statement of the uses of sampling in censuses of population, agriculture, public health, and commerce," *United Nations Publication,* vol. 17 (1948).

32. Deming, W., *Some Theory of Sampling.* John Wiley & Sons, Inc., New York, 1950.

33. Dixon, W. J., "Analysis of extreme values," *Annals of Mathematical Statistics,* vol. 21 (1950), p. 488.

34. Dixon, W. J., Mood, A. M., "The statistical sign test," *Journal of the American Statistical Association,* vol. 41 (1946), p. 557.

35. Dixon, W. J., Mood, A. M., "A method for obtaining and analyzing sensitivity data," *Journal of the American Statistical Association,* vol. 43 (1948), p. 109.

36. Edwards, A. L., *Statistical Analysis.* Rinehart & Company, Inc., New York, 1946.

37. Edwards, A. L., *Experimental Design in Psychological Research.* Rinehart & Company, Inc., New York, 1950.

38. Eisenhart, C., "The interpretation of certain regression methods and their use in biological and industrial research," *Annals of Mathematical Statistics,* vol. 10 (1939), p. 162.

39. Eisenhart, C., Wilson, P. W., "Statistical methods and control in bacteriology," *Bacteriological Reviews,* vol. 7 (1943), p. 57.

40. Eisenhart, C., "The assumptions underlying the analysis of variance," *Biometrics,* vol. 3 (1947), p. 1.

41. Eisenhart, C., Hastay, M. W., Wallis, W. A., *Techniques of Statistical Analysis.* McGraw-Hill Book Company, Inc., New York, 1947.

42. Federer, W. T., *Experimental Design.* The Macmillan Company, New York, 1955.

43. Feller, W., *An Introduction to Probability Theory and Its Applications,* vol. 1. John Wiley & Sons, Inc., New York, 1950.

44. Ferris, C. D., Grubbs, F. E., Weaver, C. L., "Operating characteristics for the common tests of significance," *Annals of Mathematical Statistics,* vol. 17 (1946), p. 178.

45. Festinger, L., "The significance of differences between means without reference to the frequency distribution function," *Psychometrika,* vol. 11 (1946), p. 97.

46. Finney, D. J., *Statistical Method in Biological Assay.* Charles Griffin & Co., Ltd., London, 1952.

47. Fisher, R. A., *Statistical Methods for Research Workers.* Oliver & Boyd, Ltd., Edinburgh and London, 1954.

48. Fisher, R. A., Yates, F., *Statistical Tables for Biological, Agricultural and Medical Research,* 4th ed. Oliver & Boyd, Ltd., Edinburgh and London, 1953.

49. Fisher, R. A., *The Design of Experiments.* Oliver & Boyd, Ltd., Edinburgh and London, 1951.

50. Fry, T. C., "The χ^2 test of significance," *Journal of the American Statistical Association,* vol. 33 (1938), p. 513.

51. Godwin, H. J., "On the estimation of the dispersion by linear systematic statistics," *Biometrika,* vol. 36 (1949), p. 92.

52. Goulden, C. H., *Methods of Statistical Analysis,* 2d ed. John Wiley & Sons, Inc., New York, 1952.

53. Grant, E. L., *Statistical Quality Control*, 2d ed. McGraw-Hill Book Company, Inc., New York, 1952.

54. Hald, A., *Statistical Tables and Formulas*. John Wiley & Sons, Inc., New York, 1952.

55. Hansen, M. H., Hurwitz, W. N., Madow, W. G., *Sample Survey Methods and Theory*. John Wiley & Sons, Inc., New York, 1953.

56. Harris, M., Horvitz, D. G., Mood, A. M., "On the determination of sample sizes in designing experiments," *Journal of the American Statistical Association*, vol. 43 (1948), p. 391.

57. Harvard University, *Tables of the Cumulative Binomial Probability Distribution*. Annals of the Computation Laboratory, Cambridge, Mass., vol. 35.

58. Hill, A. B., *Principles of Medical Statistics*, 6th ed. Oxford University Press, New York, 1955.

59. Jackson, R. W. B., *Application of the Analysis of Variance and Covariance Method to Educational Problems, Bulletin* 11. Department of Educational Research, University of Toronto, Toronto, 1940.

60. Johnson, N. L., Welch, B. L., "Applications of the non-central t-distribution," *Biometrika*, vol. 31 (1940), p. 362.

61. Johnson, P. O., *Statistical Methods from the Viewpoint of Quality Control*. Graduate School of the U.S. Department of Agriculture, Washington, 1939.

62. Johnson, P. O., *Statistical Methods in Research*. Prentice-Hall, Inc., New York, 1949.

63. Kempthorne, O., *The Design and Analysis of Experiments*. John Wiley & Sons Inc., New York, 1952.

64. Kendall, M. G., *Rank Correlation Methods*. Charles Griffin & Co., Ltd., London, 1948.

65. Kruskal, W. H., Wallis, W. A., "Use of ranks in one-criterion variance analysis," *Journal of the American Statistical Association*, vol. 47 (1952), p. 583.

66. Lehmer, E., "Inverse tables of probabilities of errors of the second kind," *Annals of Mathematical Statistics*, vol. 15 (1944), p. 388.

67. Leland, O. M., *Practical Least Squares*. McGraw-Hill Book Company, Inc., New York, 1921.

68. Levinson, H. C., *The Science of Chance*. Rinehart & Company, Inc., New York, 1950.

69. Lindquist, E. F., *Design and Analysis of Experiments in Psychology and Education*. Houghton Mifflin Company, Boston, 1953.

70. Link, R. F., "On the ratio of two ranges," *Annals of Mathematical Statistics*, vol. 21 (1950), p. 112.

71. Lord, E., "The use of the range in place of the standard deviation in the t-test," *Biometrika*, vol. 34 (1947), p. 41.

72. Mainland, D., "Statistical methods in medical research. I. Qualitative statistics (enumeration data)," *Canadian Journal of Research*, vol. 26 (1948), p. 1.

73. Mainland, D., *Elementary Medical Statistics*. W. B. Saunders Company, Philadelphia, 1952.

74. Mann, H. B., Whitney, D. R., "On a test of whether one of two random variables is stochastically larger than the other," *Annals of Mathematical Statistics*, vol. 18 (1947), p. 50.

75. Massey, F. J., "The distribution of the maximum deviation between two sample cumulative step functions," *Annals of Mathematical Statistics*, vol. 22 (1951), p. 125.

76. Massey, F. J., "The Kolmogorov-Smirnov test for goodness of fit," *Journal of the American Statistical Association*, vol. 46 (1951), p. 68.
77. Massey, F. J., "Distribution table for the deviation between two sample cumulatives," *Annals of Mathematical Statistics*, vol. 23 (1952), p. 435.
78. Merrington, M., Thompson, C. M., "Tables of percentage points of the inverted beta (F) distribution," *Biometrika*, vol. 33 (1943), p. 73.
79. Molina, E. C., *Poisson's Exponential Binomial Limit.* D. Van Nostrand Company, Inc., New York, 1942.
80. Mood, A. M., "The distribution theory of runs," *Annals of Mathematical Statistics*, vol. 11 (1940), p. 367.
81. Mood, A. M., *Introduction to the Theory of Statistics.* McGraw-Hill Book Company, Inc., 1950.
82. Moroney, M. J., *Facts from Figures.* Penguin Books, Inc., Baltimore, 1953.
83. Moses, L., "Non-parametric statistics for psychological research," *Psychological Bulletin*, vol. 49 (1952), p. 122.
84. Mosteller, F., "On some useful 'inefficient' statistics," *Annals of Mathematical Statistics*, vol. 17 (1946), p. 377.
85. Mosteller, F., Tukey, J. W., "The uses and usefulness of binomial probability paper," *Journal of the American Statistical Association*, vol. 44 (1949), p. 174.
86. Murphy, R. B., "Non-parametric tolerance limits," *Annals of Mathematical Statistics*, vol. 19 (1948), p. 581.
87. Nair, K. R., "Table of confidence intervals for the median in samples from any continuous population," *Sankhyā*, vol. 4 (1940), p. 551.
88. National Bureau of Standards, *Tables of Probability Functions*, vols. I, II. Mathematical Tables 8, Washington, 1941.
89. National Bureau of Standards, *Tables of the Binomial Probability Distribution.* Applied Mathematics Series, 6, Washington, 1949.
90. Neyman, J., Pearson, E. S., "On the problem of the most efficient tests of statistical hypotheses," *Philosophical Transactions of the Royal Society (London)*, ser. A, vol. 231 (1933), p. 289.
91. Neyman, J., Tokarska, B., "Errors of the second kind in testing 'Student's' hypothesis," *Journal of the American Statistical Association*, vol. 31 (1936), p. 318.
92. Neyman, J., *First Course in Probability and Statistics.* Henry Holt and Company, Inc., New York, 1950.
93. Neyman, J., *Lectures and Conferences on Mathematical Statistics and Probability*, 2d ed. Graduate School of the U.S. Department of Agriculture, Washington, 1952.
94. Nicholson, W. L., "A computing formula for the power of the analysis of variance tests," *Annals of Mathematical Statistics*, vol. 25 (1954), p. 607.
95. Noether, G. E., "Use of the range instead of the standard deviation," *Journal of the American Statistical Association*, vol. 50 (1955), p. 1040.
96. Olds, E. G., "Distributions of sums of squares of rank differences for small numbers of individuals," *Annals of Mathematical Statistics*, vol. 9 (1938), p. 133.
97. Olds, E. G., Knowler, L. A., "Teaching statistical quality control for town and gown," *Journal of the American Statistical Association*, vol. 44 (1949), p. 213.
98. Olmstead, P. S., Tukey, J. W., "A corner test for association," *Annals of Mathematical Statistics*, vol. 18 (1947), p. 495.
99. Ostle, B., *Statistics in Research.* Iowa State College Press, Ames, Iowa, 1954.
100. Paull, A. E., "On a preliminary test for pooling mean squares in the analysis of variance," *Annals of Mathematical Statistics*, vol. 21 (1950), p. 539.

101. Paulson, E., "An approximate normalization of the analysis of variance distribution," *Annals of Mathematical Statistics*, vol. 13 (1942), p. 233.
102. Pearson, E. S., "The probability integral of the range in samples of n observations from a normal population," *Biometrika*, vol. 32 (1942), p. 301.
103. Pearson, E. S., Hartley, H. O., "Charts of the power function for analysis of variance tests, derived from the non-central F-distribution," *Biometrika*, vol. 38 (1951), p. 112.
104. Pearson, E. S., Hartley, H. O., *Biometrika Tables for Statisticians*, vol. 1. Cambridge University Press, New York, 1954.
105. Romig, H. G., 50–100 *Binomial Tables*. John Wiley & Sons, Inc., New York, 1953.
106. Scheffé, H. "A method for judging all contrasts in the analysis of variance," *Biometrika*, vol. 40 (1953), p. 87.
107. Shewhart, W. A., *Statistical Method from the Viewpoint of Quality Control*. Graduate School of the U.S. Department of Agriculture, Washington, 1939.
108. Snedecor, G. W., *Statistical Methods*, 4th ed. Iowa State College Press, Ames, Iowa, 1946.
109. Sprowls, R. C., *Elementary Statistics—For Students of Social Science and Business*. McGraw-Hill Book Company, Inc., New York, 1955.
110. Statistical Research Group, Columbia University, *Sequential Analysis of Statistical Data: Applications*, rev. ed. Columbia University Press, New York, 1945.
111. Stearman, R. L., "Statistical concepts in microbiology," *Bacteriological Reviews*, vol. 19 (1955), p. 160.
112. Swed, F., Eisenhart, C., "Tables for testing randomness of grouping in a sequence of alternatives," *Annals of Mathematical Statistics*, vol. 14 (1943), p. 66.
113. Tang, P. C., "The power function of the analysis of variance tests with tables and illustration of their use," *Statistical Research Memoirs*, vol. 2 (1938), p. 143.
114. Tukey, J. W., "Comparing individual means in the analysis of variance," *Biometrics*, vol. 5 (1949), p. 99.
115. Uspensky, J. V., *Introduction to Mathematical Probability*. McGraw-Hill Book Company, Inc., New York, 1937.
116. Wald, A., *Sequential Analysis*. John Wiley & Sons, Inc., New York, 1947.
117. Walker, H. M., "The sampling problem in educational research," *Teachers College Record*, vol. 30 (1929), p. 760.
118. Walker, H. M., *Mathematics Essential for Elementary Statistics*, 2d ed. Henry Holt and Company, Inc., New York, 1951.
119. Walker, H. M., *Elementary Statistical Methods*. Henry Holt and Company, Inc., New York, 1943.
120. Walker, H. M., Lev, J., *Statistical Inference*. Henry Holt and Company, Inc., New York, 1953.
121. Wallis, W. A., "Tolerance intervals for linear regression," *Second Berkeley Symposium on Mathematical Statistics and Probability*, p. 43, edited by J. Neyman. University of California Press, Berkeley, Calif., 1951.
122. Wallis, W. A., Roberts, H. V., *Statistics: A New Approach*. Free Press, Glencoe, Ill., 1956.
123. Walsh, J. E., "On the range-midrange test and some tests with bounded significance levels," *Annals of Mathematical Statistics*, vol. 20 (1949), p. 257.
124. Walsh, J. E., "Applications of some significance tests for the median which are valid under very general conditions," *Journal of the American Statistical Association*, vol. 44 (1949), p. 342.

125. Welch, B. L., "The generalization of 'Student's' problem when several different population variances are involved," *Biometrika*, vol. 34 (1947), p. 28.

126. Wilcoxon, F., "Individual comparisons by ranking methods," *Biometrics*, vol. 1 (1945), p. 80.

127. Wilcoxon, F., "Probability tables for individual comparisons by ranking methods," *Biometrics*, vol. 3 (1947), p. 119.

128. Wilcoxon, F., *Some Rapid Approximate Statistical Procedures*. American Cyanimid Co., Stamford, Conn., 1949.

129. Wilks, S. S., *Elementary Statistical Analysis*. Princeton University Press, Princeton, N.J., 1948.

130. Winsor, C. P., "Which regression?" *Biometrics*, vol. 2 (1946), p. 101.

131. Yates, F., *Sampling Methods for Censuses and Surveys*. Hafner Publishing Company, New York, 1949.

132. Yost, E. K., "Joint estimation of mean and standard deviation by percentiles," unpublished master's thesis, University of Oregon, Eugene, Ore., 1948.

133. Youden, W. J., *Statistical Methods for Chemists*. John Wiley & Sons, Inc., 1951.

APPENDIX

LIST OF TABLES

Table A-1. Random Numbers*

10 09 73 25 33	76 52 01 35 86	34 67 35 48 76	80 95 90 91 17	39 29 27 49 45
37 54 20 48 05	64 89 47 42 96	24 80 52 40 37	20 63 61 04 02	00 82 29 16 65
08 42 26 89 53	19 64 50 93 03	23 20 90 25 60	15 95 33 47 64	35 08 03 36 06
99 01 90 25 29	09 37 67 07 15	38 31 13 11 65	88 67 67 43 97	04 43 62 76 59
12 80 79 99 70	80 15 73 61 47	64 03 23 66 53	98 95 11 68 77	12 17 17 68 33
66 06 57 47 17	34 07 27 68 50	36 69 73 61 70	65 81 33 98 85	11 19 92 91 70
31 06 01 08 05	45 57 18 24 06	35 30 34 26 14	86 79 90 74 39	23 40 30 97 32
85 26 97 76 02	02 05 16 56 92	68 66 57 48 18	73 05 38 52 47	18 62 38 85 79
63 57 33 21 35	05 32 54 70 48	90 55 35 75 48	28 46 82 87 09	83 49 12 56 24
73 79 64 57 53	03 52 96 47 78	35 80 83 42 82	60 93 52 03 44	35 27 38 84 35
98 52 01 77 67	14 90 56 86 07	22 10 94 05 58	60 97 09 34 33	50 50 07 39 98
11 80 50 54 31	39 80 82 77 32	50 72 56 82 48	29 40 52 42 01	52 77 56 78 51
83 45 29 96 34	06 28 89 80 83	13 74 67 00 78	18 47 54 06 10	68 71 17 78 17
88 68 54 02 00	86 50 75 84 01	36 76 66 79 51	90 36 47 64 93	29 60 91 10 62
99 59 46 73 48	87 51 76 49 69	91 82 60 89 28	93 78 56 13 68	23 47 83 41 13
65 48 11 76 74	17 46 85 09 50	58 04 77 69 74	73 03 95 71 86	40 21 81 65 44
80 12 43 56 35	17 72 70 80 15	45 31 82 23 74	21 11 57 82 53	14 38 55 37 63
74 35 09 98 17	77 40 27 72 14	43 23 60 02 10	45 52 16 42 37	96 28 60 26 55
69 91 62 68 03	66 25 22 91 48	36 93 68 72 03	76 62 11 39 90	94 40 05 64 18
09 89 32 05 05	14 22 56 85 14	46 42 75 67 88	96 29 77 88 22	54 38 21 45 98
91 49 91 45 23	68 47 92 76 86	46 16 28 35 54	94 75 08 99 23	37 08 92 00 48
80 33 69 45 98	26 94 03 68 58	70 29 73 41 35	53 14 03 33 40	42 05 08 23 41
44 10 48 19 49	85 15 74 79 54	32 97 92 65 75	57 60 04 08 81	22 22 20 64 13
12 55 07 37 42	11 10 00 20 40	12 86 07 46 97	96 64 48 94 39	28 70 72 58 15
63 60 64 93 29	16 50 53 44 84	40 21 95 25 63	43 65 17 70 82	07 20 73 17 90
61 19 69 04 46	26 45 74 77 74	51 92 43 37 29	65 39 45 95 93	42 58 26 05 27
15 47 44 52 66	95 27 07 99 53	59 36 78 38 48	82 39 61 01 18	33 21 15 94 66
94 55 72 85 73	67 89 75 43 87	54 62 24 44 31	91 19 04 25 92	92 92 74 59 73
42 48 11 62 13	97 34 40 87 21	16 86 84 87 67	03 07 11 20 59	25 70 14 66 70
23 52 37 83 17	73 20 88 98 37	68 93 59 14 16	26 25 22 96 63	05 52 28 25 62
04 49 35 24 94	75 24 63 38 24	45 86 25 10 25	61 96 27 93 35	65 33 71 24 72
00 54 99 76 54	64 05 18 81 59	96 11 96 38 96	54 69 28 23 91	23 28 72 95 29
35 96 31 53 07	26 89 80 93 54	33 35 13 54 62	77 97 45 00 24	90 10 33 93 33
59 80 80 83 91	45 42 72 68 42	83 60 94 97 00	13 02 12 48 92	78 56 52 01 06
46 05 88 52 36	01 39 09 22 86	77 28 14 40 77	93 91 08 36 47	70 61 74 29 41
32 17 90 05 97	87 37 92 52 41	05 56 70 70 07	86 74 31 71 57	85 39 41 18 38
69 23 46 14 06	20 11 74 52 04	15 95 66 00 00	18 74 39 24 23	97 11 89 63 38
19 56 54 14 30	01 75 87 53 79	40 41 92 15 85	66 67 43 68 06	84 96 28 52 07
45 15 51 49 38	19 47 60 72 46	43 66 79 45 43	59 04 79 00 33	20 82 66 95 41
94 86 43 19 94	36 16 81 08 51	34 88 88 15 53	01 54 03 54 56	05 01 45 11 76
98 08 62 48 26	45 24 02 84 04	44 99 90 88 96	39 09 47 34 07	35 44 13 18 80
33 18 51 62 32	41 94 15 09 49	89 43 54 85 81	88 69 54 19 94	37 54 87 30 43
80 95 10 04 06	96 38 27 07 74	20 15 12 33 87	25 01 62 52 98	94 62 46 11 71
79 75 24 91 40	71 96 12 82 96	69 86 10 25 91	74 85 22 05 39	00 38 75 95 79
18 63 33 25 37	98 14 50 65 71	31 01 02 46 74	05 45 56 14 27	77 93 89 19 36
74 02 94 39 02	77 55 73 22 70	97 79 01 71 19	52 52 75 80 21	80 81 45 17 48
54 17 84 56 11	80 99 33 71 43	05 33 51 29 69	56 12 71 92 55	36 04 09 03 24
11 66 44 98 83	52 07 98 48 27	59 38 17 15 39	09 97 33 34 40	88 46 12 33 56
48 32 47 79 28	31 24 96 47 10	02 29 53 68 70	32 30 75 75 46	15 02 00 99 94
69 07 49 41 38	87 63 79 19 76	35 58 40 44 01	10 51 82 16 15	01 84 87 69 38

* This table is reproduced with permission from tables of the RAND Corporation.

TABLE A-1. RANDOM NUMBERS (*Continued*)

09 18 82 00 97	32 82 53 95 27	04 22 08 63 04	83 38 98 73 74	64 27 85 80 44
90 04 58 54 97	51 98 15 06 54	94 93 88 19 97	91 87 07 61 50	68 47 66 46 59
73 18 95 02 07	47 67 72 62 69	62 29 06 44 64	27 12 46 70 18	41 36 18 27 60
75 76 87 64 90	20 97 18 17 49	90 42 91 22 72	95 37 50 58 71	93 82 34 31 78
54 01 64 40 56	66 28 13 10 03	00 68 22 73 98	20 71 45 32 95	07 70 61 78 13
08 35 86 99 10	78 54 24 27 85	13 66 15 88 73	04 61 89 75 53	31 22 30 84 20
28 30 60 32 64	81 33 31 05 91	40 51 00 78 93	32 60 46 04 75	94 11 90 18 40
53 84 08 62 33	81 59 41 36 28	51 21 59 02 90	28 46 66 87 95	77 76 22 07 91
91 75 75 37 41	61 61 36 22 69	50 26 39 02 12	55 78 17 65 14	83 48 34 70 55
89 41 59 26 94	00 39 75 83 91	12 60 71 76 46	48 94 97 23 06	94 54 13 74 08
77 51 30 38 20	86 83 42 99 01	68 41 48 27 74	51 90 81 39 80	72 89 35 55 07
19 50 23 71 74	69 97 92 02 88	55 21 02 97 73	74 28 77 52 51	65 34 46 74 15
21 81 85 93 13	93 27 88 17 57	05 68 67 31 56	07 08 28 50 46	31 85 33 84 52
51 47 46 64 99	68 10 72 36 21	94 04 99 13 45	42 83 60 91 91	08 00 74 54 49
99 55 96 83 31	62 53 52 41 70	69 77 71 28 30	74 81 97 81 42	43 86 07 28 34
33 71 34 80 07	93 58 47 28 69	51 92 66 47 21	58 30 32 98 22	93 17 49 39 72
85 27 48 68 93	11 30 32 92 70	28 83 43 41 37	73 51 59 04 00	71 14 84 36 43
84 13 38 96 40	44 03 55 21 66	73 85 27 00 91	61 22 26 05 61	62 32 71 84 23
56 73 21 62 34	17 39 59 61 31	10 12 39 16 22	85 49 65 75 60	81 60 41 88 80
65 13 85 68 06	87 64 88 52 61	34 31 36 58 61	45 87 52 10 69	85 64 44 72 77
38 00 10 21 76	81 71 91 17 11	71 60 29 29 37	74 21 96 40 49	65 58 44 96 98
37 40 29 63 97	01 30 47 75 86	56 27 11 00 86	47 32 46 26 05	40 03 03 74 38
97 12 54 03 48	87 08 33 14 17	21 81 53 92 50	75 23 76 20 47	15 50 12 95 78
21 82 64 11 34	47 14 33 40 72	64 63 88 59 02	49 13 90 64 41	03 85 65 45 52
73 13 54 27 42	95 71 90 90 35	85 79 47 42 96	08 78 98 81 56	64 69 11 92 02
07 63 87 79 29	03 06 11 80 72	96 20 74 41 56	23 82 19 95 38	04 71 36 69 94
60 52 88 34 41	07 95 41 98 14	59 17 52 06 95	05 53 35 21 39	61 21 20 64 55
83 59 63 56 55	06 95 89 29 83	05 12 80 97 19	77 43 35 37 83	92 30 15 04 98
10 85 06 27 46	99 59 91 05 07	13 49 90 63 19	53 07 57 18 39	06 41 01 93 62
39 82 09 89 52	43 62 26 31 47	64 42 18 08 14	43 80 00 93 51	31 02 47 31 67
59 58 00 64 78	75 56 97 88 00	88 83 55 44 86	23 76 80 61 56	04 11 10 84 08
38 50 80 73 41	23 79 34 87 63	90 82 29 70 22	17 71 90 42 07	95 95 44 99 53
30 69 27 06 68	94 68 81 61 27	56 19 68 00 91	82 06 76 34 00	05 46 26 92 00
65 44 39 56 59	18 28 82 74 37	49 63 22 40 41	08 33 76 56 76	96 29 99 08 36
27 26 75 02 64	13 19 27 22 94	07 47 74 46 06	17 98 54 89 11	97 34 13 03 58
91 30 70 69 91	19 07 22 42 10	36 69 95 37 28	28 82 53 57 93	28 97 66 62 52
68 43 49 46 88	84 47 31 36 22	62 12 69 84 08	12 84 38 25 90	09 81 59 31 46
48 90 81 58 77	54 74 52 45 91	35 70 00 47 54	83 82 45 26 92	54 13 05 51 60
06 91 34 51 97	42 67 27 86 01	11 88 30 95 28	63 01 19 89 01	14 97 44 03 44
10 45 51 60 19	14 21 03 37 12	91 34 23 78 21	88 32 58 08 51	43 66 77 08 83
12 88 39 73 43	65 02 76 11 84	04 28 50 13 92	17 97 41 50 77	90 71 22 67 69
21 77 83 09 76	38 80 73 69 61	31 64 94 20 96	63 28 10 20 23	08 81 64 74 49
19 52 35 95 15	65 12 25 96 59	86 28 36 82 58	69 57 21 37 98	16 43 59 15 29
67 24 55 26 70	35 58 31 65 63	79 24 68 66 86	76 46 33 42 22	26 65 59 08 02
60 58 44 73 77	07 50 03 79 92	45 13 42 65 29	26 76 08 36 37	41 32 64 43 44
53 85 34 13 77	36 06 69 48 50	58 83 87 38 59	49 36 47 33 31	96 24 04 36 42
24 63 73 87 36	74 38 48 93 42	52 62 30 79 92	12 36 91 86 01	03 74 28 38 73
83 08 01 24 51	38 99 22 28 15	07 75 95 17 77	97 37 72 75 85	51 97 23 78 67
16 44 42 43 34	36 15 19 90 73	27 49 37 09 39	85 13 03 25 52	54 84 65 47 59
60 79 01 81 57	57 17 86 57 62	11 16 17 85 76	45 81 95 29 79	65 13 00 48 60

TABLE A-1. RANDOM NUMBERS (*Continued*)

03 99 11 04 61	93 71 61 68 94	66 08 32 46 53	84 60 95 82 32	88 61 81 91 61
38 55 59 55 54	32 88 65 97 80	08 35 56 08 60	29 73 54 77 62	71 29 92 38 53
17 54 67 37 04	92 05 24 62 15	55 12 12 92 81	59 07 60 79 36	27 95 45 89 09
32 64 35 28 61	95 81 90 68 31	00 91 19 89 36	76 35 59 37 79	80 86 30 05 14
69 57 26 87 77	39 51 03 59 05	14 06 04 06 19	29 54 96 96 16	33 56 46 07 80
24 12 26 65 91	27 69 90 64 94	14 84 54 66 72	61 95 87 71 00	90 89 97 57 54
61 19 63 02 31	92 96 26 17 73	41 83 95 53 82	17 26 77 09 43	78 03 87 02 67
30 53 22 17 04	10 27 41 22 02	39 68 52 33 09	10 06 16 88 29	55 98 66 64 85
03 78 89 75 99	75 86 72 07 17	74 41 65 31 66	35 20 83 33 74	87 53 90 88 23
48 22 86 33 79	85 78 34 76 19	53 15 26 74 33	35 66 35 29 72	16 81 86 03 11
60 36 59 46 53	35 07 53 39 49	42 61 42 92 97	01 91 82 83 16	98 95 37 32 31
83 79 94 24 02	56 62 33 44 42	34 99 44 13 74	70 07 11 47 36	09 95 81 80 65
32 96 00 74 05	36 40 98 32 32	99 38 54 16 00	11 13 30 75 86	15 91 70 62 53
19 32 25 38 45	57 62 05 26 06	66 49 76 86 46	78 13 86 65 59	19 64 09 94 13
11 22 09 47 47	07 39 93 74 08	48 50 92 39 29	27 48 24 54 76	85 24 43 51 59
31 75 15 72 60	68 98 00 53 39	15 47 04 83 55	88 65 12 25 96	03 15 21 91 21
88 49 29 93 82	14 45 40 45 04	20 09 49 89 77	74 84 39 34 13	22 10 97 85 08
30 93 44 77 44	07 48 18 38 28	73 78 80 65 33	28 59 72 04 05	94 20 52 03 80
22 88 84 88 93	27 49 99 87 48	60 53 04 51 28	74 02 28 46 17	82 03 71 02 68
78 21 21 69 93	35 90 29 13 86	44 37 21 54 86	65 74 11 40 14	87 48 13 72 20
41 84 98 45 47	46 85 05 23 26	34 67 75 83 00	74 91 06 43 45	19 32 58 15 49
46 35 23 30 49	69 24 89 34 60	45 30 50 75 21	61 31 83 18 55	14 41 37 09 51
11 08 79 62 94	14 01 33 17 92	59 74 76 72 77	76 50 33 45 13	39 66 37 75 44
52 70 10 83 37	56 30 38 73 15	16 52 06 96 76	11 65 49 98 93	02 18 16 81 61
57 27 53 68 98	81 30 44 85 85	68 65 22 73 76	92 85 25 58 66	88 44 80 35 84
20 85 77 31 56	70 28 42 43 26	79 37 59 52 20	01 15 96 32 67	10 62 24 83 91
15 63 38 49 24	90 41 59 36 14	33 52 12 66 65	55 82 34 76 41	86 22 53 17 04
92 69 44 82 97	39 90 40 21 15	59 58 94 90 67	66 82 14 15 75	49 76 70 40 37
77 61 31 90 19	88 15 20 00 80	20 55 49 14 09	96 27 74 82 57	50 81 60 76 16
38 68 83 24 86	45 13 46 35 45	59 40 47 20 59	43 94 75 16 80	43 85 25 96 93
25 16 30 18 89	70 01 41 50 21	41 29 06 73 12	71 85 71 59 57	68 97 11 14 03
65 25 10 76 29	37 23 93 32 95	05 87 00 11 19	92 78 42 63 40	18 47 76 56 22
36 81 54 36 25	18 63 73 75 09	82 44 49 90 05	04 92 17 37 01	14 70 79 39 97
64 39 71 16 92	05 32 78 21 62	20 24 78 17 59	45 19 72 53 32	83 74 52 25 67
04 51 52 56 24	95 09 66 79 46	48 46 08 55 58	15 19 11 87 82	16 93 03 33 61
83 76 16 08 73	43 25 38 41 45	60 83 32 59 83	01 29 14 13 49	20 36 80 71 26
14 38 70 63 45	80 85 40 92 79	43 52 90 63 18	38 38 47 47 61	41 19 63 74 80
51 32 19 22 46	80 08 87 70 74	88 72 25 67 36	66 16 44 94 31	66 91 93 16 78
72 47 20 00 08	80 89 01 80 02	94 81 33 19 00	54 15 58 34 36	35 35 25 41 31
05 46 65 53 06	93 12 81 84 64	74 45 79 05 61	72 84 81 18 34	79 98 26 84 16
39 52 87 24 84	82 47 42 55 93	48 54 53 52 47	18 61 91 36 74	18 61 11 92 41
81 61 61 87 11	53 34 24 42 76	75 12 21 17 24	74 62 77 37 07	58 31 91 59 97
07 58 61 61 20	82 64 12 28 20	92 90 41 31 41	32 39 21 97 63	61 19 96 79 40
90 76 70 42 35	13 57 41 72 00	69 90 26 37 42	78 46 42 25 01	18 62 79 08 72
40 18 82 81 93	29 59 38 86 27	94 97 21 15 98	62 09 53 67 87	00 44 15 89 97
34 41 48 21 57	86 88 75 50 87	19 15 20 00 23	12 30 28 07 83	32 62 46 86 91
63 43 97 53 63	44 98 91 68 22	36 02 40 08 67	76 37 84 16 05	65 96 17 34 88
67 04 90 90 70	93 39 94 55 47	94 45 87 42 84	05 04 14 98 07	20 28 83 40 60
79 49 50 41 46	52 16 29 02 86	54 15 83 42 43	46 97 83 54 82	59 36 29 59 38
91 70 43 05 52	04 73 72 10 31	75 05 19 30 29	47 66 56 43 82	99 78 29 34 78

TABLE A-1. RANDOM NUMBERS (*Continued*)

94 01 54 68 74	32 44 44 82 77	59 82 09 61 63	64 65 42 58 43	41 14 54 28 20
74 10 88 82 22	88 57 07 40 15	25 70 49 10 35	01 75 51 47 50	48 96 83 86 03
62 88 08 78 73	95 16 05 92 21	22 30 49 03 14	72 87 71 73 34	39 28 30 41 49
11 74 81 21 02	80 58 04 18 67	17 71 05 96 21	06 55 40 78 50	73 95 07 95 52
17 94 40 56 00	60 47 80 33 43	25 85 25 89 05	57 21 63 96 18	49 85 69 93 26
66 06 74 27 92	95 04 35 26 80	46 78 05 64 87	09 97 15 94 81	37 00 62 21 86
54 24 49 10 30	45 54 77 08 18	59 84 99 61 69	61 45 92 16 47	87 41 71 71 98
30 94 55 75 89	31 73 25 72 60	47 67 00 76 54	46 37 62 53 66	94 74 64 95 80
69 17 03 74 03	86 99 59 03 07	94 30 47 18 03	26 82 50 55 11	12 45 99 13 14
08 34 58 89 75	35 84 18 57 71	08 10 55 99 87	87 11 22 14 76	14 71 37 11 81
27 76 74 35 84	85 30 18 89 77	29 49 06 97 14	73 03 54 12 07	74 69 90 93 10
13 02 51 43 38	54 06 61 52 43	47 72 46 67 33	47 43 14 39 05	31 04 85 66 99
80 21 73 62 92	98 52 52 43 35	24 43 22 48 96	43 27 75 88 74	11 46 61 60 82
10 87 56 20 04	90 39 16 11 05	57 41 10 63 68	53 85 63 07 43	08 67 08 47 41
54 12 75 73 26	26 62 91 90 87	24 47 28 87 79	30 54 02 78 86	61 73 27 54 54
60 31 14 28 24	37 30 14 26 78	45 99 04 32 42	17 37 45 20 03	70 70 77 02 14
49 73 97 14 84	92 00 39 80 86	76 66 87 32 09	59 20 21 19 73	02 90 23 32 50
78 62 65 15 94	16 45 39 46 14	39 01 49 70 66	83 01 20 98 32	25 57 17 76 28
66 69 21 39 86	99 83 70 05 82	81 23 24 49 87	09 50 49 64 12	90 19 37 95 68
44 07 12 80 91	07 36 29 77 03	76 44 74 25 37	98 52 49 78 31	65 70 40 95 14
41 46 88 51 49	49 55 41 79 94	14 92 43 96 50	95 29 40 05 56	70 48 10 69 05
94 55 93 75 59	49 67 85 31 19	70 31 20 56 82	66 98 63 40 99	74 47 42 07 40
41 61 57 03 60	64 11 45 86 60	90 85 06 46 18	80 62 05 17 90	11 43 63 80 72
50 27 39 31 13	41 79 48 68 61	24 78 18 96 83	55 41 18 56 67	77 53 59 98 92
41 39 68 05 04	90 67 00 82 89	40 90 20 50 69	95 08 30 67 83	28 10 25 78 16
25 80 72 42 60	71 52 97 89 20	72 68 20 73 85	90 72 65 71 66	98 88 40 85 83
06 17 09 79 65	88 30 29 80 41	21 44 34 18 08	68 98 48 36 20	89 74 79 88 82
60 80 85 44 44	74 41 28 11 05	01 17 62 88 38	36 42 11 64 89	18 05 95 10 61
80 94 04 48 93	10 40 83 62 22	80 58 27 19 44	92 63 84 03 33	67 05 41 60 67
19 51 69 01 20	46 75 97 16 43	13 17 75 52 92	21 03 68 28 08	77 50 19 74 27
49 38 65 44 80	23 60 42 35 54	21 78 54 11 01	91 17 81 01 74	29 42 09 04 38
06 31 28 89 40	15 99 56 93 21	47 45 86 48 09	98 18 98 18 51	29 65 18 42 15
60 94 20 03 07	11 89 79 26 74	40 40 56 80 32	96 71 75 42 44	10 70 14 13 93
92 32 99 89 32	78 28 44 63 47	71 20 99 20 61	39 44 89 31 36	25 72 20 85 64
77 93 66 35 74	31 38 45 19 24	85 56 12 96 71	58 13 71 78 20	22 75 13 65 18
38 10 17 77 56	11 65 71 38 97	95 88 95 70 67	47 64 81 38 85	70 66 99 34 06
39 64 16 94 57	91 33 92 25 02	92 61 38 97 19	11 94 75 62 03	19 32 42 05 04
84 05 44 04 55	99 39 66 36 80	67 66 76 06 31	69 18 19 68 45	38 52 51 16 00
47 46 80 35 77	57 64 96 32 66	24 70 07 15 94	14 00 42 31 53	69 24 90 57 47
43 32 13 13 70	28 97 72 38 96	76 47 96 85 62	62 34 20 75 89	08 89 90 59 85
64 28 16 18 26	18 55 56 49 37	13 17 33 33 65	78 85 11 64 99	87 06 41 30 75
66 84 77 04 95	32 35 00 29 85	86 71 63 87 46	26 31 37 74 63	55 38 77 26 81
72 46 13 32 30	21 52 95 34 24	92 58 10 22 62	78 43 86 62 76	18 39 67 35 38
21 03 29 10 50	13 05 81 62 18	12 47 05 65 00	15 29 27 61 39	59 52 65 21 13
95 33 26 70 11	06 65 11 61 36	01 01 60 08 57	55 01 85 63 74	35 82 47 17 08
49 71 29 73 80	10 40 45 54 52	34 03 06 07 26	75 21 11 02 71	36 63 36 84 24
58 27 56 17 64	97 58 65 47 16	50 25 94 63 45	87 19 54 60 92	26 78 76 09 39
89 51 41 17 88	68 22 42 34 17	73 95 97 61 45	30 34 24 02 77	11 04 97 20 49
15 47 25 06 69	48 13 93 67 32	46 87 43 70 88	73 46 50 98 19	58 86 93 52 20
12 12 08 61 24	51 24 74 43 02	60 88 35 21 09	21 43 73 67 86	49 22 67 78 37

Table A-1. Random Numbers (*Continued*)

19 61 27 84 30	11 66 19 47 70	77 60 36 56 69	86 86 81 26 65	30 01 27 59 89
39 14 17 74 00	28 00 06 42 38	73 25 87 17 94	31 34 02 62 56	66 45 33 70 16
64 75 68 04 57	08 74 71 28 36	03 46 95 06 78	03 27 44 34 23	66 67 78 25 56
92 90 15 18 78	56 44 12 29 98	29 71 83 84 47	06 45 32 53 11	07 56 55 37 71
03 55 19 00 70	09 48 39 40 50	45 93 81 81 35	36 90 84 33 21	11 07 35 18 03
98 88 46 62 09	06 83 05 36 56	14 66 35 63 46	71 43 00 49 09	19 81 80 57 07
27 36 98 68 82	53 47 30 75 41	53 63 37 08 63	03 74 81 28 22	19 36 04 90 88
59 06 67 59 74	63 33 52 04 83	43 51 43 74 81	58 27 82 69 67	49 32 54 39 51
91 64 79 37 83	64 16 94 90 22	98 58 80 94 95	49 82 95 90 68	38 83 10 48 38
83 60 59 24 19	39 54 20 77 72	71 56 87 56 73	35 18 58 97 59	44 90 17 42 91
24 89 58 85 30	70 77 43 54 39	46 75 87 04 72	70 20 79 26 75	91 62 36 12 75
35 72 02 65 56	95 59 62 00 94	73 75 08 57 88	34 26 40 17 03	46 83 36 52 48
14 14 15 34 10	38 64 90 63 43	57 25 66 13 42	72 70 97 53 18	90 37 93 75 62
27 41 67 56 70	92 17 67 25 35	93 11 95 60 77	06 88 61 82 44	92 34 43 13 74
82 07 10 74 29	81 00 74 77 49	40 74 45 69 74	23 33 68 88 21	53 84 11 05 36
21 44 58 27 93	24 83 19 32 41	14 19 97 62 68	70 88 36 80 02	03 82 91 74 43
72 51 37 64 00	52 22 59 23 48	62 30 89 84 81	29 74 43 31 65	33 14 16 10 20
71 47 94 50 27	76 16 05 74 11	13 78 01 36 32	52 30 87 77 62	88 87 43 36 97
83 21 05 14 66	09 08 85 03 95	26 74 30 53 06	21 70 67 00 01	99 43 98 07 67
68 74 99 51 48	94 89 77 86 36	96 75 00 90 24	94 53 89 11 43	96 69 36 18 86
05 18 47 57 63	47 07 58 81 58	05 31 35 34 39	14 90 80 88 30	60 09 62 15 51
13 65 16 25 46	96 89 22 52 40	47 51 15 84 83	87 34 27 88 18	07 85 53 92 69
00 56 62 12 20	00 29 22 40 69	25 07 22 95 19	52 54 85 40 91	21 28 22 12 96
50 95 81 76 95	58 07 26 89 90	60 32 99 59 55	71 58 66 34 17	35 94 76 78 07
57 62 16 45 47	46 85 03 79 81	38 52 70 90 37	64 75 60 33 24	04 98 68 36 66
09 28 22 58 44	79 13 97 84 35	35 42 84 35 61	69 79 96 33 14	12 99 19 35 16
23 39 49 42 06	93 43 23 78 36	94 91 92 68 46	02 55 57 44 10	94 91 54 81 99
05 28 03 74 70	93 62 20 43 45	15 09 21 95 10	18 09 41 66 13	78 23 45 00 01
95 49 19 79 76	38 30 63 21 92	82 63 95 46 24	72 43 49 26 06	23 19 17 46 93
78 52 10 01 04	18 24 87 55 83	90 32 65 07 85	54 03 46 62 51	35 77 41 46 92
96 34 54 45 79	85 93 24 40 53	75 70 42 08 40	86 58 38 39 44	52 45 67 37 66
77 96 33 11 51	32 36 49 16 91	47 35 74 03 38	23 43 52 40 65	08 45 89 53 66
07 52 01 12 94	23 23 80 17 48	41 69 06 73 28	54 81 43 77 77	10 05 74 23 32
38 42 30 23 09	70 70 38 57 36	46 14 81 42 58	29 23 61 21 52	05 08 86 58 25
02 46 36 55 33	21 19 96 05 55	33 92 80 18 17	07 39 68 92 15	30 72 22 21 02
15 88 09 22 61	17 29 28 81 90	61 78 14 88 98	92 52 52 12 83	88 58 16 00 98
71 92 60 08 19	59 14 40 02 24	30 57 09 01 94	18 32 90 69 99	26 85 71 92 38
64 42 52 81 08	16 55 41 60 16	00 04 28 32 29	10 33 33 61 68	65 61 79 48 34
79 78 22 39 24	49 44 03 04 32	81 07 73 15 43	95 21 66 48 65	13 65 85 10 81
35 33 77 45 38	44 55 36 46 72	90 96 04 18 49	93 86 54 46 08	93 17 63 48 51
05 24 92 93 29	19 71 59 40 82	14 73 88 66 67	43 70 86 63 54	93 69 22 55 27
56 46 39 93 80	38 79 38 57 74	19 05 61 39 39	46 06 22 76 47	66 14 66 32 10
96 29 63 31 21	54 19 63 41 08	75 81 48 59 86	71 17 11 51 02	28 99 26 31 65
98 38 03 62 69	60 01 40 72 01	62 44 84 63 85	42 17 58 83 50	46 18 24 91 26
52 56 76 43 50	16 31 55 39 69	80 39 58 11 14	54 35 86 45 78	47 26 91 57 47
78 49 89 08 30	25 95 59 92 36	43 28 69 10 64	99 96 99 51 44	64 42 47 73 77
49 55 32 42 41	08 15 08 95 35	08 70 39 10 41	77 32 38 10 79	45 12 79 36 86
32 15 10 70 75	83 15 51 02 52	73 10 08 86 18	23 89 18 74 18	45 41 72 02 68
11 31 45 03 63	26 86 02 77 99	49 41 68 35 34	19 18 70 80 59	76 67 70 21 10
12 36 47 12 10	87 05 25 02 41	90 78 59 78 89	81 39 95 81 30	64 43 90 56 14

TABLE A-2. RANDOM NORMAL NUMBERS, $\mu = 0$, $\sigma = 1$*

01	02	03	04	05	06	07	08	09	10
0.464	0.137	2.455	−0.323	−0.068	0.296	−0.288	1.298	0.241	−0.957
0.060	−2.526	−0.531	−0.194	0.543	−1.558	0.187	−1.190	0.022	0.525
1.486	−0.354	−0.634	0.697	0.926	1.375	0.785	−0.963	−0.853	−1.865
1.022	−0.472	1.279	3.521	0.571	−1.851	0.194	1.192	−0.501	−0.273
1.394	−0.555	0.046	0.321	2.945	1.974	−0.258	0.412	0.439	−0.035
0.906	−0.513	−0.525	0 595	0.881	−0.934	1.579	0.161	−1.885	0.371
1.179	−1.055	0.007	0.769	0.971	0.712	1.090	−0.631	−0.255	−0.702
−1.501	−0.488	−0.162	−0.136	1.033	0.203	0.448	0.748	−0.423	−0.432
−0.690	0.756	−1.618	−0.345	−0.511	−2.051	−0.457	−0.218	0.857	−0.465
1.372	0.225	0.378	0.761	0.181	−0.736	0.960	−1.530	−0.260	0.120
−0.482	1.678	−0.057	−1.229	−0.486	0.856	−0.491	−1.983	−2.830	−0.238
−1.376	−0.150	1.356	−0.561	−0.256	−0.212	0.219	0.779	0.953	−0.869
−1.010	0.598	−0.918	1.598	0.065	0.415	−0.169	0.313	−0.973	−1.016
−0.005	−0.899	0.012	−0.725	1.147	−0.121	1.096	0.481	−1.691	0.417
1.393	−1.163	−0.911	1.231	−0.199	−0.246	1.239	−2.574	−0.558	0.056
−1.787	−0.261	1.237	1.046	−0.508	−1.630	−0.146	−0.392	−0.627	0.561
−0.105	−0.357	−1.384	0.360	−0.992	−0.116	−1.698	−2.832	−1.108	−2.357
−1.339	1.827	−0.959	0.424	0.969	−1.141	−1.041	0.362	−1.726	1.956
1.041	0.535	0.731	1.377	0.983	−1.330	1.620	−1.040	0.524	−0.281
0.279	−2.056	0.717	−0.873	−1.096	−1.396	1.047	0.089	−0.573	0.932
−1.805	−2.008	−1.633	0.542	0.250	−0.166	0.032	0.079	0.471	−1.029
−1.186	1.180	1.114	0.882	1.265	−0.202	0.151	−0.376	−0.310	0.479
0.658	−1.141	1.151	−1.210	−0.927	0.425	0.290	−0.902	0.610	2.709
−0.439	0.358	−1.939	0.891	−0.227	0.602	0.873	−0.437	−0.220	−0.057
−1.399	−0.230	0.385	−0.649	−0.577	0.237	−0.289	0.513	0.738	−0.300
0.199	0.208	−1.083	−0.219	−0.291	1.221	1.119	0.004	−2.015	−0.594
0.159	0.272	−0.313	0.084	−2.828	−0.439	−0.792	−1.275	−0.623	−1.047
2.273	0.606	0.606	−0.747	0.247	1.291	0.063	−1.793	−0.699	−1.347
0.041	−0.307	0.121	0.790	−0.584	0.541	0.484	−0.986	0.481	0.996
−1.132	−2.098	0.921	0.145	0.446	−1.661	1.045	−1.363	−0.586	−1.023
0.768	0.079	−1.473	0.034	−2.127	0.665	0.084	−0.880	−0.579	0.551
0.375	−1.658	−0.851	0.234	−0.656	0.340	−0.086	−0.158	−0.120	0.418
−0.513	−0.344	0.210	−0.736	1.041	0.008	0.427	−0.831	0.191	0.074
0.292	−0.521	1.266	−1.206	−0.899	0.110	−0.528	−0.813	0.071	0.524
1.026	2.990	−0.574	−0.491	−1.114	1.297	−1.433	−1.345	−3.001	0.479
−1.334	1.278	−0.568	−0.109	−0.515	−0.566	2.923	0.500	0.359	0.326
−0.287	−0.144	−0.254	0.574	−0.451	−1.181	−1.190	−0.318	−0.094	1.114
0.161	−0.886	−0.921	−0.509	1.410	−0.518	0.192	−0.432	1.501	1.068
−1.346	0.193	−1.202	0.394	−1.045	0.843	0.942	1.045	0.031	0.772
1.250	−0.199	−0.288	1.810	1.378	0.584	1.216	0.733	0.402	0.226
0.630	−0.537	0.782	0.060	0.499	−0.431	1.705	1.164	0.884	−0.298
0.375	−1.941	0.247	−0.491	0.665	−0.135	−0.145	−0.498	0.457	1.064
−1.420	0.489	−1.711	−1.186	0.754	−0.732	−0.066	1.006	−0.798	0.162
−0.151	−0.243	−0.430	−0.762	0.298	1.049	1.810	2.885	−0.768	−0.129
−0.309	0.531	0.416	−1.541	1.456	2.040	−0.124	0.196	0.023	−1.204
0.424	−0.444	0.593	0.993	−0.106	0.116	0.484	−1.272	1.066	1.097
0.593	0.658	−1.127	−1.407	−1.579	−1.616	1.458	1.262	0.736	−0.916
0.862	−0.885	−0.142	−0.504	0.532	1.381	0.022	−0.281	−0.342	1.222
0.235	−0.628	−0.023	−0.463	−0.899	−0.394	−0.538	1.707	−0.188	−1.153
−0.853	0.402	0.777	0.833	0.410	−0.349	−1.094	0.580	1.395	1.298

* This table is reproduced with permission from tables of the RAND Corporation.

TABLE A-2. RANDOM NORMAL NUMBERS, $\mu = 0$, $\sigma = 1$ (*Continued*)

11	12	13	14	15	16	17	18	19	20
-1.329	-0.238	-0.838	-0.988	-0.445	0.964	-0.266	-0.322	-1.726	2.252
1.284	-0.229	1.058	0.090	0.050	0.523	0.016	0.277	1.639	0.554
0.619	0.628	0.005	0.973	-0.058	0.150	-0.635	-0.917	0.313	-1.203
0.699	-0.269	0.722	-0.994	-0.807	-1.203	1.163	1.244	1.306	-1.210
0.101	0.202	-0.150	0.731	0.420	0.116	-0.496	-0.037	-2.466	0.794
-1.381	0.301	0.522	0.233	0.791	-1.017	-0.182	0.926	-1.096	1.001
-0.574	1.366	-1.843	0.746	0.890	0.824	-1.249	-0.806	-0.240	0.217
0.096	0.210	1.091	0.990	0.900	-0.837	-1.097	-1.238	0.030	-0.311
1.389	-0.236	0.094	3.282	0.295	-0.416	0.313	0.720	0.007	0.354
1.249	0.706	1.453	0.366	-2.654	-1.400	0.212	0.307	-1.145	0.639
0.756	-0.397	-1.772	-0.257	1.120	1.188	-0.527	0.709	0.479	0.317
-0.860	0.412	-0.327	0.178	0.524	-0.672	-0.831	0.758	0.131	0.771
-0.778	-0.979	0.236	-1.033	1.497	-0.661	0.906	1.169	-1.582	1.303
0.037	0.062	0.426	1.220	0.471	0.784	-0.719	0.465	1.559	-1.326
2.619	-0.440	0.477	1.063	0.320	1.406	-0.701	-0.128	0.518	-0.676
-0.420	-0.287	-0.050	-0.481	1.521	-1.367	0.609	0.292	0.048	0.592
1.048	0.220	1.121	-1.789	-1.211	-0.871	-0.740	0.513	-0.558	-0.395
1.000	-0.638	1.261	0.510	-0.150	0.034	0.054	-0.055	0.639	-0.825
0.170	-1.131	-0.985	0.102	-0.939	-1.457	1.766	1.087	-1.275	2.362
0.389	-0.435	0.171	0.891	1.158	1.041	1.048	-0.324	-0.404	1.060
-0.305	0.838	-2.019	-0.540	0.905	1.195	-1.190	0.106	0.571	0.298
-0.321	-0.039	1.799	-1.032	-2.225	-0.148	0.758	-0.862	0.158	-0.726
1.900	1.572	-0.244	-1.721	1.130	0.495	-0.484	0.014	-0.778	-1.483
-0.778	-0.288	-0.224	-1.324	-0.072	0.890	-0.410	0.752	0.376	-0.224
0.617	-1.718	-0.183	-0.100	1.719	0.696	-1.339	-0.614	1.071	-0.386
-1.430	-0.953	0.770	-0.007	-1.872	1.075	-0.913	-1.168	1.775	0.238
0.267	-0.048	0.972	0.734	-1.408	-1.955	-0.848	2.002	0.232	-1.273
0.978	-0.520	-0.368	1.690	-1.479	0.985	1.475	-0.098	-1.633	2.399
-1.235	-1.168	0.325	1.421	2.652	-0.486	-1.253	0.270	-1.103	0.118
-0.258	0.638	2.309	0.741	-0.161	-0.679	0.336	1.973	0.370	-2.277
0.243	0.629	-1.516	-0.157	0.693	1.710	0.800	-0.265	1.218	0.655
-0.292	-1.455	-1.451	1.492	-0.713	0.821	-0.031	-0.780	1.330	0.977
-0.505	0.389	0.544	-0.042	1.615	-1.440	-0.989	-0.580	0.156	0.052
0.397	-0.287	1.712	0.289	-0.904	0.259	-0.600	-1.635	-0.009	-0.799
-0.605	-0.470	0.007	0.721	-1.117	0.635	0.592	-1.362	-1.441	0.672
1.360	0.182	-1.476	-0.599	-0.875	0.292	-0.700	0.058	-0.340	-0.639
0.480	-0.699	1.615	-0.225	1.014	-1.370	-1.097	0.294	0.309	-1.389
-0.027	-0.487	-1.000	-0.015	0.119	-1.990	-0.687	-1.964	-0.366	1.759
-1.482	-0.815	-0.121	1.884	-0.185	0.601	0.793	0.430	-1.181	0.426
-1.256	-0.567	-0.994	1.011	-1.071	-0.623	-0.420	-0.309	1.362	0.863
-1.132	2.039	1.934	-0.222	0.386	1.100	0.284	1.597	-1.718	-0.560
-0.780	-0.239	-0.497	-0.434	-0.284	-0.241	-0.333	1.348	-0.478	-0.169
-0.859	-0.215	0.241	1.471	0.389	-0.952	0.245	0.781	1.093	-0.240
0.447	1.479	0.067	0.426	-0.370	-0.675	-0.972	0.225	0.815	0.389
0.269	0.735	-0.066	-0.271	-1.439	1.036	-0.306	-1.439	-0.122	-0.336
0.097	-1.883	-0.218	0.202	-0.357	0.019	1.631	1.400	0.223	-0.793
-0.686	1.596	-0.286	0.722	0.655	-0.275	1.245	-1.504	0.066	-1.280
0.957	0.057	-1.153	0.701	-0.280	1.747	-0.745	1.338	-1.421	0.386
-0.976	-1.789	-0.696	-1.799	-0.354	0.071	2.355	0.135	-0.598	1.883
0.274	0.226	-0.909	-0.572	0.181	1.115	0.406	0.453	-1.218	-0.115

TABLE A-2. RANDOM NORMAL NUMBERS, $\mu = 0$, $\sigma = 1$ (*Continued*)

21	22	23	24	25	26	27	28	29	30
−1.752	−0.329	−1.256	0.318	1.531	0.349	−0.958	−0.059	0.415	−1.084
−0.291	0.085	1.701	−1.087	−0.443	−0.292	0.248	−0.539	−1.382	0.318
−0.933	0.130	0.634	0.899	1.409	−0.883	−0.095	0.229	0.129	0.367
−0.450	−0.244	0.072	1.028	1.730	−0.056	−1.488	−0.078	−2.361	−0.992
0.512	−0.882	0.490	−1.304	−0.266	0.757	−0.361	0.194	−1.078	0.529
−0.702	0.472	0.429	−0.664	−0.592	1.443	−1.515	−1.209	−1.043	0.278
0.284	0.039	−0.518	1.351	1.473	0.889	0.300	0.339	−0.206	1.392
−0.509	1.420	−0.782	−0.429	−1.266	0.627	−1.165	0.819	−0.261	0.409
−1.776	−1.033	1.977	0.014	0.702	−0.435	−0.816	1.131	0.656	0.061
−0.044	1.807	0.342	−2.510	1.071	−1.220	−0.060	−0.764	0.079	−0.964
0.263	−0.578	1.612	−0.148	−0.383	−1.007	−0.414	0.638	−0.186	0.507
0.986	0.439	−0.192	−0.132	0.167	0.883	−0.400	−1.440	−0.385	−1.414
−0.441	−0.852	−1.446	−0.605	−0.348	1.018	0.963	−0.004	2.504	−0.847
−0.866	0.489	0.097	0.379	0.192	−0.842	0.065	1.420	0.426	−1.191
−1.215	0.675	1.621	0.394	−1.447	2.199	−0.321	−0.540	−0.037	0.185
−0.475	−1.210	0.183	0.526	0.495	1.297	−1.613	1.241	−1.016	−0.090
1.200	0.131	2.502	0.344	−1.060	−0.909	−1.695	−0.666	−0.838	−0.866
−0.498	−1.202	−0.057	−1.354	−1.441	−1.590	0.987	0.441	0.637	−1.116
−0.743	0.894	−0.028	1.119	−0.598	0.279	2.241	0.830	0.267	−0.156
0.779	−0.780	−0.954	0.705	−0.361	−0.734	1.365	1.297	−0.142	−1.387
−0.206	−0.195	1.017	−1.167	−0.079	−0.452	0.058	−1.068	−0.394	−0.406
−0.092	−0.927	−0.439	0.256	0.503	0.338	1.511	−0.465	−0.118	−0.454
−1.222	−1.582	1.786	−0.517	−1.080	−0.409	−0.474	−1.890	0.247	0.575
0.068	0.075	−1.383	−0.084	0.159	1.276	1.141	0.186	−0.973	−0.266
0.183	1.600	−0.335	1.553	0.889	0.896	−0.035	0.461	0.486	1.246
−0.811	−2.904	0.618	0.588	0.533	0.803	−0.696	0.690	0.820	0.557
−1.010	1.149	1.033	0.336	1.306	0.835	1.523	0.296	−0.426	0.004
1.453	1.210	−0.043	0.220	−0.256	−1.161	−2.030	−0.046	0.243	1.082
0.759	−0.838	−0.877	−0.177	1.183	−0.218	−3.154	−0.963	−0.822	−1.114
0.287	0.278	−0.454	0.897	−0.122	0.013	0.346	0.921	0.238	−0.586
−0.669	0.035	−2.077	1.077	0.525	−0.154	−1.036	0.015	−0.220	0.882
0.392	0.106	−1.430	−0.204	−0.326	0.825	−0.432	−0.094	−1.566	0.679
−0.337	0.199	−0.160	0.625	−0.891	−1.464	−0.318	1.297	0.932	−0.032
0.369	−1.990	−1.190	0.666	−1.614	0.082	0.922	−0.139	−0.833	0.091
−1.694	0.710	−0.655	−0.546	1.654	0.134	0.466	0.033	−0.039	0.838
0.985	0.340	0.276	0.911	−0.170	−0.551	1.000	−0.838	0.275	−0.304
−1.063	−0.594	−1.526	−0.787	0.873	−0.405	−1.324	0.162	−0.163	−2.716
0.033	−1.527	1.422	0.308	0.845	−0.151	0.741	0.064	1.212	0.823
0.597	0.362	−3.760	1.159	0.874	−0.794	−0.915	1.215	1.627	−1.248
−1.601	−0.570	0.133	−0.660	1.485	0.682	−0.898	0.686	0.658	0.346
−0.266	−1.309	0.597	0.989	0.934	1.079	−0.656	−0.999	−0.036	−0.537
0.901	1.531	−0.889	−1.019	0.084	1.531	−0.144	−1.920	0.678	−0.402
−1.433	−1.008	−0.990	0.090	0.940	0.207	−0.745	0.638	1.469	1.214
1.327	0.763	−1.724	−0.709	−1.100	−1.346	−0.946	−0.157	0.522	−1.264
−0.248	0.788	−0.577	0.122	−0.536	0.293	1.207	−2.243	1.642	1.353
−0.401	−0.679	0.921	0.476	1.121	−0.864	0.128	−0.551	−0.872	1.511
0.344	−0.324	0.686	−1.487	−0.126	0.803	−0.961	0.183	−0.358	−0.184
0.441	−0.372	−1.336	0.062	1.506	−0.315	−0.112	−0.452	1.594	−0.264
0.824	0.040	−1.734	0.251	0.054	−0.379	1.298	−0.126	0.104	−0.529
1.385	1.320	−0.509	−0.381	−1.671	−0.524	−0.805	1.348	0.676	0.799

TABLE A-2. RANDOM NORMAL NUMBERS, $\mu = 0$, $\sigma = 1$ (*Continued*)

31	32	33	34	35	36	37	38	39	40
1.556	0.119	−0.078	0.164	−0.455	0.077	−0.043	−0.299	0.249	−0.182
0.647	1.029	1.186	0.887	1.204	−0.657	0.644	−0.410	−0.652	−0.165
0.329	0.407	1.169	−2.072	1.661	0.891	0.233	−1.628	−0.762	−0.717
−1.188	1.171	−1.170	−0.291	0.863	−0.045	−0.205	0.574	−0.926	1.407
−0.917	−0.616	−1.589	1.184	0.266	0.559	−1.833	−0.572	−0.648	−1.090
0.414	0.469	−0.182	0.397	1.649	1.198	0.067	−1.526	−0.081	−0.192
0.107	−0.187	1.343	0.472	−0.112	1.182	0.548	2.748	0.249	0.154
−0.497	1.907	0.191	0.136	−0.475	0.458	0.183	−1.640	−0.058	1.278
0.501	0.083	−0.321	1.133	1.126	−0.299	1.299	1.617	1.581	2.455
−1.382	−0.738	1.225	1.564	−0.363	−0.548	1.070	0.390	−1.398	0.524
−0.590	0.699	−0.162	−0.011	1.049	−0.689	1.225	0.339	−0.539	−0.445
−1.125	1.111	−1.065	0.534	0.102	0.425	−1.026	0.695	−0.057	0.795
0.849	0.169	−0.351	0.584	2.177	0.009	−0.696	−0.426	−0.692	−1.638
−1.233	−0.585	0.306	0.773	1.304	−1.304	0.282	−1.705	0.187	−0.880
0.104	−0.468	0.185	0.498	−0.624	−0.322	−0.875	1.478	−0.691	−0.281
0.261	−1.883	−0.181	1.675	−0.324	−1.029	−0.185	0.004	−0.101	−1.187
−0.007	1.280	0.568	−1.270	1.405	1.731	2.072	1.686	0.728	−0.417
0.794	−0.111	0.040	−0.536	−0.976	2.192	1.609	−0.190	−0.279	−1.611
0.431	−2.300	−1.081	−1.370	2.943	0.653	−2.523	0.756	0.886	−0.983
−0.149	1.294	−0.580	0.482	−1.449	−1.067	1.996	−0.274	0.721	0.490
−0.216	−1.647	1.043	0.481	−0.011	−0.587	−0.916	−1.016	−1.040	−1.117
1.604	−0.851	−0.317	−0.686	−0.008	1.939	0.078	−0.465	0.533	0.652
−0.212	0.005	0.535	0.837	0.362	1.103	0.219	0.488	1.332	−0.200
0.007	−0.076	1.484	0.455	−0.207	−0.554	1.120	0.913	−0.681	1.751
−0.217	0.937	0.860	0.323	1.321	−0.492	−1.386	−0.003	−0.230	0.539
−0.649	0.300	−0.698	0.900	0.569	0.842	0.804	1.025	0.603	−1.546
−1.541	0.193	2.047	−0.552	1.190	−0.087	2.062	−2.173	−0.791	−0.520
0.274	−0.530	0.112	0.385	0.656	0.436	0.882	0.312	−2.265	−0.218
0.876	−1.498	−0.128	−0.387	−1.259	−0.856	−0.353	0.714	0.863	1.169
−0.859	−1.083	1.288	−0.078	−0.081	0.210	0.572	1.194	−1.118	−1.543
−0.015	−0.567	0.113	2.127	−0.719	3.256	−0.721	−0.663	−0.779	−0.930
−1.529	−0.231	1.223	0.300	−0.995	−0.651	0.505	0.138	−0.064	1.341
0.278	−0.058	−2.740	−0.296	−1.180	0.574	1.452	0.846	−0.243	−1.208
1.428	0.322	2.302	−0.852	0.782	−1.322	−0.092	−0.546	0.560	−1.430
0.770	−1.874	0.347	0.994	−0.485	−1.179	0.048	−1.324	1.061	0.449
−0.303	−0.629	0.764	0.013	−1.192	−0.475	−1.085	−0.880	1.738	−1.225
−0.263	−2.105	0.509	−0.645	1.362	0.504	−0.755	1.274	1.448	0.604
0.997	−1.187	−0.242	0.121	2.510	−1.935	0.350	0.073	0.458	−0.446
−0.063	−0.475	−1.802	−0.476	0.193	−1.199	0.339	0.364	−0.684	1.353
−0.168	1.904	−0.485	−0.032	−0.554	0.056	−0.710	−0.778	0.722	−0.024
0.366	−0.491	0.301	−0.008	−0.894	−0.945	0.384	−1.748	−1.118	0.394
0.436	−0.464	0.539	0.942	−0.458	0.445	−1.883	1.228	1.113	−0.218
0.597	−1.471	−0.434	0.705	−0.788	0.575	0.086	0.504	1.445	−0.513
−0.805	−0.624	1.344	0.649	−1.124	0.680	−0.986	1.845	−1.152	−0.393
1.681	−1.910	0.440	0.067	−1.502	−0.755	−0.989	−0.054	−2.320	0.474
−0.007	−0.459	1.940	0.220	−1.259	−1.729	0.137	−0.520	−0.412	2.847
0.209	−0.633	0.299	0.174	1.975	−0.271	0.119	−0.199	0.007	2.315
1.254	1.672	−1.186	−1.310	0.474	0.878	−0.725	−0.191	0.642	−1.212
−1.016	−0.697	0.017	−0.263	−0.047	−1.294	−0.339	2.257	−0.078	−0.049
−1.169	−0.355	1.086	−0.199	0.031	0.396	−0.143	1.572	0.276	0.027

TABLE A-2. RANDOM NORMAL NUMBERS, $\mu = 0$, $\sigma = 1$ (*Continued*)

41	42	43	44	45	46	47	48	49	50
−0.856	−0.063	0.787	−2.052	−1.192	−0.831	1.623	1.135	0.759	−0.189
−0.276	−1.110	0.752	−1.378	−0.583	0.360	0.365	1.587	0.621	1.344
0.379	−0.440	0.858	1.453	−1.356	0.503	−1.134	1.950	−1.816	−0.283
1.468	0.131	0.047	0.355	0.162	−1.491	−0.739	−1.182	−0.533	−0.497
−1.805	−0.772	1.286	−0.636	−1.312	−1.045	1.559	−0.871	−0.102	−0.123
2.285	0.554	0.418	−0.577	−1.489	−1.255	0.092	−0.597	−1.051	−0.980
−0.602	0.399	1.121	−1.026	0.087	1.018	−1.437	0.661	0.091	−0.637
0.229	−0.584	0.705	0.124	0.341	1.320	−0.824	−1.541	−0.163	2.329
1.382	−1.454	1.537	−1.299	0.363	−0.356	−0.025	0.294	2.194	−0.395
0.978	0.109	1.434	−1.094	−0.265	−0.857	−1.421	−1.773	0.570	−0.053
−0.678	−2.335	1.202	−1.697	0.547	−0.201	−0.373	−1.363	−0.081	0.958
−0.366	−1.084	−0.626	0.798	1.706	−1.160	−0.838	1.462	0.636	0.570
−1.074	−1.379	0.086	−0.331	−0.288	−0.309	−1.527	−0.408	0.183	0.856
−0.600	−0.096	0.696	0.446	1.417	−2.140	0.599	−0.157	1.485	1.387
0.918	1.163	−1.445	0.759	0.878	−1.781	−0.056	−2.141	−0.234	0.975
−0.791	−0.528	0.946	1.673	−0.680	−0.784	1.494	−0.086	−1.071	−1.196
0.598	−0.352	0.719	−0.341	0.056	−1.041	1.429	0.235	0.314	−1.693
0.567	−1.156	−0.125	−0.534	0.711	−0.511	0.187	−0.644	−1.090	−1,281
0.963	0.052	0.037	0.637	−1.335	0.055	0.010	−0.860	−0.621	0.713
0.489	−0.209	1.659	0.054	1.635	0.169	0.794	−1.550	1.845	−0.388
−1.627	−0.017	0.699	0.661	−0.073	0.188	1.183	−1.054	−1.615	−0.765
−1.096	1.215	0.320	0.738	1.865	−1.169	−0.667	−0.674	−0.062	1.378
−2.532	1.031	−0.799	1.665	−2.756	−0.151	−0.704	0.602	−0.672	1.264
0.024	−1.183	−0.927	−0.629	0.204	−0.825	0.496	2.543	0.262	−0.785
0.192	0.125	0.373	−0.931	−0.079	0.186	−0.306	0.621	−0.292	1.131
−1.324	−1.229	−0.648	−0.430	0.811	0.868	0.787	1.845	−0.374	−0.651
−0.726	−0.746	1.572	−1.420	1.509	−0.361	−0.310	−3.117	1.637	0.642
−1.618	1.082	−0.319	0.300	1.524	−0.418	−1.712	0.358	−1.032	0.537
1.695	0.843	2.049	0.388	−0.297	1.077	−0.462	0.655	0.940	−0.354
0.790	0.605	−3.077	1.009	−0.906	−1.004	0.693	−1.098	1.300	0.549
1.792	−0.895	−0.136	−1.765	1.077	0.418	−0.150	0.808	0.697	0.435
0.771	−0.741	−0.492	−0.770	−0.458	−0.021	1.385	−1.225	−0.066	−1.471
−1.438	0.423	−1.211	0.723	−0.731	0.883	−2.109	−2.455	−0.210	1.644
−0.294	1.266	−1.994	−0.730	0.545	0.397	1.069	−0.383	−0.097	−0.985
−1.966	0.909	0.400	0.685	−0.800	1.759	0.268	1.387	−0.414	1.615
−0.999	1.587	1.423	0.937	−0.943	0.090	1.185	−1.204	0.300	−1.354
0.581	0.481	−2.400	0.000	0.231	0.079	−2.842	−0.846	−0.508	−0.516
0.370	−1.452	−0.580	−1.462	−0.972	1.116	−0.994	0.374	−3.336	−0.058
0.834	−1.227	−0.709	−1.039	−0.014	−0.383	−0.512	−0.347	0.881	−0.638
−0.376	−0.813	0.660	−1.029	−0.137	0.371	0.376	0.968	1.338	−0.786
−1.621	0.815	−0.544	−0.376	−0.852	0.436	1.562	0.815	−1.048	0.188
0.163	−0.161	2.501	−0.265	−0.285	1.934	1.070	0.215	−0.876	0.073
1.786	−0.538	−0.437	0.324	0.105	−0.421	−0.410	−0.947	0.700	−1.006
2.140	1.218	−0.351	−0.068	0.254	0.448	−1.461	0.784	0.317	1.013
0.064	0.410	0.368	0.419	−0.982	1.371	0.100	−0.505	0.856	0.890
0.789	−0.131	1.330	0.506	−0.645	−1.414	2.426	1.389	−0.169	−0.194
−0.011	−0.372	−0.699	2.382	−1.395	−0.467	1.256	−0.585	−1.359	−1.804
−0.463	0.003	−1.470	1.493	0.960	0.364	−1.267	−0.007	0.616	0.624
−1.210	−0.669	0.009	1.284	−0.617	0.355	−0.589	−0.243	−0.015	−0.712
−1.157	0.481	0.560	1.287	1.129	−0.126	0.006	1.532	1.328	0.980

TABLE A-2. RANDOM NORMAL NUMBERS, $\mu = 0$, $\sigma = 1$ (*Continued*)

51	52	53	54	55	56	57	58	59	60
0.240	1.774	0.210	−1.471	1.167	−1.114	0.182	−0.485	−0.318	1.156
0.627	−0.758	−0.930	1.641	0.162	−0.874	−0.235	0.203	−0.724	−0.155
−0.594	0.098	0.158	−0.722	1.385	−0.985	−1.707	0.175	0.449	0.654
1.082	−0.753	−1.944	−1.964	−2.131	−2.796	−1.286	0.807	−0.122	0.527
0.060	−0.014	1.577	−0.814	−0.633	0.275	−0.087	0.517	0.474	−1.432
−0.013	0.402	−0.086	−0.394	0.292	−2.862	−1.660	−1.658	1.610	−2.205
1.586	−0.833	1.444	−0.615	−1.157	−0.220	−0.517	−1.668	−2.036	−0.850
−0.405	−1.315	−1.355	−1.331	1.394	−0.381	−0.729	−0.447	−0.906	0.622
−0.329	1.701	0.427	0.627	−0.271	−0.971	−1.010	1.182	−0.143	0.844
0.992	0.708	−0.115	−1.630	0.596	0.499	−0.862	0.508	0.474	−0.974
0.296	−0.390	2.047	−0.363	0.724	0.788	−0.089	0.930	−0.497	0.058
−2.069	−1.422	−0.948	−1.742	−1.173	0.215	0.661	0.842	−0.984	−0.577
−0.211	−1.727	−0.277	1.592	−0.707	0.327	−0.527	0.912	0.571	−0.525
−0.467	1.848	−0.263	−0.862	0.706	−0.533	0.626	−0.200	−2.221	0.368
1.284	0.412	1.512	0.328	0.203	−1.231	−1.480	−0.400	−0.491	0.913
0.821	−1.503	−1.066	1.624	1.345	0.440	−1.416	0.301	−0.355	0.106
1.056	1.224	0.281	−0.098	1.868	−0.395	0.610	−1.173	−1.449	1.171
1.090	−0.790	0.882	1.687	−0.009	−2.053	−0.030	−0.421	1.253	−0.081
0.574	0.129	1.203	0.280	1.438	−2.052	−0.443	0.522	0.468	−1.211
−0.531	2.155	0.334	0.898	−1.114	0.243	1.026	0.391	−0.011	−0.024
0.896	0.181	−0.941	−0.511	0.648	−0.710	−0.181	−1.417	−0.585	0.087
0.042	0.579	−0.316	0.394	1.133	−0.305	−0.683	−1.318	−0.050	0.993
2.328	−0.243	0.534	0.241	0.275	0.060	0.727	−1.459	0.174	−1.072
0.486	−0.558	0.426	0.728	−0.360	−0.068	0.058	1.471	−0.051	0.337
−0.304	−0.309	0.646	0.309	−1.320	0.311	−1.407	−0.011	0.387	0.128
−2.319	−0.129	0.866	−0.424	0.236	0.419	−1.359	−1.088	−0.045	1.096
1.098	−0.875	0.659	−1.086	−0.424	−1.462	0.743	−0.787	1.472	1.677
−0.038	−0.118	−1.285	−0.545	−0.140	1.244	−1.104	0.146	0.058	1.245
−0.207	−0.746	1.681	0.137	0.104	−0.491	−0.935	0.671	−0.448	−0.129
0.333	−1.386	1.840	1.089	0.837	−1.642	−0.273	−0.798	0.067	0.334
1.190	−0.547	−1.016	0.540	−0.993	0.443	−0.190	1.019	−1.021	−1.276
−1.416	−0.749	0.325	0.846	2.417	−0.479	−0.655	−1.326	−1.952	1.234
0.622	0.661	0.028	1.302	−0.032	−0.157	1.470	−0.766	0.697	−0.303
−1.134	0.499	0.538	0.564	−2.392	−1.398	0.010	1.874	1.386	0.000
0.725	−0.242	0.281	1.355	−0.036	0.204	−0.345	0.395	−0.753	1.645
−0.210	0.611	−0.219	0.450	0.308	0.993	−0.146	0.225	−1.496	0.246
0.219	0.302	0.000	−0.437	−2.127	0.883	−0.599	−1.516	0.826	1.242
−1.098	−0.252	−2.480	−0.973	0.712	−1.430	−0.167	−1.237	0.750	−0.763
0.144	0.489	−0.637	1.990	0.411	−0.563	0.027	1.278	2.105	−1.130
−1.738	−1.295	0.431	−0.503	2.327	−0.007	−1.293	−1.206	−0.066	1.370
−0.487	−0.097	−1.361	−0.340	0.204	0.938	−0.148	−1.099	−0.252	−0.384
−0.636	−0.626	1.967	1.677	−0.331	−0.440	−1.440	1.281	1.070	−1.167
−1.464	−1.493	0.945	0.180	−0.672	−0.035	−0.293	−0.905	0.196	−1.122
0.561	−0.375	−0.657	1.304	0.833	−1.159	1.501	1.265	0.438	−0.437
−0.525	−0.017	1.815	0.789	−1.908	−0.353	1.383	−1.208	−1.135	1.082
0.980	−0.111	−0.804	−1.078	−1.930	0.171	−1.318	2.377	−0.303	1.062
0.501	0.835	−0.518	−1.034	−1.493	0.712	0.421	−1.165	0.782	−1.484
1.081	−1.176	−0.542	0.321	0.688	0.670	−0.771	−0.090	−0.611	−0.813
−0.148	−1.203	−1.553	1.244	0.826	0.077	0.128	−0.772	1.683	0.318
0.096	−0.286	0.362	0.888	0.551	1.782	0.335	2.083	0.350	0.260

TABLE A-2. RANDOM NORMAL NUMBERS, $\mu = 0$, $\sigma = 1$ (*Continued*)

61	62	63	64	65	66	67	68	69	70
0.052	1.504	−1.350	−1.124	−0.521	0.515	0.839	0.778	0.438	−0.550
−0.315	−0.865	0.851	0.127	−0.379	1.640	−0.441	0.717	0.670	−0.301
0.938	−0.055	0.947	1.275	1.557	−1.484	−1.137	0.398	1.333	1.988
0.497	0.502	0.385	−0.467	2.468	−1.810	−1.438	0.283	1.740	0.420
2.308	−0.399	−1.798	0.018	0.780	1.030	0.806	−0.408	−0.547	−0.280
1.815	0.101	−0.561	0.236	0.166	0.227	−0.309	0.056	0.610	0.732
−0.421	0.432	0.586	1.059	0.278	−1.672	1.859	1.433	−0.919	−1.770
0.008	0.555	−1.310	−1.440	−0.142	−0.295	−0.630	−0.911	0.133	−0.308
1.191	−0.114	1.039	1.083	0.185	−0.492	0.419	−0.433	−1.019	−2.260
1.299	1.918	0.318	1.348	0.935	1.250	−0.175	−0.828	−0.336	0.726
0.012	−0.739	−1.181	−0.645	−0.736	1.801	−0.209	−0.389	0.867	−0.555
−0.586	−0.044	−0.983	0.332	0.371	−0.072	−1.212	1.047	−1.930	0.812
−0.122	1.515	0.338	−1.040	−0.008	0.467	−0.600	0.923	1.126	−0.752
0.879	0.516	−0.920	2.121	0.674	1.481	0.660	−0.986	1.644	−2.159
0.435	1.149	−0.065	1.391	0.707	0.548	−0.490	−1.139	0.249	−0.933
0.645	0.878	−0.904	0.896	−1.284	0.237	−0.378	−0.510	−1.123	−0.129
−0.514	−1.017	0.529	0.973	−1.202	0.005	−0.644	−0.167	−0.664	0.167
0.242	−0.427	−0.727	−1.150	−1.092	−0.736	0.925	−0.050	−0.200	−0.770
0.443	0.445	−1.287	−1.463	−0.650	0.412	−2.714	−0.903	−0.341	0.957
0.273	0.203	0.423	1.423	0.508	1.058	−0.828	0.143	−1.059	0.345
0.255	1.036	1.471	0.476	0.592	−0.658	0.677	0.155	1.068	−0.759
0.858	−0.370	0.522	−1.890	−0.389	0.609	1.210	0.489	−0.006	0.834
0.097	−1.709	1.790	−0.929	0.405	0.024	−0.036	0.580	−0.642	−1.121
0.520	0.889	−0.540	0.266	−0.354	0.524	−0.788	−0.497	−0.973	1.481
−0.311	−1.772	−0.496	1.275	−0.904	0.147	1.497	0.657	−0.469	−0.783
−0.604	0.857	−0.695	0.397	0.296	−0.285	0.191	0.158	1.672	1.190
−0.001	0.287	−0.868	−0.013	−1.576	−0.168	0.047	−0.159	0.086	−1.077
1.160	0.989	0.205	0.937	−0.099	−1.281	−0.276	0.845	0.752	0.663
1.579	−0.303	−1.174	−0.960	−0.470	−0.556	−0.689	1.535	−0.711	−0.743
−0.615	−0.154	0.008	1.353	−0.381	1.137	0.022	0.175	0.586	2.941
1.578	1.529	−0.294	−1.301	0.614	0.099	−0.700	−0.003	1.052	1.643
0.626	−0.447	−1.261	−2.029	0.182	−1.176	0.083	1.868	0.872	0.965
−0.493	−0.020	0.920	1.473	1.873	−0.289	0.410	0.394	0.881	0.054
−0.217	0.342	1.423	0.364	−0.119	0.509	−2.266	0.189	0.149	1.041
−0.792	0.347	−1.367	−0.632	−1.238	−0.136	−0.352	−0.157	−1.163	1.305
0.568	−0.226	0.391	−0.074	−0.312	0.400	1.583	0.481	−1.048	0.759
0.051	0.549	−2.192	1.257	−1.460	0.363	0.127	−1.020	−1.192	0.449
−0.891	0.490	0.279	0.372	−0.578	−0.836	2.285	−0.448	0.720	0.510
0.622	−0.126	−0.637	1.255	−0.354	0.032	−1.076	0.352	0.103	−0.496
0.623	0.819	−0.489	0.354	−0.943	−0.694	0.248	0.092	−0.673	−1.428
−1.208	−1.038	0.140	−0.762	−0.854	−0.249	2.431	0.067	−0.317	−0.874
−0.487	−2.117	0.195	2.154	1.041	−1.314	−0.785	−0.414	−0.695	2.310
0.522	0.314	−1.003	0.134	−1.748	−0.107	0.459	1.550	1.118	−1.004
0.838	0.613	0.227	0.308	−0.757	0.912	2.272	0.556	−0.041	0.008
−1.534	−0.407	1.202	1.251	−0.891	−1.588	−2.380	0.059	0.682	−0.878
−0.099	2.391	1.067	−2.060	−0.464	−0.103	3.486	1.121	0.632	−1.626
0.070	1.465	−0.080	−0.526	−1.090	−1.002	0.132	1.504	0.050	−0.393
0.115	−0.601	1.751	1.956	−0.196	0.400	−0.522	0.571	−0.101	−2.160
0.252	−0.329	−0.586	−0.118	−0.242	−0.521	0.818	−0.167	−0.469	0.430
0.017	0.185	0.377	1.883	−0.443	−0.039	−1.244	−0.820	−1.171	0.104

Table A-2. Random Normal Numbers, $\mu = 0$, $\sigma = 1$ (*Continued*)

71	72	73	74	75	76	77	78	79	80
2.988	0.423	−1.261	−1.893	0.187	−0.412	−0.228	0.002	−0.384	−1.032
0.760	0.995	−0.256	−0.505	0.750	−0.654	0.647	0.613	0.086	−0.118
−0.650	−0.927	−1.071	−0.796	1.130	−1.042	−0.181	−1.020	1.648	−1.327
−0.394	−0.452	0.893	1.410	1.133	0.319	0.537	−0.789	0.078	−0.062
−1.168	1.902	0.206	0.303	1.413	2.012	0.278	−0.566	−0.900	0.200
1.343	−0.377	−0.131	−0.585	0.053	0.137	−1.371	−0.175	−0.878	0.118
−0.733	−1.921	0.471	−1.394	−0.885	−0.523	0.553	0.344	−0.775	1.545
−0.172	−0.575	0.066	−0.310	1.795	−1.148	0.772	−1.063	0.818	0.302
1.457	0.862	1.677	−0.507	−1.691	−0.034	0.270	0.075	−0.554	1.420
−0.087	0.744	1.829	1.203	−0.436	−0.618	−0.200	−1.134	−1.352	−0.098
−0.092	1.043	−0.255	0.189	0.270	−1.034	−0.571	−0.336	−0.742	2.141
0.441	−0.379	−1.757	0.608	0.527	−0.338	−1.995	0.573	−0.034	−0.056
0.073	−0.250	0.531	−0.695	1.402	−0.462	−0.938	1.130	1.453	−0.106
0.637	0.276	−0.013	1.968	−0.205	0.486	0.727	1.416	0.963	1.349
−0.792	−1.778	1.284	−0.452	0.602	0.668	0.516	−0.210	0.040	−0.103
−1.223	1.561	−2.099	1.419	0.223	−0.482	1.098	0.513	0.418	−1.686
−0.407	1.587	0.335	−2.475	−0.284	1.567	−0.248	−0.759	1.792	−2.319
−0.462	−0.193	−0.012	−1.208	2.151	1.336	−1.968	−1.767	−0.374	0.783
1.457	0.883	1.001	−0.169	0.836	−1.236	1.632	−0.142	−0.222	0.340
−1.918	−1.246	−0.209	0.780	−0.330	−2.953	−0.447	−0.094	1.344	−0.196
−0.126	1.094	−1.206	−1.426	1.474	−1.080	0.000	0.764	1.476	−0.016
−0.306	−0.847	0.639	−0.262	−0.427	0.391	−1.298	−1.013	2.024	−0.539
0.477	1.595	−0.762	0.424	0.799	0.312	1.151	−1.095	1.199	−0.765
0.369	−0.709	1.283	−0.007	−1.440	−0.782	0.061	1.427	1.656	0.974
−0.579	0.606	−0.866	−0.715	−0.301	−0.180	0.188	0.668	−1.091	1.476
−0.418	−0.588	0.919	−0.083	1.084	0.944	0.253	−1.833	1.305	0.171
0.128	−0.834	0.009	0.742	0.539	−0.948	−1.055	−0.689	−0.338	1.091
−0.291	0.235	−0.971	−1.696	1.119	0.272	0.635	−0.792	−1.355	1.291
−1.024	1.212	−1.100	−0.348	1.741	0.035	1.268	0.192	0.729	−0.467
−0.378	1.026	0.093	0.468	−0.967	0.675	0.807	−2.109	−1.214	0.559
1.232	−0.815	0.608	1.429	−0.748	0.201	0.400	−1.230	−0.398	−0.674
1.793	−0.581	−1.076	0.512	−0.442	−1.488	−0.580	0.172	−0.891	0.311
0.766	0.310	−0.070	0.624	−0.389	1.035	−0.101	−0.926	0.816	−1.048
−0.606	−1.224	1.465	0.012	1.061	0.491	−1.023	1.948	0.866	−0.737
0.106	−2.715	0.363	0.343	−0.159	2.672	1.119	0.731	−1.012	−0.889
−0.060	0.444	1.596	−0.630	0.362	−0.306	1.163	−0.974	0.486	−0.373
2.081	1.161	−1.167	0.021	0.053	−0.094	0.381	−0.628	−2.581	−1.243
−1.727	−1.266	0.088	0.936	0.368	0.648	−0.799	1.115	−0.968	−2.588
0.091	1.364	1.677	0.644	1.505	0.440	−0.329	0.498	0.869	−0.965
−1.114	−0.239	−0.409	−0.334	−0.605	0.501	−1.921	−0.470	2.354	−0.660
0.189	−0.547	−1.758	−0.295	−0.279	−0.515	−1.053	0.553	−0.297	0.496
−0.065	−0.023	−0.267	−0.247	1.318	0.904	−0.712	−1.152	−0.543	0.176
−1.742	−0.599	0.430	−0.615	1.165	0.084	2.017	−1.207	2.614	1.490
0.732	0.188	2.343	0.526	−0.812	0.389	1.036	−0.023	0.229	−2.262
−1.490	0.014	0.167	1.422	0.015	0.069	0.133	0.897	−1.678	0.323
1.507	−0.571	−0.724	1.741	−0.152	−0.147	−0.158	−0.076	0.652	0.447
0.513	0.168	−0.076	−0.171	0.428	0.205	−0.865	0.107	1.023	0.077
−0.834	−1.121	1.441	0.492	0.559	1.724	−1.659	0.245	1.354	−0.041
0.258	1.880	−0.536	1.246	−0.188	−0.746	1.097	0.258	1.547	1.238
−0.818	0.273	0.159	−0.765	0.526	1.281	1.154	−0.687	−0.793	0.795

TABLE A-2. RANDOM NORMAL NUMBERS, $\mu = 0$, $\sigma = 1$ (*Continued*)

81	82	83	84	85	86	87	88	89	90
−0.713	−0.541	−0.571	−0.807	−1.560	1.000	0.140	−0.549	0.887	2.237
−0.117	0.530	−1.599	−1.602	0.412	−1.450	−1.217	1.074	−1.021	−0.424
1.187	−1.523	1.437	0.051	1.237	−0.798	1.616	−0.823	−1.207	1.258
−0.182	−0.186	0.517	1.438	0.831	−1.319	−0.539	−0.192	0.150	2.127
1.964	−0.629	−0.944	−0.028	0.948	1.005	0.242	−0.432	−0.329	0.113
0.230	1.523	1.658	0.753	0.724	0.183	−0.147	0.505	0.448	−0.053
0.839	−0.849	−0.145	−1.843	−1.276	0.481	−0.142	−0.534	0.403	0.370
−0.801	0.343	−1.822	0.447	−0.931	−0.824	−0.484	0.864	−1.069	0.860
−0.124	0.727	1.654	−0.182	−1.381	−1.146	−0.572	0.159	0.186	1.221
−0.088	0.032	−0.564	0.654	1.141	−0.056	−0.343	0.067	−0.267	−0.219
0.912	−1.114	−1.035	−1.070	−0.297	1.195	0.030	0.022	0.406	−0.414
1.397	−0.473	0.433	0.023	−1.204	1.254	0.551	−1.012	−0.789	0.906
−0.652	−0.029	0.064	0.511	1.117	−0.465	0.523	−0.083	0.386	0.259
1.236	−0.457	−1.354	−0.898	−0.270	−1.837	1.641	−0.657	−0.753	−1.686
−0.498	1.302	0.816	−0.936	1.404	0.555	2.450	−0.789	−0.120	0.505
−0.005	2.174	1.893	−1.361	−0.991	0.508	−0.823	0.918	0.524	0.488
0.115	−1.373	−0.900	−1.010	0.624	0.946	0.312	−1.384	0.224	2.343
0.167	0.254	1.219	1.153	−0.510	−0.007	−0.285	−0.631	−0.356	0.254
0.976	1.158	−0.469	1.099	0.509	−1.324	−0.102	−0.296	−0.907	0.449
0.653	−0.366	0.450	−2.653	−0.592	−0.510	0.983	0.023	−0.881	0.876
−0.150	−0.088	0.457	−0.448	0.605	0.668	−0.613	0.261	0.023	−0.050
0.060	0.276	0.229	−1.527	−0.316	−0.834	−1.652	−0.387	0.632	0.895
−0.678	0.547	0.243	−2.183	−0.368	1.158	−0.996	−0.705	−0.314	1.464
2.139	0.395	−0.376	−0.175	0.406	0.309	−1.021	−0.460	−0.217	0.307
0.091	1.793	0.822	0.054	0.573	−0.729	−0.517	0.589	1.927	0.940
−0.003	0.344	1.242	−1.105	0.234	−1.222	−0.474	1.831	0.124	−0.840
−0.965	0.268	−1.543	0.690	0.917	2.017	−0.297	1.087	0.371	1.495
−0.076	−0.495	−0.103	0.646	2.427	−2.172	0.660	−1.541	−0.852	0.583
−0.365	−3.305	0.805	−0.418	−1.201	0.623	−0.223	0.109	0.205	−0.663
0.578	0.145	−1.438	1.122	−1.406	1.172	0.272	−2.245	1.207	1.227
−0.398	−0.304	0.529	−0.514	−0.681	−0.366	0.338	0.801	−0.301	−0.790
−0.951	−1.483	−0.613	−0.171	−0.459	1.231	−1.232	−0.497	−0.779	0.247
1.025	−0.039	−0.721	0.813	1.203	0.245	0.402	1.541	0.691	−1.420
−0.958	0.791	0.948	0.222	−0.704	−0.375	−0.246	−0.682	−0.871	0.056
1.097	−1.428	1.402	−1.425	−0.877	0.536	0.988	2.529	0.768	−1.321
0.377	2.240	0.854	−1.158	0.066	−1.222	0.821	−1.602	−0.760	−0.871
1.729	0.073	1.022	0.891	0.659	−1.040	0.251	−0.710	−1.734	−0.038
−1.329	−0.381	−0.515	1.484	−0.430	−0.466	−0.167	−0.788	−0.660	0.003
−0.132	0.391	2.205	−1.165	0.200	0.415	−0.765	0.239	−1.182	1.135
0.336	0.657	−0.805	0.150	−0.938	1.057	−1.090	1.604	−0.598	−0.760
0.124	−1.812	1.750	0.270	−0.114	0.517	−0.226	0.127	0.129	−0.751
−0.036	0.365	0.766	0.877	−0.804	−0.140	0.182	−0.483	−0.376	−0.564
−0.609	−0.019	−0.992	−1.193	−0.516	0.517	1.677	0.839	−1.134	0.675
−0.894	0.318	0.607	−0.865	0.526	−0.971	1.365	0.319	1.804	1.740
−0.357	−0.802	0.635	−0.491	−1.110	0.785	−0.042	−1.042	−0.572	0.243
−0.258	−0.383	−1.013	0.001	−1.673	0.561	−1.054	−0.106	−0.760	−1.009
2.245	−0.431	−0.496	0.796	0.193	1.202	−0.429	−0.217	0.333	−0.643
1.956	0.477	0.812	−0.117	0.606	−0.330	0.425	−0.232	0.802	0.656
1.358	0.139	0.199	−0.475	−0.120	0.184	−0.020	−1.326	0.517	−1.708
0.656	1.081	0.180	0.145	0.376	−1.363	−0.491	0.352	−1.477	1.280

TABLE A-2. RANDOM NORMAL NUMBERS, $\mu = 0$, $\sigma = 1$ (*Continued*)

91	92	93	94	95	96	97	98	99	100
−0.181	0.583	−1.478	−0.181	0.281	−0.559	1.985	−1.122	−1.106	1.441
1.549	−1.183	−2.089	−1.997	−0.343	1.275	0.676	−0.212	1.252	0.163
0.978	−1.067	−2.640	0.134	0.328	−0.052	−0.030	−0.273	−0.570	1.026
−0.596	−0.420	−0.318	−0.057	−0.695	−1.148	0.333	−0.531	−2.037	−1.587
−0.440	0.032	0.163	1.029	0.079	1.148	0.762	−1.961	−0.674	−0.486
0.443	−1.100	0.728	−2.397	−0.543	0.872	−0.568	0.980	−0.174	0.728
−2.401	−1.375	−1.332	−2.177	−2.064	−0.245	−0.039	0.585	1.344	1.386
0.311	0.322	−0.158	0.359	0.103	0.371	0.735	0.011	2.091	0.490
−1.209	0.241	−1.488	−0.667	−1.772	−0.197	0.741	−1.303	−1.149	2.251
0.575	−1.227	−1.674	1.400	0.289	0.005	0.185	−1.072	0.431	−1.096
−0.190	0.272	1.216	0.227	1.358	0.215	−2.306	−1.301	−0.597	−1.401
−0.817	−0.769	−0.470	−0.633	0.187	−0.517	−0.888	−1.712	1.774	−0.162
0.265	−0.676	0.244	1.897	−0.629	−0.206	−1.419	1.049	0.266	−0.438
−0.221	0.678	2.149	1.486	−1.361	1.402	−0.028	0.493	0.744	0.195
−0.436	0.358	−0.602	0.107	0.085	0.573	0.529	1.577	0.239	1.898
−0.010	0.475	0.655	0.659	−0.029	−0.029	0.126	−1.335	−1.261	2.036
−0.244	1.654	1.335	−0.610	0.617	0.642	0.371	0.241	0.001	−1.799
−0.932	−1.275	−1.134	−1.246	−1.508	0.949	1.743	−0.271	−1.333	−1.875
−0.199	−1.285	−0.387	0.191	0.726	−0.151	0.064	−0.803	−0.062	0.780
−0.251	−0.431	−0.831	0.036	−0.464	−1.089	0.284	−0.451	1.693	1.004
1.074	−1.323	−1.659	−0.186	−0.612	1.612	−2.159	−1.210	0.596	−1.421
1.518	2.101	0.397	0.516	−1.169	−1.821	1.346	2.435	1.165	−0.428
0.935	−0.206	1.117	−0.241	−0.963	−0.099	0.412	−1.344	0.411	0.583
1.360	−0.380	0.031	1.066	0.893	0.431	−0.081	0.099	0.500	−2.441
0.115	−0.211	1.471	0.332	0.750	0.652	−0.812	1.383	−0.355	−0.638
0.082	−0.309	−0.355	−0.402	0.774	0.150	0.015	2.539	−0.756	−1.049
−1.492	0.259	0.323	0.697	−0.509	0.968	−0.053	1.033	−0.220	−2.322
−0.203	0.548	1.494	1.185	0.083	−1.196	−0.749	−1.105	1.324	0.689
1.857	−0.167	−1.531	1.551	0.848	0.120	0.415	−0.317	1.446	1.002
0.669	−1.017	−2.437	−0.558	−0.657	0.940	0.985	0.483	−0.361	0.095
0.128	1.463	−0.436	−0.239	−1.443	0.732	0.168	−0.144	−0.392	0.989
1.879	−2.456	0.029	0.429	0.618	−1.683	−2.262	0.034	−0.002	1.914
0.680	0.252	0.130	1.658	−1.023	0.407	−0.235	−0.224	−0.434	0.253
−0.631	0.225	−0.951	1.072	−0.285	−1.731	−0.427	−1.446	−0.873	0.619
−1.273	0.723	0.201	0.505	−0.370	−0.421	−0.015	−0.463	0.288	1.734
−0.643	−1.485	0.403	0.003	−0.243	0.000	0.964	−0.703	0.844	−0.686
−0.435	−2.162	−0.169	−1.311	−1.639	0.193	2.692	−1.994	0.326	0.562
−1.706	0.119	−1.566	0.637	−1.948	−1.068	0.935	0.738	0.650	0.491
−0.498	1.640	0.384	−0.945	−1.272	0.945	−1.013	−0.913	−0.469	2.250
−0.065	−0.005	0.618	−0.523	−0.055	1.071	0.758	−0.736	−0.959	0.598
0.190	−1.020	−1.104	0.936	−0.029	−1.004	−0.657	1.270	−0.060	−0.809
0.879	−0.642	1.155	−0.523	−0.757	−1.027	0.985	−1.222	1.078	0.163
0.559	1.094	1.587	−0.384	−1.701	0.418	0.327	0.669	0.019	0.782
−0.261	1.234	−0.505	−0.664	−0.446	−0.747	0.427	−0.369	0.089	−1.302
3.136	1.120	−0.591	2.515	−2.853	1.375	2.421	0.672	1.817	−0.067
−1.307	−0.586	−0.311	−0.026	1.633	−1.340	−1.209	0.110	−0.126	−0.288
1.455	1.099	−1.225	−0.817	0.667	−0.212	0.684	0.349	−1.161	−2.432
−0.443	−0.415	−0.660	0.098	0.435	−0.846	−0.375	−0.410	−1.747	−0.790
−0.326	0.798	0.349	0.524	0.690	−0.520	−0.522	0.602	−0.193	−0.535
−1.027	−1.459	−0.840	−1.637	−0.462	0.607	−0.760	1.342	−1.916	0.424

TABLE A-3. NORMAL DISTRIBUTION

Ordinates Y at $\pm z$, and areas A between $-z$ and $+z$, of the normal distribution.

z	X	Y	A	$1 - A$	z	X	Y	A	$1 - A$
0	μ	.399	.0000	1.0000	±1.50	$\mu \pm 1.50\sigma$	.1295	.8664	.1336
± .05	$\mu \pm .05\sigma$	.398	.0399	.9601	±1.55	$\mu \pm 1.55\sigma$	.1200	.8789	.1211
± .10	$\mu \pm .10\sigma$	.397	.0797	.9203	±1.60	$\mu \pm 1.60\sigma$	.1109	.8904	.1096
± .15	$\mu \pm .15\sigma$	.394	.1192	.8808	±1.65	$\mu \pm 1.65\sigma$	.1023	.9011	.0989
± .20	$\mu \pm .20\sigma$	.391	.1585	.8415	±1.70	$\mu \pm 1.70\sigma$	.0940	.9109	.0891
± .25	$\mu \pm .25\sigma$	.387	.1974	.8026	±1.75	$\mu \pm 1.75\sigma$	.0863	.9199	.0801
± .30	$\mu \pm .30\sigma$	.381	.2358	.7642	±1.80	$\mu \pm 1.80\sigma$	.0790	.9281	.0719
± .35	$\mu \pm .35\sigma$	.375	.2737	.7263	±1.85	$\mu \pm 1.85\sigma$	.0721	.9357	.0643
± .40	$\mu \pm .40\sigma$	.368	.3108	.6892	±1.90	$\mu \pm 1.90\sigma$	.0656	.9426	.0574
± .45	$\mu \pm .45\sigma$	.361	.3473	.6527	±1.95	$\mu \pm 1.95\sigma$	.0596	.9488	.0512
± .50	$\mu \pm .50\sigma$	.352	.3829	.6171	±2.00	$\mu \pm 2.00\sigma$	.0540	.9545	.0455
± .55	$\mu \pm .55\sigma$	.343	.4177	.5823	±2.05	$\mu \pm 2.05\sigma$	.0488	.9596	.0404
± .60	$\mu \pm .60\sigma$	.333	.4515	.5485	±2.10	$\mu \pm 2.10\sigma$	.0440	.9643	.0357
± .65	$\mu \pm .65\sigma$	.323	.4843	.5157	±2.15	$\mu \pm 2.15\sigma$	.0396	.9684	.0316
± .70	$\mu \pm .70\sigma$	.312	.5161	.4839	±2.20	$\mu \pm 2.20\sigma$	.0355	.9722	.0278
± .75	$\mu \pm .75\sigma$	.301	.5467	.4533	±2.25	$\mu \pm 2.25\sigma$	.0317	.9756	.0244
± .80	$\mu \pm .80\sigma$	.290	.5763	.4237	±2.30	$\mu \pm 2.30\sigma$	.0283	.9786	.0214
± .85	$\mu \pm .85\sigma$	.278	.6047	.3953	±2.35	$\mu + 2.35\sigma$	.0252	.9812	.0188
± .90	$\mu \pm .90\sigma$	.266	.6319	.3681	±2.40	$\mu \pm 2.40\sigma$	.0224	.9836	.0164
± .95	$\mu \pm .95\sigma$	.254	.6579	.3421	±2.45	$\mu \pm 2.45\sigma$	.0198	.9857	.0143
±1.00	$\mu \pm 1.00\sigma$	.242	.6827	.3173	±2.50	$\mu \pm 2.50\sigma$	.0175	.9876	.0124
±1.05	$\mu \pm 1.05\sigma$	.230	.7063	.2937	±2.55	$\mu \pm 2.55\sigma$	.0154	.9892	.0108
±1.10	$\mu \pm 1.10\sigma$	.218	.7287	.2713	±2.60	$\mu \pm 2.60\sigma$	.0136	.9907	.0093
±1.15	$\mu \pm 1.15\sigma$	.206	.7499	.2501	±2.65	$\mu \pm 2.65\sigma$	.0119	.9920	.0080
±1.20	$\mu \pm 1.20\sigma$	.194	.7699	.2301	±2.70	$\mu \pm 2.70\sigma$	.0104	.9931	.0069
±1.25	$\mu \pm 1.25\sigma$	.183	.7887	.2113	±2.75	$\mu \pm 2.75\sigma$	.0091	.9940	.0060
±1.30	$\mu \pm 1.30\sigma$	.171	.8064	.1936	±2.80	$\mu \pm 2.80\sigma$	.0079	.9949	.0051
±1.35	$\mu \pm 1.35\sigma$	.160	.8230	.1770	±2.85	$\mu \pm 2.85\sigma$	.0069	.9956	.0044
±1.40	$\mu \pm 1.40\sigma$	.150	.8385	.1615	±2.90	$\mu \pm 2.90\sigma$	.0060	.9963	.0037
±1.45	$\mu \pm 1.45\sigma$	.139	.8529	.1471	±2.95	$\mu \pm 2.95\sigma$	.0051	.9968	.0032
±1.50	$\mu \pm 1.50\sigma$	.130	.8664	.1336	±3.00	$\mu \pm 3.00\sigma$	.0044	.9973	.0027
					±4.00	$\mu \pm 4.00\sigma$	.0001	.99994	.00006
					±5.00	$\mu \pm 5.00\sigma$	.000001	.9999994	.0000006
± .000	μ	.3989	.0000	1.0000	±1.036	$\mu \pm 1.036\sigma$	.2331	.7000	.3000
± .126	$\mu \pm .126\sigma$	.3958	.1000	.9000	±1.282	$\mu \pm 1.282\sigma$	.1755	.8000	.2000
± .253	$\mu \pm .253\sigma$	.3863	.2000	.8000	±1.645	$\mu \pm 1.645\sigma$	.1031	.9000	.1000
± .385	$\mu \pm .385\sigma$	.3704	.3000	.7000	±1.960	$\mu \pm 1.960\sigma$	.0584	.9500	.0500
± .524	$\mu \pm .524\sigma$	.3477	.4000	.6000	±2.576	$\mu \pm 2.576\sigma$	.0145	.9900	.0100
± .674	$\mu \pm .674\sigma$	.3178	.5000	.5000	±3.291	$\mu \pm 3.291\sigma$	.0018	.9990	.0010
± .842	$\mu \pm .842\sigma$	.2800	.6000	.4000	±3.891	$\mu \pm 3.891\sigma$	.0002	.9999	.0001

TABLE A-4. CUMULATIVE NORMAL DISTRIBUTION

z	X	Area	z	X	Area
−3.25	$\mu - 3.25\sigma$	.0006	−1.00	$\mu - 1.00\sigma$	.1587
−3.20	$\mu - 3.20\sigma$	.0007	− .95	$\mu - .95\sigma$	.1711
−3.15	$\mu - 3.15\sigma$	.0008	− .90	$\mu - .90\sigma$	.1841
−3.10	$\mu - 3.10\sigma$	.0010	− .85	$\mu - .85\sigma$	.1977
−3.05	$\mu - 3.05\sigma$	.0011	− .80	$\mu - .80\sigma$	.2119
−3.00	$\mu - 3.00\sigma$	.0013	− .75	$\mu - .75\sigma$	.2266
−2.95	$\mu - 2.95\sigma$	.0016	− .70	$\mu - .70\sigma$	.2420
−2.90	$\mu - 2.90\sigma$	.0019	− .65	$\mu - .65\sigma$	.2578
−2.85	$\mu - 2.85\sigma$	.0022	− .60	$\mu - .60\sigma$	.2743
−2.80	$\mu - 2.80\sigma$	.0026	− .55	$\mu - .55\sigma$	.2912
−2.75	$\mu - 2.75\sigma$	.0030	− .50	$\mu - .50\sigma$	.3085
−2.70	$\mu - 2.70\sigma$	.0035	− .45	$\mu - .45\sigma$	.3264
−2.65	$\mu - 2.65\sigma$	.0040	− .40	$\mu - .40\sigma$	.3446
−2.60	$\mu - 2.60\sigma$	.0047	− .35	$\mu - .35\sigma$	.3632
−2.55	$\mu - 2.55\sigma$	.0054	− .30	$\mu - .30\sigma$	.3821
−2.50	$\mu - 2.50\sigma$	.0062	− .25	$\mu - .25\sigma$	.4013
−2.45	$\mu - 2.45\sigma$	.0071	− .20	$\mu - .20\sigma$	.4207
−2.40	$\mu - 2.40\sigma$	.0082	− .15	$\mu - .15\sigma$	.4404
−2.35	$\mu - 2.35\sigma$	.0094	− .10	$\mu - .10\sigma$	.4602
−2.30	$\mu - 2.30\sigma$	.0107	− .05	$\mu - .05\sigma$	.4801
−2.25	$\mu - 2.25\sigma$	.0122			
−2.20	$\mu - 2.20\sigma$	.0139			
−2.15	$\mu - 2.15\sigma$	.0158	.00	μ	.5000
−2.10	$\mu - 2.10\sigma$	.0179			
−2.05	$\mu - 2.05\sigma$	.0202			
−2.00	$\mu - 2.00\sigma$	.0228	.05	$\mu + .05\sigma$	.5199
−1.95	$\mu - 1.95\sigma$	.0256	.10	$\mu + .10\sigma$	.5398
−1.90	$\mu - 1.90\sigma$	.0287	.15	$\mu + .15\sigma$	.5596
−1.85	$\mu - 1.85\sigma$	.0322	.20	$\mu + .20\sigma$	.5793
−1.80	$\mu - 1.80\sigma$	.0359	.25	$\mu + .25\sigma$	.5987
−1.75	$\mu - 1.75\sigma$	.0401	.30	$\mu + .30\sigma$	.6179
−1.70	$\mu - 1.70\sigma$	.0446	.35	$\mu + .35\sigma$	.6368
−1.65	$\mu - 1.65\sigma$	.0495	.40	$\mu + .40\sigma$	.6554
−1.60	$\mu - 1.60\sigma$	.0548	.45	$\mu + .45\sigma$	.6736
−1.55	$\mu - 1.55\sigma$	.0606	.50	$\mu + .50\sigma$	.6915
−1.50	$\mu - 1.50\sigma$	.0668	.55	$\mu + .55\sigma$	.7088
−1.45	$\mu - 1.45\sigma$	.0735	.60	$\mu + .60\sigma$	.7257
−1.40	$\mu - 1.40\sigma$	.0808	.65	$\mu + .65\sigma$	.7422
−1.35	$\mu - 1.35\sigma$	.0885	.70	$\mu + .70\sigma$	.7580
−1.30	$\mu - 1.30\sigma$	.0968	.75	$\mu + .75\sigma$	.7734
−1.25	$\mu - 1.25\sigma$	.1056	.80	$\mu + .80\sigma$	.7881
−1.20	$\mu - 1.20\sigma$	.1151	.85	$\mu + .85\sigma$	.8023
−1.15	$\mu - 1.15\sigma$	.1251	.90	$\mu + .90\sigma$	.8159
−1.10	$\mu - 1.10\sigma$	.1357	.95	$\mu + .95\sigma$	.8289
−1.05	$\mu - 1.05\sigma$	.1469	1.00	$\mu + 1.00\sigma$	.8413

TABLE A-4. CUMULATIVE NORMAL DISTRIBUTION (*Continued*)

z	X	Area	z	X	Area
1.05	$\mu + 1.05\sigma$	.8531	−4.265	$\mu - 4.265\sigma$	.00001
1.10	$\mu + 1.10\sigma$	.8643	−3.719	$\mu - 3.719\sigma$	.0001
1.15	$\mu + 1.15\sigma$	.8749	−3.090	$\mu - 3.090\sigma$	.001
1.20	$\mu + 1.20\sigma$	.8849	−2.576	$\mu - 2.576\sigma$	.005
1.25	$\mu + 1.25\sigma$	.8944	−2.326	$\mu - 2.326\sigma$	.01
1.30	$\mu + 1.30\sigma$	.9032	−2.054	$\mu - 2.054\sigma$	.02
1.35	$\mu + 1.35\sigma$	.9115	−1.960	$\mu - 1.960\sigma$	.025
1.40	$\mu + 1.40\sigma$	.9192	−1.881	$\mu - 1.881\sigma$	.03
1.45	$\mu + 1.45\sigma$	.9265	−1.751	$\mu - 1.751\sigma$	.04
1.50	$\mu + 1.50\sigma$	.9332	−1.645	$\mu - 1.645\sigma$	.05
1.55	$\mu + 1.55\sigma$	.9394	−1.555	$\mu - 1.555\sigma$	.06
1.60	$\mu + 1.60\sigma$	.9452	−1.476	$\mu - 1.476\sigma$	.07
1.65	$\mu + 1.65\sigma$	.9505	−1.405	$\mu - 1.405\sigma$	.08
1.70	$\mu + 1.70\sigma$	.9554	−1.341	$\mu - 1.341\sigma$	.09
1.75	$\mu + 1.75\sigma$	.9599	−1.282	$\mu - 1.282\sigma$	.10
1.80	$\mu + 1.80\sigma$	.9641	−1.036	$\mu - 1.036\sigma$	.15
1.85	$\mu + 1.85\sigma$	.9678	− .842	$\mu - .842\sigma$	.20
1.90	$\mu + 1.90\sigma$	.9713	− .674	$\mu - .674\sigma$	.25
1.95	$\mu + 1.95\sigma$	.9744	− .524	$\mu - .524\sigma$	.30
2.00	$\mu + 2.00\sigma$	.9772	− .385	$\mu - .385\sigma$	.35
2.05	$\mu + 2.05\sigma$	.9798	− .253	$\mu - .253\sigma$	.40
2.10	$\mu + 2.10\sigma$	.9821	− .126	$\mu - .126\sigma$	.45
2.15	$\mu + 2.15\sigma$	.9842	0	μ	.50
2.20	$\mu + 2.20\sigma$	.9861	.126	$\mu + .126\sigma$	.55
2.25	$\mu + 2.25\sigma$	.9878	.253	$\mu + .253\sigma$	.60
2.30	$\mu + 2.30\sigma$	.9893	.385	$\mu + .385\sigma$	.65
2.35	$\mu + 2.35\sigma$	.9906	.524	$\mu + .524\sigma$	.70
2.40	$\mu + 2.40\sigma$	.9918	.674	$\mu + .674\sigma$	.75
2.45	$\mu + 2.45\sigma$	.9929	.842	$\mu + .842\sigma$	.80
2.50	$\mu + 2.50\sigma$	.9938	1.036	$\mu + 1.036\sigma$	.85
2.55	$\mu + 2.55\sigma$	.9946	1.282	$\mu + 1.282\sigma$	.90
2.60	$\mu + 2.60\sigma$	.9953	1.341	$\mu + 1.341\sigma$	.91
2.65	$\mu + 2.65\sigma$	.9960	1.405	$\mu + 1.405\sigma$	.92
2.70	$\mu + 2.70\sigma$	.9965	1.476	$\mu + 1.476\sigma$	.93
2.75	$\mu + 2.75\sigma$	.9970	1.555	$\mu + 1.555\sigma$	.94
2.80	$\mu + 2.80\sigma$	.9974	1.645	$\mu + 1.645\sigma$	.95
2.85	$\mu + 2.85\sigma$	.9978	1.751	$\mu + 1.751\sigma$	.96
2.90	$\mu + 2.90\sigma$	.9981	1.881	$\mu + 1.881\sigma$	.97
2.95	$\mu + 2.95\sigma$	.9984	1.960	$\mu + 1.960\sigma$	.975
3.00	$\mu + 3.00\sigma$	.9987	2.054	$\mu + 2.054\sigma$	.98
3.05	$\mu + 3.05\sigma$	.9989	2.326	$\mu + 2.326\sigma$	.99
3.10	$\mu + 3.10\sigma$	.9990	2.576	$\mu + 2.576\sigma$	.995
3.15	$\mu + 3.15\sigma$	.9992	3.090	$\mu + 3.090\sigma$	.999
3.20	$\mu + 3.20\sigma$	.9993	3.719	$\mu + 3.719\sigma$	.9999
3.25	$\mu + 3.25\sigma$	.9994	4.265	$\mu + 4.265\sigma$	.99999

TABLE A-5. PERCENTILES OF THE t DISTRIBUTION*

df	$t_{.60}$	$t_{.70}$	$t_{.80}$	$t_{.90}$	$t_{.95}$	$t_{.975}$	$t_{.99}$	$t_{.995}$
1	.325	.727	1.376	3.078	6.314	12.706	31.821	63.657
2	.289	.617	1.061	1.886	2.920	4.303	6.965	9.925
3	.277	.584	.978	1.638	2.353	3.182	4.541	5.841
4	.271	.569	.941	1.533	2.132	2.776	3.747	4.604
5	.267	.559	.920	1.476	2.015	2.571	3.365	4.032
6	.265	.553	.906	1.440	1.943	2.447	3.143	3.707
7	.263	.549	.896	1.415	1.895	2.365	2.998	3.499
8	.262	.546	.889	1.397	1.860	2.306	2.896	3.355
9	.261	.543	.883	1.383	1.833	2.262	2.821	3.250
10	.260	.542	.879	1.372	1.812	2.228	2.764	3.169
11	.260	.540	.876	1.363	1.796	2.201	2.718	3.106
12	.259	.539	.873	1.356	1.782	2.179	2.681	3.055
13	.259	.538	.870	1.350	1.771	2.160	2.650	3.012
14	.258	.537	.868	1.345	1.761	2.145	2.624	2.977
15	.258	.536	.866	1.341	1.753	2.131	2.602	2.947
16	.258	.535	.865	1.337	1.746	2.120	2.583	2.921
17	.257	.534	.863	1.333	1.740	2.110	2.567	2.898
18	.257	.534	.862	1.330	1.734	2.101	2.552	2.878
19	.257	.533	.861	1.328	1.729	2.093	2.539	2.861
20	.257	.533	.860	1.325	1.725	2.086	2.528	2.845
21	.257	.532	.859	1.323	1.721	2.080	2.518	2.831
22	.256	.532	.858	1.321	1.717	2.074	2.508	2.819
23	.256	.532	.858	1.319	1.714	2.069	2.500	2.807
24	.256	.531	.857	1.318	1.711	2.064	2.492	2.797
25	.256	.531	.856	1.316	1.708	2.060	2.485	2.787
26	.256	.531	.856	1.315	1.706	2.056	2.479	2.779
27	.256	.531	.855	1.314	1.703	2.052	2.473	2.771
28	.256	.530	.855	1.313	1.701	2.048	2.467	2.763
29	.256	.530	.854	1.311	1.699	2.045	2.462	2.756
30	.256	.530	.854	1.310	1.697	2.042	2.457	2.750
40	.255	.529	.851	1.303	1.684	2.021	2.423	2.704
60	.254	.527	.848	1.296	1.671	2.000	2.390	2.660
120	.254	.526	.845	1.289	1.658	1.980	2.358	2.617
∞	.253	.524	.842	1.282	1.645	1.960	2.326	2.576
df	$-t_{.40}$	$-t_{.30}$	$-t_{.20}$	$-t_{.10}$	$-t_{.05}$	$-t_{.025}$	$-t_{.01}$	$-t_{.005}$

When the table is read from the foot, the tabled values are to be prefixed with a negative sign. Interpolation should be performed using the reciprocals of the degrees of freedom.

* The data of this table extracted from Table III of Fisher and Yates, *Statistical Tables,* with the permission of the authors and publishers, Oliver & Boyd, Ltd., Edinburgh and London.

TABLE A-6a. PERCENTILES OF THE χ^2 DISTRIBUTION

df	Per Cent									
	.5	1	2.5	5	10	90	95	97.5	99	99.5
1	.000039	.00016	.00098	.0039	.0158	2.71	3.84	5.02	6.63	7.88
2	.0100	.0201	.0506	.1026	.2107	4.61	5.99	7.38	9.21	10.60
3	.0717	.115	.216	.352	.584	6.25	7.81	9.35	11.34	12.84
4	.207	.297	.484	.711	1.064	7.78	9.49	11.14	13.28	14.86
5	.412	.554	.831	1.15	1.61	9.24	11.07	12.83	15.09	16.75
6	.676	.872	1.24	1.64	2.20	10.64	12.59	14.45	16.81	18.55
7	.989	1.24	1.69	2.17	2.83	12.02	14.07	16.01	18.48	20.28
8	1.34	1.65	2.18	2.73	3.49	13.36	15.51	17.53	20.09	21.96
9	1.73	2.09	2.70	3.33	4.17	14.68	16.92	19.02	21.67	23.59
10	2.16	2.56	3.25	3.94	4.87	15.99	18.31	20.48	23.21	25.19
11	2.60	3.05	3.82	4.57	5.58	17.28	19.68	21.92	24.73	26.76
12	3.07	3.57	4.40	5.23	6.30	18.55	21.03	23.34	26.22	28.30
13	3.57	4.11	5.01	5.89	7.04	19.81	22.36	24.74	27.69	29.82
14	4.07	4.66	5.63	6.57	7.79	21.06	23.68	26.12	29.14	31.32
15	4.60	5.23	6.26	7.26	8.55	22.31	25.00	27.49	30.58	32.80
16	5.14	5.81	6.91	7.96	9.31	23.54	26.30	28.85	32.00	34.27
18	6.26	7.01	8.23	9.39	10.86	25.99	28.87	31.53	34.81	37.16
20	7.43	8.26	9.59	10.85	12.44	28.41	31.41	34.17	37.57	40.00
24	9.89	10.86	12.40	13.85	15.66	33.20	36.42	39.36	42.98	45.56
30	13.79	14.95	16.79	18.49	20.60	40.26	43.77	46.98	50.89	53.67
40	20.71	22.16	24.43	26.51	29.05	51.81	55.76	59.34	63.69	66.77
60	35.53	37.48	40.48	43.19	46.46	74.40	79.08	83.30	88.38	91.95
120	83.85	86.92	91.58	95.70	100.62	140.23	146.57	152.21	158.95	163.64

For large values of degrees of freedom the approximate formula

$$\chi_\alpha^2 = n\left(1 - \frac{2}{9n} + z_\alpha\sqrt{\frac{2}{9n}}\right)^3$$

where z_α is the normal deviate and n is the number of degrees of freedom, may be used. For example $\chi_{.99}^2 = 60[1 - .00370 + 2.326(.06086)]^3 = 60(1.1379)^3 = 88.4$ for the 99th percentile for 60 degrees of freedom.

TABLE A-6*b*. PERCENTILES OF THE χ^2/df DISTRIBUTIONS

df	.05	.1	.5	1.0	2.5	5.0	10	20	30	40	50	60
1	$.0^{6}39$	$.0^{5}157$	$.0^{4}39$	$.0^{3}16$	$.0^{3}98$	$.0^{2}39$	.016	.064	.148	.275	.455	.708
2	.001	.001	.005	.010	.025	.052	.106	.223	.356	.511	.693	.916
3	.005	.008	.024	.038	.072	.117	.195	.335	.475	.623	.789	.982
4	.016	.023	.052	.074	.121	.178	.266	.412	.549	.688	.839	1.011
5	.032	.042	.082	.111	.166	.229	.322	.469	.600	.731	.870	1.03
6	.050	.064	.113	.145	.206	.272	.367	.512	.638	.762	.891	1.04
7	.069	.085	.141	.177	.241	.310	.405	.546	.667	.785	.907	1.04
8	.089	.107	.168	.206	.272	.342	.436	.574	.691	.803	.918	1.04
9	.108	.128	.193	.232	.300	.369	.463	.598	.710	.817	.927	1.05
10	.126	.148	.216	.256	.325	.394	.487	.618	.727	.830	.934	1.05
11	.144	.167	.237	.278	.347	.416	.507	.635	.741	.840	.940	1.05
12	.161	.184	.256	.298	.367	.436	.525	.651	.753	.848	.945	1.05
13	.177	.201	.274	.316	.385	.453	.542	.664	.764	.856	.949	1.05
14	.193	.217	.291	.333	.402	.469	.556	.676	.773	.863	.953	1.05
15	.207	.232	.307	.349	.418	.484	.570	.687	.781	.869	.956	1.05
16	.221	.246	.321	.363	.432	.498	.582	.697	.789	.874	.959	1.05
17	.234	.260	.335	.377	.445	.510	.593	.706	.796	.879	.961	1.05
18	.247	.272	.348	.390	.457	.522	.604	.714	.802	.883	.963	1.05
19	.258	.285	.360	.402	.469	.532	.613	.722	.808	.887	.965	1.05
20	.270	.296	.372	.413	.480	.543	.622	.729	.813	.890	.967	1.05
22	.291	.317	.393	.434	.499	.561	.638	.742	.823	.897	.970	1.05
24	.310	.337	.412	.452	.517	.577	.652	.753	.831	.902	.972	1.05
26	.328	.355	.429	.469	.532	.592	.665	.762	.838	.907	.974	1.05
28	.345	.371	.445	.484	.547	.605	.676	.771	.845	.911	.976	1.04
30	.360	.386	.460	.498	.560	.616	.687	.779	.850	.915	.978	1.04
35	.394	.420	.491	.529	.588	.642	.708	.795	.862	.922	.981	1.04
40	.423	.448	.518	.554	.611	.663	.726	.809	.872	.928	.983	1.04
45	.448	.472	.540	.576	.630	.680	.741	.820	.880	.933	.985	1.04
50	.469	.494	.560	.594	.647	.695	.754	.829	.886	.937	.987	1.04
55	.488	.512	.577	.610	.662	.708	.765	.837	.892	.941	.988	1.04
60	.506	.529	.592	.625	.675	.720	.774	.844	.897	.944	.989	1.04
70	.535	.558	.618	.649	.697	.739	.790	.856	.905	.949	.990	1.03
80	.560	.582	.640	.669	.714	.755	.803	.865	.911	.952	.992	1.03
90	.581	.602	.658	.686	.729	.768	.814	.873	.917	.955	.993	1.03
100	.599	.619	.673	.701	.742	.779	.824	.879	.921	.958	.993	1.03
120	.629	.648	.699	.724	.763	.798	.839	.890	.929	.962	.994	1.03
140	.653	.671	.719	.743	.780	.812	.850	.898	.934	.965	.995	1.03
160	.673	.690	.736	.758	.793	.824	.860	.905	.939	.968	.996	1.02
180	.689	.706	.749	.771	.804	.833	.868	.910	.942	.970	.996	1.02
200	.703	.719	.761	.782	.814	.841	.874	.915	.945	.972	.997	1.02
250	.732	.746	.785	.804	.832	.858	.887	.924	.951	.975	.997	1.02
300	.753	.767	.802	.820	.846	.870	.897	.931	.956	.977	.998	1.02
350	.770	.783	.816	.833	.857	.879	.904	.936	.959	.979	.998	1.02
400	.784	.796	.827	.843	.866	.887	.911	.940	.962	.981	.998	1.02
450	.795	.807	.837	.852	.874	.893	.916	.944	.964	.982	.999	1.02
500	.805	.816	.845	.859	.880	.898	.920	.946	.966	.983	.999	1.01
750	.839	.848	.872	.884	.901	.917	.934	.956	.972	.986	.999	1.01
1000	.859	.868	.889	.899	.914	.928	.943	.962	.976	.988	.999	1.01
5000	.936	.939	.949	.954	.961	.967	.974	.983	.989	.995	1.00	1.00
∞	1	1	1	1	1	1	1	1	1	1	1	1

Read $.0^{3}16$ as .00016, etc.

TABLE A-6*b*. PERCENTILES OF THE χ^2/df DISTRIBUTIONS (*Continued*)

70	80	90	95	97.5	99	99.5	99.9	99.95	df
1.07	1.64	2.71	3.84	5.02	6.64	7.88	10.83	12.12	1
1.20	1.61	2.30	3.00	3.69	4.61	5.30	6.91	7.60	2
1.22	1.55	2.08	2.60	3.12	3.78	4.28	5.42	5.91	3
1.22	1.50	1.94	2.37	2.79	3.32	3.72	4.62	5.00	4
1.21	1.46	1.85	2.21	2.57	3.02	3.35	4.10	4.42	5
1.21	1.43	1.77	2.10	2.41	2.80	3.09	3.74	4.02	6
1.20	1.40	1.72	2.01	2.29	2.64	2.90	3.47	3.72	7
1.19	1.38	1.67	1.94	2.19	2.51	2.74	3.27	3.48	8
1.18	1.36	1.63	1.88	2.11	2.41	2.62	3.10	3.30	9
1.18	1.34	1.60	1.83	2.05	2.32	2.52	2.96	3.14	10
1.17	1.33	1.57	1.79	1.99	2.25	2.43	2.84	3.01	11
1.17	1.32	1.55	1.75	1.94	2.18	2.36	2.74	2.90	12
1.16	1.31	1.52	1.72	1.90	2.13	2.29	2.66	2.81	13
1.16	1.30	1.50	1.69	1.87	2.08	2.24	2.58	2.72	14
1.15	1.29	1.49	1.67	1.83	2.04	2.19	2.51	2.65	15
1.15	1.28	1.47	1.64	1.80	2.00	2.14	2.45	2.58	16
1.15	1.27	1.46	1.62	1.78	1.97	2.10	2.40	2.52	17
1.14	1.26	1.44	1.60	1.75	1.93	2.06	2.35	2.47	18
1.14	1.26	1.43	1.59	1.73	1.90	2.03	2.31	2.42	19
1.14	1.25	1.42	1.57	1.71	1.88	2.00	2.27	2.37	20
1.13	1.24	1.40	1.54	1.67	1.83	1.95	2.19	2.30	22
1.13	1.23	1.38	1.52	1.64	1.79	1.90	2.13	2.23	24
1.12	1.22	1.37	1.50	1.61	1.76	1.86	2.08	2.17	26
1.12	1.22	1.35	1.48	1.59	1.72	1.82	2.03	2.12	28
1.12	1.21	1.34	1.46	1.57	1.70	1.79	1.99	2.07	30
1.11	1.19	1.32	1.42	1.52	1.64	1.72	1.90	1.98	35
1.10	1.18	1.30	1.39	1.48	1.59	1.67	1.84	1.90	40
1.10	1.17	1.28	1.37	1.45	1.55	1.63	1.78	1.84	45
1.09	1.16	1.26	1.35	1.43	1.52	1.59	1.73	1.79	50
1.09	1.16	1.25	1.33	1.41	1.50	1.56	1.69	1.75	55
1.09	1.15	1.24	1.32	1.39	1.47	1.53	1.66	1.71	60
1.08	1.14	1.22	1.29	1.36	1.43	1.49	1.60	1.65	70
1.08	1.13	1.21	1.27	1.33	1.40	1.45	1.56	1.60	80
1.07	1.12	1.20	1.26	1.31	1.38	1.43	1.52	1.56	90
1.07	1.12	1.18	1.24	1.30	1.36	1.40	1.49	1.53	100
1.06	1.11	1.17	1.22	1.27	1.32	1.36	1.45	1.48	120
1.06	1.10	1.16	1.20	1.25	1.30	1.33	1.41	1.44	140
1.06	1.09	1.15	1.19	1.23	1.28	1.31	1.38	1.41	160
1.05	1.09	1.14	1.18	1.22	1.26	1.29	1.36	1.38	180
1.05	1.08	1.13	1.17	1.21	1.25	1.28	1.34	1.36	200
1.04	1.07	1.12	1.15	1.18	1.22	1.25	1.30	1.32	250
1.04	1.07	1.11	1.14	1.17	1.20	1.22	1.27	1.29	300
1.04	1.06	1.10	1.13	1.15	1.18	1.21	1.25	1.27	350
1.04	1.06	1.09	1.12	1.14	1.17	1.19	1.24	1.25	400
1.03	1.06	1.09	1.11	1.13	1.16	1.18	1.22	1.23	450
1.03	1.05	1.08	1.11	1.13	1.15	1.17	1.21	1.22	500
1.03	1.04	1.07	1.09	1.10	1.12	1.14	1.17	1.18	750
1.02	1.04	1.06	1.07	1.09	1.11	1.12	1.14	1.15	1000
1.01	1.02	1.02	1.03	1.04	1.05	1.05	1.06	1.07	5000
1	1	1	1	1	1	1	1	1	∞

TABLE A-7a. F DISTRIBUTION, UPPER 5% POINTS ($F_{.95}$)*

Degrees of freedom for numerator (columns); Degrees of freedom for denominator (rows)

	1	2	3	4	5	6	7	8	9	10	12	15	20	24	30	40	60	120	∞
1	161	200	216	225	230	234	237	239	241	242	244	246	248	249	250	251	252	253	254
2	18.5	19.0	19.2	19.2	19.3	19.3	19.4	19.4	19.4	19.4	19.4	19.4	19.4	19.5	19.5	19.5	19.5	19.5	19.5
3	10.1	9.55	9.28	9.12	9.01	8.94	8.89	8.85	8.81	8.79	8.74	8.70	8.66	8.64	8.62	8.59	8.57	8.55	8.53
4	7.71	6.94	6.59	6.39	6.26	6.16	6.09	6.04	6.00	5.96	5.91	5.86	5.80	5.77	5.75	5.72	5.69	5.66	5.63
5	6.61	5.79	5.41	5.19	5.05	4.95	4.88	4.82	4.77	4.74	4.68	4.62	4.56	4.53	4.50	4.46	4.43	4.40	4.37
6	5.99	5.14	4.76	4.53	4.39	4.28	4.21	4.15	4.10	4.06	4.00	3.94	3.87	3.84	3.81	3.77	3.74	3.70	3.67
7	5.59	4.74	4.35	4.12	3.97	3.87	3.79	3.73	3.68	3.64	3.57	3.51	3.44	3.41	3.38	3.34	3.30	3.27	3.23
8	5.32	4.46	4.07	3.84	3.69	3.58	3.50	3.44	3.39	3.35	3.28	3.22	3.15	3.12	3.08	3.04	3.01	2.97	2.93
9	5.12	4.26	3.86	3.63	3.48	3.37	3.29	3.23	3.18	3.14	3.07	3.01	2.94	2.90	2.86	2.83	2.79	2.75	2.71
10	4.96	4.10	3.71	3.48	3.33	3.22	3.14	3.07	3.02	2.98	2.91	2.85	2.77	2.74	2.70	2.66	2.62	2.58	2.54
11	4.84	3.98	3.59	3.36	3.20	3.09	3.01	2.95	2.90	2.85	2.79	2.72	2.65	2.61	2.57	2.53	2.49	2.45	2.40
12	4.75	3.89	3.49	3.26	3.11	3.00	2.91	2.85	2.80	2.75	2.69	2.62	2.54	2.51	2.47	2.43	2.38	2.34	2.30
13	4.67	3.81	3.41	3.18	3.03	2.92	2.83	2.77	2.71	2.67	2.60	2.53	2.46	2.42	2.38	2.34	2.30	2.25	2.21
14	4.60	3.74	3.34	3.11	2.96	2.85	2.76	2.70	2.65	2.60	2.53	2.46	2.39	2.35	2.31	2.27	2.22	2.18	2.13
15	4.54	3.68	3.29	3.06	2.90	2.79	2.71	2.64	2.59	2.54	2.48	2.40	2.33	2.29	2.25	2.20	2.16	2.11	2.07
16	4.49	3.63	3.24	3.01	2.85	2.74	2.66	2.59	2.54	2.49	2.42	2.35	2.28	2.24	2.19	2.15	2.11	2.06	2.01
17	4.45	3.59	3.20	2.96	2.81	2.70	2.61	2.55	2.49	2.45	2.38	2.31	2.23	2.19	2.15	2.10	2.06	2.01	1.96
18	4.41	3.55	3.16	2.93	2.77	2.66	2.58	2.51	2.46	2.41	2.34	2.27	2.19	2.15	2.11	2.06	2.02	1.97	1.92
19	4.38	3.52	3.13	2.90	2.74	2.63	2.54	2.48	2.42	2.38	2.31	2.23	2.16	2.11	2.07	2.03	1.98	1.93	1.88
20	4.35	3.49	3.10	2.87	2.71	2.60	2.51	2.45	2.39	2.35	2.28	2.20	2.12	2.08	2.04	1.99	1.95	1.90	1.84
21	4.32	3.47	3.07	2.84	2.68	2.57	2.49	2.42	2.37	2.32	2.25	2.18	2.10	2.05	2.01	1.96	1.92	1.87	1.81
22	4.30	3.44	3.05	2.82	2.66	2.55	2.46	2.40	2.34	2.30	2.23	2.15	2.07	2.03	1.98	1.94	1.89	1.84	1.78
23	4.28	3.42	3.03	2.80	2.64	2.53	2.44	2.37	2.32	2.27	2.20	2.13	2.05	2.01	1.96	1.91	1.86	1.81	1.76
24	4.26	3.40	3.01	2.78	2.62	2.51	2.42	2.36	2.30	2.25	2.18	2.11	2.03	1.98	1.94	1.89	1.84	1.79	1.73
25	4.24	3.39	2.99	2.76	2.60	2.49	2.40	2.34	2.28	2.24	2.16	2.09	2.01	1.96	1.92	1.87	1.82	1.77	1.71
30	4.17	3.32	2.92	2.69	2.53	2.42	2.33	2.27	2.21	2.16	2.09	2.01	1.93	1.89	1.84	1.79	1.74	1.68	1.62
40	4.08	3.23	2.84	2.61	2.45	2.34	2.25	2.18	2.12	2.08	2.00	1.92	1.84	1.79	1.74	1.69	1.64	1.58	1.51
60	4.00	3.15	2.76	2.53	2.37	2.25	2.17	2.10	2.04	1.99	1.92	1.84	1.75	1.70	1.65	1.59	1.53	1.47	1.39
120	3.92	3.07	2.68	2.45	2.29	2.18	2.09	2.02	1.96	1.91	1.83	1.75	1.66	1.61	1.55	1.50	1.43	1.35	1.25
∞	3.84	3.00	2.60	2.37	2.21	2.10	2.01	1.94	1.88	1.83	1.75	1.67	1.57	1.52	1.46	1.39	1.32	1.22	1.00

Interpolation should be performed using reciprocals of the degrees of freedom.

* This table is reproduced with the permission of Professor E. S. Pearson from M. Merrington, C. M. Thompson, "Tables of percentage points of the inverted beta (F) distribution," *Biometrika*, vol. 33 (1943), p. 73.

TABLE A-7b. F DISTRIBUTION, UPPER 1% POINTS ($F_{.99}$)*

Degrees of freedom for numerator (columns); Degrees of freedom for denominator (rows)

	1	2	3	4	5	6	7	8	9	10	12	15	20	24	30	40	60	120	∞
1	4,052	5,000	5,403	5,625	5,764	5,859	5,928	5,982	6,023	6,056	6,106	6,157	6,209	6,235	6,261	6,287	6,313	6,339	6,366
2	98.5	99.0	99.2	99.2	99.3	99.3	99.4	99.4	99.4	99.4	99.4	99.4	99.4	99.5	99.5	99.5	99.5	99.5	99.5
3	34.1	30.8	29.5	28.7	28.2	27.9	27.7	27.5	27.3	27.2	27.1	26.9	26.7	26.6	26.5	26.4	26.3	26.2	26.1
4	21.2	18.0	16.7	16.0	15.5	15.2	15.0	14.8	14.7	14.5	14.4	14.2	14.0	13.9	13.8	13.7	13.7	13.6	13.5
5	16.3	13.3	12.1	11.4	11.0	10.7	10.5	10.3	10.2	10.1	9.89	9.72	9.55	9.47	9.38	9.29	9.20	9.11	9.02
6	13.7	10.9	9.78	9.15	8.75	8.47	8.26	8.10	7.98	7.87	7.72	7.56	7.40	7.31	7.23	7.14	7.06	6.97	6.88
7	12.2	9.55	8.45	7.85	7.46	7.19	6.99	6.84	6.72	6.62	6.47	6.31	6.16	6.07	5.99	5.91	5.82	5.74	5.65
8	11.3	8.65	7.59	7.01	6.63	6.37	6.18	6.03	5.91	5.81	5.67	5.52	5.36	5.28	5.20	5.12	5.03	4.95	4.86
9	10.6	8.02	6.99	6.42	6.06	5.80	5.61	5.47	5.35	5.26	5.11	4.96	4.81	4.73	4.65	4.57	4.48	4.40	4.31
10	10.0	7.56	6.55	5.99	5.64	5.39	5.20	5.06	4.94	4.85	4.71	4.56	4.41	4.33	4.25	4.17	4.08	4.00	3.91
11	9.65	7.21	6.22	5.67	5.32	5.07	4.89	4.74	4.63	4.54	4.40	4.25	4.10	4.02	3.94	3.86	3.78	3.69	3.60
12	9.33	6.93	5.95	5.41	5.06	4.82	4.64	4.50	4.39	4.30	4.16	4.01	3.86	3.78	3.70	3.62	3.54	3.45	3.36
13	9.07	6.70	5.74	5.21	4.86	4.62	4.44	4.30	4.19	4.10	3.96	3.82	3.66	3.59	3.51	3.43	3.34	3.25	3.17
14	8.86	6.51	5.56	5.04	4.70	4.46	4.28	4.14	4.03	3.94	3.80	3.66	3.51	3.43	3.35	3.27	3.18	3.09	3.00
15	8.68	6.36	5.42	4.89	4.56	4.32	4.14	4.00	3.89	3.80	3.67	3.52	3.37	3.29	3.21	3.13	3.05	2.96	2.87
16	8.53	6.23	5.29	4.77	4.44	4.20	4.03	3.89	3.78	3.69	3.55	3.41	3.26	3.18	3.10	3.02	2.93	2.84	2.75
17	8.40	6.11	5.19	4.67	4.34	4.10	3.93	3.79	3.68	3.59	3.46	3.31	3.16	3.08	3.00	2.92	2.83	2.75	2.65
18	8.29	6.01	5.09	4.58	4.25	4.01	3.84	3.71	3.60	3.51	3.37	3.23	3.08	3.00	2.92	2.84	2.75	2.66	2.57
19	8.19	5.93	5.01	4.50	4.17	3.94	3.77	3.63	3.52	3.43	3.30	3.15	3.00	2.92	2.84	2.76	2.67	2.58	2.49
20	8.10	5.85	4.94	4.43	4.10	3.87	3.70	3.56	3.46	3.37	3.23	3.09	2.94	2.86	2.78	2.69	2.61	2.52	2.42
21	8.02	5.78	4.87	4.37	4.04	3.81	3.64	3.51	3.40	3.31	3.17	3.03	2.88	2.80	2.72	2.64	2.55	2.46	2.36
22	7.95	5.72	4.82	4.31	3.99	3.76	3.59	3.45	3.35	3.26	3.12	2.98	2.83	2.75	2.67	2.58	2.50	2.40	2.31
23	7.88	5.66	4.76	4.26	3.94	3.71	3.54	3.41	3.30	3.21	3.07	2.93	2.78	2.70	2.62	2.54	2.45	2.35	2.26
24	7.82	5.61	4.72	4.22	3.90	3.67	3.50	3.36	3.26	3.17	3.03	2.89	2.74	2.66	2.58	2.49	2.40	2.31	2.21
25	7.77	5.57	4.68	4.18	3.86	3.63	3.46	3.32	3.22	3.13	2.99	2.85	2.70	2.62	2.53	2.45	2.36	2.27	2.17
30	7.56	5.39	4.51	4.02	3.70	3.47	3.30	3.17	3.07	2.98	2.84	2.70	2.55	2.47	2.39	2.30	2.21	2.11	2.01
40	7.31	5.18	4.31	3.83	3.51	3.29	3.12	2.99	2.89	2.80	2.66	2.52	2.37	2.29	2.20	2.11	2.02	1.92	1.80
60	7.08	4.98	4.13	3.65	3.34	3.12	2.95	2.82	2.72	2.63	2.50	2.35	2.20	2.12	2.03	1.94	1.84	1.73	1.60
120	6.85	4.79	3.95	3.48	3.17	2.96	2.79	2.66	2.56	2.47	2.34	2.19	2.03	1.95	1.86	1.76	1.66	1.53	1.38
∞	6.63	4.61	3.78	3.32	3.02	2.80	2.64	2.51	2.41	2.32	2.18	2.04	1.88	1.79	1.70	1.59	1.47	1.32	1.00

Interpolation should be performed using reciprocals of the degrees of freedom.

* This table is reproduced with the permission of Professor E. S. Pearson from M. Merrington, C. M. Thompson, "Tables of percentage points of the inverted beta (F) distribution," *Biometrika*, vol. 33 (1943), p. 73.

TABLE A-7c. PERCENTILES OF THE $F(\nu_1, \nu_2)$ DISTRIBUTION WITH DEGREES OF FREEDOM ν_1 FOR THE NUMERATOR AND ν_2 FOR THE DENOMINATOR

ν_2	Cum. Prop. \ ν_1	1	2	3	4	5	6	7	8	9	10	11	12	Cum. Prop.
1	.0005	$.0^{6}62$	$.0^{3}50$	$.0^{2}38$	$.0^{2}94$	.016	.022	.027	.032	.036	.039	.042	.045	.0005
	.001	$.0^{5}25$	$.0^{2}10$	$.0^{2}60$	.013	.021	.028	.034	.039	.044	.048	.051	.054	.001
	.005	$.0^{4}62$	$.0^{2}51$	.018	.032	.044	.054	.062	.068	.073	.078	.082	.085	.005
	.010	$.0^{3}25$	.010	.029	.047	.062	.073	.082	.089	.095	.100	.104	.107	.010
	.025	$.0^{2}15$	.026	.057	.082	.100	.113	.124	.132	.139	.144	.149	.153	.025
	.05	$.0^{2}62$	.054	.099	.130	.151	.167	.179	.188	.195	.201	.207	.211	.05
	.10	.025	.117	.181	.220	.246	.265	.279	.289	.298	.304	.310	.315	.10
	.25	.172	.389	.494	.553	.591	.617	.637	.650	.661	.670	.680	.684	.25
	.50	1.00	1.50	1.71	1.82	1.89	1.94	1.98	2.00	2.03	2.04	2.05	2.07	.50
	.75	5.83	7.50	8.20	8.58	8.82	8.98	9.10	9.19	9.26	9.32	9.36	9.41	.75
	.90	39.9	49.5	53.6	55.8	57.2	58.2	58.9	59.4	59.9	60.2	60.5	60.7	.90
	.95	161	200	216	225	230	234	237	239	241	242	243	244	.95
	.975	648	800	864	900	922	937	948	957	963	969	973	977	.975
	.99	405^{1}	500^{1}	540^{1}	562^{1}	576^{1}	586^{1}	593^{1}	598^{1}	602^{1}	606^{1}	608^{1}	611^{1}	.99
	.995	162^{2}	200^{2}	216^{2}	225^{2}	231^{2}	234^{2}	237^{2}	239^{2}	241^{2}	242^{2}	243^{2}	244^{2}	.995
	.999	406^{3}	500^{3}	540^{3}	562^{3}	576^{3}	586^{3}	593^{3}	598^{3}	602^{3}	606^{3}	609^{3}	611^{3}	.999
	.9995	162^{4}	200^{4}	216^{4}	225^{4}	231^{4}	234^{4}	237^{4}	239^{4}	241^{4}	242^{4}	243^{4}	244^{4}	.9995
2	.0005	$.0^{6}50$	$.0^{3}50$	$.0^{2}42$	.011	.020	.029	.037	.044	.050	.056	.061	.065	.0005
	.001	$.0^{5}20$	$.0^{2}10$	$.0^{2}68$	.016	.027	.037	.046	.054	.061	.067	.072	.077	.001
	.005	$.0^{4}50$	$.0^{2}50$	.020	.038	.055	.069	.081	.091	.099	.106	.112	.118	.005
	.01	$.0^{3}20$	.010	.032	.056	.075	.092	.105	.116	.125	.132	.139	.144	.01
	.025	$.0^{2}13$	.026	.062	.094	.119	.138	.153	.165	.175	.183	.190	.196	.025
	.05	$.0^{2}50$	.053	.105	.144	.173	.194	.211	.224	.235	.244	.251	.257	.05
	.10	.020	.111	.183	.231	.265	.289	.307	.321	.333	.342	.350	.356	.10
	.25	.133	.333	.439	.500	.540	.568	.588	.604	.616	.626	.633	.641	.25
	.50	.667	1.00	1.13	1.21	1.25	1.28	1.30	1.32	1.33	1.34	1.35	1.36	.50
	.75	2.57	3.00	3.15	3.23	3.28	3.31	3.34	3.35	3.37	3.38	3.39	3.39	.75
	.90	8.53	9.00	9.16	9.24	9.29	9.33	9.35	9.37	9.38	9.39	9.40	9.41	.90
	.95	18.5	19.0	19.2	19.2	19.3	19.3	19.4	19.4	19.4	19.4	19.4	19.4	.95
	.975	38.5	39.0	39.2	39.2	39.3	39.3	39.4	39.4	39.4	39.4	39.4	39.4	.975
	.99	98.5	99.0	99.2	99.2	99.3	99.3	99.4	99.4	99.4	99.4	99.4	99.4	.99
	.995	198	199	199	199	199	199	199	199	199	199	199	199	.995
	.999	998	999	999	999	999	999	999	999	999	999	999	999	.999
	.9995	200^{1}	200^{1}	200^{1}	200^{1}	200^{1}	200^{1}	200^{1}	200^{1}	200^{1}	200^{1}	200^{1}	200^{1}	.9995
3	.0005	$.0^{6}46$	$.0^{3}50$	$.0^{2}44$	.012	.023	.033	.043	.052	.060	.067	.074	.079	.0005
	.001	$.0^{5}19$	$.0^{2}10$	$.0^{2}71$	.018	.030	.042	.053	.063	.072	.079	.086	.093	.001
	.005	$.0^{4}46$	$.0^{2}50$	.021	.041	.060	.077	.092	.104	.115	.124	.132	.138	.005
	.01	$.0^{3}19$	.010	.034	.060	.083	.102	.118	.132	.143	.153	.161	.168	.01
	.025	$.0^{2}12$	.026	.065	.100	.129	.152	.170	.185	.197	.207	.216	.224	.025
	.05	$.0^{2}46$	.052	.108	.152	.185	.210	.230	.246	.259	.270	.279	.287	.05
	.10	.019	.109	.185	.239	.276	.304	.325	.342	.356	.367	.376	.384	.10
	.25	.122	.317	.424	.489	.531	.561	.582	.600	.613	.624	.633	.641	.25
	.50	.585	.881	1.00	1.06	1.10	1.13	1.15	1.16	1.17	1.18	1.19	1.20	.50
	.75	2.02	2.28	2.36	2.39	2.41	2.42	2.43	2.44	2.44	2.44	2.45	2.45	.75
	.90	5.54	5.46	5.39	5.34	5.31	5.28	5.27	5.25	5.24	5.23	5.22	5.22	.90
	.95	10.1	9.55	9.28	9.12	9.01	8.94	8.89	8.85	8.81	8.79	8.76	8.74	.95
	.075	17.4	16.0	15.4	15.1	14.9	14.7	14.6	14.5	14.5	14.4	14.4	14.3	.975
	.99	34.1	30.8	29.5	28.7	28.2	27.9	27.7	27.5	27.3	27.2	27.1	27.1	.99
	.995	55.6	49.8	47.5	46.2	45.4	44.8	44.4	44.1	43.9	43.7	43.5	43.4	.995
	.999	167	149	141	137	135	133	132	131	130	129	129	128	.999
	.9995	266	237	225	218	214	211	209	208	207	206	204	204	.9995

Read $.0^{3}56$ as .00056, 200^{1} as 2000, 162^{4} as 1620000, etc.

Table A-7c. Percentiles of the $F(\nu_1, \nu_2)$ Distributions (*Continued*)

Cum. Prop. \ ν_1	15	20	24	30	40	50	60	100	120	200	500	∞	Cum. Prop.	ν_2
.0005	.051	.058	062	.066	.069	.072	.074	.077	.078	.080	.081	.083	.0005	**1**
.001	.060	.067	.071	.075	.079	.082	.084	.087	.088	.089	.091	.092	.001	
.005	.093	.101	.105	.109	.113	.116	.118	.121	.122	.124	.126	.127	.005	
.01	.115	.124	.128	.132	.137	.139	.141	.145	.146	.148	.150	.151	.01	
.025	.161	.170	.175	.180	.184	.187	.189	.193	.194	.196	.198	.199	.025	
.05	.220	.230	.235	.240	.245	.248	.250	.254	.255	.257	.259	.261	.05	
.10	.325	.336	.342	.347	.353	.356	.358	.362	.364	.366	.368	.370	.10	
.25	.698	.712	.719	.727	.734	.738	.741	.747	.749	.752	.754	.756	.25	
.50	2.09	2.12	2.13	2.15	2.16	2.17	2.17	2.18	2.18	2.19	2.19	2.20	.50	
.75	9.49	9.58	9.63	9.67	9.71	9.74	9.76	9.78	9.80	9.82	9.84	9.85	.75	
.90	61.2	61.7	62.0	62.3	62.5	62.7	62.8	63.0	63.1	63.2	63.3	63.3	.90	
.95	246	248	249	250	251	252	252	253	253	254	254	254	.95	
.975	985	993	997	100^1	101^1	101^1	101^1	101^1	101^1	102^1	102^1	102^1	.975	
.99	616^1	621^1	623^1	626^1	629^1	630^1	631^1	633^1	634^1	635^1	636^1	637^1	.99	
.995	246^2	248^2	249^2	250^2	251^2	252^2	253^2	253^2	254^2	254^2	254^2	255^2	.995	
.999	616^3	621^3	623^3	626^3	629^3	630^3	631^3	633^3	634^3	635^3	636^3	637^3	.999	
.9995	246^4	248^4	249^4	250^4	251^4	252^4	252^4	253^4	253^4	253^4	254^4	254^4	.9995	
.0005	.076	.088	.094	.101	.108	.113	.116	.122	.124	.127	.130	.132	.0005	**2**
.001	.088	.100	.107	.114	.121	.126	.129	.135	.137	.140	.143	.145	.001	
.005	.130	.143	.150	.157	.165	.169	.173	.179	.181	.184	.187	.189	.005	
.01	.157	.171	.178	.186	.193	.198	.201	.207	.209	.212	.215	.217	.01	
.025	.210	.224	.232	.239	.247	.251	.255	.261	.263	.266	.269	.271	.025	
.05	.272	.286	.294	.302	.309	.314	.317	.324	.326	.329	.332	.334	.05	
.10	.371	.386	.394	.402	.410	.415	.418	.424	.426	.429	.433	.434	.10	
.25	.657	.672	.680	.689	.697	.702	.705	.711	.713	.716	.719	.721	.25	
.50	1.38	1.39	1.40	1.41	1.42	1.42	1.43	1.43	1.43	1.44	1.44	1.44	.50	
.75	3.41	3.43	3.43	3.44	3.45	3.45	3.46	3.47	3.47	3.48	3.48	3.48	.75	
.90	9.42	9.44	9.45	9.46	9.47	9.47	9.47	9.48	9.48	9.49	9.49	9.49	.90	
.95	19.4	19.4	19.5	19.5	19.5	19.5	19.5	19.5	19.5	19.5	19.5	19.5	.95	
.975	39.4	39.4	39.5	39.5	39.5	39.5	39.5	39.5	39.5	39.5	39.5	39.5	.975	
.99	99.4	99.4	99.5	99.5	99.5	99.5	99.5	99.5	99.5	99.5	99.5	99.5	.99	
.995	199	199	199	199	199	199	199	199	199	199	199	200	.995	
.999	999	999	999	999	999	999	999	999	999	999	999	999	.999	
.9995	200^1	200^1	200^1	200^1	200^1	200^1	200^1	200^1	200^1	200^1	200^1	200^1	.9995	
.0005	.093	.109	.117	.127	.136	.143	.147	.156	.158	.162	.166	.169	.0005	**3**
.001	.107	.123	.132	.142	.152	.158	.162	.171	.173	.177	.181	.184	.001	
.005	.154	.172	.181	.191	.201	.207	.211	.220	.222	.227	.231	.234	.005	
.01	.185	.203	.212	.222	.232	.238	.242	.251	.253	.258	.262	.264	.01	
.025	.241	.259	.269	.279	.289	.295	.299	.308	.310	.314	.318	.321	.025	
.05	.304	.323	.332	.342	.352	.358	.363	.370	.373	.377	.382	.384	.05	
.10	.402	.420	.430	.439	.449	.455	.459	.467	.469	.474	.476	.480	.10	
.25	.658	.675	.684	.693	.702	.708	.711	.719	.721	.724	.728	.730	.25	
.50	1.21	1.23	1.23	1.24	1.25	1.25	1.25	1.26	1.26	1.26	1.27	1.27	.50	
.75	2.46	2.46	2.46	2.47	2.47	2.47	2.47	2.47	2.47	2.47	2.47	2.47	.75	
.90	5.20	5.18	5.18	5.17	5.16	5.15	5.15	5.14	5.14	5.14	5.14	5.13	.90	
.95	8.70	8.66	8.63	8.62	8.59	8.58	8.57	8.55	8.55	8.54	8.53	8.53	.95	
.975	14.3	14.2	14.1	14.1	14.0	14.0	14.0	14.0	13.9	13.9	13.9	13.9	.975	
.99	26.9	26.7	26.6	26.5	26.4	26.4	26.3	26.2	26.2	26.2	26.1	26.1	.99	
.995	43.1	42.8	42.6	42.5	42.3	42.2	42.1	42.0	42.0	41.9	41.9	41.8	.995	
.999	127	126	126	125	125	125	124	124	124	124	124	123	.999	
.9995	203	201	200	199	199	198	198	197	197	197	196	196	.9995	

TABLE A-7c. PERCENTILES OF THE $F(\nu_1, \nu_2)$ DISTRIBUTIONS (*Continued*)

ν_2	Cum. Prop. \ ν_1	1	2	3	4	5	6	7	8	9	10	11	12	Cum. Prop.
4	.0005	$.0^{6}44$	$.0^{3}50$	$.0^{2}46$	.013	.024	.036	.047	.057	.066	.075	.082	.089	.0005
	.001	$.0^{5}18$	$.0^{2}10$	$.0^{2}73$	.019	.032	.046	.058	.069	.079	.089	.097	.104	.001
	.005	$.0^{4}44$	$.0^{2}50$	.022	.043	.064	.083	.100	.114	.126	.137	.145	.153	.005
	.01	$.0^{3}18$	.010	.035	.063	.088	.109	.127	.143	.156	.167	.176	.185	.01
	.025	$.0^{2}11$	.026	.066	.104	.135	.161	.181	.198	.212	.224	.234	.243	.025
	.05	$.0^{2}44$	.052	.110	.157	.193	.221	.243	.261	.275	.288	.298	.307	.05
	.10	.018	.108	.187	.243	.284	.314	.338	.356	.371	.384	.394	.403	.10
	.25	.117	.309	.418	.484	.528	.560	.583	.601	.615	.627	.637	.645	.25
	.50	.549	.828	.941	1.00	1.04	1.06	1.08	1.09	1.10	1.11	1.12	1.13	.50
	.75	1.81	2.00	2.05	2.06	2.07	2.08	2.08	2.08	2.08	2.08	2.08	2.08	.75
	.90	4.54	4.32	4.19	4.11	4.05	4.01	3.98	3.95	3.94	3.92	3.91	3.90	.90
	.95	7.71	6.94	6.59	6.39	6.26	6.16	6.09	6.04	6.00	5.96	5.94	5.91	.95
	.975	12.2	10.6	9.98	9.60	9.36	9.20	9.07	8.98	8.90	8.84	8.79	8.75	.975
	.99	21.2	18.0	16.7	16.0	15.5	15.2	15.0	14.8	14.7	14.5	14.4	14.4	.99
	.995	31.3	26.3	24.3	23.2	22.5	22.0	21.6	21.4	21.1	21.0	20.8	20.7	.995
	.999	74.1	61.2	56.2	53.4	51.7	50.5	49.7	49.0	48.5	48.0	47.7	47.4	.999
	.9995	106	87.4	80.1	76.1	73.6	71.9	70.6	69.7	68.9	68.3	67.8	67.4	.9995
5	.0005	$.0^{6}43$	$.0^{3}50$	$.0^{2}47$	.014	.025	.038	.050	.061	.070	.081	.089	.096	.0005
	.001	$.0^{5}17$	$.0^{2}10$	$.0^{2}75$	.019	.034	.048	.062	.074	.085	.095	.104	.112	.001
	.005	$.0^{4}43$	$.0^{2}50$	.022	.045	.067	.087	.105	.120	.134	.146	.156	.165	.005
	.01	$.0^{3}17$	.010	.035	.064	.091	.114	.134	.151	.165	.177	.188	.197	.01
	.025	$.0^{2}11$	.025	.067	.107	.140	.167	.189	.208	.223	.236	.248	.257	.025
	.05	$.0^{2}43$	.052	.111	.160	.198	.228	.252	.271	.287	.301	.313	.322	.05
	.10	.017	.108	.188	.247	.290	.322	.347	.367	.383	.397	.408	.418	.10
	.25	.113	.305	.415	.483	.528	.560	.584	.604	.618	.631	.641	.650	.25
	.50	.528	.799	.907	.965	1.00	1.02	1.04	1.05	1.06	1.07	1.08	1.09	.50
	.75	1.69	1.85	1.88	1.89	1.89	1.89	1.89	1.89	1.89	1.89	1.89	1.89	.75
	.90	4.06	3.78	3.62	3.52	3.45	3.40	3.37	3.34	3.32	3.30	3.28	3.27	.90
	.95	6.61	5.79	5.41	5.19	5.05	4.95	4.88	4.82	4.77	4.74	4.71	4.68	.95
	.975	10.0	8.43	7.76	7.39	7.15	6.98	6.85	6.76	6.68	6.62	6.57	6.52	.975
	.99	16.3	13.3	12.1	11.4	11.0	10.7	10.5	10.3	10.2	10.1	9.96	9.89	.99
	.995	22.8	18.3	16.5	15.6	14.9	14.5	14.2	14.0	13.8	13.6	13.5	13.4	.995
	.999	47.2	37.1	33.2	31.1	29.7	28.8	28.2	27.6	27.2	26.9	26.6	26.4	.999
	.9995	63.6	49.8	44.4	41.5	39.7	38.5	37.6	36.9	36.4	35.9	35.6	35.2	.9995
6	.0005	$.0^{6}43$	$.0^{3}50$	$.0^{2}47$	.014	.026	.039	.052	.064	.075	.085	.094	.103	.0005
	.001	$.0^{5}17$	$.0^{2}10$	$.0^{2}75$	.020	.035	.050	.064	.078	.090	.101	.111	.119	.001
	.005	$.0^{4}43$	$.0^{2}50$	.022	.045	.069	.090	.109	.126	.140	.153	.164	.174	.005
	.01	$.0^{3}17$	.010	.036	.066	.094	.118	.139	.157	.172	.186	.197	.207	.01
	.025	$.0^{2}11$	.025	.068	.109	.143	.172	.195	.215	.231	.246	.258	.268	.025
	.05	$.0^{2}43$	.052	.112	.162	.202	.233	.259	.279	.296	.311	.324	.334	.05
	.10	.017	.107	.189	.249	.294	.327	.354	.375	.392	.406	.418	.429	.10
	.25	.111	.302	.413	.481	.524	.561	.586	.606	.622	.635	.645	.654	.25
	.50	.515	.780	.886	.942	.977	1.00	1.02	1.03	1.04	1.05	1.05	1.06	.50
	.75	1.62	1.76	1.78	1.79	1.79	1.78	1.78	1.78	1.77	1.77	1.77	1.77	.75
	.90	3.78	3.46	3.29	3.18	3.11	3.05	3.01	2.98	2.96	2.94	2.92	2.90	.90
	.95	5.99	5.14	4.76	4.53	4.39	4.28	4.21	4.15	4.10	4.06	4.03	4.00	.95
	.975	8.81	7.26	6.60	6.23	5.99	5.82	5.70	5.60	5.52	5.46	5.41	5.37	.975
	.99	13.7	10.9	9.78	9.15	8.75	8.47	8.26	8.10	7.98	7.87	7.79	7.72	.99
	.995	18.6	14.5	12.9	12.0	11.5	11.1	10.8	10.6	10.4	10.2	10.1	10.0	.995
	.999	35.5	27.0	23.7	21.9	20.8	20.0	19.5	19.0	18.7	18.4	18.2	18.0	.999
	.9995	46.1	34.8	30.4	28.1	26.6	25.6	24.9	24.3	23.9	23.5	23.2	23.0	.9995

TABLE A-7c. PERCENTILES OF THE $F(\nu_1, \nu_2)$ DISTRIBUTIONS (*Continued*)

Cum. Prop. \ ν_1	15	20	24	30	40	50	60	100	120	200	500	∞	Cum. Prop.	ν_2
.0005	.105	.125	.135	.147	.159	.166	.172	.183	.186	.191	.196	.200	.0005	4
.001	.121	.141	.152	.163	.176	.183	.188	.200	.202	.208	.213	.217	.001	
.005	.172	.193	.204	.216	.229	.237	.242	.253	.255	.260	.266	.269	.005	
.01	.204	.226	.237	.249	.261	.269	.274	.285	.287	.293	.298	.301	.01	
.025	.263	.284	.296	.308	.320	.327	.332	.342	.346	.351	.356	.359	.025	
.05	.327	.349	.360	.372	.384	.391	.396	.407	.409	.413	.418	.422	.05	
.10	.424	.445	.456	.467	.478	.485	.490	.500	.502	.508	.510	.514	.10	
.25	.664	.683	.692	.702	.712	.718	.722	.731	.733	.737	.740	.743	.25	
.50	1.14	1.15	1.16	1.16	1.17	1.18	1.18	1.18	1.18	1.19	1.19	1.19	.50	
.75	2.08	2.08	2.08	2.08	2.08	2.08	2.08	2.08	2.08	2.08	2.08	2.08	.75	
.90	3.87	3.84	3.83	3.82	3.80	3.80	3.79	3.78	3.78	3.77	3.76	3.76	.90	
.95	5.86	5.80	5.77	5.75	5.72	5.70	5.69	5.66	5.66	5.65	5.64	5.63	.95	
.975	8.66	8.56	8.51	8.46	8.41	8.38	8.36	8.32	8.31	8.29	8.27	8.26	.975	
.99	14.2	14.0	13.9	13.8	13.7	13.7	13.7	13.6	13.6	13.5	13.5	13.5	.99	
.995	20.4	20.2	20.0	19.9	19.8	19.7	19.6	19.5	19.5	19.4	19.4	19.3	.995	
.999	46.8	46.1	45.8	45.4	45.1	44.9	44.7	44.5	44.4	44.3	44.1	44.0	.999	
.9995	66.5	65.5	65.1	64.6	64.1	63.8	63.6	63.2	63.1	62.9	62.7	62.6	.9995	
.0005	.115	.137	.150	.163	.177	.186	.192	.205	.209	.216	.222	.226	.0005	5
.001	.132	.155	.167	.181	.195	.204	.210	.223	.227	.233	.239	.244	.001	
.005	.186	.210	.223	.237	.251	.260	.266	.279	.282	.288	.294	.299	.005	
.01	.219	.244	.257	.270	.285	.293	.299	.312	.315	.322	.328	.331	.01	
.025	.280	.304	.317	.330	.344	.353	.359	.370	.374	.380	.386	.390	.025	
.05	.345	.369	.382	.395	.408	.417	.422	.432	.437	.442	.448	.452	.05	
.10	.440	.463	.476	.488	.501	.508	.514	.524	.527	.532	.538	.541	.10	
.25	.669	.690	.700	.711	.722	.728	.732	.741	.743	.748	.752	.755	.25	
.50	1.10	1.11	1.12	1.12	1.13	1.13	1.14	1.14	1.14	1.15	1.15	1.15	.50	
.75	1.89	1.88	1.88	1.88	1.88	1.88	1.87	1.87	1.87	1.87	1.87	1.87	.75	
.90	3.24	3.21	3.19	3.17	3.16	3.15	3.14	3.13	3.12	3.12	3.11	3.10	.90	
.95	4.62	4.56	4.53	4.50	4.46	4.44	4.43	4.41	4.40	4.39	4.37	4.36	.95	
.975	6.43	6.33	6.28	6.23	6.18	6.14	6.12	6.08	6.07	6.05	6.03	6.02	.975	
.99	9.72	9.55	9.47	9.38	9.29	9.24	9.20	9.13	9.11	9.08	9.04	9.02	.99	
.995	13.1	12.9	12.8	12.7	12.5	12.5	12.4	12.3	12.3	12.2	12.2	12.1	.995	
.999	25.9	25.4	25.1	24.9	24.6	24.4	24.3	24.1	24.1	23.9	23.8	23.8	.999	
.9995	34.6	33.9	33.5	33.1	32.7	32.5	32.3	32.1	32.0	31.8	31.7	31.6	.9995	
.0005	.123	.148	.162	.177	.193	.203	.210	.225	.229	.236	.244	.249	.0005	6
.001	.141	.166	.180	.195	.211	.222	.229	.243	.247	.255	.262	.267	.001	
.005	.197	.224	.238	.253	.269	.279	.286	.301	.304	.312	.318	.324	.005	
.01	.232	.258	.273	.288	.304	.313	.321	.334	.338	.346	.352	.357	.01	
.025	.293	.320	.334	.349	.364	.375	.381	.394	.398	.405	.412	.415	.025	
.05	.358	.385	.399	.413	.428	.437	.444	.457	.460	.467	.472	.476	.05	
.10	.453	.478	.491	.505	.519	.526	.533	.546	.548	.556	.559	.564	.10	
.25	.675	.696	.707	.718	.729	.736	.741	.751	.753	.758	.762	.765	.25	
.50	1.07	1.08	1.09	1.10	1.10	1.11	1.11	1.11	1.12	1.12	1.12	1.12	.50	
.75	1.76	1.76	1.75	1.75	1.75	1.75	1.74	1.74	1.74	1.74	1.74	1.74	.75	
.90	2.87	2.84	2.82	2.80	2.78	2.77	2.76	2.75	2.74	2.73	2.73	2.72	.90	
.95	3.94	3.87	3.84	3.81	3.77	3.75	3.74	3.71	3.70	3.69	3.68	3.67	.95	
.975	5.27	5.17	5.12	5.07	5.01	4.98	4.96	4.92	4.90	4.88	4.86	4.85	.975	
.99	7.56	7.40	7.31	7.23	7.14	7.09	7.06	6.99	6.97	6.93	6.90	6.88	.99	
.995	9.81	9.59	9.47	9.36	9.24	9.17	9.12	9.03	9.00	8.95	8.91	8.88	.995	
.999	17.6	17.1	16.9	16.7	16.4	16.3	16.2	16.0	16.0	15.9	15.8	15.7	.999	
.9995	22.4	21.9	21.7	21.4	21.1	20.9	20.7	20.5	20.4	20.3	20.2	20.1	.9995	

TABLE A-7c. PERCENTILES OF THE $F(\nu_1,\nu_2)$ DISTRIBUTIONS (*Continued*)

ν_2	ν_1 / Cum. Prop.	1	2	3	4	5	6	7	8	9	10	11	12	Cum. Prop.
7	.0005	$.0^{6}42$	$.0^{3}50$	$.0^{2}48$	.014	.027	.040	.053	.066	.078	.088	.099	.108	.0005
	.001	$.0^{5}17$	$.0^{2}10$	$.0^{2}76$	.020	.035	.051	.067	.081	.093	.105	.115	.125	.001
	.005	$.0^{4}42$	$.0^{2}50$	.023	.046	.070	.093	.113	.130	.145	.159	.171	.181	.005
	.01	$.0^{3}17$	.010	.036	.067	.096	.121	.143	.162	.178	.192	.205	.216	.01
	.025	$.0^{2}10$	.025	.068	.110	.146	.176	.200	.221	.238	.253	.266	.277	.025
	.05	$.0^{2}42$	.052	.113	.164	.205	.238	.264	.286	.304	.319	.332	.343	.05
	.10	.017	.107	.190	.251	.297	.332	.359	.381	.399	.414	.427	.438	.10
	.25	.110	.300	.412	.481	.528	.562	.588	.608	.624	.637	.649	.658	.25
	.50	.506	.767	.871	.926	.960	.983	1.00	1.01	1.02	1.03	1.04	1.04	.50
	.75	1.57	1.70	1.72	1.72	1.71	1.71	1.70	1.70	1.69	1.69	1.69	1.68	.75
	.90	3.59	3.26	3.07	2.96	2.88	2.83	2.78	2.75	2.72	2.70	2.68	2.67	.90
	.95	5.59	4.74	4.35	4.12	3.97	3.87	3.79	3.73	3.68	3.64	3.60	3.57	.95
	.975	8.07	6.54	5.89	5.52	5.29	5.12	4.99	4.90	4.82	4.76	4.71	4.67	.975
	.99	12.2	9.55	8.45	7.85	7.46	7.19	6.99	6.84	6.72	6.62	6.54	6.47	.99
	.995	16.2	12.4	10.9	10.0	9.52	9.16	8.89	8.68	8.51	8.38	8.27	8.18	.995
	.999	29.2	21.7	18.8	17.2	16.2	15.5	15.0	14.6	14.3	14.1	13.9	13.7	.999
	.9995	37.0	27.2	23.5	21.4	20.2	19.3	18.7	18.2	17.8	17.5	17.2	17.0	.9995
8	.0005	$.0^{3}42$	$.0^{3}50$	$.0^{2}48$	.014	.027	.041	.055	.068	.081	.092	.102	.112	.0005
	.001	$.0^{5}17$	$.0^{2}10$	$.0^{2}76$	.020	.036	.053	.068	.083	.096	.109	.120	.130	.001
	.005	$.0^{4}42$	$.0^{2}50$	.027	.047	.072	.095	.115	.133	.149	.164	.176	.187	.005
	.01	$.0^{3}17$	.010	.036	.068	.097	.123	.146	.166	.183	.198	.211	.222	.01
	.025	$.0^{2}10$	.025	.069	.111	.148	.179	.204	.226	.244	.259	.273	.285	.025
	.05	$.0^{2}42$	.052	.113	.166	.208	.241	.268	.291	.310	.326	.339	.351	.05
	.10	.017	.107	.190	.253	.299	.335	.363	.386	.405	.421	.435	.445	.10
	.25	.109	.298	.411	.481	.529	.563	.589	.610	.627	.640	.654	.661	.25
	.50	.499	.757	.860	.915	.948	.971	.988	1.00	1.01	1.02	1.02	1.03	.50
	.75	1.54	1.66	1.67	1.66	1.66	1.65	1.64	1.64	1.64	1.63	1.63	1.62	.75
	.90	3.46	3.11	2.92	2.81	2.73	2.67	2.62	2.59	2.56	2.54	2.52	2.50	.90
	.95	5.32	4.46	4.07	3.84	3.69	3.58	3.50	3.44	3.39	3.35	3.31	3.28	.95
	.975	7.57	6.06	5.42	5.05	4.82	4.65	4.53	4.43	4.36	4.30	4.24	4.20	.975
	.99	11.3	8.65	7.59	7.01	6.63	6.37	6.18	6.03	5.91	5.81	5.73	5.67	.99
	.995	14.7	11.0	9.60	8.81	8.30	7.95	7.69	7.50	7.34	7.21	7.10	7.01	.995
	.999	25.4	18.5	15.8	14.4	13.5	12.9	12.4	12.0	11.8	11.5	11.4	11.2	.999
	.9995	31.6	22.8	19.4	17.6	16.4	15.7	15.1	14.6	14.3	14.0	13.8	13.6	.9995
9	.0005	$.0^{6}41$	$.0^{3}50$	$.0^{2}48$	.015	.027	.042	.056	.070	.083	.094	.105	.115	.0005
	.001	$.0^{5}17$	$.0^{2}10$	$.0^{2}77$	.021	.037	.054	.070	.085	.099	.112	.123	.134	.001
	.005	$.0^{4}42$	$.0^{2}50$	.023	.047	.073	.096	.117	.136	.153	.168	.181	.192	.005
	.01	$.0^{3}17$	.010	.037	.068	.098	.125	.149	.169	.187	.202	.216	.228	.01
	.025	$.0^{2}10$	.025	.069	.112	.150	.181	.207	.230	.248	.265	.279	.291	.025
	.05	$.0^{2}40$	.052	.113	.167	.210	.244	.272	.296	.315	.331	.345	.358	.05
	.10	.017	.107	.191	.254	.302	.338	.367	.390	.410	.426	.441	.452	.10
	.25	.108	.297	.410	.480	.529	.564	.591	.612	.629	.643	.654	.664	.25
	.50	.494	.749	.852	.906	.939	.962	.978	.990	1.00	1.01	1.01	1.02	.50
	.75	1.51	1.62	1.63	1.63	1.62	1.61	1.60	1.60	1.59	1.59	1.58	1.58	.75
	.90	3.36	3.01	2.81	2.69	2.61	2.55	2.51	2.47	2.44	2.42	2.40	2.38	.90
	.95	5.12	4.26	3.86	3.63	3.48	3.37	3.29	3.23	3.18	3.14	3.10	3.07	.95
	.975	7.21	5.71	5.08	4.72	4.48	4.32	4.20	4.10	4.03	3.96	3.91	3.87	.975
	.99	10.6	8.02	6.99	6.42	6.06	5.80	5.61	5.47	5.35	5.26	5.18	5.11	.99
	.995	13.6	10.1	8.72	7.96	7.47	7.13	6.88	6.69	6.54	6.42	6.31	6.23	.995
	.999	22.9	16.4	13.9	12.6	11.7	11.1	10.7	10.4	10.1	9.89	9.71	9.57	.999
	.9995	28.0	19.9	16.8	15.1	14.1	13.3	12.8	12.4	12.1	11.8	11.6	11.4	.9995

TABLE A-7c. PERCENTILES OF THE $F(\nu_1,\nu_2)$ DISTRIBUTIONS (*Continued*)

Cum. Prop. \ ν_1	15	20	24	30	40	50	60	100	120	200	500	∞	Cum. Prop.	ν_2
.0005	.130	.157	.172	.188	.206	.217	.225	.242	.246	.255	.263	.268	.0005	7
.001	.148	.176	.191	.208	.225	.237	.245	.261	.266	.274	.282	.288	.001	
.005	.206	.235	.251	.267	.285	.296	.304	.319	.324	.332	.340	.345	.005	
.01	.241	.270	.286	.303	.320	.331	.339	.355	.358	.366	.373	.379	.01	
.025	.304	.333	.348	.364	.381	.392	.399	.413	.418	.426	.433	.437	.025	
.05	.369	.398	.413	.428	.445	.455	.461	.476	.479	.485	.493	.498	.05	
.10	.463	.491	.504	.519	.534	.543	.550	.562	.566	.571	.578	.582	.10	
.25	.679	.702	.713	.725	.737	.745	.749	.760	.762	.767	.772	.775	.25	
.50	1.05	1.07	1.07	1.08	1.08	1.09	1.09	1.10	1.10	1.10	1.10	1.10	.50	
.75	1.68	1.67	1.67	1.66	1.66	1.66	1.65	1.65	1.65	1.65	1.65	1.65	.75	
.90	2.63	2.59	2.58	2.56	2.54	2.52	2.51	2.50	2.49	2.48	2.48	2.47	.90	
.95	3.51	3.44	3.41	3.38	3.34	3.32	3.30	3.27	3.27	3.25	3.24	3.23	.95	
.975	4.57	4.47	4.42	4.36	4.31	4.28	4.25	4.21	4.20	4.18	4.16	4.14	.975	
.99	6.31	6.16	6.07	5.99	5.91	5.86	5.82	5.75	5.74	5.70	5.67	5.65	.99	
.995	7.97	7.75	7.65	7.53	7.42	7.35	7.31	7.22	7.19	7.15	7.10	7.08	.995	
.999	13.3	12.9	12.7	12.5	12.3	12.2	12.1	11.9	11.9	11.8	11.7	11.7	.999	
.9995	16.5	16.0	15.7	15.5	15.2	15.1	15.0	14.7	14.7	14.6	14.5	14.4	.9995	
.0005	.136	.164	.181	.198	.218	.230	.239	.257	.262	.271	.281	.287	.0005	8
.001	.155	.184	.200	.218	.238	.250	.259	.277	.282	.292	.300	.306	.001	
.005	.214	.244	.261	.279	.299	.311	.319	.337	.341	.351	.358	.364	.005	
.01	.250	.281	.297	.315	.334	.346	.354	.372	.376	.385	.392	.398	.01	
.025	.313	.343	.360	.377	.395	.407	.415	.431	.435	.442	.450	.456	.025	
.05	.379	.409	.425	.441	.459	.469	.477	.493	.496	.505	.510	.516	.05	
.10	.472	.500	.515	.531	.547	.556	.563	.578	.581	.588	.595	.599	.10	
.25	.684	.707	.718	.730	.743	.751	.756	.767	.769	.775	.780	.783	.25	
.50	1.04	1.05	1.06	1.07	1.07	1.07	1.08	1.08	1.08	1.09	1.09	1.09	.50	
.75	1.62	1.61	1.60	1.60	1.59	1.59	1.59	1.58	1.58	1.58	1.58	1.58	.75	
.90	2.46	2.42	2.40	2.38	2.36	2.35	2.34	2.32	2.32	2.31	2.30	2.29	.90	
.95	3.22	3.15	3.12	3.08	3.04	3.02	3.01	2.97	2.97	2.95	2.94	2.93	.95	
.975	4.10	4.00	3.95	3.89	3.84	3.81	3.78	3.74	3.73	3.70	3.68	3.67	.975	
.99	5.52	5.36	5.28	5.20	5.12	5.07	5.03	4.96	4.95	4.91	4.88	4.86	.99	
.995	6.81	6.61	6.50	6.40	6.29	6.22	6.18	6.09	6.06	6.02	5.98	5.95	.995	
.999	10.8	10.5	10.3	10.1	9.92	9.80	9.73	9.57	9.54	9.46	9.39	9.34	.999	
.9995	13.1	12.7	12.5	12.2	12.0	11.8	11.8	11.6	11.5	11.4	11.4	11.3	.9995	
.0005	.141	.171	.188	.207	.228	.242	.251	.270	.276	.287	.297	.303	.0005	9
.001	.160	.191	.208	.228	.249	.262	.271	.291	.296	.307	.316	.323	.001	
.005	.220	.253	.271	.290	.310	.324	.332	.351	.356	.366	.376	.382	.005	
.01	.257	.289	.307	.326	.346	.358	.368	.386	.391	.400	.410	.415	.01	
.025	.320	.352	.370	.388	.408	.420	.428	.446	.450	.459	.467	.473	.025	
.05	.386	.418	.435	.452	.471	.483	.490	.508	.510	.518	.526	.532	.05	
.10	.479	.509	.525	.541	.558	.568	.575	.588	.594	.602	.610	.613	.10	
.25	.687	.711	.723	.736	.749	.757	.762	.773	.776	.782	.787	.791	.25	
.50	1.03	1.04	1.05	1.05	1.06	1.06	1.07	1.07	1.07	1.08	1.08	1.08	.50	
.75	1.57	1.56	1.56	1.55	1.55	1.54	1.54	1.53	1.53	1.53	1.53	1.53	.75	
.90	2.34	2.30	2.28	2.25	2.23	2.22	2.21	2.19	2.18	2.17	2.17	2.16	.90	
.95	3.01	2.94	2.90	2.86	2.83	2.80	2.79	2.76	2.75	2.73	2.72	2.71	.95	
.975	3.77	3.67	3.61	3.56	3.51	3.47	3.45	3.40	3.39	3.37	3.35	3.33	.975	
.99	4.96	4.81	4.73	4.65	4.57	4.52	4.48	4.42	4.40	4.36	4.33	4.31	.99	
.995	6.03	5.83	5.73	5.62	5.52	5.45	5.41	5.32	5.30	5.26	5.21	5.19	.995	
.999	9.24	8.90	8.72	8.55	8.37	8.26	8.19	8.04	8.00	7.93	7.86	7.81	.999	
.9995	11.0	10.6	10.4	10.2	9.94	9.80	9.71	9.53	9.49	9.40	9.32	9.26	.9995	

TABLE A-7c. PERCENTILES OF THE $F(\nu_1, \nu_2)$ DISTRIBUTIONS (*Continued*)

ν_2	Cum. Prop. \ V_1	1	2	3	4	5	6	7	8	9	10	11	12	Cum. Prop.
10	.0005	$.0^{6}41$	$.0^{3}50$	$.0^{2}49$	.015	.028	.043	.057	.071	.085	.097	.108	.119	.0005
	.001	$.0^{5}17$	$.0^{2}10$	$.0^{2}77$	.021	.037	.054	.071	.087	.101	.114	.126	.137	.001
	.005	$.0^{4}41$	$.0^{2}50$	.023	.048	.073	.098	.119	.139	.156	.171	.185	.197	.005
	.01	$.0^{3}17$	.010	.037	.069	.100	.127	.151	.172	.190	.206	.220	.233	.01
	.025	$.0^{2}10$	.025	.069	.113	.151	.183	.210	.233	.252	.269	.283	.296	.025
	.05	$.0^{2}41$	.052	.114	.168	.211	.246	.275	.299	.319	.336	.351	.363	.05
	.10	.017	.106	.191	.255	.303	.340	.370	.394	.414	.430	.444	.457	.10
	.25	.107	.296	.409	.480	.529	.565	.592	.613	.631	.645	.657	.667	.25
	.50	.490	.743	.845	.899	.932	.954	.971	.983	.992	1.00	1.01	1.01	.50
	.75	1.49	1.60	1.60	1.59	1.59	1.58	1.57	1.56	1.56	1.55	1.55	1.54	.75
	.90	3.28	2.92	2.73	2.61	2.52	2.46	2.41	2.38	2.35	2.32	2.30	2.28	.90
	.95	4.96	4.10	3.71	3.48	3.33	3.22	3.14	3.07	3.02	2.98	2.94	2.91	.95
	.975	6.94	5.46	4.83	4.47	4.24	4.07	3.95	3.85	3.78	3.72	3.66	3.62	.975
	.99	10.0	7.56	6.55	5.99	5.64	5.39	5.20	5.06	4.94	4.85	4.77	4.71	.99
	.995	12.8	9.43	8.08	7.34	6.87	6.54	6.30	6.12	5.97	5.85	5.75	5.66	.995
	.999	21.0	14.9	12.6	11.3	10.5	9.92	9.52	9.20	8.96	8.75	8.58	8.44	.999
	.9995	25.5	17.9	15.0	13.4	12.4	11.8	11.3	10.9	10.6	10.3	10.1	9.93	.9995
11	.0005	$.0^{6}41$	$.0^{3}50$	$.0^{2}49$	.015	.028	.043	.058	.072	.086	.099	.111	.121	.0005
	.001	$.0^{5}16$	$.0^{2}10$	$.0^{2}78$	.021	.038	.055	.072	.088	.103	.116	.129	.140	.001
	.005	$.0^{4}40$	$.0^{2}50$	.023	.048	.074	.099	.121	.141	.158	.174	.188	.200	.005
	.01	$.0^{3}16$	.010	.037	.069	.100	.128	.153	.175	.193	.210	.224	.237	.01
	.025	$.0^{2}10$	.025	.069	.114	.152	.185	.212	.236	.256	.273	.288	.301	.025
	.05	$.0^{2}41$	.052	.114	.168	.212	.248	.278	.302	.323	.340	.355	.368	.05
	.10	.017	.106	.192	.256	.305	.342	.373	.397	.417	.435	.448	.461	.10
	.25	.107	.295	.408	.481	.529	.565	.592	.614	.633	.645	.658	.667	.25
	.50	.486	.739	.840	.893	.926	.948	.964	.977	.986	.994	1.00	1.01	.50
	.75	1.47	1.58	1.58	1.57	1.56	1.55	1.54	1.53	1.53	1.52	1.52	1.51	.75
	.90	3.23	2.86	2.66	2.54	2.45	2.39	2.34	2.30	2.27	2.25	2.23	2.21	.90
	.95	4.84	3.98	3.59	3.36	3.20	3.09	3.01	2.95	2.90	2.85	2.82	2.79	.95
	.975	6.72	5.26	4.63	4.28	4.04	3.88	3.76	3.66	3.59	3.53	3.47	3.43	.975
	.99	9.65	7.21	6.22	5.67	5.32	5.07	4.89	4.74	4.63	4.54	4.46	4.40	.99
	.995	12.2	8.91	7.60	6.88	6.42	6.10	5.86	5.68	5.54	5.42	5.32	5.24	.995
	.999	19.7	13.8	11.6	10.3	9.58	9.05	8.66	8.35	8.12	7.92	7.76	7.62	.999
	.9995	23.6	16.4	13.6	12.2	11.2	10.6	10.1	9.76	9.48	9.24	9.04	8.88	.9995
12	.0005	$.0^{6}41$	$.0^{3}50$	$.0^{2}49$	.015	.028	.044	.058	.073	.087	.101	.113	.124	.0005
	.001	$.0^{5}16$	$.0^{2}10$	$.0^{2}78$	.021	.038	.056	.073	.089	.104	.118	.131	.143	.001
	.005	$.0^{4}39$	$.0^{2}50$	.023	.048	.075	.100	.122	.143	.161	.177	.191	.204	.005
	.01	$.0^{3}16$	.010	.037	.070	.101	.130	.155	.176	.196	.212	.227	.241	.01
	.025	$.0^{2}10$	.025	.070	.114	.153	.186	.214	.238	.259	.276	.292	.305	.025
	.05	$.0^{2}41$	.052	.114	.169	.214	.250	.280	.305	.325	.343	.358	.372	.05
	.10	.016	.106	.192	.257	.306	.344	.375	.400	.420	.438	.452	.466	.10
	.25	.106	.295	.408	.480	.530	.566	.594	.616	.633	.649	.662	.671	.25
	.50	.484	.735	.835	.888	.921	.943	.959	.972	.981	.989	.995	1.00	.50
	.75	1.46	1.56	1.56	1.55	1.54	1.53	1.52	1.51	1.51	1.50	1.50	1.49	.75
	.90	3.18	2.81	2.61	2.48	2.39	2.33	2.28	2.24	2.21	2.19	2.17	2.15	.90
	.95	4.75	3.89	3.49	3.26	3.11	3.00	2.91	2.85	2.80	2.75	2.72	2.69	.95
	.975	6.55	5.10	4.47	4.12	3.89	3.73	3.61	3.51	3.44	3.37	3.32	3.28	.975
	.99	9.33	6.93	5.95	5.41	5.06	4.82	4.64	4.50	4.39	4.30	4.22	4.16	.99
	.995	11.8	8.51	7.23	6.52	6.07	5.76	5.52	5.35	5.20	5.09	4.99	4.91	.995
	.999	18.6	13.0	10.8	9.63	8.89	8.38	8.00	7.71	7.48	7.29	7.14	7.01	.999
	.9995	22.2	15.3	12.7	11.2	10.4	9.74	9.28	8.94	8.66	8.43	8.24	8.08	.9995

TABLE A-7c. PERCENTILES OF THE $F(\nu_1,\nu_2)$ DISTRIBUTIONS (*Continued*)

Cum. Prop. \ ν_1	15	20	24	30	40	50	60	100	120	200	500	∞	Cum. Prop.	ν_2
.0005	.145	.177	.195	.215	.238	.251	.262	.282	.288	.299	.311	.319	.0005	**10**
.001	.164	.197	.216	.236	.258	.272	.282	.303	.309	.321	.331	.338	.001	
.005	.226	.260	.279	.299	.321	.334	.344	.365	.370	.380	.391	.397	.005	
.01	.263	.297	.316	.336	.357	.370	.380	.400	.405	.415	.424	.431	.01	
.025	.327	.360	.379	.398	.419	.431	.441	.459	.464	.474	.483	.488	.025	
.05	.393	.426	.444	.462	.481	.493	.502	.518	.523	.532	.541	.546	.05	
.10	.486	.516	.532	.549	.567	.578	.586	.602	.605	.614	.621	.625	.10	
.25	.691	.714	.727	.740	.754	.762	.767	.779	.782	.788	.793	.797	.25	
.50	1.02	1.03	1.04	1.05	1.05	1.06	1.06	1.06	1.06	1.07	1.07	1.07	.50	
.75	1.53	1.52	1.52	1.51	1.51	1.50	1.50	1.49	1.49	1.49	1.48	1.48	.75	
.90	2.24	2.20	2.18	2.16	2.13	2.12	2.11	2.09	2.08	2.07	2.06	2.06	.90	
.95	2.85	2.77	2.74	2.70	2.66	2.64	2.62	2.59	2.58	2.56	2.55	2.54	.95	
.975	3.52	3.42	3.37	3.31	3.26	3.22	3.20	3.15	3.14	3.12	3.09	3.08	.975	
.99	4.56	4.41	4.33	4.25	4.17	4.12	4.08	4.01	4.00	3.96	3.93	3.91	.99	
.995	5.47	5.27	5.17	5.07	4.97	4.90	4.86	4.77	4.75	4.71	4.67	4.64	.995	
.999	8.13	7.80	7.64	7.47	7.30	7.19	7.12	6.98	6.94	6.87	6.81	6.76	.999	
.9995	9.56	9.16	8.96	8.75	8.54	8.42	8.33	8.16	8.12	8.04	7.96	7.90	.9995	
.0005	.148	.182	.201	.222	.246	.261	.271	.293	.299	.312	.324	.331	.0005	**11**
.001	.168	.202	.222	.243	.266	.282	.292	.313	.320	.332	.343	.353	.001	
.005	.231	.266	.286	.308	.330	.345	.355	.376	.382	.394	.403	.412	.005	
.01	.268	.304	.324	.344	.366	.380	.391	.412	.417	.427	.439	.444	.01	
.025	.332	.368	.386	.407	.429	.442	.450	.472	.476	.485	.495	.503	.025	
.05	.398	.433	.452	.469	.490	.503	.513	.529	.535	.543	.552	.559	.05	
.10	.490	.524	.541	.559	.578	.588	.595	.614	.617	.625	.633	.637	.10	
.25	.694	.719	.730	.744	.758	.767	.773	.780	.788	.794	.799	.803	.25	
.50	1.02	1.03	1.03	1.04	1.05	1.05	1.05	1.06	1.06	1.06	1.06	1.06	.50	
.75	1.50	1.49	1.49	1.48	1.47	1.47	1.47	1.46	1.46	1.46	1.45	1.45	.75	
.90	2.17	2.12	2.10	2.08	2.05	2.04	2.03	2.00	2.00	1.99	1.98	1.97	.90	
.95	2.72	2.65	2.61	2.57	2.53	2.51	2.49	2.46	2.45	2.43	2.42	2.40	.95	
.975	3.33	3.23	3.17	3.12	3.06	3.03	3.00	2.96	2.94	2.92	2.90	2.88	.975	
.99	4.25	4.10	4.02	3.94	3.86	3.81	3.78	3.71	3.69	3.66	3.62	3.60	.99	
.995	5.05	4.86	4.76	4.65	4.55	4.49	4.45	4.36	4.34	4.29	4.25	4.23	.995	
.999	7.32	7.01	6.85	6.68	6.52	6.41	6.35	6.21	6.17	6.10	6.04	6.00	.999	
.9995	8.52	8.14	7.94	7.75	7.55	7.43	7.35	7.18	7.14	7.06	6.98	6.93	.9995	
.0005	.152	.186	.206	.228	.253	.269	.280	.305	.311	.323	.337	.345	.0005	**12**
.001	.172	.207	.228	.250	.275	.291	.302	.326	.332	.344	.357	.365	.001	
.005	.235	.272	.292	.315	.339	.355	.365	.388	.393	.405	.417	.424	.005	
.01	.273	.310	.330	.352	.375	.391	.401	.422	.428	.441	.450	.458	.01	
.025	.337	.374	.394	.416	.437	.450	.461	.481	.487	.498	.508	.514	.025	
.05	.404	.439	.458	.478	.499	.513	.522	.541	.545	.556	.565	.571	.05	
.10	.496	.528	.546	.564	.583	.595	.604	.621	.625	.633	.641	.647	.10	
.25	.695	.721	.734	.748	.762	.771	.777	.789	.792	.799	.804	.808	.25	
.50	1.01	1.02	1.03	1.03	1.04	1.04	1.05	1.05	1.05	1.05	1.06	1.06	.50	
.75	1.48	1.47	1.46	1.45	1.45	1.44	1.44	1.43	1.43	1.43	1.42	1.42	.75	
.90	2.11	2.06	2.04	2.01	1.99	1.97	1.96	1.94	1.93	1.92	1.91	1.90	.90	
.95	2.62	2.54	2.51	2.47	2.43	2.40	2.38	2.35	2.34	2.32	2.31	2.30	.95	
.975	3.18	3.07	3.02	2.96	2.91	2.87	2.85	2.80	2.79	2.76	2.74	2.72	.975	
.99	4.01	3.86	3.78	3.70	3.62	3.57	3.54	3.47	3.45	3.41	3.38	3.36	.99	
.995	4.72	4.53	4.43	4.33	4.23	4.17	4.12	4.04	4.01	3.97	3.93	3.90	.995	
.999	6.71	6.40	6.25	6.09	5.93	5.83	5.76	5.63	5.59	5.52	5.46	5.42	.999	
.9995	7.74	7.37	7.18	7.00	6.80	6.68	6.61	6.45	6.41	6.33	6.25	6.20	.9995	

TABLE A-7c. PERCENTILES OF THE $F(\nu_1,\nu_2)$ DISTRIBUTIONS (*Continued*)

ν_2	Cum. Prop. \ ν_1	1	2	3	4	5	6	7	8	9	10	11	12	Cum. Prop.
15	.0005	$.0^{6}41$	$.0^{3}50$	$.0^{2}49$	.015	.029	.045	.061	.076	.091	.105	.117	.129	.0005
	.001	$.0^{5}16$	$.0^{2}10$	$.0^{2}79$	.021	.039	.057	.075	.092	.108	.123	.137	.149	.001
	.005	$.0^{4}39$	$.0^{2}50$	.023	.049	.076	.102	.125	.147	.166	.183	.198	.212	.005
	.01	$.0^{3}16$	.010	.037	.070	.103	.132	.158	.181	.202	.219	.235	.249	.01
	.025	$.0^{2}10$	.025	.070	.116	.156	.190	.219	.244	.265	.284	.300	.315	.025
	.05	$.0^{2}41$	.051	.115	.170	.216	.254	.285	.311	.333	.351	.368	.382	.05
	.10	.016	.106	.192	.258	.309	.348	.380	.406	.427	.446	.461	.475	.10
	.25	.105	.293	.407	.480	.531	.568	.596	.618	.637	.652	.667	.676	.25
	.50	.478	.726	.826	.878	.911	.933	.948	.960	.970	.977	.984	.989	.50
	.75	1.43	1.52	1.52	1.51	1.49	1.48	1.47	1.46	1.46	1.45	1.44	1.44	.75
	.90	3.07	2.70	2.49	2.36	2.27	2.21	2.16	2.12	2.09	2.06	2.04	2.02	.90
	.95	4.54	3.68	3.29	3.06	2.90	2.79	2.71	2.64	2.59	2.54	2.51	2.48	.95
	.975	6.20	4.76	4.15	3.80	3.58	3.41	3.29	3.20	3.12	3.06	3.01	2.96	.975
	.99	8.68	6.36	5.42	4.89	4.56	4.32	4.14	4.00	3.89	3.80	3.73	3.67	.99
	.995	10.8	7.70	6.48	5.80	5.37	5.07	4.85	4.67	4.54	4.42	4.33	4.25	.995
	.999	16.6	11.3	9.34	8.25	7.57	7.09	6.74	6.47	6.26	6.08	5.93	5.81	.999
	.9995	19.5	13.2	10.8	9.48	8.66	8.10	7.68	7.36	7.11	6.91	6.75	6.60	.9995
20	.0005	$.0^{6}40$	$.0^{3}50$	$.0^{2}50$	.015	.029	.046	.063	.079	.094	.109	.123	.136	.0005
	.001	$.0^{5}16$	$.0^{2}10$	$.0^{2}79$	.022	.039	.058	.077	.095	.112	.128	.143	.156	.001
	.005	$.0^{4}39$	$.0^{2}50$	.023	.050	.077	.104	.129	.151	.171	.190	.206	.221	.005
	.01	$.0^{3}16$	.010	.037	.071	.105	.135	.162	.187	.208	.227	.244	.259	.01
	.025	$.0^{2}10$	.025	.071	.117	.158	.193	.224	.250	.273	.292	.310	.325	.025
	.05	$.0^{2}40$	.051	.115	.172	.219	.258	.290	.318	.340	.360	.377	.393	.05
	.10	.016	.106	.193	.260	.312	.353	.385	.412	.435	.454	.472	.485	.10
	.25	.104	.292	.407	.480	.531	.569	.598	.622	.641	.656	.671	.681	.25
	.50	.472	.718	.816	.868	.900	.922	.938	.950	.959	.966	.972	.977	.50
	.75	1.40	1.49	1.48	1.47	1.45	1.44	1.43	1.42	1.41	1.40	1.39	1.39	.75
	.90	2.97	2.59	2.38	2.25	2.16	2.09	2.04	2.00	1.96	1.94	1.91	1.89	.90
	.95	4.35	3.49	3.10	2.87	2.71	2.60	2.51	2.45	2.39	2.35	2.31	2.28	.95
	.975	5.87	4.46	3.86	3.51	3.29	3.13	3.01	2.91	2.84	2.77	2.72	2.68	.975
	.99	8.10	5.85	4.94	4.43	4.10	3.87	3.70	3.56	3.46	3.37	3.29	3.23	.99
	.995	9.94	6.99	5.82	5.17	4.76	4.47	4.26	4.09	3.96	3.85	3.76	3.68	.995
	.999	14.8	9.95	8.10	7.10	6.46	6.02	5.69	5.44	5.24	5.08	4.94	4.82	.999
	.9995	17.2	11.4	9.20	8.02	7.28	6.76	6.38	6.08	5.85	5.66	5.51	5.38	.9995
24	.0005	$.0^{6}40$	$.0^{3}50$	$.0^{2}50$	.015	.030	.046	.064	.080	.096	.112	.126	.139	.0005
	.001	$.0^{5}16$	$.0^{2}10$	$.0^{2}79$	.022	.040	.059	.079	.097	.115	.131	.146	.160	.001
	.005	$.0^{4}40$	$.0^{2}50$	.023	.050	.078	.106	.131	.154	.175	.193	.210	.226	.005
	.01	$.0^{3}16$	.010	.038	.072	.106	.137	.165	.189	.211	.231	.249	.264	.01
	.025	$.0^{2}10$	.025	.071	.117	.159	.195	.227	.253	.277	.297	.315	.331	.025
	.05	$.0^{2}40$	.051	.116	.173	.221	.260	.293	.321	.345	.365	.383	.399	.05
	.10	.016	.106	.193	.261	.313	.355	.388	.416	.439	.459	.476	.491	.10
	.25	.104	.291	.406	.480	.532	.570	.600	.623	.643	.659	.671	.684	.25
	.50	.469	.714	.812	.863	.895	.917	.932	.944	.953	.961	.967	.972	.50
	.75	1.39	1.47	1.46	1.44	1.43	1.41	1.40	1.39	1.38	1.38	1.37	1.36	.75
	.90	2.93	2.54	2.33	2.19	2.10	2.04	1.98	1.94	1.91	1.88	1.85	1.83	.90
	.95	4.26	3.40	3.01	2.78	2.62	2.51	2.42	2.36	2.30	2.25	2.21	2.18	.95
	.975	5.72	4.32	3.72	3.38	3.15	2.99	2.87	2.78	2.70	2.64	2.59	2.54	.975
	.99	7.82	5.61	4.72	4.22	3.90	3.67	3.50	3.36	3.26	3.17	3.09	3.03	.99
	.995	9.55	6.66	5.52	4.89	4.49	4.20	3.99	3.83	3.69	3.59	3.50	3.42	.995
	.999	14.0	9.34	7.55	6.59	5.98	5.55	5.23	4.99	4.80	4.64	4.50	4.39	.999
	.9995	16.2	10.6	8.52	7.39	6.68	6.18	5.82	5.54	5.31	5.13	4.98	4.85	.9995

TABLE A-7c. PERCENTILES OF THE $F(\nu_1,\nu_2)$ DISTRIBUTIONS (*Continued*)

Cum. Prop. \ ν_1	15	20	24	30	40	50	60	100	120	200	500	∞	Cum. Prop.	ν_2
.0005	.159	.197	.220	.244	.272	.290	.303	.330	.339	.353	.368	.377	.0005	**15**
.001	.181	.219	.242	.266	.294	.313	.325	.352	.360	.375	.388	.398	.001	
.005	.246	.286	.308	.333	.360	.377	.389	.415	.422	.435	.448	.457	.005	
.01	.284	.324	.346	.370	.397	.413	.425	.450	.456	.469	.483	.490	.01	
.025	.349	.389	.410	.433	.458	.474	.485	.508	.514	.526	.538	.546	.025	
.05	.416	.454	.474	.496	.519	.535	.545	.565	.571	.581	.592	.600	.05	
.10	.507	.542	.561	.581	.602	.614	.624	.641	.647	.658	.667	.672	.10	
.25	.701	.728	.742	.757	.772	.782	.788	.802	.805	.812	.818	.822	.25	
.50	1.00	1.01	1.02	1.02	1.03	1.03	1.03	1.04	1.04	1.04	1.04	1.05	.50	
.75	1.43	1.41	1.41	1.40	1.39	1.39	1.38	1.38	1.37	1.37	1.36	1.36	.75	
.90	1.97	1.92	1.90	1.87	1.85	1.83	1.82	1.79	1.79	1.77	1.76	1.76	.90	
.95	2.40	2.33	2.39	2.25	2.20	2.18	2.16	2.12	2.11	2.10	2.08	2.07	.95	
.975	2.86	2.76	2.70	2.64	2.59	2.55	2.52	2.47	2.46	2.44	2.41	2.40	.975	
.99	3.52	3.37	3.29	3.21	3.13	3.08	3.05	2.98	2.96	2.92	2.89	2.87	.99	
.995	4.07	3.88	3.79	3.69	3.59	3.52	3.48	3.39	3.37	3.33	3.29	3.26	.995	
.999	5.54	5.25	5.10	4.95	4.80	4.70	4.64	4.51	4.47	4.41	4.35	4.31	.999	
.9995	6.27	5.93	5.75	5.58	5.40	5.29	5.21	5.06	5.02	4.94	4.87	4.83	.9995	
.0005	.169	.211	.235	.263	.295	.316	.331	.364	.375	.391	.408	.422	.0005	**20**
.001	.191	.233	.258	.286	.318	.339	.354	.386	.395	.413	.429	.441	.001	
.005	.258	.301	.327	.354	.385	.405	.419	.448	.457	.474	.490	.500	.005	
.01	.297	.340	.365	.392	.422	.441	.455	.483	.491	.508	.521	.532	.01	
.025	.363	.406	.430	.456	.484	.503	.514	.541	.548	.562	.575	.585	.025	
.05	.430	.471	.493	.518	.544	.562	.572	.595	.603	.617	.629	.637	.05	
.10	.520	.557	.578	.600	.623	.637	.648	.671	.675	.685	.694	.704	.10	
.25	.708	.736	.751	.767	.784	.794	.801	.816	.820	.827	.835	.840	.25	
.50	.989	1.00	1.01	1.01	1.02	1.02	1.02	1.03	1.03	1.03	1.03	1.03	.50	
.75	1.37	1.36	1.35	1.34	1.33	1.33	1.32	1.31	1.31	1.30	1.30	1.29	.75	
.90	1.84	1.79	1.77	1.74	1.71	1.69	1.68	1.65	1.64	1.63	1.62	1.61	.90	
.95	2.20	2.12	2.08	2.04	1.99	1.97	1.95	1.91	1.90	1.88	1.86	1.84	.95	
.975	2.57	2.46	2.41	2.35	2.29	2.25	2.22	2.17	2.16	2.13	2.10	2.09	.975	
.99	3.09	2.94	2.86	2.78	2.69	2.64	2.61	2.54	2.52	2.48	2.44	2.42	.99	
.995	3.50	3.32	3.22	3.12	3.02	2.96	2.92	2.83	2.81	2.76	2.72	2.69	.995	
.999	4.56	4.29	4.15	4.01	3.86	3.77	3.70	3.58	3.54	3.48	3.42	3.38	.999	
.9995	5.07	4.75	4.58	4.42	4.24	4.15	4.07	3.93	3.90	3.82	3.75	3.70	.9995	
.0005	.174	.218	.244	.274	.309	.331	.349	.384	.395	.416	.434	.449	.0005	**24**
.001	.196	.241	.268	.298	.332	.354	.371	.405	.417	.437	.455	.469	.001	
.005	.264	.310	.337	.367	.400	.422	.437	.469	.479	.498	.515	.527	.005	
.01	.304	.350	.376	.405	.437	.459	.473	.505	.513	.529	.546	.558	.01	
.025	.370	.415	.441	.468	.498	.518	.531	.562	.568	.585	.599	.610	.025	
.05	.437	.480	.504	.530	.558	.575	.588	.613	.622	.637	.649	.659	.05	
.10	.527	.566	.588	.611	.635	.651	.662	.685	.691	.704	.715	.723	.10	
.25	.712	.741	.757	.773	.791	.802	.809	.825	.829	.837	.844	.850	.25	
.50	.983	.994	1.00	1.01	1.01	1.02	1.02	1.02	1.02	1.02	1.03	1.03	.50	
.75	1.35	1.33	1.32	1.31	1.30	1.29	1.29	1.28	1.28	1.27	1.27	1.26	.75	
.90	1.78	1.73	1.70	1.67	1.64	1.62	1.61	1.58	1.57	1.56	1.54	1.53	.90	
.95	2.11	2.03	1.98	1.94	1.89	1.86	1.84	1.80	1.79	1.77	1.75	1.73	.95	
.975	2.44	2.33	2.27	2.21	2.15	2.11	2.08	2.02	2.01	1.98	1.95	1.94	.975	
.99	2.89	2.74	2.66	2.58	2.49	2.44	2.40	2.33	2.31	2.27	2.24	2.21	.99	
.995	3.25	3.06	2.97	2.87	2.77	2.70	2.66	2.57	2.55	2.50	2.46	2.43	.995	
.999	4.14	3.87	3.74	3.59	3.45	3.35	3.29	3.16	3.14	3.07	3.01	2.97	.999	
.9995	4.55	4.25	4.09	3.93	3.76	3.66	3.59	3.44	3.41	3.33	3.27	3.22	.9995	

Table A-7c. Percentiles of the $F(\nu_1, \nu_2)$ Distributions (*Continued*)

ν_2	Cum. Prop \ ν_1	1	2	3	4	5	6	7	8	9	10	11	12	Cum. Prop.
30	.0005	$.0^{6}40$	$.0^{3}50$	$.0^{2}50$	.015	.030	.047	.065	.082	.098	.114	.129	.143	.0005
	.001	$.0^{5}16$	$.0^{2}10$	$.0^{2}80$	.022	.040	.060	.080	.099	.117	.134	.150	.164	.001
	.005	$.0^{4}40$	$.0^{2}50$	.024	.050	.079	.107	.133	.156	.178	.197	.215	.231	.005
	.01	$.0^{3}16$	.010	.038	.072	.107	.138	.167	.192	.215	.235	.254	.270	.01
	.025	$.0^{2}10$	.025	.071	.118	.161	.197	.229	.257	.281	.302	.321	.337	.025
	.05	$.0^{2}40$	.051	.116	.174	.222	.263	.296	.325	.349	.370	.389	.406	.05
	.10	.016	.106	.193	.262	.315	.357	.391	.420	.443	.464	.481	.497	.10
	.25	.103	.290	.406	.480	.532	.571	.601	.625	.645	.661	.676	.688	.25
	.50	.466	.709	.807	.858	.890	.912	.927	.939	.948	.955	.961	.966	.50
	.75	1.38	1.45	1.44	1.42	1.41	1.39	1.38	1.37	1.36	1.35	1.35	1.34	.75
	.90	2.88	2.49	2.28	2.14	2.05	1.98	1.93	1.88	1.85	1.82	1.79	1.77	.90
	.95	4.17	3.32	2.92	2.69	2.53	2.42	2.33	2.27	2.21	2.16	2.13	2.09	.95
	.975	5.57	4.18	3.59	3.25	3.03	2.87	2.75	2.65	2.57	2.51	2.46	2.41	.975
	.99	7.56	5.39	4.51	4.02	3.70	3.47	3.30	3.17	3.07	2.98	2.91	2.84	.99
	.995	9.18	6.35	5.24	4.62	4.23	3.95	3.74	3.58	3.45	3.34	3.25	3.18	.995
	.999	13.3	8.77	7.05	6.12	5.53	5.12	4.82	4.58	4.39	4.24	4.11	4.00	.999
	.9995	15.2	9.90	7.90	6.82	6.14	5.66	5.31	5.04	4.82	4.65	4.51	4.38	.9995
40	.0005	$.0^{6}40$	$.0^{3}50$	$.0^{2}50$	.016	.030	.048	.066	.084	.100	.117	.132	.147	.0005
	.001	$.0^{5}16$	$.0^{2}10$	$.0^{2}80$	.022	.042	.061	.081	.101	.119	.137	.153	.169	.001
	.005	$.0^{4}40$	$.0^{2}50$	.024	.051	.080	.108	.135	.159	.181	.201	.220	.237	.005
	.01	$.0^{3}16$	.010	.038	.073	.108	.140	.169	.195	.219	.240	.259	.276	.01
	.025	$.0^{3}99$	.025	.071	.119	.162	.199	.232	.260	.285	.307	.327	.344	.025
	.05	$.0^{2}40$	.051	.116	.175	.224	.265	.299	.329	.354	.376	.395	.412	.05
	.10	.016	.106	.194	.263	.317	.360	.394	.424	.448	.469	.488	.504	.10
	.25	.103	.290	.405	.480	.533	.572	.603	.627	.647	.664	.680	.691	.25
	.50	.463	.705	.802	.854	.885	.907	.922	.934	.943	.950	.956	.961	.50
	.75	1.36	1.44	1.42	1.40	1.39	1.37	1.36	1.35	1.34	1.33	1.32	1.31	.75
	.90	2.84	2.44	2.23	2.09	2.00	1.93	1.87	1.83	1.79	1.76	1.73	1.71	.90
	.95	4.08	3.23	2.84	2.61	2.45	2.34	2.25	2.18	2.12	2.08	2.04	2.00	.95
	.975	5.42	4.05	3.46	3.13	2.90	2.74	2.62	2.53	2.45	2.39	2.33	2.29	.975
	.99	7.31	5.18	4.31	3.83	3.51	3.29	3.12	2.99	2.89	2.80	2.73	2.66	.99
	.995	8.83	6.07	4.98	4.37	3.99	3.71	3.51	3.35	3.22	3.12	3.03	2.95	.995
	.999	12.6	8.25	6.60	5.70	5.13	4.73	4.44	4.21	4.02	3.87	3.75	3.64	.999
	.9995	14.4	9.25	7.33	6.30	5.64	5.19	4.85	4.59	4.38	4.21	4.07	3.95	.9995
60	.0005	$.0^{6}40$	$.0^{3}50$	$.0^{2}51$	.016	.031	.048	.067	.085	.103	.120	.136	.152	.0005
	.001	$.0^{5}16$	$.0^{2}10$	$.0^{2}80$	.022	.041	.062	.083	.103	.122	.140	.157	.174	.001
	.005	$.0^{4}40$	$.0^{2}50$	.024	.051	.081	.110	.137	.162	.185	.206	.225	.243	.005
	.01	$.0^{3}16$	.010	.038	.073	.109	.142	.172	.199	.223	.245	.265	.283	.01
	.025	$.0^{3}99$	.025	.071	.120	.163	.202	.235	.264	.290	.313	.333	.351	.025
	.05	$.0^{2}40$	.051	.116	.176	.226	.267	.303	.333	.359	.382	.402	.419	.05
	.10	.016	.106	.194	.264	.318	.362	.398	.428	.453	.475	.493	.510	.10
	.25	.102	.289	.405	.480	.534	.573	.604	.629	.650	.667	.680	.695	.25
	.50	.461	.701	.798	.849	.880	.901	.917	.928	.937	.945	.951	.956	.50
	.75	1.35	1.42	1.41	1.38	1.37	1.35	1.33	1.32	1.31	1.30	1.29	1.29	.75
	.90	2.79	2.39	2.18	2.04	1.95	1.87	1.82	1.77	1.74	1.71	1.68	1.66	.90
	.95	4.00	3.15	2.76	2.53	2.37	2.25	2.17	2.10	2.04	1.99	1.95	1.92	.95
	.975	5.29	3.93	3.34	3.01	2.79	2.63	2.51	2.41	2.33	2.27	2.22	2.17	.975
	.99	7.08	4.98	4.13	3.65	3.34	3.12	2.95	2.82	2.72	2.63	2.56	2.50	.99
	.995	8.49	5.80	4.73	4.14	3.76	3.49	3.29	3.13	3.01	2.90	2.82	2.74	.995
	.999	12.0	7.76	6.17	5.31	4.76	4.37	4.09	3.87	3.69	3.54	3.43	3.31	.999
	.9995	13.6	8.65	6.81	5.82	5.20	4.76	4.44	4.18	3.98	3.82	3.69	3.57	.9995

TABLE A-7c. PERCENTILES OF THE $F(\nu_1, \nu_2)$ DISTRIBUTIONS (*Continued*)

Cum. Prop. \ ν_1	15	20	24	30	40	50	60	100	120	200	500	∞	Cum. Prop.	ν_2
.0005	.179	.226	.254	.287	.325	.350	.369	.410	.420	.444	.467	.483	.0005	**30**
.001	.202	.250	.278	.311	.348	.373	.391	.431	.442	.465	.488	.503	.001	
.005	.271	.320	.349	.381	.416	.441	.457	.495	.504	.524	.543	.559	.005	
.01	.311	.360	.388	.419	.454	.476	.493	.529	.538	.559	.575	.590	.01	
.025	.378	.426	.453	.482	.515	.535	.551	.585	.592	.610	.625	.639	.025	
.05	.445	.490	.516	.543	.573	.592	.606	.637	.644	.658	.676	.685	.05	
.10	.534	.575	.598	.623	.649	.667	.678	.704	.710	.725	.735	.746	.10	
.25	.716	.746	.763	.780	.798	.810	.818	.835	.839	.848	.856	.862	.25	
.50	.978	.989	.994	1.00	1.01	1.01	1.01	1.02	1.02	1.02	1.02	1.02	.50	
.75	1.32	1.30	1.29	1.28	1.27	1.26	1.26	1.25	1.24	1.24	1.23	1.23	.75	
.90	1.72	1.67	1.64	1.61	1.57	1.55	1.54	1.51	1.50	1.48	1.47	1.46	.90	
.95	2.01	1.93	1.89	1.84	1.79	1.76	1.74	1.70	1.68	1.66	1.64	1.62	.95	
.975	2.31	2.20	2.14	2.07	2.01	1.97	1.94	1.88	1.87	1.84	1.81	1.79	.975	
.99	2.70	2.55	2.47	2.39	2.30	2.25	2.21	2.13	2.11	2.07	2.03	2.01	.99	
.995	3.01	2.82	2.73	2.63	2.52	2.46	2.42	2.32	2.30	2.25	2.21	2.18	.995	
.999	3.75	3.49	3.36	3.22	3.07	2.98	2.92	2.79	2.76	2.69	2.63	2.59	.999	
.9995	4.10	3.80	3.65	3.48	3.32	3.22	3.15	3.00	2.97	2.89	2.82	2.78	.9995	
.0005	.185	.236	.266	.301	.343	.373	.393	.441	.453	.480	.504	.525	.0005	**40**
.001	.209	.259	.290	.326	.367	.396	.415	.461	.473	.500	.524	.545	.001	
.005	.279	.331	.362	.396	.436	.463	.481	.524	.534	.559	.581	.599	.005	
.01	.319	.371	.401	.435	.473	.498	.516	.556	.567	.592	.613	.628	.01	
.025	.387	.437	.466	.498	.533	.556	.573	.610	620	.641	.662	.674	.025	
.05	.454	.502	.529	.558	.591	.613	.627	.658	.669	.685	.704	.717	.05	
.10	.542	.585	.609	.636	.664	.683	.696	.724	.731	.747	.762	.772	.10	
.25	.720	.752	.769	.787	.806	.819	.828	.846	.851	.861	.870	.877	.25	
.50	.972	.983	.989	.994	1.00	1.00	1.01	1.01	1.01	1.01	1.02	1.02	.50	
.75	1.30	1.28	1.26	1.25	1.24	1.23	1.22	1.21	1.21	1.20	1.19	1.19	.75	
.90	1.66	1.61	1.57	1.54	1.51	1.48	1.47	1.43	1.42	1.41	1.39	1.38	.90	
.95	1.92	1.84	1.79	1.74	1.69	1.66	1.64	1.59	1.58	1.55	1.53	1.51	.95	
.975	2.18	2.07	2.01	1.94	1.88	1.83	1.80	1.74	1.72	1.69	1.66	1.64	.975	
.99	2.52	2.37	2.29	2.20	2.11	2.06	2.02	1.94	1.92	1.87	1.83	1.80	.99	
.995	2.78	2.60	2.50	2.40	2.30	2.23	2.18	2.09	2.06	2.01	1.96	1.93	.995	
.999	3.40	3.15	3.01	2.87	2.73	2.64	2.57	2.44	2.41	2.34	2.28	2.23	.999	
.9995	3.68	3.39	3.24	3.08	2.92	2.82	2.74	2.60	2.57	2.49	2.41	2.37	.9995	
.0005	.192	.246	.278	.318	.365	.398	.421	.478	.493	.527	.561	.585	.0005	**60**
.001	.216	.270	.304	.343	.389	.421	.444	.497	.512	.545	.579	.602	.001	
.005	.287	.343	.376	.414	.458	.488	.510	.559	.572	.602	.633	.652	.005	
.01	.328	.383	.416	.453	.495	.524	.545	.592	.604	.633	.658	.679	.01	
.025	.396	.450	.481	.515	.555	.581	.600	.641	.654	.680	.704	.720	.025	
.05	.463	.514	.543	.575	.611	.633	.652	.690	.700	.719	.746	.759	.05	
.10	.550	.596	.622	.650	.682	.703	.717	.750	.758	.776	.793	.806	.10	
.25	.725	.758	.776	.796	.816	.830	.840	.860	.865	.877	.888	.896	.25	
.50	.967	.978	.983	.989	.994	.998	1.00	1.00	1.01	1.01	1.01	1.01	.50	
.75	1.27	1.25	1.24	1.22	1.21	1.20	1.19	1.17	1.17	1.16	1.15	1.15	.75	
.90	1.60	1.54	1.51	1.48	1.44	1.41	1.40	1.36	1.35	1.33	1.31	1.29	.90	
.95	1.84	1.75	1.70	1.65	1.59	1.56	1.53	1.48	1.47	1.44	1.41	1.39	.95	
.975	2.06	1.94	1.88	1.82	1.74	1.70	1.67	1.60	1.58	1.54	1.51	1.48	.975	
.99	2.35	2.20	2.12	2.03	1.94	1.88	1.84	1.75	1.73	1.68	1.63	1.60	.99	
.995	2.57	2.39	2.29	2.19	2.08	2.01	1.96	1.86	1.83	1.78	1.73	1.69	.995	
.999	3.08	2.83	2.69	2.56	2.41	2.31	2.25	2.11	2.09	2.01	1.93	1.89	.999	
.9995	3.30	3.02	2.87	2.71	2.55	2.45	2.38	2.23	2.19	2.11	2.03	1.98	.9995	

TABLE A-7c. PERCENTILES OF THE $F(\nu_1,\nu_2)$ DISTRIBUTIONS (*Continued*)

ν_2	ν_1 / Cum. Prop.	1	2	3	4	5	6	7	8	9	10	11	12	Cum. Prop.
120	.0005	$.0^{6}40$	$.0^{3}50$	$.0^{2}51$	.016	.031	.049	.067	.087	.105	.123	.140	.156	.0005
	.001	$.0^{5}16$	$.0^{2}10$	$.0^{2}81$	.023	.042	.063	.084	.105	.125	.144	.162	.179	.001
	.005	$.0^{4}39$	$.0^{2}50$	.024	.051	.081	.111	.139	.165	.189	.211	.230	.249	.005
	.01	$.0^{3}16$	.010	.038	.074	.110	.143	.174	.202	.227	.250	.271	.290	.01
	.025	$.0^{3}99$	.025	.072	.120	.165	.204	.238	.268	.295	.318	.340	.359	.025
	.05	$.0^{2}39$	.051	.117	.177	.227	.270	.306	.337	.364	.388	.408	.427	.05
	.10	.016	.105	.194	.265	.320	.365	.401	.432	.458	.480	.500	.518	.10
	.25	.102	.288	.405	.481	.534	.574	.606	.631	.652	.670	.685	.699	.25
	.50	.458	.697	.793	.844	.875	.896	.912	.923	.932	.939	.945	.950	.50
	.75	1.34	1.40	1.39	1.37	1.35	1.33	1.31	1.30	1.29	1.28	1.27	1.26	.75
	.90	2.75	2.35	2.13	1.99	1.90	1.82	1.77	1.72	1.68	1.65	1.62	1.60	.90
	.95	3.92	3.07	2.68	2.45	2.29	2.18	2.09	2.02	1.96	1.91	1.87	1.83	.95
	.975	5.15	3.80	3.23	2.89	2.67	2.52	2.39	2.30	2.22	2.16	2.10	2.05	.975
	.99	6.85	4.79	3.95	3.48	3.17	2.96	2.79	2.66	2.56	2.47	2.40	2.34	.99
	.995	8.18	5.54	4.50	3.92	3.55	3.28	3.09	2.93	2.81	2.71	2.62	2.54	.995
	.999	11.4	7.32	5.79	4.95	4.42	4.04	3.77	3.55	3.38	3.24	3.12	3.02	.999
	.9995	12.8	8.10	6.34	5.39	4.79	4.37	4.07	3.82	3.63	3.47	3.34	3.22	.9995
∞	.0005	$.0^{6}39$	$.0^{3}50$	$.0^{2}51$	.016	.032	.050	.069	.088	.108	.127	.144	.161	.0005
	.001	$.0^{5}16$	$.0^{2}10$	$.0^{2}81$	.023	.042	.063	.085	.107	.128	.148	.167	.185	.001
	.005	$.0^{4}39$	$.0^{2}50$	.024	.052	.082	.113	.141	.168	.193	.216	.236	.256	.005
	.01	$.0^{3}16$	.010	.038	.074	.111	.145	.177	.206	.232	.256	.278	.298	.01
	.025	$.0^{3}98$	.025	.072	.121	.166	.206	.241	.272	.300	.325	.347	.367	.025
	.05	$.0^{2}39$	.051	.117	.178	.229	.273	.310	.342	.369	.394	.417	.436	.05
	.10	.016	.105	.195	.266	.322	.367	.405	.436	.463	.487	.508	.525	.10
	.25	.102	.288	.404	.481	.535	.576	.608	.634	.655	.674	.690	.703	.25
	.50	.455	.693	.789	.839	.870	.891	.907	.918	.927	.934	.939	.945	.50
	.75	1.32	1.39	1.37	1.35	1.33	1.31	1.29	1.28	1.27	1.25	1.24	1.24	.75
	.90	2.71	2.30	2.08	1.94	1.85	1.77	1.72	1.67	1.63	1.60	1.57	1.55	.90
	.95	3.84	3.00	2.60	2.37	2.21	2.10	2.01	1.94	1.88	1.83	1.79	1.75	.95
	.975	5.02	3.69	3.12	2.79	2.57	2.41	2.29	2.19	2.11	2.05	1.99	1.94	.975
	.99	6.63	4.61	3.78	3.32	3.02	2.80	2.64	2.51	2.41	2.32	2.25	2.18	.99
	.995	7.88	5.30	4.28	3.72	3.35	3.09	2.90	2.74	2.62	2.52	2.43	2.36	.995
	.999	10.8	6.91	5.42	4.62	4.10	3.74	3.47	3.27	3.10	2.96	2.84	2.74	.999
	.9995	12.1	7.60	5.91	5.00	4.42	4.02	3.72	3.48	3.30	3.14	3.02	2.90	.9995

For sample sizes larger than, say, 30, a fairly good approximation to the F distribution percentiles can be obtained from

$$\log_{10} F_\alpha(\nu_1,\nu_2) \approx \left(\frac{a}{\sqrt{h-b}}\right) - cg$$

where $h = 2\nu_1\nu_2/(\nu_1 + \nu_2)$, $g = (\nu_2 - \nu_1)/\nu_1\nu_2$, and a, b, c are functions of α given below:

α	.50	.75	.90	.95	.975	.99	.995	.999	.9995
a	0	0.5859	1.1131	1.4287	1.7023	2.0206	2.2373	2.6841	2.8580
b	—	0.58	0.77	0.95	1.14	1.40	1.61	2.09	2.30
c	0.290	0.355	0.527	0.681	0.846	1.073	1.250	1.672	1.857

TABLE A-7c. PERCENTILES OF THE $F(\nu_1, \nu_2)$ DISTRIBUTIONS (*Continued*)

Cum. Prop. \ ν_1	15	20	24	30	40	50	60	100	120	200	500	∞	Cum. Prop.	ν_2
.0005	.199	.256	.293	.338	.390	.429	.458	.524	.543	.578	.614	.676	.0005	**120**
.001	.223	.282	.319	.363	.415	.453	.480	.542	.568	.595	.631	.691	.001	
.005	.297	.356	.393	.434	.484	.520	.545	.605	.623	.661	.702	.733	.005	
.01	.338	.397	.433	.474	.522	.556	.579	.636	.652	.688	.725	.755	.01	
.025	.406	.464	.498	.536	.580	.611	.633	.684	.698	.729	.762	.789	.025	
.05	.473	.527	.559	.594	.634	.661	.682	.727	.740	.767	.785	.819	.05	
.10	.560	.609	.636	.667	.702	.726	.742	.781	.791	.815	.838	.855	.10	
.25	.730	.765	.784	.805	.828	.843	.853	.877	.884	.897	.911	.923	.25	
.50	.961	.972	.978	.983	.989	.992	.994	1.00	1.00	1.00	1.01	1.01	.50	
.75	1.24	1.22	1.21	1.19	1.18	1.17	1.16	1.14	1.13	1.12	1.11	1.10	.75	
.90	1.55	1.48	1.45	1.41	1.37	1.34	1.32	1.27	1.26	1.24	1.21	1.19	.90	
.95	1.75	1.66	1.61	1.55	1.50	1.46	1.43	1.37	1.35	1.32	1.28	1.25	.95	
.975	1.95	1.82	1.76	1.69	1.61	1.56	1.53	1.45	1.43	1.39	1.34	1.31	.975	
.99	2.19	2.03	1.95	1.86	1.76	1.70	1.66	1.56	1.53	1.48	1.42	1.38	.99	
.995	2.37	2.19	2.09	1.98	1.87	1.80	1.75	1.64	1.61	1.54	1.48	1.43	.995	
.999	2.78	2.53	2.40	2.26	2.11	2.02	1.95	1.82	1.76	1.70	1.62	1.54	.999	
.9995	2.96	2.67	2.53	2.38	2.21	2.11	2.01	1.88	1.84	1.75	1.67	1.60	.9995	
.0005	.207	.270	.311	.360	.422	.469	.505	.599	.624	.704	.804	1.00	.0005	∞
.001	.232	.296	.338	.386	.448	.493	.527	.617	.649	.719	.819	1.00	.001	
.005	.307	.372	.412	.460	.518	.559	.592	.671	.699	.762	.843	1.00	.005	
.01	.349	.413	.452	.499	.554	.595	.625	.699	.724	.782	.858	1.00	.01	
.025	.418	.480	.517	.560	.611	.645	.675	.741	.763	.813	.878	1.00	.025	
.05	.484	.543	.577	.617	.663	.694	.720	.781	.797	.840	.896	1.00	.05	
.10	.570	.622	.652	.687	.726	.752	.774	.826	.838	.877	.919	1.00	.10	
.25	.736	.773	.793	.816	.842	.860	.872	.901	.910	.932	.957	1.00	.25	
.50	.956	.967	.972	.978	.983	.987	.989	.993	.994	.997	.999	1.00	.50	
.75	1.22	1.19	1.18	1.16	1.14	1.13	1.12	1.09	1.08	1.07	1.04	1.00	.75	
.90	1.49	1.42	1.38	1.34	1.30	1.26	1.24	1.18	1.17	1.13	1.08	1.00	.90	
.95	1.67	1.57	1.52	1.46	1.39	1.35	1.32	1.24	1.22	1.17	1.11	1.00	.95	
.975	1.83	1.71	1.64	1.57	1.48	1.43	1.39	1.30	1.27	1.21	1.13	1.00	.975	
.99	2.04	1.88	1.79	1.70	1.59	1.52	1.47	1.36	1.32	1.25	1.15	1.00	.99	
.995	2.19	2.00	1.90	1.79	1.67	1.59	1.53	1.40	1.36	1.28	1.17	1.00	.995	
.999	2.51	2.27	2.13	1.99	1.84	1.73	1.66	1.49	1.45	1.34	1.21	1.00	.999	
.9995	2.65	2.37	2.22	2.07	1.91	1.79	1.71	1.53	1.48	1.36	1.22	1.00	.9995	

The values given in this table are abstracted with permission from the following sources:

1. All values for ν_1, ν_2 equal to 50, 100, 200, 500 are from A. Hald, *Statistical Tables and Formulas*, John Wiley & Sons, Inc., New York, 1952.
2. For cumulative proportions .5, .75, .9, .95, .975, .99, .995 most of the values are from M. Merrington and C. M. Thompson, *Biometrika*, vol. 33 (1943), p. 73.
3. For cumulative proportions .999 the values are from C. Colcord and L. S. Deming, *Sankhyā*, vol. 2 (1936), p. 423.
4. For cum. prop. $= \alpha < .5$ the values are the reciprocals of values for $1 - \alpha$ (with ν_1 and ν_2 interchanged). The values in Merrington and Thompson and in Colcord and Deming are to five significant figures, and it is hoped (but not expected) that the reciprocals are correct as given. The values in Hald are to three significant figures, and the reciprocals are probably accurate within one to two digits in the third significant figure except for those values very close to unity, where they may be off four to five digits in the third significant figure.
5. Gaps remaining in the table after using the above sources were filled in by interpolation.

$$\alpha = \frac{(\nu_1/\nu_2)^{\frac{1}{2}\nu_1}}{\beta(\frac{1}{2}\nu_1, \frac{1}{2}\nu_2)} \int_{-\infty}^{F_\alpha} F^{\frac{1}{2}\nu_1 - 1} \left(1 + \frac{\nu_1 F}{\nu_2}\right)^{-(\nu_1+\nu_2)/2} dF$$

Table A-8. Simplified Statistics

8a. Percentile estimates in large samples

8a(1) Mean

	Percentile estimate	Eff.
1	P_{50}	.64
2	$.5(P_{25} + P_{75})$	.81
3	$.3333(P_{17} + P_{50} + P_{83})$	.88
4	$.25(P_{12.5} + P_{37.5} + P_{62.5} + P_{87.5})$	.91
5	$.20(P_{10} + P_{30} + P_{50} + P_{70} + P_{90})$	.93
...	. . . .	...
10	$.10(P_{05} + P_{15} + P_{25} + P_{35} + P_{45} + P_{55} + P_{65} + P_{75} + P_{85} + P_{95})$	.97

8a(2) Standard deviation

	Percentile estimate	Eff.
2	$.3388(P_{93} - P_{07})$	.65
4	$.1714(P_{97} + P_{85} - P_{15} - P_{03})$	.80
6	$.1180(P_{98} + P_{91} + P_{80} - P_{20} - P_{09} - P_{02})$	.87
8	$.0935(P_{98} + P_{93} + P_{86} + P_{77} - P_{23} - P_{14} - P_{07} - P_{02})$	.90
10	$.0739(P_{98.5} + P_{95} + P_{90} + P_{84} + P_{75} - P_{25} - P_{16} - P_{10} - P_{05} - P_{01.5})$	.92

8a(3) Mean and standard deviation

	Percentile	Efficiency		K
		Mean	Standard deviation	
2	15, 85	.73	.56	.4824
4	05, 30, 70, 95	.80	.74	.2305
6	05, 15, 40, 60, 85, 95	.89	.80	.1704
8	03, 10, 25, 45, 55, 75, 90, 97	.90	.86	.1262
10	03, 10, 20, 30, 50, 50, 70, 80, 90, 97	.94	.87	.1104

8b. Estimates of mean and dispersion in small samples

8b(1) Unbiased estimate of σ using w (Variance to be multiplied by σ^2)

Sample size	Estimate	Variance	Eff.	Sample size	Estimate	Variance	Eff.
2	$.886w$	.571	1.000	11	$.315w$	.0616	.831
3	$.591w$	.275	.992	12	$.307w$	.0571	.814
4	$.486w$	.183	.975	13	$.300w$	.0533	.797
5	$.430w$	.138	.955	14	$.294w$	.0502	.781
6	$.395w$	.112	.933	15	$.288w$	.0474	.766
7	$.370w$	.0949	.911	16	$.283w$	.0451	.751
8	$.351w$	.0829	.890	17	$.279w$	.0430	.738
9	$.337w$	.0740	.869	18	$.275w$	.0412	.725
10	$.325w$	.0671	.850	19	$.271w$	.0395	.712
				20	$.268w$	.0381	.700

TABLE A-8. SIMPLIFIED STATISTICS (*Continued*)

Percentiles of the distribution of w/σ

Sample size	$P_{0.1}$	$P_{0.5}$	P_{01}	$P_{02.5}$	P_{05}	P_{10}	P_{90}	P_{95}	$P_{97.5}$	P_{99}	$P_{99.5}$	$P_{99.9}$
2	.00	.01	.02	.04	.09	.18	2.33	2.77	3.17	3.64	3.97	4.65
3	.06	.13	.19	.30	.43	.62	2.90	3.31	3.68	4.12	4.42	5.06
4	.20	.34	.43	.59	.76	.98	3.24	3.63	3.98	4.40	4.69	5.31
5	.37	.55	.66	.85	1.03	1.26	3.48	3.86	4.20	4.60	4.89	5.48
6	.54	.75	.87	1.06	1.25	1.49	3.66	4.03	4.36	4.76	5.03	5.62
7	.69	.92	1.05	1.25	1.44	1.68	3.81	4.17	4.49	4.88	5.15	5.73
8	.83	1.08	1.20	1.41	1.60	1.83	3.93	4.29	4.61	4.99	5.26	5.82
9	.96	1.21	1.34	1.55	1.74	1.97	4.04	4.39	4.70	5.08	5.34	5.90
10	1.08	1.33	1.47	1.67	1.86	2.09	4.13	4.47	4.79	5.16	5.42	5.97
11	1.20	1.45	1.58	1.78	1.97	2.20	4.21	4.55	4.86	5.23	5.49	6.04
12	1.30	1.55	1.68	1.88	2.07	2.30	4.29	4.62	4.92	5.29	5.54	6.09
13	1.38	1.64	1.77	1.97	2.16	2.39	4.35	4.69	4.98	5.35	5.60	6.15
14	1.47	1.72	1.85	2.06	2.24	2.47	4.41	4.74	5.04	5.40	5.65	6.20
15	1.55	1.80	1.93	2.14	2.32	2.54	4.47	4.80	5.09	5.45	5.70	6.23
16	1.62	1.87	2.00	2.21	2.39	2.61	4.52	4.85	5.14	5.49	5.74	6.27
17	1.69	1.94	2.07	2.27	2.45	2.67	4.57	4.89	5.18	5.54	5.79	6.30
18	1.75	2.01	2.14	2.33	2.52	2.73	4.61	4.93	5.22	5.58	5.82	6.35
19	1.82	2.07	2.20	2.39	2.57	2.79	4.65	4.97	5.26	5.61	5.86	6.38
20	1.88	2.13	2.25	2.45	2.63	2.84	4.69	5.01	5.30	5.65	5.89	6.40

Unbiased estimate of σ based on s

Sample size	Estimate	Variance	Sample size	Estimate	Variance
2	$1.253s$	$.571\sigma^2$	7	$1.042s$	$.0865\sigma^2$
3	$1.128s$	$.273\sigma^2$	8	$1.036s$	$.0738\sigma^2$
4	$1.085s$	$.178\sigma^2$	9	$1.032s$	$.0643\sigma^2$
5	$1.064s$	$.132\sigma^2$	10	$1.028s$	$.0570\sigma^2$
6	$1.051s$	$.104\sigma^2$	∞	$\left[1 + \frac{1}{4(N-1)}\right] s$	$\sigma^2/2N$

8*b*(2) Mean deviation estimate of σ

Sample size	Estimate	Eff.
2	$.8862(X_2 - X_1)$	1.00
3	$.5908(X_3 - X_1)$	.99
4	$.3770(X_4 + X_3 - X_2 - X_1)$	.91
5	$.3016(X_5 + X_4 - X_2 - X_1)$	.94
6	$.2369(X_6 + X_5 + X_4 - X_3 - X_2 - X_1)$	.90
7	$.2031(X_7 + X_6 + X_5 - X_3 - X_2 - X_1)$	.92
8	$.1723(X_8 + X_7 + X_6 + X_5 - X_4 - X_3 - X_2 - X_1)$	.90
9	$.1532(X_9 + X_8 + X_7 + X_6 - X_4 - X_3 - X_2 - X_1)$	.91
10	$.1353(X_{10} + X_9 + X_8 + X_7 + X_6 - X_5 - X_4 - X_3 - X_2 - X_1)$	.89

TABLE A-8. SIMPLIFIED STATISTICS (*Continued*)

8*b*(3) Modified linear estimate of σ (Variance to be multiplied by σ^2)

Sample size	Estimate	Variance	Eff.
2	$.8862(X_2 - X_1)$	.571	1.000
3	$.5908(X_3 - X_1)$	.275	.992
4	$.4857(X_4 - X_1)$	.183	.975
5	$.4299(X_5 - X_1)$	.138	.955
6	$.2619(X_6 + X_5 - X_2 - X_1)$	.109	.957
7	$.2370(X_7 + X_6 - X_2 - X_1)$	.0895	.967
8	$.2197(X_8 + X_7 - X_2 - X_1)$	.0761	.970
9	$.2068(X_9 + X_8 - X_2 - X_1)$	.0664	.968
10	$.1968(X_{10} + X_9 - X_2 - X_1)$	.0591	.964
11	$.1608(X_{11} + X_{10} + X_8 - X_4 - X_2 - X_1)$	.0529	.967
12	$.1524(X_{12} + X_{11} + X_9 - X_4 - X_2 - X_1)$	.0478	.972
13	$.1456(X_{13} + X_{12} + X_{10} - X_4 - X_2 - X_1)$	.0436	.975
14	$.1399(X_{14} + X_{13} + X_{11} - X_4 - X_2 - X_1)$	.0401	.977
15	$.1352(X_{15} + X_{14} + X_{12} - X_4 - X_2 - X_1)$	.0372	.977
16	$.1311(X_{16} + X_{15} + X_{13} - X_4 - X_2 - X_1)$	.0347	.975
17	$.1050(X_{17} + X_{16} + X_{15} + X_{13} - X_5 - X_3 - X_2 - X_1)$	.0325	.978
18	$.1020(X_{18} + X_{17} + X_{16} + X_{14} - X_5 - X_3 - X_2 - X_1)$	.0305	.978
19	$.09939(X_{19} + X_{18} + X_{17} + X_{15} - X_5 - X_3 - X_2 - X_1)$	.0288	.979
20	$.09706(X_{20} + X_{19} + X_{18} + X_{16} - X_5 - X_3 - X_2 - X_1)$	.0272	.978

8*b*(4) Several estimates of the mean (Variance to be multiplied by σ^2)

N	Median		Midrange		Av. of best two			$(X_2 + X_3 + \cdots + X_{N-1})/(N - 2)$	
	Var.	Eff.	Var.	Eff.	Statistic	Var.	Eff.	Var.	Eff.
2	.500	1.000	.500	1.000	$\frac{1}{2}(X_1 + X_2)$	.500	1.000		
3	.449	.743	.362	.920	$\frac{1}{2}(X_1 + X_3)$	.362	.920	.449	.743
4	.298	.838	.298	.838	$\frac{1}{2}(X_2 + X_3)$	.298	.838	.298	.838
5	.287	.697	.261	.767	$\frac{1}{2}(X_2 + X_4)$	.231	.867	.227	.881
6	.215	.776	.236	.706	$\frac{1}{2}(X_2 + X_5)$	.193	.865	.184	.906
7	.210	.679	.218	.654	$\frac{1}{2}(X_2 + X_6)$	.168	.849	.155	.922
8	.168	.743	.205	.610	$\frac{1}{2}(X_3 + X_6)$	.149	.837	.134	.934
9	.166	.669	.194	.572	$\frac{1}{2}(X_3 + X_7)$	.132	.843	.118	.942
10	.138	.723	.186	.539	$\frac{1}{2}(X_3 + X_8)$	.119	.840	.105	.949
11	.137	.663	.178	.510	$\frac{1}{2}(X_3 + X_9)$	.109	.832	.0952	.955
12	.118	.709	.172	.484	$\frac{1}{2}(X_4 + X_9)$	.100	.831	.0869	.959
13	.117	.659	.167	.461	$\frac{1}{2}(X_4 + X_{10})$	.0924	.833	.0799	.963
14	.102	.699	.162	.440	$\frac{1}{2}(X_4 + X_{11})$	.0860	.830	.0739	.966
15	.102	.656	.158	.422	$\frac{1}{2}(X_4 + X_{12})$	.0808	.825	.0688	.969
16	.0904	.692	.154	.392	$\frac{1}{2}(X_5 + X_{12})$	.0756	.827	.0644	.971
17	.0901	.653	.151	.389	$\frac{1}{2}(X_5 + X_{13})$	.0711	.827	.0605	.973
18	.0810	.686	.148	.375	$\frac{1}{2}(X_5 + X_{14})$	.0673	.825	.0570	.975
19	.0808	.651	.145	.362	$\frac{1}{2}(X_6 + X_{14})$	.0640	.823	.0539	.976
20	.0734	.681	.143	.350	$\frac{1}{2}(X_6 + X_{15})$	.0607	.824	.0511	.978
∞	$1.57/N$	.637		.000	$\frac{1}{2}(P_{25} + P_{75})$	$1.24/N$	.808		1.000

TABLE A-8. SIMPLIFIED STATISTICS (*Continued*)

8b(5) Mean values of the order statistics. Values given are in deviations from the mean in standard-deviation units

Sample size	X_1	X_2	X_3	X_4	X_5	X_6	X_7	X_8	X_9	X_{10}
2	−.564	.564								
3	−.846	.000	.846							
4	−1.029	−.297	.297	1.029						
5	−1.163	−.495	.000	.495	1.163					
6	−1.267	−.642	−.202	.202	.642	1.267				
7	−1.352	−.757	−.353	.000	.353	.757	1.352			
8	−1.424	−.852	−.473	−.153	.153	.473	.852	1.424		
9	−1.485	−.932	−.572	−.275	.000	.275	.572	.932	1.485	
10	−1.539	−1.001	−.656	−.376	−.123	.123	.376	.656	1.001	1.539
11	−1.586	−1.062	−.729	−.462	−.225	.000	.225	.462	.729	1.062
12	−1.629	−1.116	−.793	−.537	−.312	−.103	.103	.312	.537	.793
13	−1.668	−1.164	−.850	−.603	−.388	−.191	.000	.191	.388	.603
14	−1.703	−1.208	−.901	−.662	−.456	−.267	−.088	.088	.267	.456
15	−1.736	−1.248	−.948	−.715	−.516	−.335	−.165	.000	.165	.335
16	−1.766	−1.285	−.990	−.763	−.570	−.396	−.234	−.077	.077	.234
17	−1.794	−1.319	−1.029	−.807	−.619	−.451	−.295	−.146	.000	.146
18	−1.820	−1.350	−1.066	−.848	−.665	−.502	−.351	−.208	−.069	.069
19	−1.844	−1.380	−1.099	−.886	−.707	−.548	−.402	−.264	−.131	.000
20	−1.867	−1.408	−1.131	−.921	−.745	−.590	−.448	−.315	−.187	−.062

For sample sizes greater than 10 the mean values of X_{11}, X_{12}, etc., can be obtained by symmetry. For example, for $N = 17$ the expected value of X_{15} is the same except for sign as the expected value of X_3.

8b(6) Best linear estimate of σ

Sample size	Estimate	Eff.
2	$.8862(X_2 - X_1)$	1.000
3	$.5908(X_3 - X_1)$	.992
4	$.4539(X_4 - X_1) + .1102(X_3 - X_2)$	.989
5	$.3724(X_5 - X_1) + .1352(X_4 - X_2)$	.988
6	$.3175(X_6 - X_1) + .1386(X_5 - X_2) + .0432(X_4 - X_3)$	.988
7	$.2778(X_7 - X_1) + .1351(X_6 - X_2) + .0625(X_5 - X_3)$	.989
8	$.2476(X_8 - X_1) + .1294(X_7 - X_2) + .0713(X_6 - X_3) + .0230(X_5 - X_4)$	.989
9	$.2237(X_9 - X_1) + .1233(X_8 - X_2) + .0751(X_7 - X_3) + .0360(X_6 - X_4)$	.989
10	$.2044(X_{10} - X_1) + .1172(X_9 - X_2) + .0763(X_8 - X_3) + .0436(X_7 - X_4) + .0142(X_6 - X_5)$	.990

TABLE A-8. SIMPLIFIED STATISTICS (*Continued*)

8*c*. Substitute *t* ratios

8*c*(1) Percentiles* for $\tau_1 = \dfrac{\bar{X} - \mu}{w}$

Sample size	P_{95}	$P_{97.5}$	P_{99}	$P_{99.5}$	$P_{99.9}$	$P_{99.95}$
2	3.175	6.353	15.910	31.828	159.16	318.31
3	.885	1.304	2.111	3.008	6.77	9.58
4	.529	.717	1.023	1.316	2.29	2.85
5	.388	.507	.685	.843	1.32	1.58
6	.312	.399	.523	.628	.92	1.07
7	.263	.333	.429	.507	.71	.82
8	.230	.288	.366	.429	.59	.67
9	.205	.255	.322	.374	.50	.57
10	.186	.230	.288	.333	.44	.50
11	.170	.210	.262	.302	.40	.44
12	.158	.194	.241	.277	.36	.40
13	.147	.181	.224	.256	.33	.37
14	.138	.170	.209	.239	.31	.34
15	.131	.160	.197	.224	.29	.32
16	.124	.151	.186	.212	.27	.30
17	.118	.144	.177	.201	.26	.28
18	.113	.137	.168	.191	.24	.26
19	.108	.131	.161	.182	.23	.25
20	.104	.126	.154	.175	.22	.24
	$-P_{05}$	$-P_{02.5}$	$-P_{01}$	$-P_{0.5}$	$-P_{0.1}$	$-P_{0.05}$

* When the table is read from the foot, the tabled values are to be prefixed with a negative sign.

TABLE A-8. SIMPLIFIED STATISTICS (*Continued*)

8c(2) Percentiles* for $\tau_d = \dfrac{\bar{X}_1 - \bar{X}_2}{\frac{1}{2}(w_1 + w_2)}$

Sample sizes $N_1 = N_2$	P_{95}	$P_{97.5}$	P_{99}	$P_{99.5}$	$P_{99.9}$	$P_{99.95}$
2	2.322	3.427	5.553	7.916	17.81	25.23
3	.974	1.272	1.715	2.093	3.27	4.18
4	.644	.813	1.047	1.237	1.74	1.99
5	.493	.613	.772	.896	1.21	1.35
6	.405	.499	.621	.714	.94	1.03
7	.347	.426	.525	.600	.77	.85
8	.306	.373	.459	.521	.67	.73
9	.275	.334	.409	.464	.59	.64
10	.250	.304	.371	.419	.53	.58
11	.233	.280	.340	.384	.48	.52
12	.214	.260	.315	.355	.44	.48
13	.201	.243	.294	.331	.41	.45
14	.189	.228	.276	.311	.39	.42
15	.179	.216	.261	.293	.36	.39
16	.170	.205	.247	.278	.34	.37
17	.162	.195	.236	.264	.33	.35
18	.155	.187	.225	.252	.31	.34
19	.149	.179	.216	.242	.30	.32
20	.143	.172	.207	.232	.29	.31
	$-P_{05}$	$-P_{02.5}$	$-P_{01}$	$-P_{0.5}$	$-P_{0.1}$	$-P_{0.05}$

* When the table is read from the foot, the tabled values are to be prefixed with a negative sign.

8c(3) Percentiles for $\tau_2 = \dfrac{\frac{1}{2}(X_1 + X_N) - \mu}{w}$

Sample size	P_{95}	$P_{97.5}$	P_{99}	$P_{99.5}$
2	3.16	6.35	15.91	31.83
3	.90	1.30	2.11	3.02
4	.55	.74	1.04	1.37
5	.42	.52	.71	.85
6	.35	.43	.56	.66
7	.30	.37	.47	.55
8	.26	.33	.42	.47
9	.24	.30	.38	.42
10	.22	.27	.35	.39
	$-P_{05}$	$-P_{02.5}$	$-P_{01}$	$-P_{0.5}$

TABLE A-8. SIMPLIFIED STATISTICS (*Continued*)

8*d*. Substitute F ratio, ratio of ranges

Sample size for denominator	Cum. prop.	Sample size for numerator								
		2	3	4	5	6	7	8	9	10
2	.005	.0078	.096	.21	.30	.38	.44	.49	.54	.57
	.01	.0157	.136	.26	.38	.46	.53	.59	.64	.68
	.025	.039	.217	.37	.50	.60	.68	.74	.79	.83
	.05	.079	.31	.50	.62	.74	.80	.86	.91	.95
	.95	12.7	19.1	23	26	29	30	32	34	35
	.975	25.5	38.2	52	57	60	62	64	67	68
	.99	63.7	95	116	132	142	153	160	168	174
	.995	127	191	230	250	260	270	280	290	290
3	.005	.0052	.071	.16	.24	.32	.38	.43	.47	.50
	.01	.0105	.100	.20	.30	.37	.43	.49	.53	.57
	.025	.026	.160	.28	.39	.47	.54	.59	.64	.68
	.05	.052	.23	.37	.49	.57	.64	.70	.75	.80
	.95	3.19	4.4	5.0	5.7	6.2	6.6	6.9	7.2	7.4
	.975	4.61	6.3	7.3	8.0	8.7	9.3	9.8	10.2	10.5
	.99	7.37	10	12	13	14	15	15	16	17
	.995	10.4	14	17	18	20	21	22	23	25
4	.005	.0043	.059	.14	.22	.28	.34	.39	.43	.46
	.01	.0086	.084	.18	.26	.33	.39	.44	.48	.52
	.025	.019	.137	.25	.34	.42	.48	.53	.57	.61
	.05	.043	.20	.32	.42	.50	.57	.62	.67	.70
	.95	2.02	2.7	3.1	3.4	3.6	3.8	4.0	4.2	4.4
	.975	2.72	3.5	4.0	4.4	4.7	5.0	5.2	5.4	5.6
	.99	3.83	5.0	5.5	6.0	6.4	6.7	7.0	7.2	7.5
	.995	4.85	6.1	7.0	7.6	8.1	8.5	8.8	9.3	9.6
5	.005	.0039	.054	.13	.20	.26	.32	.36	.40	.44
	.01	.0076	.079	.17	.24	.31	.36	.41	.45	.49
	.025	.018	.124	.23	.32	.38	.44	.49	.53	.57
	.05	.038	.18	.29	40	.46	.52	.57	.61	.65
	.95	1.61	2.1	2.4	2.6	2.8	2.9	3.0	3.1	3.2
	.975	2.01	2.6	2.9	3.2	3.4	3.6	3.7	3.8	3.9
	.99	2.64	3.4	3.8	4.1	4.3	4.6	4.7	4.9	5.0
	.995	3.36	4.1	4.6	4.9	5.2	5.5	5.7	5.9	6.1

TABLE A-8. SIMPLIFIED STATISTICS (*Continued*)

Sample size for denominator	cum. prop.	Sample size for numerator 2	3	4	5	6	7	8	9	10
6	.005	.0038	.051	.12	.19	.25	.30	.35	.38	.42
	.01	.0070	.073	.16	.23	.29	.34	.39	.43	.46
	.025	.017	.115	.21	.30	.36	.42	.46	.50	.54
	.05	.035	.16	.27	.36	.43	.49	.54	.58	.61
	.95	1.36	1.8	2.0	2.2	2.3	2.4	2.5	2.6	2.7
	.975	1.67	2.1	2.4	2.6	2.8	2.9	3.0	3.1	3.2
	.99	2.16	2.7	3.0	3.2	3.4	3.6	3.7	3.8	3.9
	.995	2.67	3.1	3.5	3.8	4.0	4.1	4.3	4.5	4.6
7	.005	.0037	.048	.12	.18	.24	.29	.33	.37	.40
	.01	.0066	.069	.15	.22	.28	.33	.37	.41	.45
	.025	.016	.107	.20	.28	.34	.40	.44	.48	.52
	.05	.032	.15	.26	.35	.41	.47	.51	.55	.59
	.95	1.26	1.6	1.8	1.9	2.0	2.1	2.2	2.3	2.4
	.975	1.48	1.9	2.1	2.3	2.4	2.5	2.6	2.7	2.8
	.99	1.87	2.3	2.6	2.8	2.9	3.0	3.1	3.2	3.3
	.995	2.28	2.7	2.9	3.1	3.3	3.5	3.6	3.7	3.8
8	.005	.0036	.045	.11	.18	.23	.28	.32	.36	.39
	.01	.0063	.065	.14	.21	.27	.32	.36	.40	.43
	.025	.016	.102	.19	.27	.33	.38	.43	.47	.50
	.05	.031	.14	.25	.33	.40	.45	.50	.53	.57
	.95	1.17	1.4	1.6	1.8	1.9	1.9	2.0	2.1	2.1
	.975	1.36	1.7	1.9	2.0	2.2	2.3	2.3	2.4	2.5
	.99	1.69	2.1	2.3	2.4	2.6	2.7	2.8	2.8	2.9
	.995	2.03	2.3	2.6	2.7	2.9	3.0	3.1	3.2	3.3
9	.005	.0035	.042	.11	.17	.22	.27	.31	.35	.38
	.01	.0060	.062	.14	.21	.26	.31	.35	.39	.42
	.025	.015	.098	.18	.26	.32	.37	.42	.46	.49
	.05	.030	.14	.24	.32	.38	.44	.48	.52	.55
	.95	1.10	1.3	1.5	1.6	1.7	1.8	1.9	1.9	2.0
	.975	1.27	1.6	1.8	1.9	2.0	2.1	2.1	2.2	2.3
	.99	1.56	1.9	2.1	2.2	2.3	2.4	2.5	2.6	2.6
	.995	1.87	2.1	2.3	2.5	2.6	2.7	2.8	2.9	3.0
10	.005	.0034	.041	.10	.16	.22	.26	.30	.34	.37
	.01	.0058	.060	.13	.20	.26	.30	.34	.38	.41
	.025	.015	.095	.18	.25	.31	.36	.41	.44	.48
	.05	.029	.13	.23	.31	.37	.43	.47	.51	.54
	.95	1.05	1.3	1.4	1.5	1.6	1.7	1.8	1.8	1.9
	.975	1.21	1.5	1.6	1.8	1.9	1.9	2.0	2.0	2.1
	.99	1.47	1.8	1.9	2.1	2.2	2.2	2.3	2.4	2.4
	.995	1.75	2.0	2.2	2.3	2.4	2.5	2.6	2.6	2.7

TABLE A-8. SIMPLIFIED STATISTICS (*Continued*)

8*e*. Criteria for Testing for Extreme Mean

Statistic	Number of obs., k	Critical values						
		$\alpha =$ .30	$\alpha =$ .20	$\alpha =$ .10	$\alpha =$ .05	$\alpha =$ .02	$\alpha =$ .01	$\alpha =$ .005
$r_{10} = \dfrac{X_2 - X_1}{X_k - X_1}$	3	.684	.781	.886	.941	.976	.988	.994
	4	.471	.560	.679	.765	.846	.889	.926
	5	.373	.451	.557	.642	.729	.780	.821
	6	.318	.386	.482	.560	.644	.698	.740
	7	.281	.344	.434	.507	.586	.637	.680
$r_{11} = \dfrac{X_2 - X_1}{X_{k-1} - X_1}$	8	.318	.385	.479	.554	.631	.683	.725
	9	.288	.352	.441	.512	.587	.635	.677
	10	.265	.325	.409	.477	.551	.597	.639
$r_{21} = \dfrac{X_3 - X_1}{X_{k-1} - X_1}$	11	.391	.442	.517	.576	.638	.679	.713
	12	.370	.419	.490	.546	.605	.642	.675
	13	.351	.399	.467	.521	.578	.615	.649
$r_{22} = \dfrac{X_3 - X_1}{X_{k-2} - X_1}$	14	.370	.421	.492	.546	.602	.641	.674
	15	.353	.402	.472	.525	.579	.616	.647
	16	.338	.386	.454	.507	.559	.595	.624
	17	.325	.373	.438	.490	.542	.577	.605
	18	.314	.361	.424	.475	.527	.561	.589
	19	.304	.350	.412	.462	.514	.547	.575
	20	.295	.340	.401	.450	.502	.535	.562
	21	.287	.331	.391	.440	.491	.524	.551
	22	.280	.323	.382	.430	.481	.514	.541
	23	.274	.316	.374	.421	.472	.505	.532
	24	.268	.310	.367	.413	.464	.497	.524
	25	.262	.304	.360	.406	.457	.489	.516

Table A-8*a*(1) is reproduced with permission from F. Mosteller, "On some useful 'inefficient' statistics," *Annals of Mathematical Statistics*, vol. 17 (1946), p. 377. Tables A-8*a*(2) and (3) are reproduced with permission from E. K. Yost, "Joint estimation of mean and standard deviation by percentiles," unpublished master's thesis, University of Oregon, Eugene, Ore., 1948. Table A-8*b*(1) is reproduced with permission from E. S. Pearson, "The probability integral of the range in samples of n observations from a normal population," *Biometrika*, vol. 32 (1942), p. 301. Tables A-8*b*(2) to (5) are reproduced from an unpublished manuscript, W. J. Dixon, University of California, Los Angeles. Tables A-8*c*(1), (2) are reproduced with the permission of E. S. Pearson from E. Lord, "The use of the range in place of the standard deviation in the *t* test," *Biometrika*, vol. 34 (1947), p. 41. Table A-8*c*(3) is reproduced with permission from J. E. Walsh, "On the range-midrange test and some tests with bounded significance levels," *Annals of Mathematical Statistics*, vol. 20 (1949), p. 257. Table A-8*d* is reproduced and extended from R. F. Link, "On the ratio of two ranges," *Annals of Mathematical Statistics*, vol. 21 (1950), p. 112. Table A-8*e* is reproduced from W. J. Dixon, "Processing data for outliers," *Biometrics*, vol. 9 (1953), p. 74.

TABLE A-9a. CONFIDENCE BELTS FOR PROPORTIONS
(Confidence coefficient .80)

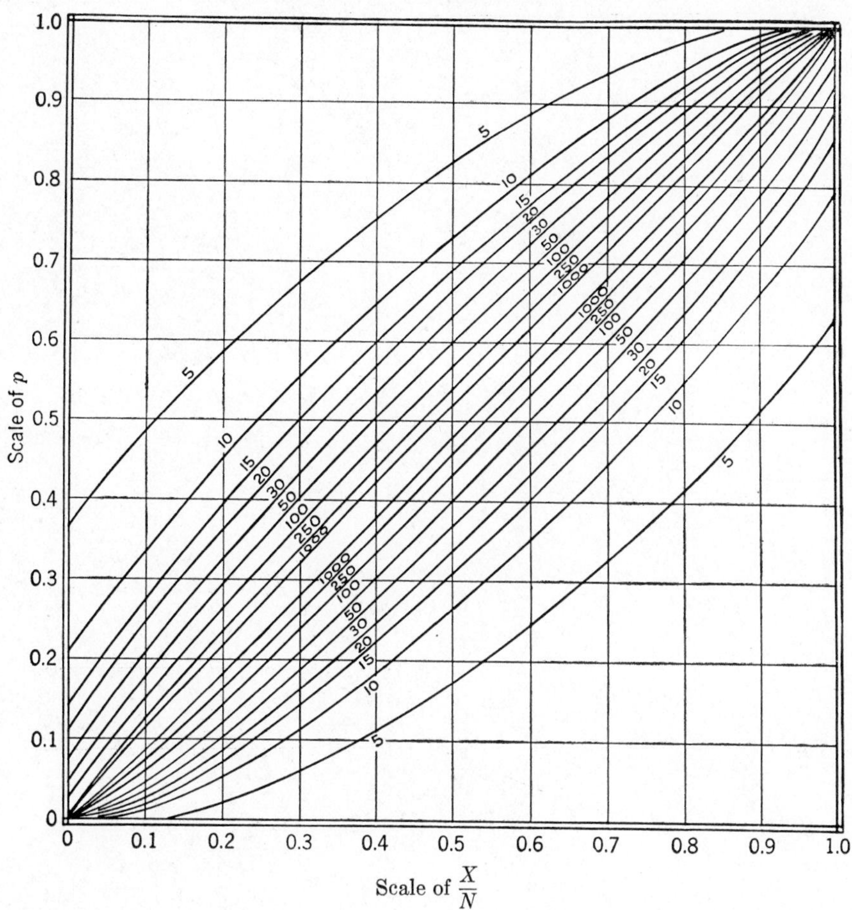

TABLE A-9b. CONFIDENCE BELTS FOR PROPORTIONS
(Confidence coefficient .90)

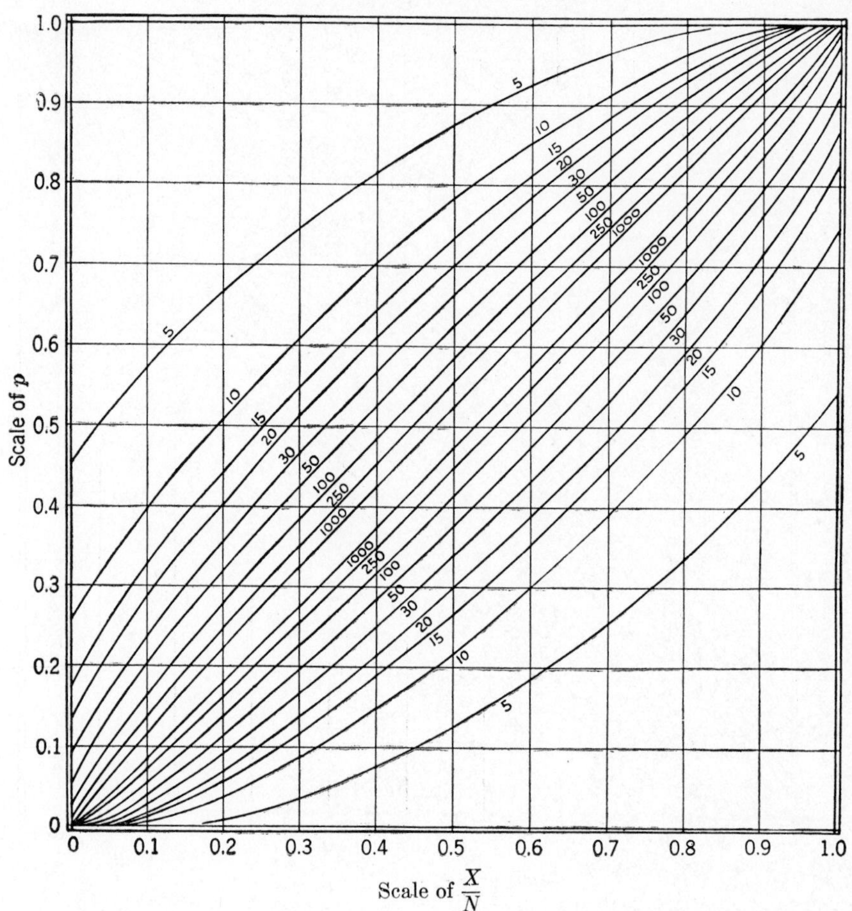

TABLE A-9c. CONFIDENCE BELTS FOR PROPORTIONS*
(Confidence coefficient .95)

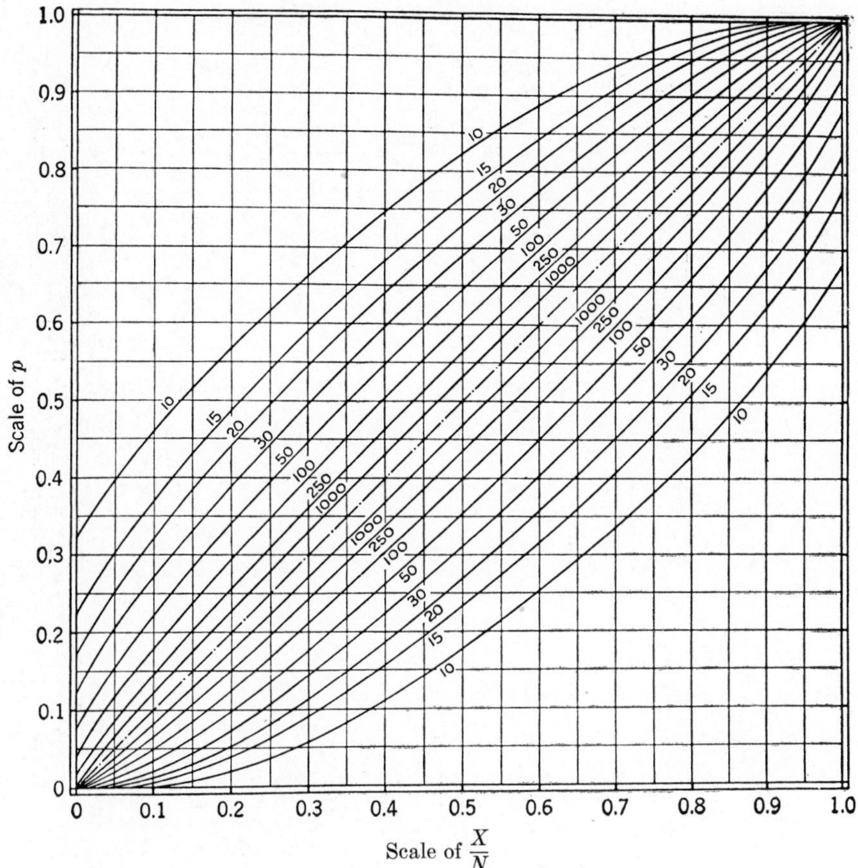

* This chart is reproduced with the permission of Professor E. S. Pearson from C. J. Clopper, E. S. Pearson, "The use of confidence or fiducial limits illustrated in the case of the binomial," *Biometrika*, vol. 26 (1934), p. 404.

TABLE A-9*d*. CONFIDENCE BELTS FOR PROPORTIONS*
(Confidence coefficient .99)

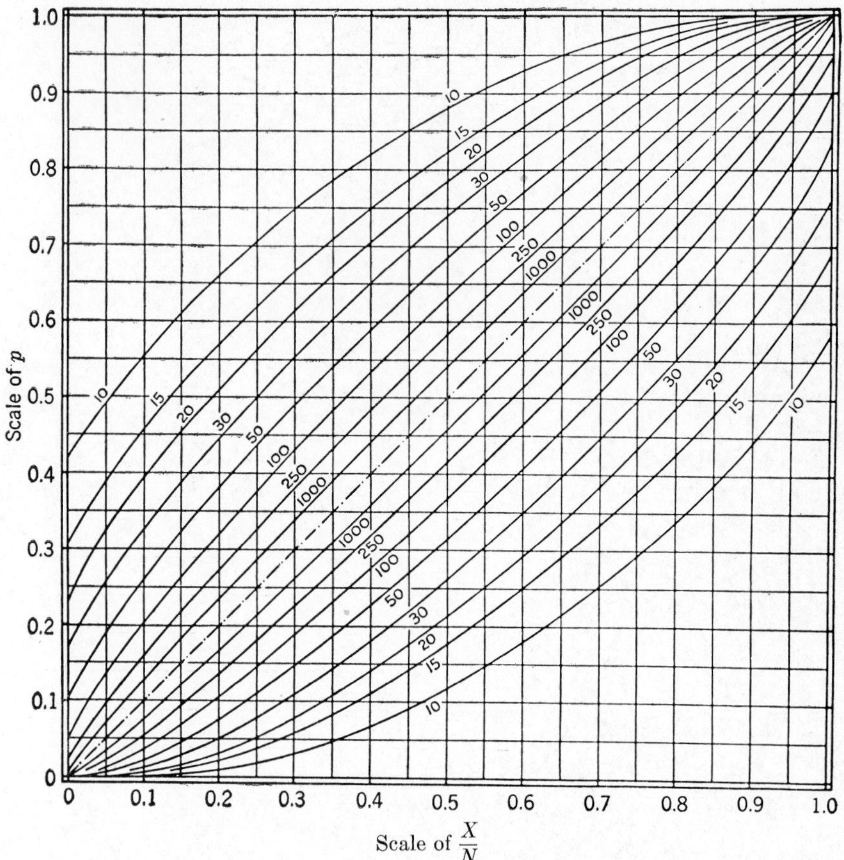

Scale of $\frac{X}{N}$

*This chart is reproduced with the permission of Professor E. S. Pearson from C. J. Clopper, E. S. Pearson, "The use of confidence or fiducial limits illustrated in the case of the binomial," *Biometrika*, vol. 26 (1934), p. 404.

TABLE. A-10*a*. CRITICAL VALUES OF r FOR THE SIGN TEST
(Two-tail percentage points for the binomial for $p = .5$)

N	1%	5%	10%	25%	N	1%	5%	10%	25%
1					46	13	15	16	18
2					47	14	16	17	19
3				0	48	14	16	17	19
4				0	49	15	17	18	19
5			0	0	50	15	17	18	20
6		0	0	1	51	15	18	19	20
7		0	0	1	52	16	18	19	21
8	0	0	1	1	53	16	18	20	21
9	0	1	1	2	54	17	19	20	22
10	0	1	1	2	55	17	19	20	22
11	0	1	2	3	56	17	20	21	23
12	1	2	2	3	57	18	20	21	23
13	1	2	3	3	58	18	21	22	24
14	1	2	3	4	59	19	21	22	24
15	2	3	3	4	60	19	21	23	25
16	2	3	4	5	61	20	22	23	25
17	2	4	4	5	62	20	22	24	25
18	3	4	5	6	63	20	23	24	26
19	3	4	5	6	64	21	23	24	26
20	3	5	5	6	65	21	24	25	27
21	4	5	6	7	66	22	24	25	27
22	4	5	6	7	67	22	25	26	28
23	4	6	7	8	68	22	25	26	28
24	5	6	7	8	69	23	25	27	29
25	5	7	7	9	70	23	26	27	29
26	6	7	8	9	71	24	26	28	30
27	6	7	8	10	72	24	27	28	30
28	6	8	9	10	73	25	27	28	31
29	7	8	9	10	74	25	28	29	31
30	7	9	10	11	75	25	28	29	32
31	7	9	10	11	76	26	28	30	32
32	8	9	10	12	77	26	29	30	32
33	8	10	11	12	78	27	29	31	33
34	9	10	11	13	79	27	30	31	33
35	9	11	12	13	80	28	30	32	34
36	9	11	12	14	81	28	31	32	34
37	10	12	13	14	82	28	31	33	35
38	10	12	13	14	83	29	32	33	35
39	11	12	13	15	84	29	32	33	36
40	11	13	14	15	85	30	32	34	36
41	11	13	14	16	86	30	33	34	37
42	12	14	15	16	87	31	33	35	37
43	12	14	15	17	88	31	34	35	38
44	13	15	16	17	89	31	34	36	38
45	13	15	16	18	90	32	35	36	39

For values of N larger than 90, approximate values of r may be found by taking the nearest integer less than $(N - 1)/2 - k\sqrt{N+1}$, where k is 1.2879, 0.9800, 0.8224, 0.5752 for the 1, 5, 10, 25% values, respectively.

Table A-10b. Distribution for the Sign Test
(Percentage points for the binomial for $p = .5$)

The percentiles listed cover the range from $\alpha = .005$ to $\alpha = .125$ for every value of N up to 100. Percentiles from $\alpha = .875$ to $\alpha = .995$ may be read by entering the table with $N - x$ and $1 - \alpha$. x is the number of plus signs.

N	x	α
$N = 3$	0	.125
$N = 4$	0	.062
	1	.312
$N = 5$	0	.031
	1	.188
$N = 6$	0	.016
	1	.109
	2	.344
$N = 7$	0	.008
	1	.062
	2	.227
$N = 8$	0	.004
	1	.035
	2	.145
$N = 9$	0	.002
	1	.020
	2	.090
	3	.254
$N = 10$	0	.001
	1	.011
	2	.055
	3	.172
$N = 11$	0	.000
	1	.006
	2	.033
	3	.113
	4	.274
$N = 12$	1	.003
	2	.019
	3	.073
	4	.194
$N = 13$	1	.002
	2	.011
	3	.046
	4	.133
$N = 14$	1	.001
	2	.006
	3	.029
	4	.090
	5	.212
$N = 15$	1	.000
	2	.004
	3	.018
	4	.059
	5	.151
$N = 16$	2	.002
	3	.011
	4	.038
	5	.105
	6	.227
$N = 17$	2	.001
	3	.006
	4	.025
	5	.072
	6	.166
$N = 18$	3	.004
	4	.015
	5	.048
	6	.119
	7	.240
$N = 19$	3	.002
	4	.010
	5	.032
	6	.084
	7	.180
$N = 20$	3	.001
	4	.006
	5	.021
	6	.058
	7	.132
$N = 21$	4	.004
	5	.013
	6	.039
	7	.095
	8	.192
$N = 22$	4	.002
	5	.008
	6	.026
	7	.067
	8	.143
$N = 23$	4	.001
	5	.005
	6	.017
	7	.047
	8	.105
	9	.202
$N = 24$	5	.003
	6	.011
	7	.032
	8	.076
	9	.154
$N = 25$	5	.002
	6	.007
	7	.022
	8	.054
	9	.115
	10	.212
$N = 26$	6	.005
	7	.014
	8	.038
	9	.084
	10	.163
$N = 27$	6	.003
	7	.010
	8	.026
	9	.061
	10	.124
	11	.221
$N = 28$	6	.002
	7	.006
	8	.018
	9	.044
	10	.092
	11	.172
$N = 29$	7	.004
	8	.012
	9	.031
	10	.068
	11	.132
$N = 30$	7	.003
	8	.008
	9	.021
	10	.049
	11	.100
	12	.181
$N = 31$	7	.002
	8	.005
	9	.015
	10	.035
	11	.075
	12	.141
$N = 32$	8	.004
	9	.010
	10	.025
	11	.055
	12	.108
	13	.189
$N = 33$	8	.002
	9	.007
	10	.018
	11	.040
	12	.081
	13	.148
$N = 34$	9	.005
	10	.012
	11	.029
	12	.061
	13	.115
	14	.196
$N = 35$	9	.003
	10	.008
	11	.020
	12	.045
	13	.088
	14	.155
$N = 36$	9	.002
	10	.006
	11	.014
	12	.033
	13	.066
	14	.121
	15	.203
$N = 37$	10	.004
	11	.010
	12	.024
	13	.049
	14	.094
	15	.162
$N = 38$	10	.003
	11	.007
	12	.017
	13	.036
	14	.072
	15	.128
$N = 39$	11	.005
	12	.012
	13	.027
	14	.054
	15	.100
	16	.168
$N = 40$	11	.003
	12	.008
	13	.019
	14	.040
	15	.077
	16	.134
$N = 41$	11	.002
	12	.006
	13	.014
	14	.030
	15	.059
	16	.106
	17	.174
$N = 42$	12	.004
	13	.010
	14	.022
	15	.044
	16	.082
	17	.140

Table A-10b. Distribution for the Sign Test (*Continued*)

x	α
$N = 43$	
12	.003
13	.007
14	.016
15	.033
16	.063
17	.111
18	.180
$N = 44$	
13	.005
14	.011
15	.024
16	.048
17	.087
18	.146
$N = 45$	
13	.003
14	.008
15	.018
16	.036
17	.068
18	.116
19	.186
$N = 46$	
13	.002
14	.006
15	.013
16	.027
17	.052
18	.092
19	.151
$N = 47$	
14	.004
15	.009
16	.020
17	.039
18	.072
19	.121
20	.191
$N = 48$	
14	.003
15	.007
16	.015
17	.030
18	.056
19	.097
20	.156

x	α
$N = 49$	
15	.005
16	.011
17	.022
18	.043
19	.076
20	.126
$N = 50$	
15	.003
16	.008
17	.016
18	.032
19	.059
20	.101
21	.161
$N = 51$	
15	.002
16	.005
17	.012
18	.024
19	.046
20	.080
21	.131
$N = 52$	
16	.004
17	.009
18	.018
19	.035
20	.063
21	.106
22	.166
$N = 53$	
16	.003
17	.006
18	.014
19	.027
20	.049
21	.084
22	.136
$N = 54$	
17	.005
18	.010
19	.020
20	.038
21	.067
22	.110
23	.170

x	α
$N = 55$	
17	.003
18	.007
19	.015
20	.029
21	.052
22	.089
23	.140
$N = 56$	
17	.002
18	.005
19	.011
20	.022
21	.041
22	.070
23	.114
24	.175
$N = 57$	
18	.004
19	.008
20	.017
21	.031
22	.056
23	.092
24	.145
$N = 58$	
18	.003
19	.006
20	.012
21	.024
22	.043
23	.074
24	.119
25	.179
$N = 59$	
19	.004
20	.009
21	.018
22	.034
23	.059
24	.096
25	.149

x	α
$N = 60$	
19	.003
20	.007
21	.014
22	.026
23	.046
24	.078
25	.123
26	.183
$N = 61$	
20	.005
21	.010
22	.020
23	.036
24	.062
25	.100
26	.153
$N = 62$	
20	.004
21	.008
22	.015
23	.028
24	.049
25	.081
26	.126
$N = 63$	
20	.003
21	.006
22	.011
23	.021
24	.038
25	.065
26	.104
27	.157
$N = 64$	
21	.004
22	.008
23	.016
24	.030
25	.052
26	.084
27	.130

x	α
$N = 65$	
21	.003
22	.006
23	.012
24	.023
25	.041
26	.068
27	.107
28	.161
$N = 66$	
22	.005
23	.009
24	.018
25	.032
26	.054
27	.088
28	.134
$N = 67$	
22	.003
23	.007
24	.014
25	.025
26	.043
27	.071
28	.111
29	.164
$N = 68$	
22	.002
23	.005
24	.010
25	.019
26	.034
27	.057
28	.091
29	.137
$N = 69$	
23	.004
24	.008
25	.015
26	.027
27	.046
28	.074
29	.114
30	.168

x	α
$N = 70$	
23	.003
24	.006
25	.011
26	.021
27	.036
28	.060
29	.094
30	.141
$N = 71$	
24	.004
25	.008
26	.016
27	.028
28	.048
29	.077
30	.118
31	.171
$N = 72$	
24	.003
25	.006
26	.012
27	.022
28	.038
29	.062
30	.097
31	.144
$N = 73$	
25	.005
26	.009
27	.017
28	.030
29	.050
30	.080
31	.121
32	.175
$N = 74$	
25	.004
26	.007
27	.013
28	.024
29	.040
30	.065
31	.100
32	.148

Table A-10*b*. Distribution for the Sign Test (*Continued*)

N	x	α
N = 75	25	.003
	26	.005
	27	.010
	28	.018
	29	.032
	30	.053
	31	.083
	32	.124
	33	.179
N = 76	26	.004
	27	.008
	28	.014
	29	.025
	30	.042
	31	.068
	32	.103
	33	.151
N = 77	26	.003
	27	.006
	28	.011
	29	.020
	30	.034
	31	.055
	32	.086
	33	.127
N = 78	27	.004
	28	.008
	29	.015
	30	.027
	31	.044
	32	.070
	33	.106
	34	.154
N = 79	27	.003
	28	.006
	29	.012
	30	.021
	31	.036
	32	.057
	33	.088
	34	.130
N = 80	28	.005
	29	.009
	30	.016
	31	.028
	32	.046
	33	.073
	34	.109
	35	.157
N = 81	28	.004
	29	.007
	30	.013
	31	.022
	32	.037
	33	.060
	34	.091
	35	.133
N = 82	28	.003
	29	.005
	30	.010
	31	.018
	32	.030
	33	.049
	34	.075
	35	.112
	36	.160
N = 83	29	.004
	30	.008
	31	.014
	32	.024
	33	.039
	34	.062
	35	.094
	36	.136
N = 84	29	.003
	30	.006
	31	.011
	32	.019
	33	.031
	34	.051
	35	.078
	36	.115
	37	.163
N = 85	30	.004
	31	.008
	32	.015
	33	.025
	34	.041
	35	.064
	36	.096
	37	.139
N = 86	30	.003
	31	.006
	32	.011
	33	.020
	34	.033
	35	.053
	36	.080
	37	.118
	38	.166
N = 87	31	.005
	32	.009
	33	.016
	34	.027
	35	.043
	36	.066
	37	.099
	38	.142
N = 88	31	.004
	32	.007
	33	.012
	34	.012
	35	.035
	36	.055
	37	.083
	38	.120
	39	.169
N = 89	31	.003
	32	.005
	33	.010
	34	.017
	35	.028
	36	.045
	37	.069
	38	.102
	39	.145
N = 90	32	.004
	33	.007
	34	.013
	35	.022
	36	.036
	37	.057
	38	.085
	39	.123
	40	.171
N = 91	32	.003
	33	.006
	34	.010
	35	.018
	36	.029
	37	.046
	38	.071
	39	.104
	40	.147
N = 92	33	.004
	34	.008
	35	.014
	36	.024
	37	.038
	38	.059
	39	.087
	40	.126
N = 93	33	.003
	34	.006
	35	.011
	36	.019
	37	.031
	38	.048
	39	.073
	40	.107
	41	.150
N = 94	34	.005
	35	.009
	36	.015
	37	.025
	38	.039
	39	.061
	40	.090
	41	.128
N = 95	34	.004
	35	.007
	36	.012
	37	.020
	38	.032
	39	.050
	40	.075
	41	.109
	42	.152
N = 96	34	.003
	35	.005
	36	.009
	37	.016
	38	.026
	39	.041
	40	.063
	41	.092
	42	.131
N = 97	35	.004
	36	.007
	37	.012
	38	.021
	39	.034
	40	.052
	41	.077
	42	.111
	43	.155
N = 98	35	.003
	36	.006
	37	.010
	38	.017
	39	.027
	40	.043
	41	.065
	42	.094
	43	.133
N = 99	36	.004
	37	.008
	38	.013
	39	.022
	40	.035
	41	.054
	42	.080
	43	.114
	44	.157
N = 100	36	.003
	37	.006
	38	.010
	39	.018
	40	.028
	41	.044
	42	.067
	43	.097
	44	.136

Table A-11. Distribution of the Total Number of Runs u in Samples of Size (N_1, N_2)*

$(N_1,N_2) \backslash u$	2	3	4	5	6	7	8	9	10	11	12	13	14	15	16	17	18	19	20
(2,3)	.200	.500	.900	1.000															
(2,4)	.133	.400	.800	1.000															
(2,5)	.095	.333	.714	1.000															
(2,6)	.071	.286	.643	1.000															
(2,7)	.056	.250	.583	1.000															
(2,8)	.044	.222	.533	1.000															
(2,9)	.036	.200	.491	1.000															
(2,10)	.030	.182	.455	1.000															
(3,3)	.100	.300	.700	.900	1.000														
(3,4)	.057	.200	.543	.800	.971	1.000													
(3,5)	.036	.143	.429	.714	.929	1.000													
(3,6)	.024	.107	.345	.643	.881	1.000													
(3,7)	.017	.083	.283	.583	.833	1.000													
(3,8)	.012	.067	.236	.533	.788	1.000													
(3,9)	.009	.055	.200	.491	.745	1.000													
(3,10)	.007	.045	.171	.455	.706	1.000													
(4,4)	.029	.114	.371	.629	.886	.971	1.000												
(4,5)	.016	.071	.262	.500	.786	.929	.992	1.000											
(4,6)	.010	.048	.190	.405	.690	.881	.976	1.000											
(4,7)	.006	.033	.142	.333	.606	.833	.954	1.000											
(4,8)	.004	.024	.109	.279	.533	.788	.929	1.000											
(4,9)	.003	.018	.085	.236	.471	.745	.902	1.000											
(4,10)	.002	.014	.068	.203	.419	.706	.874	1.000											
(5,5)	.008	.040	.167	.357	.643	.833	.960	.992	1.000										
(5,6)	.004	.024	.110	.262	.522	.738	.911	.976	.998	1.000									
(5,7)	.003	.015	.076	.197	.424	.652	.854	.955	.992	1.000									
(5,8)	.002	.010	.054	.152	.347	.576	.793	.929	.984	1.000									
(5,9)	.001	.007	.039	.119	.287	.510	.734	.902	.972	1.000									
(5,10)	.001	.005	.029	.095	.239	.455	.678	.874	.958	1.000									
(6,6)	.002	.013	.067	.175	.392	.608	.825	.933	.987	.998	1.000								
(6,7)	.001	.008	.043	.121	.296	.500	.733	.879	.966	.992	.999	1.000							
(6,8)	.001	.005	.028	.086	.226	.413	.646	.821	.937	.984	.998	1.000							
(6,9)	.000	.003	.019	.063	.175	.343	.566	.762	.902	.972	.994	1.000							
(6,10)	.000	.002	.013	.047	.137	.288	.497	.706	.864	.958	.990	1.000							
(7,7)	.001	.004	.025	.078	.209	.383	.617	.791	.922	.975	.996	.999	1.000						
(7,8)	.000	.002	.015	.051	.149	.296	.514	.704	.867	.949	.988	.998	1.000	1.000					
(7,9)	.000	.001	.010	.035	.108	.231	.427	.622	.806	.916	.975	.994	.999	1.000					
(7,10)	.000	.001	.006	.024	.080	.182	.355	.549	.743	.879	.957	.990	.998	1.000					
(8,8)	.000	.001	.009	.032	.100	.214	.405	.595	.786	.900	.968	.991	.999	1.000	1.000				
(8,9)	.000	.001	.005	.020	.069	.157	.319	.500	.702	.843	.939	.980	.996	.999	1.000	1.000			
(8,10)	.000	.000	.003	.013	.048	.117	.251	.419	.621	.782	.903	.964	.990	.998	1.000	1.000			
(9,9)	.000	.000	.003	.012	.044	.109	.238	.399	.601	.762	.891	.956	.988	.997	1.000	1.000	1.000		
(9,10)	.000	.000	.002	.008	.029	.077	.179	.319	.510	.681	.834	.923	.974	.992	.999	1.000	1.000	1.000	
(10,10)	.000	.000	.001	.004	.019	.051	.128	.242	.414	.586	.758	.872	.949	.981	.996	.999	1.000	1.000	1.000

* Reproduced with permission from C. Eisenhart and F. Swed, "Tables for testing randomness of grouping in a sequence of alternatives," *Annals of Mathematical Statistics*, vol. 14 (1943), p. 66.

TABLE A-11. DISTRIBUTION OF THE TOTAL NUMBER OF RUNS (*Continued*)

The values listed on the previous page give the chance that u or fewer runs will occur. For example, for two samples of size 4, the chance of three or fewer runs is .114. For sample sizes $N_1 = N_2$ larger than 10 the following table can be used. The columns headed 0.5, 1, 2.5, 5 give values of u such that u or fewer runs occur with chance less than the indicated percentage. For example, for $N_1 = N_2 = 12$ the chance of 8 or fewer runs is about .05. The columns headed 95, 97.5, 99, 99.5 give values of u for which the chance of u or more runs is less than 5, 2.5, 1, 0.5 per cent.

$N_1 = N_2$	0.5	1	2.5	5	95	97.5	99	99.5	Mean	Var.	s.d.
11	5	6	7	7	16	16	17	18	12	5.24	2.29
12	6	7	7	8	17	18	18	19	13	5.74	2.40
13	7	7	8	9	18	19	20	20	14	6.24	2.50
14	7	8	9	10	19	20	21	22	15	6.74	2.60
15	8	9	10	11	20	21	22	23	16	7.24	2.69
16	9	10	11	11	22	22	23	24	17	7.74	2.78
17	10	10	11	12	23	24	25	25	18	8.24	2.87
18	10	11	12	13	24	25	26	27	19	8.74	2.96
19	11	12	13	14	25	26	27	28	20	9.24	3.04
20	12	13	14	15	26	27	28	29	21	9.74	3.12
25	16	17	18	19	32	33	34	35	26	12.24	3.50
30	20	21	22	24	37	39	40	41	31	14.75	3.84
35	24	25	27	28	43	44	46	47	36	17.25	4.15
40	29	30	31	33	48	50	51	52	41	19.75	4.44
45	33	34	36	37	54	55	57	58	46	22.25	4.72
50	37	38	40	42	59	61	63	64	51	24.75	4.97
55	42	43	45	46	65	66	68	69	56	27.25	5.22
60	46	47	49	51	70	72	74	75	61	29.75	5.45
65	50	52	54	56	75	77	79	81	66	32.25	5.68
70	55	56	58	60	81	83	85	86	71	34.75	5.89
75	59	61	63	65	86	88	90	92	76	37.25	6.10
80	64	65	68	70	91	93	96	97	81	39.75	6.30
85	68	70	72	74	97	99	101	103	86	42.25	6.50
90	73	74	77	79	102	104	107	108	91	44.75	6.69
95	77	79	82	84	107	109	112	114	96	47.25	6.87
100	82	84	86	88	113	115	117	119	101	49.75	7.05

For large values of N_1 and N_2, particularly for $N_1 = N_2$ greater than 10, a normal approximation may be used. The mean and variance are

$$\frac{2N_1N_2}{N_1 + N_2} + 1 \quad \text{and} \quad \frac{2N_1N_2(2N_1N_2 - N_1 - N_2)}{(N_1 + N_2)^2(N_1 + N_2 - 1)}$$

respectively. For example, for $N_1 = N_2 = 20$ the mean is 21, and the variance is 9.74. The 97.5 and 2.5 percentiles are $21 + 1.96\sqrt{9.74}$ and $21 - 1.96\sqrt{9.74}$ or 27.1 and 14.9. The approximation is improved if $\frac{1}{2}$ is subtracted from the computed values. The resulting percentiles would then be 26.6 and 14.4. For two samples each of size N the mean is $N + 1$, and the variance is $N(N - 1)/(2N - 1)$.

TABLE A-12*a*. POWER CURVES FOR ONE- AND TWO-SIDED TESTS WHEN σ IS KNOWN

For one-sided tests $d = \dfrac{\mu - \mu_0}{\sigma/\sqrt{N}}$ or $d = \dfrac{(\mu_1 - \mu_2)}{\sigma\sqrt{\dfrac{1}{N_1} + \dfrac{1}{N_2}}}$.

For two-sided tests $d = \dfrac{|\mu - \mu_0|}{\sigma/\sqrt{N}}$ or $d = \dfrac{|\mu_1 - \mu_2|}{\sigma\sqrt{\dfrac{1}{N_1} + \dfrac{1}{N_2}}}$.

Curve (*a*) is for two-sided $\alpha = .10$ tests, curve (*b*) is for one-sided $\alpha = .05$ tests, curve (*c*) is for two-sided $\alpha = .05$ tests, curve (*d*) is for one-sided $\alpha = .025$ tests, curve (*e*) is for two-sided $\alpha = .01$ tests, and curve (*f*) is for one-sided $\alpha = .005$ tests.

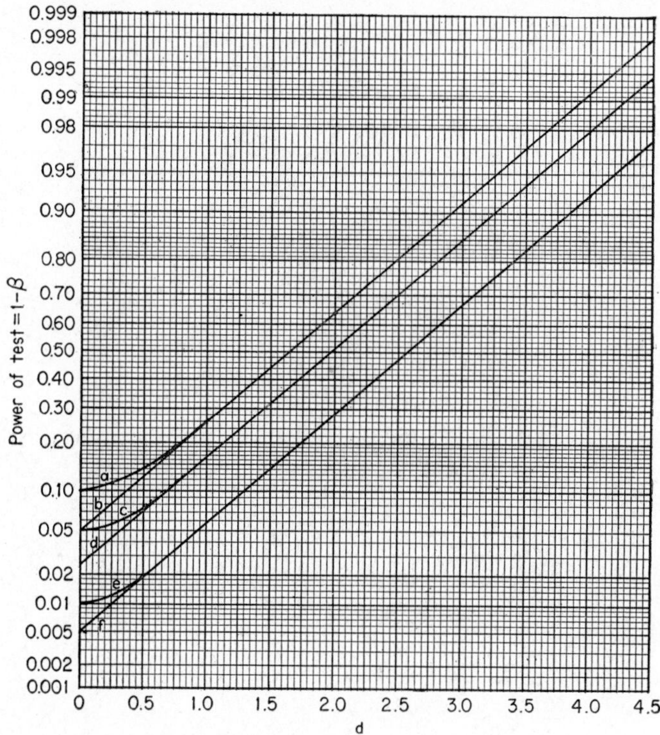

TABLE A-12b. VALUES OF $d = \frac{\mu - \mu_0}{\sigma/\sqrt{N}}$ FOR A SINGLE SAMPLE OR

$d = \frac{\mu_1 - \mu_2}{\sigma\sqrt{1/N_1 + 1/N_2}}$ FOR TWO SAMPLES SUCH THAT A ONE-SIDED TEST AT THE α LEVEL OF SIGNIFICANCE HAS POWER $1 - \beta$

The values in the tables are approximate values of $|d|$ for two-sided tests at level of significance 2α.

$\alpha = .005$, one-sided test ($\alpha = .01$, two sided test)

df \ $1-\beta$	.1	.2	.3	.4	.5	.6	.7	.8	.9	.95	.975	.99	.995	df
4	1.99	2.73	3.29	3.78	4.25	4.73	5.25	5.88	6.77	7.52	8.18	8.98	9.51	4
5	1.83	2.48	2.97	3.39	3.79	4.20	4.64	5.17	5.91	6.53	7.08	7.73	8.18	5
6	1.72	2.33	2.78	3.16	3.53	3.90	4.30	4.77	5.43	5.99	6.47	7.05	7.43	6
7	1.65	2.23	2.65	3.01	3.36	3.71	4.08	4.52	5.13	5.65	6.09	6.62	6.98	7
8	1.60	2.16	2.56	2.91	3.24	3.57	3.92	4.34	4.92	5.41	5.84	6.33	6.67	8
9	1.56	2.10	2.50	2.83	3.15	3.47	3.81	4.21	4.77	5.24	5.65	6.12	6.45	9
10	1.53	2.06	2.45	2.78	3.09	3.40	3.73	4.12	4.67	5.12	5.51	5.98	6.29	10
12	1.49	2.00	2.37	2.69	2.99	3.28	3.60	3.98	4.50	4.94	5.31	5.75	6.05	12
16	1.44	1.93	2.28	2.59	2.87	3.16	3.46	3.82	4.32	4.73	5.09	5.50	5.79	16
24	1.39	1.86	2.20	2.49	2.77	3.04	3.33	3.68	4.15	4.54	4.89	5.28	5.55	24
36	1.36	1.82	2.15	2.44	2.70	2.97	3.25	3.59	4.05	4.43	4.76	5.15	5.41	36
∞	1.294	1.734	2.052	2.323	2.576	2.829	3.100	3.418	3.858	4.221	4.536	4.902	5.152	∞

$\alpha = .0125$, one-sided test ($\alpha = .025$, two-sided test)

df \ $1-\beta$	.1	.2	.3	.4	.5	.6	.7	.8	.9	.95	.975	.99	.995	df
4	1.32	1.96	2.43	2.87	3.24	3.64	4.07	4.58	5.31	5.93	6.47	7.10	7.53	4
5	1.25	1.83	2.26	2.63	2.98	3.34	3.72	4.18	4.82	5.35	5.82	6.37	6.76	5
6	1.19	1.75	2.15	2.50	2.83	3.16	3.52	3.94	4.53	5.03	5.46	5.96	6.30	6
7	1.15	1.69	2.08	2.41	2.73	3.05	3.39	3.79	4.35	4.82	5.22	5.70	6.02	7
8	1.13	1.65	2.03	2.35	2.66	2.96	3.29	3.68	4.22	4.67	5.06	5.52	5.84	8
9	1.11	1.62	1.99	2.32	2.60	2.90	3.22	3.60	4.13	4.56	4.94	5.39	5.69	9
10	1.09	1.59	1.96	2.27	2.56	2.86	3.18	3.54	4.06	4.48	4.86	5.29	5.59	10
12	1.07	1.56	1.91	2.21	2.50	2.79	3.11	3.45	3.95	4.37	4.73	5.14	5.43	12
16	1.05	1.52	1.87	2.17	2.44	2.72	3.01	3.36	3.84	4.24	4.58	4.98	5.26	16
24	1.01	1.48	1.81	2.10	2.37	2.63	2.92	3.26	3.72	4.11	4.44	4.83	5.09	24
36	.99	1.45	1.78	2.06	2.32	2.59	2.87	3.19	3.66	4.03	4.36	4.74	5.00	36
∞	.959	1.399	1.717	1.988	2.241	2.494	2.765	3.083	3.523	3.886	4.201	4.567	4.817	∞

$\alpha = .025$, one-sided test ($\alpha = .05$, two-sided test)

df \ $1-\beta$	.1	.2	.3	.4	.5	.6	.7	.8	.9	.95	.975	.99	.995	df
4	.87	1.44	1.86	2.23	2.58	2.93	3.31	3.76	4.40	4.93	5.40	5.94	6.32	4
5	.82	1.37	1.77	2.11	2.43	2.75	3.10	3.51	4.09	4.58	5.00	5.48	5.82	5
6	.80	1.32	1.70	2.03	2.34	2.64	2.98	3.37	3.91	4.37	4.76	5.23	5.54	6
7	.78	1.29	1.66	1.98	2.27	2.57	2.89	3.27	3.80	4.23	4.61	5.06	5.36	7
8	.77	1.27	1.63	1.94	2.23	2.52	2.83	3.20	3.71	4.14	4.51	4.94	5.23	8
9	.76	1.25	1.60	1.91	2.20	2.48	2.79	3.15	3.65	4.07	4.43	4.85	5.14	9
10	.75	1.23	1.59	1.89	2.17	2.45	2.76	3.11	3.60	4.01	4.37	4.78	5.07	10
12	.74	1.21	1.56	1.86	2.13	2.41	2.71	3.05	3.54	3.94	4.28	4.69	4.96	12
16	.72	1.19	1.53	1.82	2.09	2.36	2.65	2.98	3.46	3.84	4.18	4.58	4.84	16
24	.71	1.16	1.50	1.78	2.04	2.31	2.59	2.92	3.38	3.76	4.09	4.47	4.72	24
36	.70	1.15	1.48	1.75	2.01	2.27	2.55	2.88	3.33	3.71	4.03	4.41	4.66	36
∞	.678	1.118	1.436	1.707	1.960	2.213	2.484	2.802	3.242	3.605	3.920	4.286	4.536	∞

$\alpha = .05$, one-sided test ($\alpha = .10$, two-sided test)

df \ $1-\beta$	.1	.2	.3	.4	.5	.6	.7	.8	.9	.95	.975	.99	.995	df
4	.43	.96	1.34	1.68	1.99	2.30	2.64	3.04	3.60	4.07	4.48	4.95	5.29	4
5	.42	.92	1.29	1.61	1.91	2.21	2.51	2.90	3.43	3.87	4.25	4.70	5.00	5
6	.40	.90	1.26	1.57	1.86	2.15	2.46	2.82	3.33	3.75	4.12	4.55	4.84	6
7	.40	.89	1.24	1.54	1.82	2.11	2.41	2.77	3.26	3.68	4.03	4.45	4.73	7
8	.39	.88	1.22	1.52	1.80	2.08	2.38	2.73	3.21	3.62	3.97	4.37	4.66	8
9	.39	.87	1.21	1.50	1.78	2.06	2.35	2.70	3.18	3.57	3.92	4.32	4.60	9
10	.39	.86	1.20	1.49	1.77	2.04	2.33	2.67	3.15	3.54	3.88	4.28	4.56	10
12	.38	.85	1.19	1.48	1.75	2.02	2.30	2.64	3.11	3.50	3.82	4.23	4.49	12
16	.38	.84	1.17	1.45	1.72	1.98	2.27	2.60	3.06	3.44	3.77	4.16	4.42	16
24	.37	.83	1.15	1.43	1.69	1.95	2.23	2.56	3.01	3.39	3.71	4.09	4.35	24
36	.37	.82	1.14	1.42	1.68	1.94	2.21	2.54	2.98	3.36	3.68	4.05	4.31	36
∞	.363	.803	1.121	1.392	1.645	1.898	2.169	2.487	2.927	3.290	3.605	3.971	4.221	∞

TABLE A-12c. SAMPLE SIZE NEEDED TO ATTAIN POWER $1 - \beta$ AGAINST $d' = (\mu - \mu_0)/\sigma$ IN THE ONE-SAMPLE CASE OR $d' = (\mu_1 - \mu_2)/\sigma$ IN THE TWO-SAMPLE CASE

Each sample in the two sample case should be of the given size.

α	d'	One-sided, single-sample test							One-sided, two-sample test							d'
		$1 - \beta$														
		.50	.60	.70	.80	.90	.95	.99	.50	.60	.70	.80	.90	.95	.99	
.005	.1	669	805	966	1173	1493	1785	2403	1327	1602	1922	2337	2977	3567	4806	.1
	.2	169	204	244	296	377	450	605	333	403	484	588	749	894	1206	.2
	.4	42	53	64	77	97	115	154	87	101	124	150	189	226	304	.4
	.6	22	26	31	36	45	53	71	37	44	55	65	85	100	138	.6
	.8	14	16	19	22	27	32	41	23	27	32	39	49	56	85	.8
	1.0	10	12	13	14	19	22	28	15	18	21	26	32	38	49	1.0
	1.2	8	9	10	12	14	16	21	11	13	16	18	23	27	36	1.2
	1.4	7	8	9	10	12	13	16	9	10	12	14	18	20	27	1.4
	1.6	6	7	8	8	10	11	13	7	9	10	11	14	16	21	1.6
	1.8	6	6	7	8	9	9	11	6	7	8	9	11	13	17	1.8
	2.0	4	6	6	7	8	8	10	6	6	7	8	10	11	14	2.0
	3.0	3	4	5	5	6	6	7	4	4	5	5	6	6	8	3.0
.0125	.1	506	625	768	954	1245	1514	2090	1004	1244	1529	1901	2482	3020	4180	.1
	.2	127	158	194	240	312	380	524	255	316	388	482	629	766	1057	.2
	.4	34	42	52	63	81	98	135	64	81	97	120	157	191	265	.4
	.6	17	19	24	30	37	45	61	30	37	44	54	71	84	117	.6
	.8	11	13	15	18	23	27	36	18	21	26	32	40	49	69	.8
	1.0	8	9	11	13	16	18	24	12	14	17	21	27	32	44	1.0
	1.2	7	7	8	10	12	14	18	9	11	13	15	19	23	31	1.2
	1.4	6	6	7	8	10	11	14	7	8	10	12	15	17	23	1.4
	1.6	5	6	6	7	8	9	11	6	7	8	9	12	14	18	1.6
	1.8		5	6	6	7	8	10	5	6	7	8	10	11	15	1.8
	2.0			5	6	6	7	9	4	5	6	7	8	9	12	2.0
	3.0							6		3	4	4	5	5	7	3.0
.025	.1	386	492	619	788	1054	1302	1840	771	982	1237	1574	2106	2603	3680	.1
	.2	98	124	156	201	265	327	459	193	245	310	395	527	650	922	.2
	.4	26	33	41	52	68	85	117	49	62	80	100	133	164	231	.4
	.6	13	16	20	24	32	39	53	23	29	36	45	60	77	104	.6
	.8	9	10	12	14	18	23	31	14	17	21	26	34	42	59	.8
	1.0	6	7	9	10	13	16	21	9	11	14	17	22	28	38	1.0
	1.2	6	6	7	8	10	12	15	7	8	10	12	16	19	27	1.2
	1.4	5	5	6	7	8	9	12	5	7	8	10	12	15	20	1.4
	1.6			5	6	7	8	10	5	5	6	8	10	12	16	1.6
	1.8				5	6	7	8	4	4	5	6	8	10	13	1.8
	2.0					5	6	7	4	4	5	6	7	8	11	2.0
	3.0											4	4	5	6	3.0
.05	.1	272	362	473	620	858	1084	1580	543	722	943	1235	1715	2166	3160	.1
	.2	69	92	119	156	215	272	396	138	182	237	312	430	543	793	.2
	.4	19	24	31	41	55	70	101	35	46	59	79	109	137	199	.4
	.6	9	12	15	19	26	32	46	16	21	28	35	48	62	89	.6
	.8	6	8	9	12	15	19	27	10	12	16	20	28	35	50	.8
	1.0	5	6	7	8	11	13	18	7	8	11	13	18	23	33	1.0
	1.2		5	5	6	8	10	13	5	6	8	10	13	16	23	1.2
	1.4				5	6	8	10	4	5	6	7	10	12	17	1.4
	1.6					6	6	8	4	4	5	6	8	10	14	1.6
	1.8					5	6	7		4	4	5	7	8	11	1.8
	2.0						5	6			4	4	6	7	9	2.0
	3.0												3	4	5	3.0

TABLE A-13. POWER OF THE ANALYSIS-OF-VARIANCE TEST

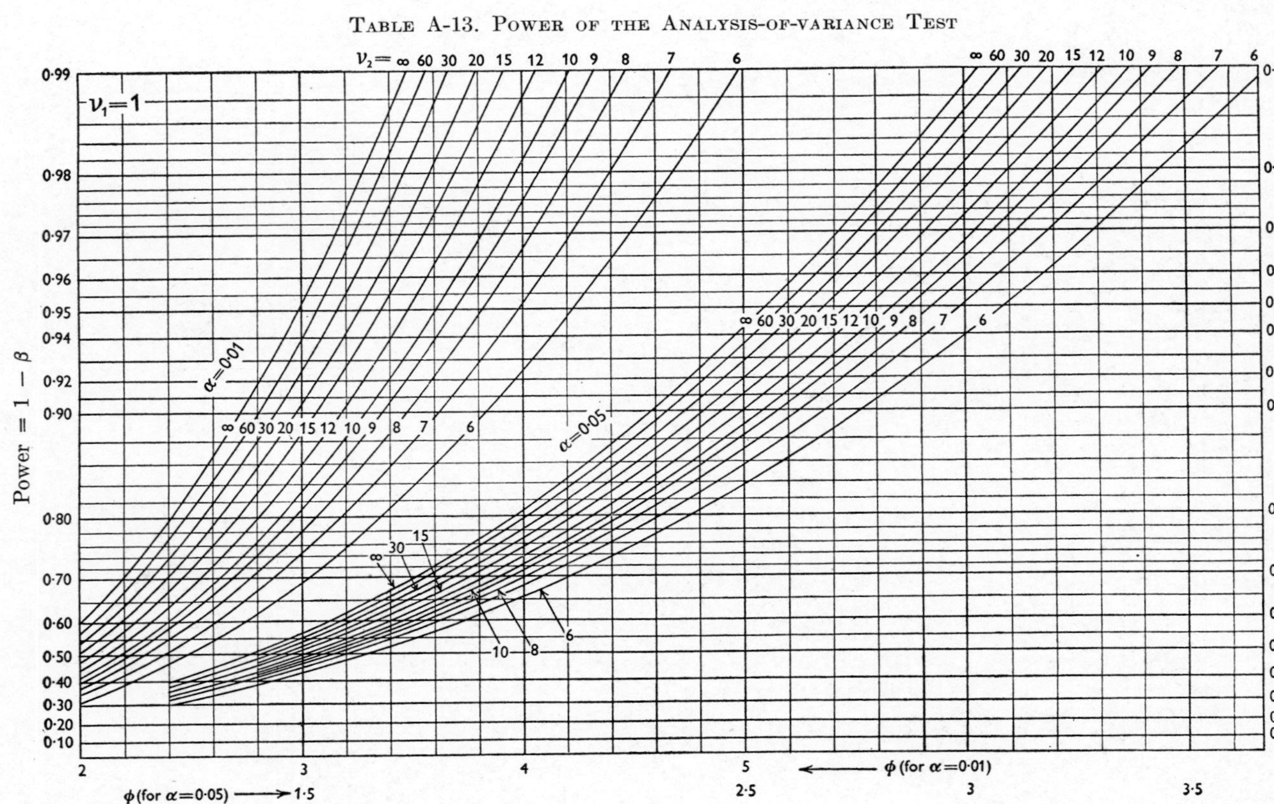

TABLE A-13. POWER OF THE ANALYSIS-OF-VARIANCE TEST (*Continued*)

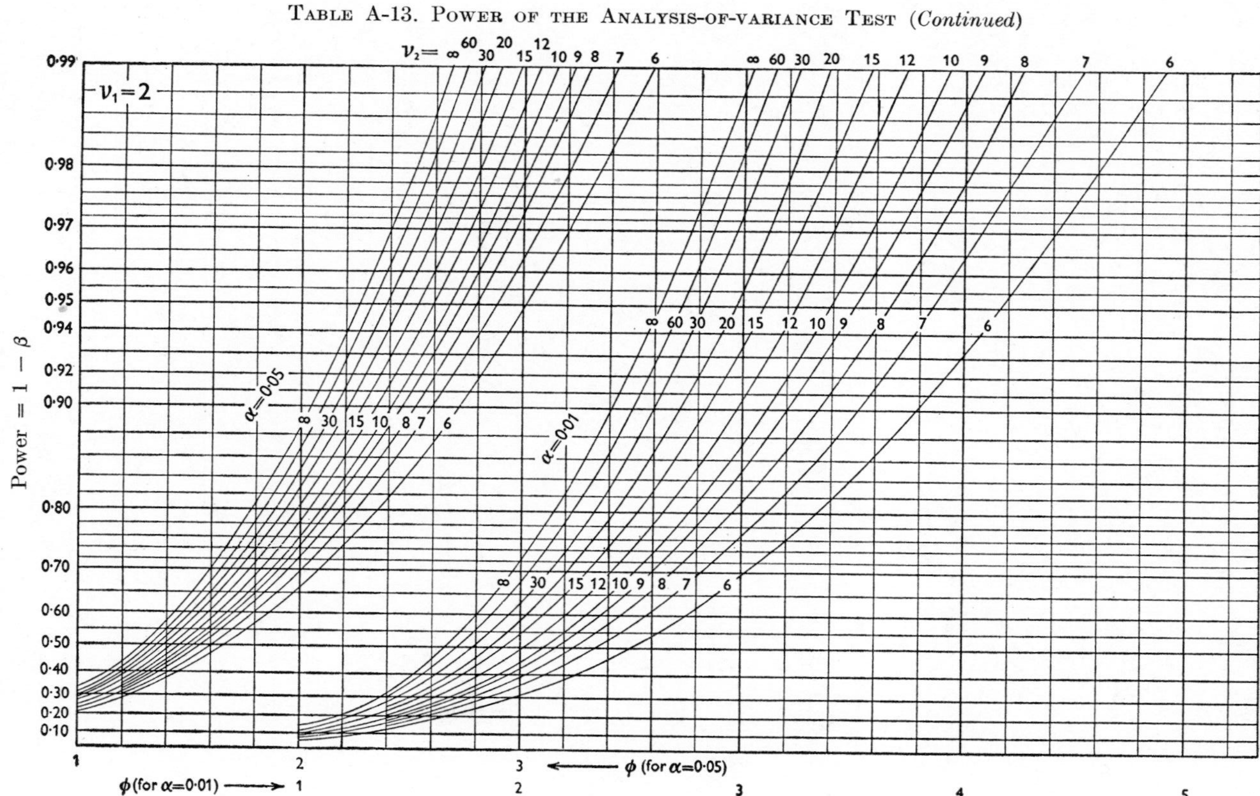

TABLE A-13. POWER OF THE ANALYSIS-OF-VARIANCE TEST (*Continued*)

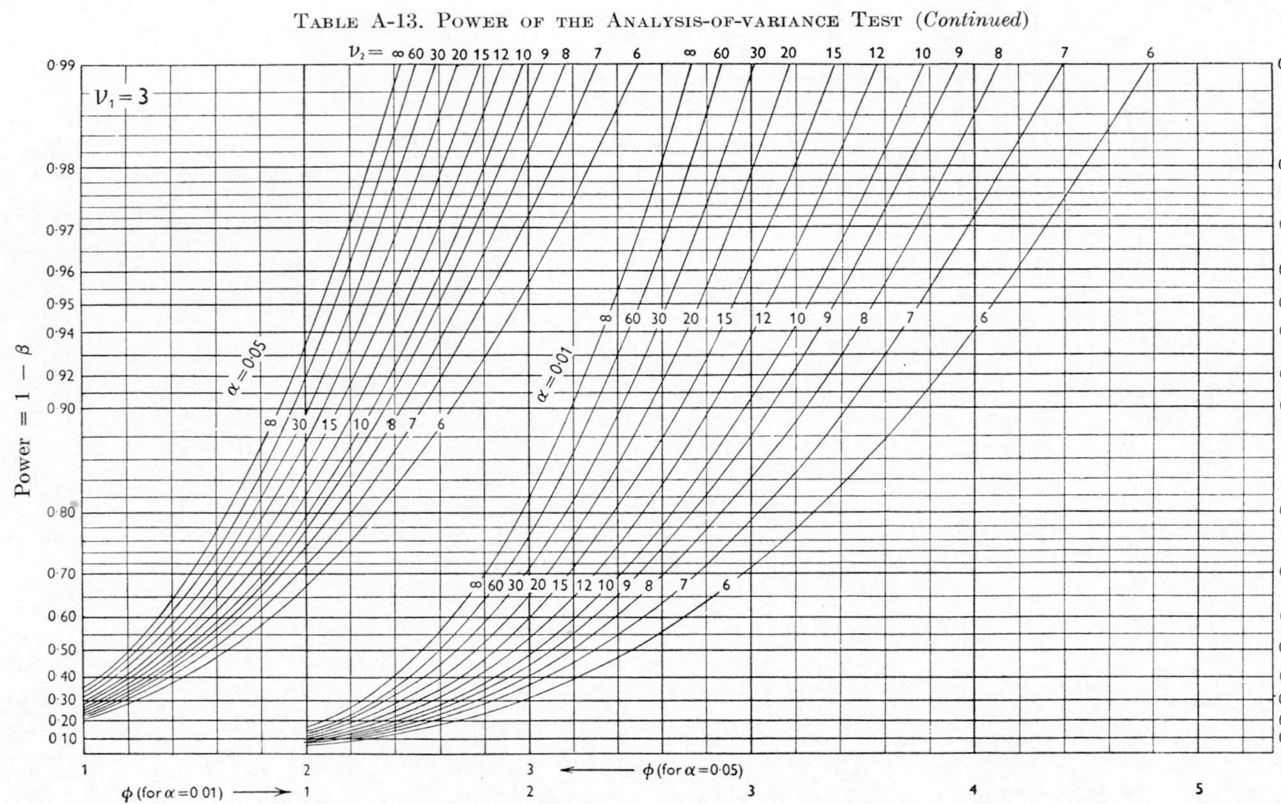

Table A-13. Power of the Analysis-of-variance Test (*Continued*)

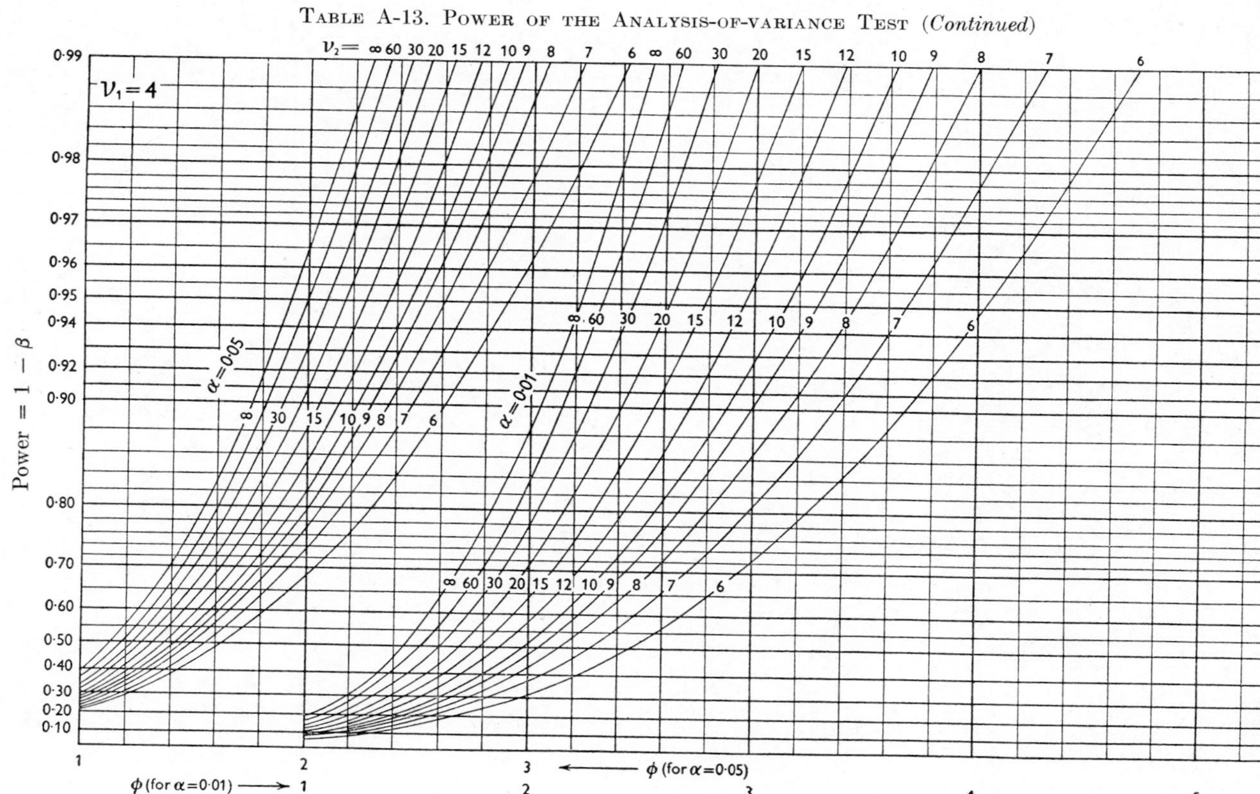

TABLE A-13. POWER OF THE ANALYSIS-OF-VARIANCE TEST (*Continued*)

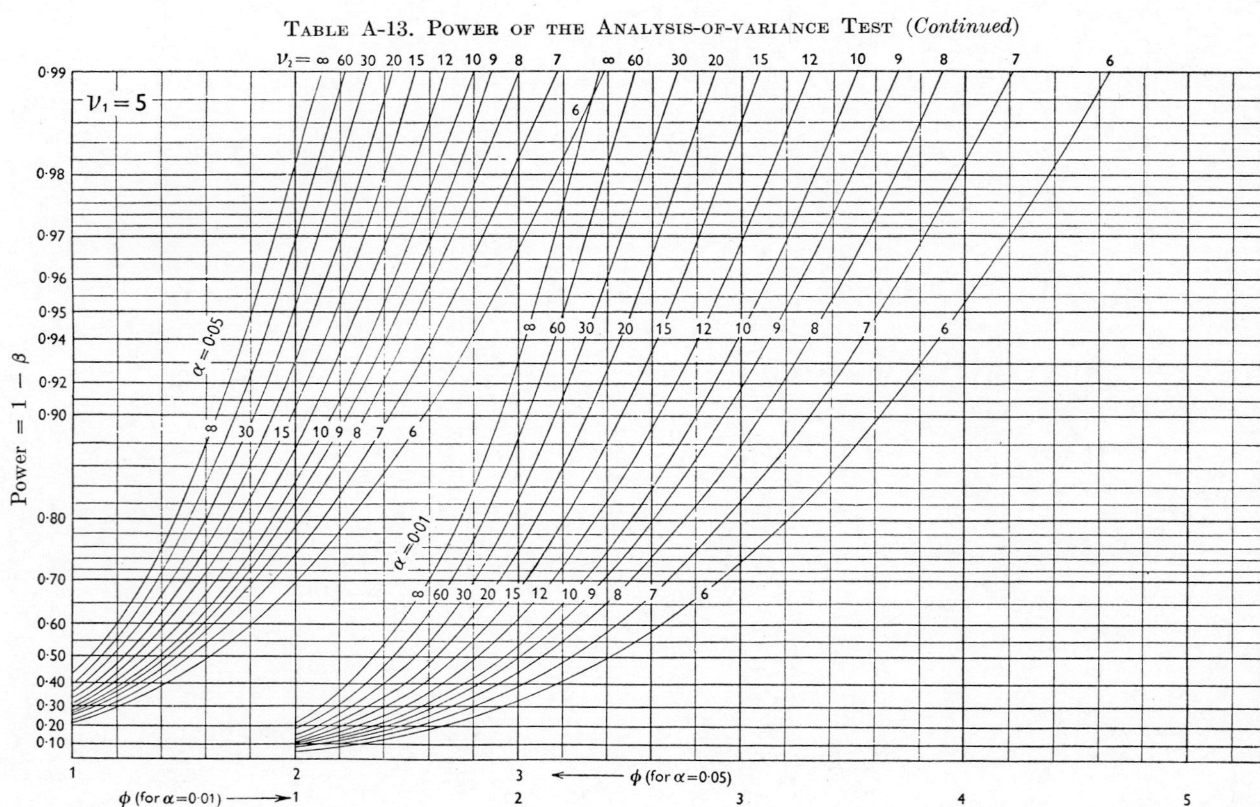

TABLE A-13. POWER OF THE ANALYSIS-OF-VARIANCE TEST (*Continued*)

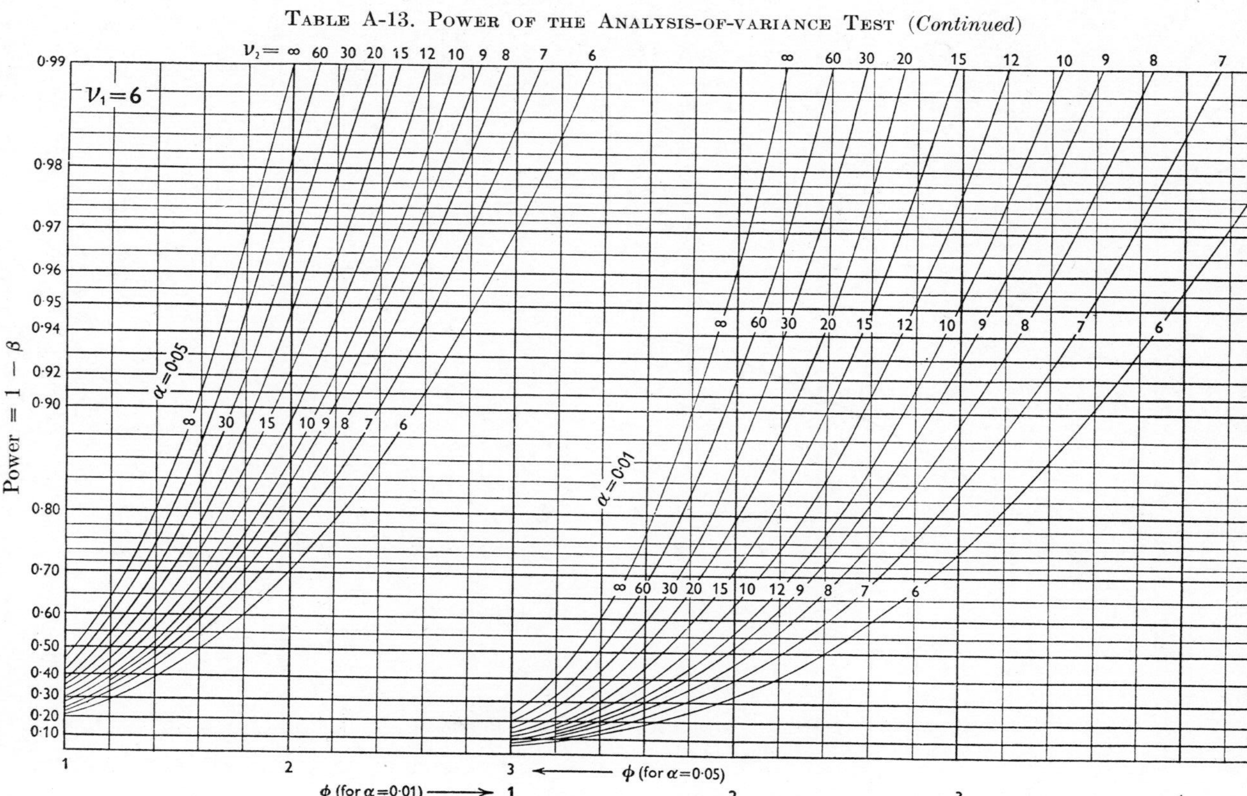

Table A-13. Power of the Analysis-of-variance Test (*Continued*)

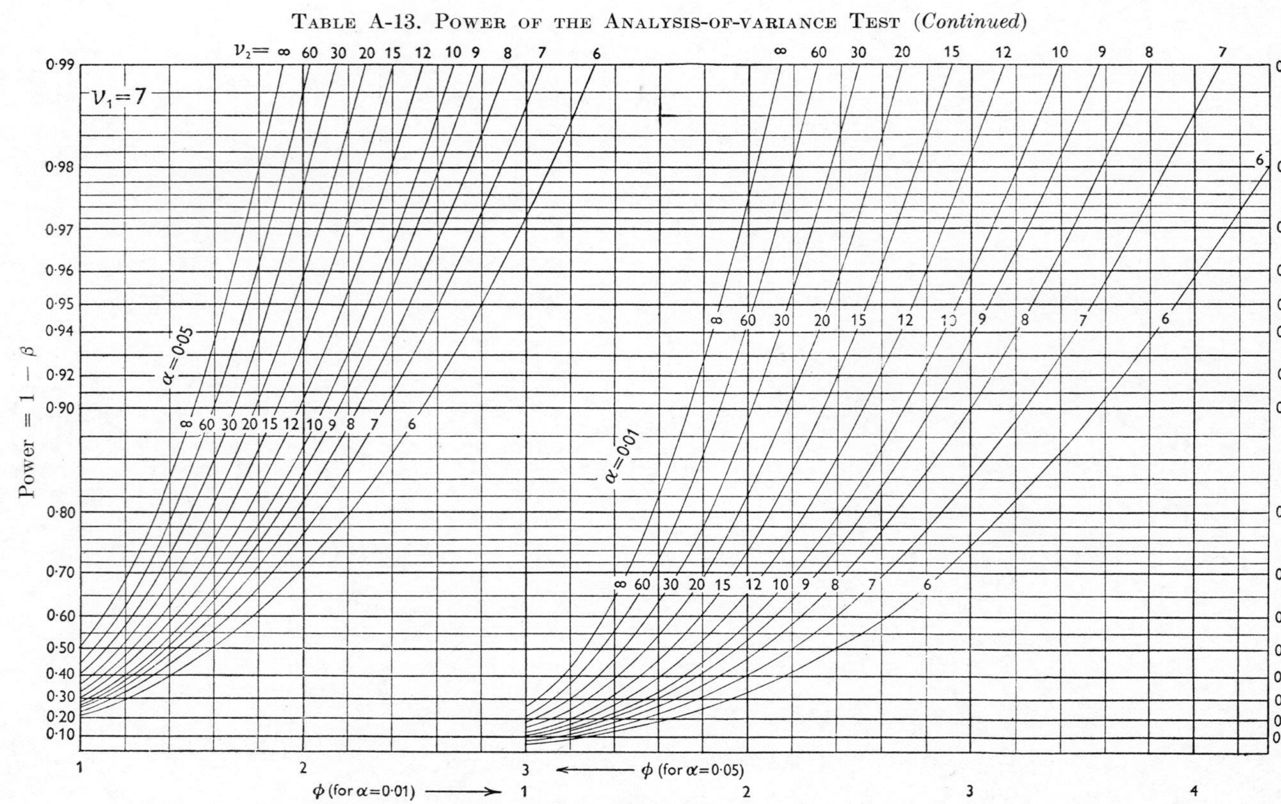

TABLE A-13. POWER OF THE ANALYSIS-OF-VARIANCE TEST (*Continued*)

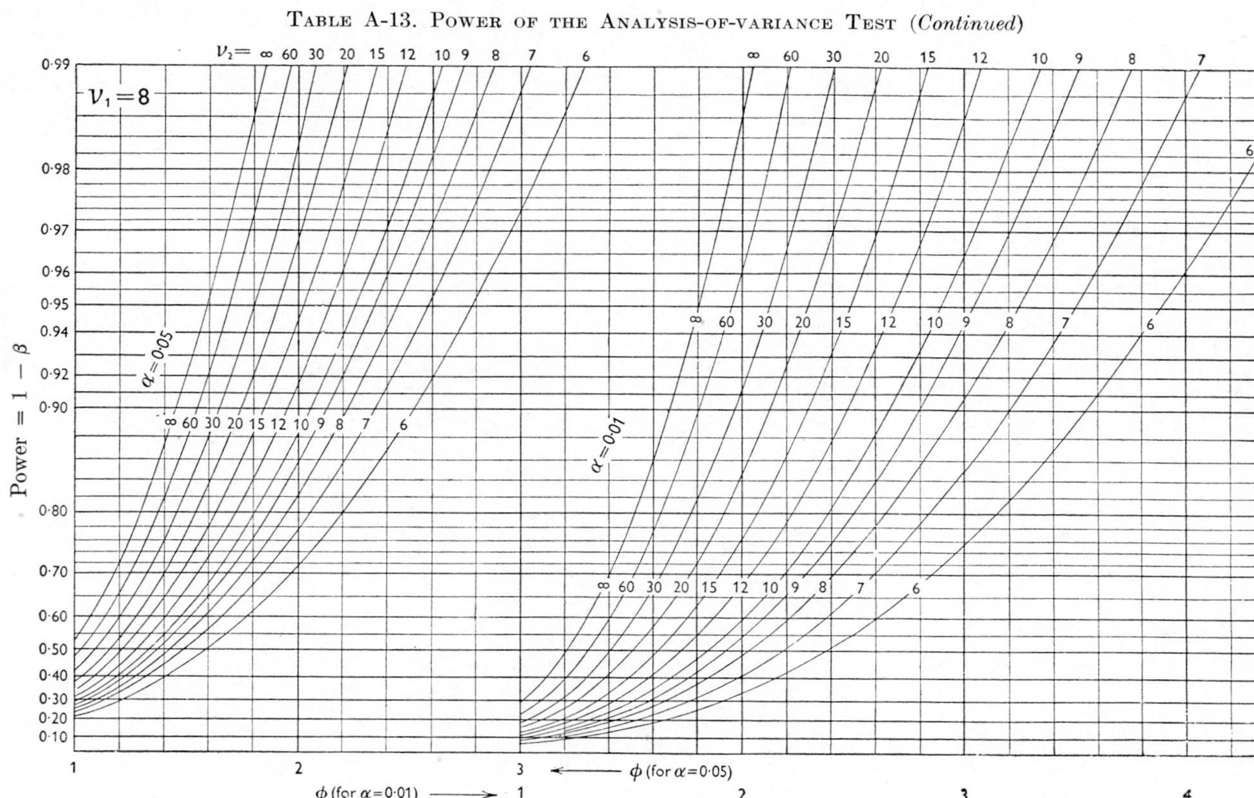

Table A-14. Natural Logarithms

.10–.99

N	.00	.01	.02	.03	.04	.05	.06	.07	.08	.09
.1	−2.303	−2.207	−2.120	−2.040	−1.966	−1.897	−1.833	−1.772	−1.715	−1.661
.2	−1.609	−1.561	−1.514	−1.470	−1.427	−1.386	−1.347	−1.309	−1.273	−1.238
.3	−1.204	−1.171	−1.139	−1.109	−1.079	−1.050	−1.022	− .994	− .968	− .942
.4	− .916	− .892	− .868	− .844	− .821	− .799	− .777	− .755	− .734	− .713
.5	− .693	− .673	− .654	− .635	− .616	− .598	− .580	− .562	− .545	− .528
.6	− .511	− .494	− .478	− .462	− .446	− .431	− .416	− .400	− .386	− .371
.7	− .357	− .342	− .329	− .315	− .301	− .288	− .274	− .261	− .248	− .236
.8	− .223	− .211	− .198	− .186	− .174	− .163	− .151	− .139	− .128	− .117
.9	− .105	− .094	− .083	− .073	− .062	− .051	− .041	− .030	− .020	− .010

1.0–9.9

N	.0	.1	.2	.3	.4	.5	.6	.7	.8	.9
1.0	.000	.095	.182	.262	.336	.405	.470	.531	.588	.642
2.0	.693	.742	.788	.833	.875	.916	.956	.993	1.030	1.065
3.0	1.099	1.131	1.163	1.194	1.224	1.253	1.281	1.308	1.335	1.361
4.0	1.386	1.411	1.435	1.459	1.482	1.504	1.526	1.548	1.569	1.589
5.0	1.609	1.629	1.649	1.668	1.686	1.705	1.723	1.740	1.758	1.775
6.0	1.792	1.808	1.825	1.841	1.856	1.872	1.887	1.902	1.917	1.932
7.0	1.946	1.960	1.974	1.988	2.001	2.015	2.028	2.041	2.054	2.067
8.0	2.079	2.092	2.104	2.116	2.128	2.140	2.152	2.163	2.175	2.186
9.0	2.197	2.208	2.219	2.230	2.241	2.251	2.262	2.272	2.282	2.293

To obtain the natural logarithm of numbers above 10:
divide the number by 10 and add 2.303 to the ln obtained,
or divide the number by 100 and add 4.605 to the ln obtained,
or divide the number by 1,000 and add 6.908 to the ln obtained, etc.

To obtain the natural logarithm of numbers less than .1:
multiply the number by 10 and subtract 2.303 from the ln obtained,
or multiply by 100 and subtract 4.605 from the ln obtained,
or multiply by 1,000 and subtract 6.908 from the ln obtained, etc.

Special Values of $\ln (1 - \beta)/\alpha$ for Sequential Tests

Note that $\ln \beta/(1 - \alpha)$ is equal to $-\ln (1 - \alpha)/\beta$, which can be read from the table by interchanging the arguments α and β and prefixing a minus sign.

α \ β	.001	.005	.01	.02	.03	.04	.05	.10	.15	.20	.25
.001	6.907	6.903	6.898	6.888	6.877	6.867	6.856	6.802	6.745	6.685	6.620
.005	5.297	5.293	5.288	5.278	5.268	5.257	5.247	5.193	5.136	5.075	5.011
.01	4.604	4.600	4.595	4.585	4.575	4.564	4.554	4.500	4.443	4.382	4.317
.02	3.911	3.907	3.902	3.892	3.882	3.871	3.861	3.807	3.750	3.689	3.624
.03	3.506	3.502	3.496	3.486	3.476	3.466	3.455	3.401	3.344	3.283	3.219
.04	3.218	3.214	3.209	3.199	3.188	3.178	3.168	3.114	3.056	2.996	2.931
.05	2.995	2.991	2.986	2.976	2.965	2.955	2.944	2.890	2.833	2.773	2.708
.10	2.302	2.298	2.293	2.282	2.272	2.261	2.251	2.197	2.140	2.079	2.015
.15	1.896	1.892	1.887	1.877	1.867	1.855	1.846	1.792	1.735	1.674	1.609
.20	1.608	1.604	1.599	1.589	1.579	1.568	1.558	1.504	1.447	1.386	1.322
.25	1.385	1.381	1.376	1.366	1.356	1.344	1.335	1.281	1.224	1.163	1.099

TABLE A-15. CUMULATIVE POISSON DISTRIBUTION
(Proportion of cases less than or equal to X)

λ \ X	0	1	2	3	4	5	6	7	8	9	10	11	12
.05	.951	.999	1.000										
.10	.905	.995	1.000										
.15	.861	.990	.999	1.000									
.20	.819	.982	.999	1.000									
.25	.779	.974	.998	1.000									
.30	.741	.963	.996	1.000									
.35	.705	.951	.994	1.000									
.40	.670	.938	.992	.999	1.000								
.45	.638	.925	.989	.999	1.000								
.50	.607	.910	.986	.998	1.000								
.55	.577	.894	.982	.998	1.000								
.60	.549	.878	.977	.997	1.000								
.65	.522	.861	.972	.996	.999	1.000							
.70	.497	.844	.966	.994	.999	1.000							
.75	.472	.827	.959	.993	.999	1.000							
.80	.449	.809	.953	.991	.999	1.000							
.85	.427	.791	.945	.989	.998	1.000							
.90	.407	.772	.937	.987	.998	1.000							
.95	.387	.754	.929	.984	.997	1.000							
1.00	.368	.736	.920	.981	.996	.999	1.000						
1.1	.333	.699	.900	.974	.995	.999	1.000						
1.2	.301	.663	.879	.966	.992	.998	1.000						
1.3	.273	.627	.857	.957	.989	.998	1.000						
1.4	.247	.592	.833	.946	.986	.997	.999	1.000					
1.5	.223	.558	.809	.934	.981	.996	.999	1.000					
1.6	.202	.525	.783	.921	.976	.994	.999	1.000					
1.7	.183	.493	.757	.907	.970	.992	.998	1.000					
1.8	.165	.463	.731	.891	.964	.990	.997	.999	1.000				
1.9	.150	.434	.704	.875	.956	.987	.997	.999	1.000				
2.0	.135	.406	.677	.857	.947	.983	.995	.999	1.000				
2.2	.111	.355	.623	.819	.928	.975	.993	.998	1.000				
2.4	.091	.308	.570	.779	.904	.964	.988	.997	.999	1.000			
2.6	.074	.267	.518	.736	.877	.951	.983	.995	.999	1.000			
2.8	.061	.231	.469	.692	.848	.935	.976	.992	.998	.999	1.000		
3.0	.050	.199	.423	.647	.815	.916	.966	.988	.996	.999	1.000		
3.2	.041	.171	.380	.603	.781	.895	.955	.983	.994	.998	1.000		
3.4	.033	.147	.340	.558	.744	.871	.942	.977	.992	.997	.999	1.000	
3.6	.027	.126	.303	.515	.706	.844	.927	.969	.988	.996	.999	1.000	
3.8	.022	.107	.269	.473	.668	.816	.909	.960	.984	.994	.998	.999	1.000
4.0	.018	.092	.238	.433	.629	.785	.889	.949	.979	.992	.997	.999	1.000

Table A-16. Tolerance Factors for Normal Distributions*

	$\gamma = 0.75$					$\gamma = 0.90$					$\gamma = 0.95$					$\gamma = 0.99$				
N \ P	0.75	0.90	0.95	0.99	0.999	0.75	0.90	0.95	0.99	0.999	0.75	0.90	0.95	0.99	0.999	0.75	0.90	0.95	0.99	0.999
2	4.498	6.301	7.414	9.531	11.920	11.407	15.978	18.800	24.167	30.227	22.858	32.019	37.674	48.430	60.573	114.363	160.193	188.491	242.300	303.054
3	2.501	3.538	4.187	5.431	6.844	4.132	5.847	6.919	8.974	11.309	5.922	8.380	9.916	12.861	16.208	13.378	18.930	22.401	29.055	36.616
4	2.035	2.892	3.431	4.471	5.657	2.932	4.166	4.943	6.440	8.149	3.779	5.369	6.370	8.299	10.502	6.614	9.398	11.150	14.527	18.383
5	1.825	2.599	3.088	4.033	5.117	2.454	3.494	4.152	5.423	6.879	3.002	4.275	5.079	6.634	8.415	4.643	6.612	7.855	10.260	13.015
6	1.704	2.429	2.889	3.779	4.802	2.196	3.131	3.723	4.870	6.188	2.604	3.712	4.414	5.775	7.337	3.743	5.337	6.345	8.301	10.548
7	1.624	2.318	2.757	3.611	4.593	2.034	2.902	3.452	4.521	5.750	2.361	3.369	4.007	5.248	6.676	3.233	4.613	5.488	7.187	9.142
8	1.568	2.238	2.663	3.491	4.444	1.921	2.743	3.264	4.278	5.446	2.197	3.136	3.732	4.891	6.226	2.905	4.147	4.936	6.468	8.234
9	1.525	2.178	2.593	3.400	4.330	1.839	2.626	3.125	4.098	5.220	2.078	2.967	3.532	4.631	5.899	2.677	3.822	4.550	5.966	7.600
10	1.492	2.131	2.537	3.328	4.241	1.775	2.535	3.018	3.959	5.046	1.987	2.839	3.379	4.433	5.649	2.508	3.582	4.265	5.594	7.129
11	1.465	2.093	2.493	3.271	4.169	1.724	2.463	2.933	3.849	4.906	1.916	2.737	3.259	4.277	5.452	2.378	3.397	4.045	5.308	6.766
12	1.443	2.062	2.456	3.223	4.110	1.683	2.404	2.863	3.758	4.792	1.858	2.655	3.162	4.150	5.291	2.274	3.250	3.870	5.079	6.477
13	1.425	2.036	2.424	3.183	4.059	1.648	2.355	2.805	3.682	4.697	1.810	2.587	3.081	4.044	5.158	2.190	3.130	3.727	4.893	6.240
14	1.409	2.013	2.398	3.148	4.016	1.619	2.314	2.756	3.618	4.615	1.770	2.529	3.012	3.955	5.045	2.120	3.029	3.608	4.737	6.043
15	1.395	1.994	2.375	3.118	3.979	1.594	2.278	2.713	3.562	4.545	1.735	2.480	2.954	3.878	4.949	2.060	2.945	3.507	4.605	5.876
16	1.383	1.977	2.355	3.092	3.946	1.572	2.246	2.676	3.514	4.484	1.705	2.437	2.903	3.812	4.865	2.009	2.872	3.421	4.492	5.732
17	1.372	1.962	2.337	3.069	3.917	1.552	2.219	2.643	3.471	4.430	1.679	2.400	2.858	3.754	4.791	1.965	2.808	3.345	4.393	5.607
18	1.363	1.948	2.321	3.048	3.891	1.535	2.194	2.614	3.433	4.382	1.655	2.366	2.819	3.702	4.725	1.926	2.753	3.279	4.307	5.497
19	1.355	1.936	2.307	3.030	3.867	1.520	2.172	2.588	3.399	4.339	1.635	2.337	2.784	3.656	4.667	1.891	2.703	3.221	4.230	5.399
20	1.347	1.925	2.294	3.013	3.846	1.506	2.152	2.564	3.368	4.300	1.616	2.310	2.752	3.615	4.614	1.860	2.659	3.168	4.161	5.312
21	1.340	1.915	2.282	2.998	3.827	1.493	2.135	2.543	3.340	4.264	1.599	2.286	2.723	3.577	4.567	1.833	2.620	3.121	4.100	5.234
22	1.334	1.906	2.271	2.984	3.809	1.482	2.118	2.524	3.315	4.232	1.584	2.264	2.697	3.543	4.523	1.808	2.584	3.078	4.044	5.163
23	1.328	1.898	2.261	2.971	3.793	1.471	2.103	2.506	3.292	4.203	1.570	2.244	2.673	3.512	4.484	1.785	2.551	3.040	3.993	5.098
24	1.322	1.891	2.252	2.959	3.778	1.462	2.089	2.489	3.270	4.176	1.557	2.225	2.651	3.483	4.447	1.764	2.522	3.004	3.947	5.039
25	1.317	1.883	2.244	2.948	3.764	1.453	2.077	2.474	3.251	4.151	1.545	2.208	2.631	3.457	4.413	1.745	2.494	2.972	3.904	4.985
26	1.313	1.877	2.236	2.938	3.751	1.444	2.065	2.460	3.232	4.127	1.534	2.193	2.612	3.432	4.382	1.727	2.469	2.941	3.865	4.935
27	1.309	1.871	2.229	2.929	3.740	1.437	2.054	2.447	3.215	4.106	1.523	2.178	2.595	3.409	4.353	1.711	2.446	2.914	3.828	4.888

30	1.297	1.855	2.210	2.904	3.708	1.417	2.025	2.413	3.170	4.049	1.497	2.140	2.549	3.350	4.278	1.668	2.385	2.841	3.733	4.768
35	1.283	1.834	2.185	2.871	3.667	1.390	1.988	2.368	3.112	3.974	1.462	2.090	2.490	3.272	4.179	1.613	2.306	2.748	3.611	4.611
40	1.271	1.818	2.166	2.846	3.635	1.370	1.959	2.334	3.066	3.917	1.435	2.052	2.445	3.213	4.104	1.571	2.247	2.677	3.518	4.493
45	1.262	1.805	2.150	2.826	3.609	1.354	1.935	2.306	3.030	3.871	1.414	2.021	2.408	3.165	4.042	1.539	2.200	2.621	3.444	4.399
50	1.255	1.794	2.138	2.809	3.588	1.340	1.916	2.284	3.001	3.833	1.396	1.996	2.379	3.126	3.993	1.512	2.162	2.576	3.385	4.323
55	1.249	1.785	2.127	2.795	3.571	1.329	1.901	2.265	2.976	3.801	1.382	1.976	2.354	3.094	3.951	1.490	2.130	2.538	3.335	4.260
60	1.243	1.778	2.118	2.784	3.556	1.320	1.887	2.248	2.955	3.774	1.369	1.958	2.333	3.066	3.916	1.471	2.103	2.506	3.293	4.206
65	1.239	1.771	2.110	2.773	3.543	1.312	1.875	2.235	2.937	3.751	1.359	1.943	2.315	3.042	3.886	1.455	2.080	2.478	3.257	4.160
70	1.235	1.765	2.104	2.764	3.531	1.304	1.865	2.222	2.920	3.730	1.349	1.929	2.299	3.021	3.859	1.440	2.060	2.454	3.225	4.120
75	1.231	1.760	2.098	2.757	3.521	1.298	1.856	2.211	2.906	3.712	1.341	1.917	2.285	3.002	3.835	1.428	2.042	2.433	3.197	4.084
80	1.228	1.756	2.092	2.749	3.512	1.292	1.848	2.202	2.894	3.696	1.334	1.907	2.272	2.986	3.814	1.417	2.026	2.414	3.173	4.053
85	1.225	1.752	2.087	2.743	3.504	1.287	1.841	2.193	2.882	3.682	1.327	1.897	2.261	2.971	3.795	1.407	2.012	2.397	3.150	4.024
90	1.223	1.748	2.083	2.737	3.497	1.283	1.834	2.185	2.872	3.669	1.321	1.889	2.251	2.958	3.778	1.398	1.999	2.382	3.130	3.999
95	1.220	1.745	2.079	2.732	3.490	1.278	1.828	2.178	2.863	3.657	1.315	1.881	2.241	2.945	3.763	1.390	1.987	2.368	3.112	3.976
100	1.218	1.742	2.075	2.727	3.484	1.275	1.822	2.172	2.854	3.646	1.311	1.874	2.233	2.934	3.748	1.383	1.977	2.355	3.096	3.954
110	1.214	1.736	2.069	2.719	3.473	1.268	1.813	2.160	2.839	3.626	1.302	1.861	2.218	2.915	3.723	1.369	1.958	2.333	3.066	3.917
120	1.211	1.732	2.063	2.712	3.464	1.262	1.804	2.150	2.826	3.610	1.294	1.850	2.205	2.898	3.702	1.358	1.942	2.314	3.041	3.885
130	1.208	1.728	2.059	2.705	3.456	1.257	1.797	2.141	2.814	3.595	1.288	1.841	2.194	2.883	3.683	1.349	1.928	2.298	3.019	3.857
140	1.206	1.724	2.054	2.700	3.449	1.252	1.791	2.134	2.804	3.582	1.282	1.833	2.184	2.870	3.666	1.340	1.916	2.283	3.000	3.833
150	1.204	1.721	2.051	2.695	3.443	1.248	1.785	2.127	2.795	3.571	1.277	1.825	2.175	2.859	3.652	1.332	1.905	2.270	2.983	3.811
160	1.202	1.718	2.047	2.691	3.437	1.245	1.780	2.121	2.787	3.561	1.272	1.819	2.167	2.848	3.638	1.326	1.896	2.259	2.968	3.792
170	1.200	1.716	2.044	2.687	3.432	1.242	1.775	2.116	2.780	3.552	1.268	1.813	2.160	2.839	3.627	1.320	1.887	2.248	2.955	3.774
180	1.198	1.713	2.042	2.683	3.427	1.239	1.771	2.111	2.774	3.543	1.264	1.808	2.154	2.831	3.616	1.314	1.879	2.239	2.942	3.759
190	1.197	1.711	2.039	2.680	3.423	1.236	1.767	2.106	2.768	3.536	1.261	1.803	2.148	2.823	3.606	1.309	1.872	2.230	2.931	3.744
200	1.195	1.709	2.037	2.677	3.419	1.234	1.764	2.102	2.762	3.529	1.258	1.798	2.143	2.816	3.597	1.304	1.865	2.222	2.921	3.731
250	1.190	1.702	2.028	2.665	3.404	1.224	1.750	2.085	2.740	3.501	1.245	1.780	2.121	2.788	3.561	1.286	1.839	2.191	2.880	3.678
300	1.186	1.696	2.021	2.656	3.393	1.217	1.740	2.073	2.725	3.481	1.236	1.767	2.106	2.767	3.535	1.273	1.820	2.169	2.850	3.641
400	1.181	1.688	2.012	2.644	3.378	1.207	1.726	2.057	2.703	3.453	1.223	1.749	2.084	2.739	3.499	1.255	1.794	2.138	2.809	3.589
500	1.177	1.683	2.006	2.636	3.368	1.201	1.717	2.046	2.689	3.434	1.215	1.737	2.070	2.721	3.475	1.243	1.777	2.117	2.783	3.555
600	1.175	1.680	2.002	2.631	3.360	1.196	1.710	2.038	2.678	3.421	1.209	1.729	2.060	2.707	3.458	1.234	1.764	2.102	2.763	3.530
700	1.173	1.677	1.998	2.626	3.355	1.192	1.705	2.032	2.670	3.411	1.204	1.722	2.052	2.697	3.445	1.227	1.755	2.091	2.748	3.511
800	1.171	1.675	1.996	2.623	3.350	1.189	1.701	2.027	2.663	3.402	1.201	1.717	2.046	2.688	3.434	1.222	1.747	2.082	2.736	3.495
900	1.170	1.673	1.993	2.620	3.347	1.187	1.697	2.023	2.658	3.396	1.198	1.712	2.040	2.682	3.426	1.218	1.741	2.075	2.726	3.483
1000	1.169	1.671	1.992	2.617	3.344	1.185	1.695	2.019	2.654	3.390	1.195	1.709	2.036	2.676	3.418	1.214	1.736	2.068	2.718	3.472
∞	1.150	1.645	1.960	2.576	3.291	1.150	1.645	1.960	2.576	3.291	1.150	1.645	1.960	2.576	3.291	1.150	1.645	1.960	2.576	3.291

* Reproduced with permission from C. Eisenhart, M. W. Hastay, W. A. Wallis, *Techniques of Statistical Analysis*, chap. 2. McGraw-Hill Book Company, Inc., New York, 1947.

TABLE A-17. CRITICAL VALUES FOR COCHRAN'S TEST*

Values given are for the statistic (Largest s^2)/(Σs_i^2), where each of the k values of s^2 has ν degrees of freedom.

Percentile 95

k \ ν	1	2	3	4	5	6	7	8	9	10	16	36	144	∞
2	0.9985	0.9750	0.9392	0.9057	0.8772	0.8534	0.8332	0.8159	0.8010	0.7880	0.7341	0.6602	0.5813	0.5000
3	0.9669	0.8709	0.7977	0.7457	0.7071	0.6771	0.6530	0.6333	0.6167	0.6025	0.5466	0.4748	0.4031	0.3333
4	0.9065	0.7679	0.6841	0.6287	0.5895	0.5598	0.5365	0.5175	0.5017	0.4884	0.4366	0.3720	0.3093	0.2500
5	0.8412	0.6838	0.5981	0.5441	0.5065	0.4783	0.4564	0.4387	0.4241	0.4118	0.3645	0.3066	0.2513	0.2000
6	0.7808	0.6161	0.5321	0.4803	0.4447	0.4184	0.3980	0.3817	0.3682	0.3568	0.3135	0.2612	0.2119	0.1667
7	0.7271	0.5612	0.4800	0.4307	0.3974	0.3726	0.3535	0.3384	0.3259	0.3154	0.2756	0.2278	0.1833	0.1429
8	0.6798	0.5157	0.4377	0.3910	0.3595	0.3362	0.3185	0.3043	0.2926	0.2829	0.2462	0.2022	0.1616	0.1250
9	0.6385	0.4775	0.4027	0.3584	0.3286	0.3067	0.2901	0.2768	0.2659	0.2568	0.2226	0.1820	0.1446	0.1111
10	0.6020	0.4450	0.3733	0.3311	0.3029	0.2823	0.2666	0.2541	0.2439	0.2353	0.2032	0.1655	0.1308	0.1000
12	0.5410	0.3924	0.3264	0.2880	0.2624	0.2439	0.2299	0.2187	0.2098	0.2020	0.1737	0.1403	0.1100	0.0833
15	0.4709	0.3346	0.2758	0.2419	0.2195	0.2034	0.1911	0.1815	0.1736	0.1671	0.1429	0.1144	0.0889	0.0667
20	0.3894	0.2705	0.2205	0.1921	0.1735	0.1602	0.1501	0.1422	0.1357	0.1303	0.1108	0.0879	0.0675	0.0500
24	0.3434	0.2354	0.1907	0.1656	0.1493	0.1374	0.1286	0.1216	0.1160	0.1113	0.0942	0.0743	0.0567	0.0417
30	0.2929	0.1980	0.1593	0.1377	0.1237	0.1137	0.1061	0.1002	0.0958	0.0921	0.0771	0.0604	0.0457	0.0333
40	0.2370	0.1576	0.1259	0.1082	0.0968	0.0887	0.0827	0.0780	0.0745	0.0713	0.0595	0.0462	0.0347	0.0250
60	0.1737	0.1131	0.0895	0.0765	0.0682	0.0623	0.0583	0.0552	0.0520	0.0497	0.0411	0.0316	0.0234	0.0167
120	0.0998	0.0632	0.0495	0.0419	0.0371	0.0337	0.0312	0.0292	0.0279	0.0266	0.0218	0.0165	0.0120	0.0083
∞	0	0	0	0	0	0	0	0	0	0	0	0	0	0

* Reproduced with permission from C. Eisenhart, M. W. Hastay, W. A. Wallis, *Techniques of Statistical Analysis*, chap. 15. McGraw-Hill Book Company, Inc., New York, 1947.

TABLE A-17. CRITICAL VALUES FOR COCHRAN'S TEST (*Continued*)

Percentile 99

k \ ν	1	2	3	4	5	6	7	8	9	10	16	36	144	∞
2	0.9999	0.9950	0.9794	0.9586	0.9373	0.9172	0.8988	0.8823	0.8674	0.8539	0.7949	0.7067	0.6062	0.5000
3	0.9933	0.9423	0.8831	0.8335	0.7933	0.7606	0.7335	0.7107	0.6912	0.6743	0.6059	0.5153	0.4230	0.3333
4	0.9676	0.8643	0.7814	0.7212	0.6761	0.6410	0.6129	0.5897	0.5702	0.5536	0.4884	0.4057	0.3251	0.2500
5	0.9279	0.7885	0.6957	0.6329	0.5875	0.5531	0.5259	0.5037	0.4854	0.4697	0.4094	0.3351	0.2644	0.2000
6	0.8828	0.7218	0.6258	0.5635	0.5195	0.4866	0.4608	0.4401	0.4229	0.4084	0.3529	0.2858	0.2229	0.1667
7	0.8376	0.6644	0.5685	0.5080	0.4659	0.4347	0.4105	0.3911	0.3751	0.3616	0.3105	0.2494	0.1929	0.1429
8	0.7945	0.6152	0.5209	0.4627	0.4226	0.3932	0.3704	0.3522	0.3373	0.3248	0.2779	0.2214	0.1700	0.1250
9	0.7544	0.5727	0.4810	0.4251	0.3870	0.3592	0.3378	0.3207	0.3067	0.2950	0.2514	0.1992	0.1521	0.1111
10	0.7175	0.5358	0.4469	0.3934	0.3572	0.3308	0.3106	0.2945	0.2813	0.2704	0.2297	0.1811	0.1376	0.1000
12	0.6528	0.4751	0.3919	0.3428	0.3099	0.2861	0.2680	0.2535	0.2419	0.2320	0.1961	0.1535	0.1157	0.0833
15	0.5747	0.4069	0.3317	0.2882	0.2593	0.2386	0.2228	0.2104	0.2002	0.1918	0.1612	0.1251	0.0934	0.0667
20	0.4799	0.3297	0.2654	0.2288	0.2048	0.1877	0.1748	0.1646	0.1567	0.1501	0.1248	0.0960	0.0709	0.0500
24	0.4247	0.2871	0.2295	0.1970	0.1759	0.1608	0.1495	0.1406	0.1338	0.1283	0.1060	0.0810	0.0595	0.0417
30	0.3632	0.2412	0.1913	0.1635	0.1454	0.1327	0.1232	0.1157	0.1100	0.1054	0.0867	0.0658	0.0480	0.0333
40	0.2940	0.1915	0.1508	0.1281	0.1135	0.1033	0.0957	0.0898	0.0853	0.0816	0.0668	0.0503	0.0363	0.0250
60	0.2151	0.1371	0.1069	0.0902	0.0796	0.0722	0.0668	0.0625	0.0594	0.0567	0.0461	0.0344	0.0245	0.0167
120	0.1225	0.0759	0.0585	0.0489	0.0429	0.0387	0.0357	0.0334	0.0316	0.0302	0.0242	0.0178	0.0125	0.0083
∞	0	0	0	0	0	0	0	0	0	0	0	0	0	0

TABLE A-18. PERCENTILES* OF THE DISTRIBUTION OF $q = w/s$

w is the range of k observations, and ν is the number of degrees of freedom in the independent standard deviation s.

ν	cum. prop. \ k	2	3	4	5	6	7	8	9	10	11	12	13	14	15	16	17	18	19	20
1	.95	18.0	27.0	32.8	37.1	40.4	43.1	45.4	47.4	49.1	50.6	52.0	53.2	54.3	55.4	56.3	57.2	58.0	58.8	59.6
	.99	90.0	135	164	186	202	216	227	237	246	253	260	266	272	277	282	286	290	294	298
2	.95	6.09	8.3	9.8	10.9	11.7	12.4	13.0	13.5	14.0	14.4	14.7	15.1	15.4	15.7	15.9	16.1	16.4	16.6	16.8
	.99	14.0	19.0	22.3	24.7	26.6	28.2	29.5	30.7	31.7	32.6	33.4	34.1	34.8	35.4	36.0	36.5	37.0	37.5	37.9
3	.95	4.50	5.91	6.82	7.50	8.04	8.48	8.85	9.18	9.46	9.72	9.95	10.2	10.4	10.5	10.7	10.8	11.0	11.1	11.2
	.99	8.26	10.6	12.2	13.3	14.2	15.0	15.6	16.2	16.7	17.1	17.5	17.9	18.2	18.5	18.8	19.1	19.3	19.5	19.8
4	.95	3.93	5.04	5.76	6.29	6.71	7.05	7.35	7.60	7.83	8.03	8.21	8.37	8.52	8.66	8.79	8.91	9.03	9.13	9.23
	.99	6.51	8.12	9.17	9.96	10.6	11.1	11.5	11.9	12.3	12.6	12.8	13.1	13.3	13.5	13.7	13.9	14.1	14.2	14.4
5	.95	3.64	4.60	5.22	5.67	6.03	6.33	6.58	6.80	6.99	7.17	7.32	7.47	7.60	7.72	7.83	7.93	8.03	8.12	8.21
	.99	5.70	6.97	7.80	8.42	8.91	9.32	9.67	9.97	10.2	10.5	10.7	10.9	11.1	11.2	11.4	11.6	11.7	11.8	11.9
6	.95	3.46	4.34	4.90	5.31	5.63	5.89	6.12	6.32	6.49	6.65	6.79	6.92	7.03	7.14	7.24	7.34	7.43	7.51	7.59
	.99	5.24	6.33	7.03	7.56	7.97	8.32	8.61	8.87	9.10	9.30	9.49	9.65	9.81	9.95	10.1	10.2	10.3	10.4	10.5
7	.95	3.34	4.16	4.68	5.06	5.36	5.61	5.82	6.00	6.16	6.30	6.43	6.55	6.66	6.76	6.85	6.94	7.02	7.09	7.17
	.99	4.95	5.92	6.54	7.01	7.37	7.68	7.94	8.17	8.37	8.55	8.71	8.86	9.00	9.12	9.24	9.35	9.46	9.55	9.65
8	.95	3.26	4.04	4.53	4.89	5.17	5.40	5.60	5.77	5.92	6.05	6.18	6.29	6.39	6.48	6.57	6.65	6.73	6.80	6.87
	.99	4.74	5.63	6.20	6.63	6.96	7.24	7.47	7.68	7.87	8.03	8.18	8.31	8.44	8.55	8.66	8.76	8.85	8.94	9.03
9	.95	3.20	3.95	4.42	4.76	5.02	5.24	5.43	5.60	5.74	5.87	5.98	6.09	6.19	6.28	6.36	6.44	6.51	6.58	6.64
	.99	4.60	5.43	5.96	6.35	6.66	6.91	7.13	7.32	7.49	7.65	7.78	7.91	8.03	8.13	8.23	8.32	8.41	8.49	8.57
10	.01	.02	.18	.42	.64	.81	.96	1.11	1.23	1.34	1.41	1.50	1.57	1.62	1.70	1.74	1.81	1.84	1.88	1.92
	.05	.09	.43	.75	1.01	1.20	1.37	1.52	1.63	1.74	1.83	1.91	1.98	2.05	2.12	2.17	2.22	2.26	2.30	2.34
	.95	3.15	3.88	4.33	4.65	4.91	5.12	5.30	5.46	5.60	5.72	5.83	5.93	6.03	6.11	6.20	6.27	6.34	6.40	6.47
	.99	4.48	5.27	5.77	6.14	6.43	6.67	6.87	7.05	7.21	7.36	7.48	7.60	7.71	7.81	7.91	7.99	8.07	8.15	8.22
11	.01	.02	.18	.42	.64	.82	.97	1.12	1.24	1.35	1.43	1.52	1.58	1.64	1.71	1.76	1.82	1.86	1.91	1.94
	.05	.09	.43	.75	1.01	1.21	1.38	1.52	1.64	1.75	1.84	1.92	2.00	2.07	2.13	2.18	2.24	2.28	2.33	2.37
	.95	3.11	3.82	4.26	4.57	4.82	5.03	5.20	5.35	5.49	5.61	5.71	5.81	5.90	5.99	6.06	6.14	6.20	6.26	6.33
	.99	4.39	5.14	5.62	5.97	6.25	6.48	6.67	6.84	6.99	7.13	7.25	7.36	7.46	7.56	7.65	7.73	7.81	7.88	7.95

12	.01	.02	.18	.42	.64	.82	.98	1.12	1.24	1.35	1.44	1.53	1.60	1.65	1.73	1.77	1.84	1.88	1.92	1.96
	.05	.09	.43	.75	1.01	1.21	1.38	1.53	1.65	1.76	1.85	1.93	2.01	2.08	2.14	2.20	2.26	2.30	2.34	2.38
	.95	3.08	3.77	4.20	4.51	4.75	4.95	5.12	5.27	5.40	5.51	5.62	5.71	5.80	5.88	5.95	6.03	6.09	6.15	6.21
	.99	4.32	5.04	5.50	5.84	6.10	6.32	6.51	6.67	6.81	6.94	7.06	7.17	7.26	7.36	7.44	7.52	7.59	7.66	7.73
13	.01	.02	.18	.42	.64	.83	.98	1.13	1.25	1.36	1.45	1.54	1.61	1.66	1.74	1.79	1.85	1.89	1.94	1.98
	.05	.09	.43	.75	1.01	1.22	1.39	1.53	1.65	1.76	1.86	1.94	2.02	2.09	2.15	2.21	2.27	2.31	2.36	2.40
	.95	3.06	3.73	4.15	4.45	4.69	4.88	5.05	5.19	5.32	5.43	5.53	5.63	5.71	5.79	5.86	5.93	6.00	6.05	6.11
	.99	4.26	4.96	5.40	5.73	5.98	6.19	6.37	6.53	6.67	6.79	6.90	7.01	7.10	7.19	7.27	7.34	7.42	7.48	7.55
14	.01	.02	.18	.42	.65	.83	.99	1.13	1.25	1.37	1.46	1.55	1.62	1.68	1.76	1.80	1.87	1.91	1.95	2.00
	.05	.09	.43	.75	1.01	1.22	1.39	1.54	1.66	1.77	1.86	1.95	2.03	2.10	2.16	2.22	2.28	2.32	2.37	2.41
	.95	3.03	3.70	4.11	4.41	4.64	4.83	4.99	5.13	5.25	5.36	5.46	5.55	5.64	5.72	5.79	5.85	5.92	5.97	6.03
	.99	4.21	4.89	5.32	5.63	5.88	6.08	6.26	6.41	6.54	6.66	6.77	6.87	6.96	7.05	7.12	7.20	7.27	7.33	7.39
15	.01	.02	.18	.42	.65	.83	.99	1.14	1.26	1.37	1.46	1.55	1.63	1.69	1.76	1.81	1.88	1.92	1.97	2.01
	.05	.09	.43	.75	1.01	1.22	1.39	1.54	1.66	1.77	1.87	1.95	2.03	2.11	2.17	2.23	2.29	2.34	2.38	2.43
	.95	3.01	3.67	4.08	4.37	4.60	4.78	4.94	5.08	5.20	5.31	5.40	5.49	5.58	5.65	5.72	5.79	5.85	5.90	5.96
	.99	4.17	4.83	5.25	5.56	5.80	5.99	6.16	6.31	6.44	6.55	6.66	6.76	6.84	6.93	7.00	7.07	7.14	7.20	7.26
16	.01	.02	.18	.42	.65	.83	.99	1.14	1.26	1.37	1.47	1.56	1.63	1.70	1.77	1.82	1.89	1.93	1.98	2.02
	.05	.09	.43	.75	1.01	1.22	1.39	1.54	1.67	1.78	1.87	1.96	2.04	2.11	2.18	2.24	2.30	2.34	2.39	2.44
	.95	3.00	3.65	4.05	4.33	4.56	4.74	4.90	5.03	5.15	5.26	5.35	5.44	5.52	5.59	5.66	5.72	5.79	5.84	5.90
	.99	4.13	4.78	5.19	5.49	5.72	5.92	6.08	6.22	6.35	6.46	6.56	6.66	6.74	6.82	6.90	6.97	7.03	7.09	7.15
17	.01	.02	.18	.42	.65	.84	1.00	1.14	1.27	1.38	1.48	1.57	1.64	1.70	1.78	1.83	1.90	1.94	1.99	2.04
	.05	.09	.43	.75	1.01	1.22	1.40	1.55	1.67	1.78	1.88	1.97	2.05	2.12	2.19	2.25	2.30	2.35	2.40	2.45
	.95	2.98	3.63	4.02	4.30	4.52	4.71	4.86	4.99	5.11	5.21	5.31	5.39	5.47	5.55	5.61	5.68	5.74	5.79	5.84
	.99	4.10	4.74	5.14	5.43	5.66	5.85	6.01	6.15	6.27	6.38	6.48	6.57	6.66	6.73	6.80	6.87	6.94	7.00	7.05
18	.01	.02	.18	.42	.65	.84	1.00	1.15	1.27	1.38	1.48	1.57	1.65	1.71	1.79	1.84	1.91	1.95	2.00	2.05
	.05	.09	.43	.75	1.02	1.22	1.40	1.55	1.67	1.79	1.88	1.97	2.05	2.12	2.19	2.25	2.31	2.36	2.41	2.45
	.95	2.97	3.61	4.00	4.28	4.49	4.67	4.82	4.96	5.07	5.17	5.27	5.35	5.43	5.50	5.57	5.63	5.69	5.74	5.79
	.99	4.07	4.70	5.09	5.38	5.60	5.79	5.94	6.08	6.20	6.31	6.41	6.50	6.58	6.65	6.72	6.79	6.85	6.91	6.96
19	.01	.02	.18	.43	.65	.84	1.00	1.15	1.28	1.39	1.48	1.58	1.65	1.72	1.80	1.85	1.91	1.96	2.01	2.06
	.05	.09	.43	.75	1.02	1.23	1.40	1.55	1.68	1.79	1.89	1.98	2.05	2.13	2.20	2.26	2.32	2.37	2.42	2.46
	.95	2.96	3.59	3.98	4.25	4.47	4.65	4.79	4.92	5.04	5.14	5.23	5.32	5.39	5.46	5.53	5.59	5.65	5.70	5.75
	.99	4.05	4.67	5.05	5.33	5.55	5.73	5.89	6.02	6.14	6.25	6.34	6.43	6.51	6.58	6.65	6.72	6.78	6.84	6.89
20	.01	.02	.18	.43	.65	.84	1.01	1.15	1.28	1.39	1.49	1.58	1.66	1.72	1.80	1.85	1.92	1.97	2.01	2.06
	.05	.09	.43	.75	1.02	1.23	1.40	1.55	1.68	1.79	1.89	1.98	2.06	2.13	2.20	2.27	2.32	2.37	2.42	2.47
	.95	2.95	3.58	3.96	4.23	4.45	4.62	4.77	4.90	5.01	5.11	5.20	5.28	5.36	5.43	5.49	5.55	5.61	5.66	5.71
	.99	4.02	4.64	5.02	5.29	5.51	5.69	5.84	5.97	6.09	6.19	6.29	6.37	6.45	6.52	6.59	6.65	6.71	6.76	6.82

* Reproduced with permission from E. S. Pearson and H. O. Hartley, *Biometrika Tables for Statisticians*, vol. 1. Cambridge University Press, New York, 1954.

TABLE A-18. PERCENTILES OF THE DISTRIBUTION OF $q = w/s$ (*Continued*)

ν	cum. prop. \ k	2	3	4	5	6	7	8	9	10	11	12	13	14	15	16	17	18	19	20
24	.01	.02	.18	.43	.65	.85	1.01	1.16	1.29	1.40	1.50	1.60	1.67	1.74	1.82	1.88	1.94	1.99	2.05	2.09
	.05	.09	.43	.75	1.02	1.23	1.41	1.56	1.69	1.80	1.90	1.99	2.08	2.15	2.22	2.28	2.34	2.39	2.45	2.49
	.95	2.92	3.53	3.90	4.17	4.37	4.54	4.68	4.81	4.92	5.01	5.10	5.18	5.25	5.32	5.38	5.44	5.50	5.54	5.59
	.99	3.96	4.54	4.91	5.17	5.37	5.54	5.69	5.81	5.92	6.02	6.11	6.19	6.26	6.33	6.39	6.45	6.51	6.56	6.61
30	.01	.02	.18	.43	.66	.85	1.02	1.17	1.30	1.41	1.52	1.61	1.69	1.76	1.84	1.90	1.97	2.02	2.07	2.12
	.05	.09	.43	.76	1.02	1.24	1.41	1.57	1.70	1.81	1.92	2.01	2.09	2.17	2.24	2.30	2.36	2.41	2.47	2.52
	.95	2.89	3.49	3.84	4.10	4.30	4.46	4.60	4.72	4.83	4.92	5.00	5.08	5.15	5.21	5.27	5.33	5.38	5.43	5.48
	.99	3.89	4.45	4.80	5.05	5.24	5.40	5.54	5.65	5.76	5.85	5.93	6.01	6.08	6.14	6.20	6.26	6.31	6.36	6.41
40	.01	.02	.18	.43	.66	.85	1.02	1.18	1.31	1.43	1.53	1.63	1.71	1.79	1.86	1.92	1.99	2.04	2.10	2.15
	.05	.09	.43	.76	1.02	1.24	1.42	1.57	1.71	1.82	1.93	2.02	2.10	2.18	2.26	2.32	2.38	2.43	2.49	2.54
	.95	2.86	3.44	3.79	4.04	4.23	4.39	4.52	4.63	4.74	4.82	4.91	4.98	5.05	5.11	5.16	5.22	5.27	5.31	5.36
	.99	3.82	4.37	4.70	4.93	5.11	5.27	5.39	5.50	5.60	5.69	5.77	5.84	5.90	5.96	6.02	6.07	6.12	6.17	6.21
60	.01	.02	.18	.43	.66	.86	1.03	1.19	1.32	1.44	1.55	1.64	1.73	1.81	1.88	1.95	2.02	2.07	2.13	2.18
	.05	.09	.43	.76	1.02	1.24	1.43	1.58	1.72	1.83	1.94	2.04	2.12	2.20	2.28	2.34	2.40	2.46	2.52	2.57
	.95	2.83	3.40	3.74	3.98	4.16	4.31	4.44	4.55	4.65	4.73	4.81	4.88	4.94	5.00	5.06	5.11	5.16	5.20	5.24
	.99	3.76	4.28	4.60	4.82	4.99	5.13	5.25	5.36	5.45	5.53	5.60	5.67	5.73	5.79	5.84	5.89	5.93	5.98	6.02
120	.01	.02	.18	.43	.66	.86	1.04	1.20	1.33	1.45	1.56	1.66	1.75	1.83	1.91	1.98	2.04	2.10	2.16	2.21
	.05	.09	.43	.76	1.03	1.25	1.43	1.59	1.73	1.85	1.96	2.06	2.14	2.22	2.30	2.36	2.43	2.49	2.54	2.60
	.95	2.80	3.36	3.69	3.92	4.10	4.24	4.36	4.48	4.56	4.64	4.72	4.78	4.84	4.90	4.95	5.00	5.05	5.09	5.13
	.99	3.70	4.20	4.50	4.71	4.87	5.01	5.12	5.21	5.30	5.38	5.44	5.51	5.56	5.61	5.66	5.71	5.75	5.79	5.83
∞	.01	.02	.19	.43	.66	.87	1.05	1.20	1.34	1.47	1.58	1.68	1.77	1.86	1.93	2.01	2.08	2.14	2.20	2.25
	.05	.09	.43	.76	1.03	1.25	1.44	1.60	1.74	1.86	1.97	2.07	2.16	2.24	2.32	2.39	2.45	2.52	2.57	2.62
	.95	2.77	3.31	3.63	3.86	4.03	4.17	4.29	4.39	4.47	4.55	4.62	4.68	4.74	4.80	4.85	4.89	4.93	4.97	5.01
	.99	3.64	4.12	4.40	4.60	4.76	4.88	4.99	5.08	5.16	5.23	5.29	5.35	5.40	5.45	5.49	5.54	5.57	5.61	5.65

Table A-19. Distribution of the Signed Rank Statistic T

The percentiles listed cover the range $\alpha = .005$ to $.125$ for every sample size up to $N = 20$. Values T_α are such that the probability is α that the signed rank statistic is less than or equal to T_α. The values $T_{1-\alpha}$ are such that the probability is α that T is greater than or equal to $T_{1-\alpha}$.

T_α	$T_{1-\alpha}$	α
	$N = 1$	
0	1	.500
	$N = 2$	
0	3	.250
	$N = 3$	
0	6	.125
	$N = 4$	
0	10	.062
1	9	.125
	$N = 5$	
0	15	.031
1	14	.062
2	13	.094
3	12	.156
	$N = 6$	
0	21	.016
1	20	.031
2	19	.047
3	18	.078
4	17	.109
5	16	.156
	$N = 7$	
0	28	.008
1	27	.016
2	26	.023
3	25	.039
4	24	.055
5	23	.078
6	22	.109
7	21	.148
	$N = 8$	
0	36	.004
1	35	.008
2	34	.012
3	33	.020
4	32	.027
5	31	.039
6	30	.055
7	29	.074
8	28	.098
9	27	.125
	$N = 9$	
1	44	.004
2	43	.006
3	42	.010
	$N = 9$ (*Cont.*)	
4	41	.014
5	40	.020
6	39	.027
7	38	.037
8	37	.049
9	36	.064
10	35	.082
11	34	.102
12	33	.125
	$N = 10$	
3	52	.005
4	51	.007
5	50	.010
6	49	.014
7	48	.019
8	47	.024
9	46	.032
10	45	.042
11	44	.053
12	43	.065
13	42	.080
14	41	.097
15	40	.116
16	39	.138
	$N = 11$	
5	61	.005
6	60	.007
7	59	.009
8	58	.012
9	57	.016
10	56	.021
11	55	.027
12	54	.034
13	53	.042
14	52	.051
15	51	.062
16	50	.074
17	49	.087
18	48	.103
19	47	.120
20	46	.139
	$N = 12$	
7	71	.005
8	70	.006
	$N = 12$ (*Cont.*)	
9	69	.008
10	68	.010
11	67	.013
12	66	.017
13	65	.021
14	64	.026
15	63	.032
16	62	.039
17	61	.046
18	60	.055
19	59	.065
20	58	.076
21	57	.088
22	56	.102
23	55	.117
24	54	.133
	$N = 13$	
9	82	.004
10	81	.005
11	80	.007
12	79	.009
13	78	.011
14	77	.013
15	76	.016
16	75	.020
17	74	.024
18	73	.029
19	72	.034
20	71	.040
21	70	.047
22	69	.055
23	68	.064
24	67	.073
25	66	.084
26	65	.095
27	64	.108
28	63	.122
29	62	.137
	$N = 14$	
12	93	.004
13	92	.005
14	91	.007
15	90	.008
16	89	.010
	$N = 14$ (*Cont.*)	
17	88	.012
18	87	.015
19	86	.018
20	85	.021
21	84	.025
22	83	.029
23	82	.034
24	81	.039
25	80	.045
26	79	.052
27	78	.059
28	77	.068
29	76	.077
30	75	.086
31	74	.097
32	73	.108
33	72	.121
34	71	.134
	$N = 15$	
15	105	.004
16	104	.005
17	103	.006
18	102	.008
19	101	.009
20	100	.011
21	99	.013
22	98	.015
23	97	.018
24	96	.021
25	95	.024
26	94	.028
27	93	.032
28	92	.036
29	91	.042
30	90	.047
31	89	.053
32	88	.060
33	87	.068
34	86	.076
35	85	.084
36	84	.094
37	83	.104
38	82	.115
39	81	.126

TABLE A-19. DISTRIBUTION OF THE SIGNED RANK STATISTIC T (*Continued*)

T_α	$T_{1-\alpha}$	α	T_α	$T_{1-\alpha}$	α	T_α	$T_{1-\alpha}$	α	T_α	$T_{1-\alpha}$	α
	$N = 16$			$N = 17$ (*Cont.*)			$N = 18$ (*Cont.*)			$N = 19$ (*Cont.*)	
19	117	.005	36	117	.028	51	120	.071	64	126	.112
20	116	.005	37	116	.032	52	119	.077	65	125	.121
21	115	.007	38	115	.036	53	118	.084	66	124	.129
22	114	.008	39	114	.040	54	117	.091		$N = 20$	
23	113	.009	40	113	.044	55	116	.098	37	173	.005
24	112	.011	41	112	.049	56	115	.106	38	172	.005
25	111	.012	42	111	.054	57	114	.114	39	171	.006
26	110	.014	43	110	.060	58	113	.123	40	170	.007
27	109	.017	44	109	.066	59	112	.132	41	169	.008
28	108	.019	45	108	.072		$N = 19$		42	168	.009
29	107	.022	46	107	.080	32	158	.005	43	167	.010
30	106	.025	47	106	.087	33	157	.005	44	166	.011
31	105	.029	48	105	.095	34	156	.006	45	165	.012
32	104	.033	49	104	.103	35	155	.007	46	164	.013
33	103	.037	50	103	.112	36	154	.008	47	163	.015
34	102	.042	51	102	.122	37	153	.009	48	162	.016
35	101	.047	52	101	.132	38	152	.010	49	161	.018
36	100	.052		$N = 18$		39	151	.011	50	160	.020
37	99	.058	27	144	.004	40	150	.013	51	159	.022
38	98	.065	28	143	.005	41	149	.014	52	158	.024
39	97	.072	29	142	.006	42	148	.016	53	157	.027
40	96	.080	30	141	.007	43	147	.018	54	156	.029
41	95	.088	31	140	.008	44	146	.020	55	155	.032
42	94	.096	32	139	.009	45	145	.022	56	154	.035
43	93	.106	33	138	.010	46	144	.025	57	153	.038
44	92	.116	34	137	.012	47	143	.027	58	152	.041
45	91	.125	35	136	.013	48	142	.030	59	151	.045
46	90	.137	36	135	.015	49	141	.033	60	150	.049
	$N = 17$		37	134	.017	50	140	.036	61	149	.053
23	130	.005	38	133	.019	51	139	.040	62	148	.057
24	129	.005	39	132	.022	52	138	.044	63	147	.061
25	128	.006	40	131	.024	53	137	.048	64	146	.066
26	127	.008	41	130	.027	54	136	.052	65	145	.071
27	126	.009	42	129	.030	55	135	.057	66	144	.077
28	125	.010	43	128	.033	56	134	.062	67	143	.082
29	124	.012	44	127	.037	57	133	.067	68	142	.088
30	123	.013	45	126	.040	58	132	.072	69	141	.095
31	122	.015	46	125	.045	59	131	.078	70	140	.101
32	121	.017	47	124	.049	60	130	.084	71	139	.108
33	120	.020	48	123	.054	61	129	.091	72	138	.115
34	119	.022	49	122	.059	62	128	.098	73	137	.123
35	118	.025	50	121	.065	63	127	.105	74	136	.131

TABLE A-20. DISTRIBUTION OF THE RANK SUM T'

The values of T'_α, $T'_{1-\alpha}$, and α are such that if the N_1 and N_2 observations are chosen at random from the same population the chance that the rank sum T' of the N_1 observations in the smaller sample is equal to or less than T'_α is α and the chance that T' is equal to or greater than $T'_{1-\alpha}$ is α. The sample sizes are shown in parentheses (N_1,N_2).

T'_α	$T'_{1-\alpha}$	α
	(1,1)	
1	2	.500
	(1,2)	
1	3	.333
2	2	.667
	(1,3)	
1	4	.250
2	3	.500
	(1,4)	
1	5	.200
2	4	.400
3	3	.600
	(1,5)	
1	6	.167
2	5	.333
3	4	.500
	(1,6)	
1	7	.143
2	6	.286
3	5	.428
4	4	.571
	(1,7)	
1	8	.125
2	7	.250
3	6	.375
4	5	.500
	(1,8)	
1	9	.111
2	8	.222
3	7	.333
4	6	.444
5	5	.556
	(1,9)	
1	10	.100
2	9	.200
3	8	.300
4	7	.400
5	6	.500
	(1,10)	
1	11	.091
2	10	.182
3	9	.273
4	8	.364
5	7	.455
6	6	.545
	(2,2)	
3	7	.167
4	6	.333
5	5	.667
	(2,3)	
3	9	.100
4	8	.200
5	7	.400
6	6	.600
	(2,4)	
3	11	.067
4	10	.133
5	9	.267
6	8	.400
7	7	.600
	(2,5)	
3	13	.047
4	12	.095
5	11	.190
6	10	.286
7	9	.429
8	8	.571
	(2,6)	
3	15	.036
4	14	.071
5	13	.143
6	12	.214
7	11	.321
8	10	.429
9	9	.571
	(2,7)	
3	17	.028
4	16	.056
5	15	.111
6	14	.167
7	13	.250
8	12	.333
9	11	.444
10	10	.556
	(2,8)	
3	19	.022
4	18	.044
5	17	.089
6	16	.133
7	15	.200
	(2,8) (*Cont.*)	
8	14	.267
9	13	.356
10	12	.444
11	11	.556
	(2,9)	
3	21	.018
4	20	.036
5	19	.073
6	18	.109
7	17	.164
8	16	.218
9	15	.291
10	14	.364
11	13	.455
12	12	.545
	(2,10)	
3	23	.015
4	22	.030
5	21	.061
6	20	.091
7	19	.136
8	18	.182
9	17	.242
10	16	.303
11	15	.379
12	14	.455
13	13	.545
	(3,3)	
6	15	.050
7	14	.100
8	13	.200
9	12	.350
10	11	.500
	(3,4)	
6	18	.028
7	17	.057
8	16	.114
9	15	.200
10	14	.314
11	13	.429
12	12	.571
	(3,5)	
6	21	.018
7	20	.036
	(3,5) (*Cont.*)	
8	19	.071
9	18	.125
10	17	.196
11	16	.286
12	15	.393
13	14	.500
	(3,6)	
6	24	.012
7	23	.024
8	22	.048
9	21	.083
10	20	.131
11	19	.190
12	18	.274
13	17	.357
14	16	.452
15	15	.548
	(3,7)	
6	27	.008
7	26	.017
8	25	.033
9	24	.058
10	23	.092
11	22	.133
12	21	.192
13	20	.258
14	19	.333
15	18	.417
16	17	.500
	(3,8)	
6	30	.006
7	29	.012
8	28	.024
9	27	.042
10	26	.067
11	25	.097
12	24	.139
13	23	.188
14	22	.248
15	21	.315
16	20	.387
17	19	.461
18	18	.539

TABLE A-20. DISTRIBUTION OF THE RANK SUM T' (*Continued*)

T'_{α}	$T'_{1-\alpha}$	α
	(3,9)	
6	33	.005
7	32	.009
8	31	.018
9	30	.032
10	29	.050
11	28	.073
12	27	.105
13	26	.141
14	25	.186
15	24	.241
16	23	.300
17	22	.363
18	21	.432
19	20	.500
	(3,10)	
6	36	.003
7	35	.007
8	34	.014
9	33	.024
10	32	.038
11	31	.056
12	30	.080
13	29	.108
14	28	.143
15	27	.185
16	26	.234
17	25	.287
18	24	.346
19	23	.406
20	22	.469
21	21	.531
	(4,4)	
10	26	.014
11	25	.029
12	24	.057
13	23	.100
14	22	.171
15	21	.243
16	20	.343
17	19	.443
18	18	.557
	(4,5)	
10	30	.008
11	29	.016
12	28	.032
13	27	.056
14	26	.095
15	25	.143
16	24	.206
	(4,5) (*Cont.*)	
17	23	.278
18	22	.365
19	21	.452
20	20	.548
	(4,6)	
10	34	.005
11	33	.010
12	32	.019
13	31	.033
14	30	.057
15	29	.086
16	28	.129
17	27	.176
18	26	.238
19	25	.305
20	24	.381
21	23	.457
22	22	.545
	(4,7)	
10	38	.003
11	37	.006
12	36	.012
13	35	.021
14	34	.036
15	33	.055
16	32	.082
17	31	.115
18	30	.158
19	29	.206
20	28	.264
21	27	.324
22	26	.394
23	25	.464
24	24	.538
	(4,8)	
10	42	.002
11	41	.004
12	40	.008
13	39	.014
14	38	.024
15	37	.036
16	36	.055
17	35	.077
18	34	.107
19	33	.141
20	32	.184
21	31	.230
22	30	.285
23	29	.341
	(4,8) (*Cont.*)	
24	28	.404
25	27	.467
26	26	.533
	(4,9)	
10	46	.001
11	45	.003
12	44	.006
13	43	.010
14	42	.017
15	41	.025
16	40	.038
17	39	.053
18	38	.074
19	37	.099
20	36	.130
21	35	.165
22	34	.207
23	33	.252
24	32	.302
25	31	.355
26	30	.413
27	29	.470
28	28	.530
	(4,10)	
10	50	.001
11	49	.002
12	48	.004
13	47	.007
14	46	.012
15	45	.018
16	44	.026
17	43	.038
18	42	.053
19	41	.071
20	40	.094
21	39	.120
22	38	.152
23	37	.187
24	36	.227
25	35	.270
26	34	.318
27	33	.367
28	32	.420
29	31	.473
30	30	.527
	(5,5)	
15	40	.004
16	39	.008
17	38	.016
	(5,5) (*Cont.*)	
18	37	.028
19	36	.048
20	35	.075
21	34	.111
22	33	.155
23	32	.210
24	31	.274
25	30	.345
26	29	.421
27	28	.500
	(5,6)	
15	45	.002
16	44	.004
17	43	.009
18	42	.015
19	41	.026
20	40	.041
21	39	.063
22	38	.089
23	37	.123
24	36	.165
25	35	.214
26	34	.268
27	33	.331
28	32	.396
29	31	.465
30	30	.535
	(5,7)	
15	50	.001
16	49	.003
17	48	.005
18	47	.009
19	46	.015
20	45	.024
21	44	.037
22	43	.053
23	42	.074
24	41	.101
25	40	.134
26	39	.172
27	38	.216
28	37	.265
29	36	.319
30	35	.378
31	34	.438
32	33	.500
	(5,8)	
15	55	.001
16	54	.002

TABLE A-20. DISTRIBUTION OF THE RANK SUM T' (*Continued*)

T'_{α}	$T'_{1-\alpha}$	α	T'_{α}	$T'_{1-\alpha}$	α	T'_{α}	$T'_{1-\alpha}$	α	T'_{α}	$T'_{1-\alpha}$	α
	(5,8) (*Cont.*)			(5,10) (*Cont.*)			(6,7) (*Cont.*)			(6,9) (*Cont.*)	
17	53	.003	20	60	.006	28	56	.026	28	68	.009
18	52	.005	21	59	.010	29	55	.037	29	67	.013
19	51	.009	22	58	.014	30	54	.051	30	66	.018
20	50	.015	23	57	.020	31	53	.069	31	65	.025
21	49	.023	24	56	.028	32	52	.090	32	64	.033
22	48	.033	25	55	.038	33	51	.117	33	63	.044
23	47	.047	26	54	.050	34	50	.147	34	62	.057
24	46	.064	27	53	.065	35	49	.183	35	61	.072
25	45	.085	28	52	.082	36	48	.223	36	60	.091
26	44	.111	29	51	.103	37	47	.267	37	59	.112
27	43	.142	30	50	.127	38	46	.314	38	58	.136
28	42	.177	31	49	.155	39	45	.365	39	57	.164
29	41	.217	32	48	.185	40	44	.418	40	56	.194
30	40	.262	33	47	.220	41	43	.473	41	55	.228
31	39	.311	34	46	.257	42	42	.527	42	54	.264
32	38	.362	35	45	.297		(6,8)		43	53	.303
33	37	.416	36	44	.339	21	69	.000	44	52	.344
34	36	.472	37	43	.384	22	68	.001	45	51	.388
35	35	.528	38	42	.430	23	67	.001	46	50	.432
	(5,9)		39	41	.477	24	66	.002	47	49	.477
15	60	.000	40	40	.523	25	65	.004	48	48	.523
16	59	.001		(6,6)		26	64	.006		(6,10)	
17	58	.002	21	57	.001	27	63	.010	21	81	.000
18	57	.003	22	56	.002	28	62	.015	22	80	.000
19	56	.006	23	55	.004	29	61	.021	23	79	.000
20	55	.009	24	54	.008	30	60	.030	24	78	.001
21	54	.014	25	53	.013	31	59	.041	25	77	.001
22	53	.021	26	52	.021	32	58	.054	26	76	.002
23	52	.030	27	51	.032	33	57	.071	27	75	.004
24	51	.041	28	50	.047	34	56	.091	28	74	.005
25	50	.056	29	49	.066	35	55	.114	29	73	.008
26	49	.073	30	48	.090	36	54	.141	30	72	.011
27	48	.095	31	47	.120	37	53	.172	31	71	.016
28	47	.120	32	46	.155	38	52	.207	32	70	.021
29	46	.149	33	45	.197	39	51	.245	33	69	.028
30	45	.182	34	44	.242	40	50	.286	34	68	.036
31	44	.219	35	43	.294	41	49	.331	35	67	.047
32	43	.259	36	42	.350	42	48	.377	36	66	.059
33	42	.303	37	41	.409	43	47	.426	37	65	.074
34	41	.350	38	40	.469	44	46	.475	38	64	.090
35	40	.399	39	39	.531	45	45	.525	39	63	.110
36	39	.449		(6,7)			(6,9)		40	62	.132
37	38	.500	21	63	.001	21	75	.000	41	61	.157
	(5,10)		22	62	.001	22	74	.000	42	60	.184
15	65	.000	23	61	.002	23	73	.001	43	59	.214
16	64	.001	24	60	.004	24	72	.001	44	58	.246
17	63	.001	25	59	.007	25	71	.002	45	57	.281
18	62	.002	26	58	.011	26	70	.004	46	56	.318
19	61	.004	27	57	.017	27	69	.006	47	55	.356

Table A-20. Distribution of the Rank Sum T' (*Continued*)

T'_{α}	$T'_{1-\alpha}$	α	T'_{α}	$T'_{1-\alpha}$	α	T'_{α}	$T'_{1-\alpha}$	α	T'_{α}	$T'_{1-\alpha}$	α
	(6,10) (*Cont.*)			(7,8) (*Cont.*)			(7,10) (*Cont.*)			(8,8) (*Cont.*)	
48	54	.396	46	66	.140	32	94	.001	52	84	.052
49	53	.437	47	65	.168	33	93	.001	53	83	.065
50	52	.479	48	64	.198	34	92	.001	54	82	.080
51	51	.521	49	63	.232	35	91	.002	55	81	.097
	(7,7)		50	62	.268	36	90	.003	56	80	.117
28	77	.000	51	61	.306	37	89	.005	57	79	.139
29	76	.001	52	60	.347	38	88	.007	58	78	.164
30	75	.001	53	59	.389	39	87	.009	59	77	.191
31	74	.002	54	58	.433	40	86	.012	60	76	.221
32	73	.003	55	57	.478	41	85	.017	61	75	.253
33	72	.006	56	56	.522	42	84	.022	62	74	.287
34	71	.009		(7,9)		43	83	.028	63	73	.323
35	70	.013	28	91	.000	44	82	.035	64	72	.360
36	69	.019	29	90	.000	45	81	.044	65	71	.399
37	68	.027	30	89	.000	46	80	.054	66	70	.439
38	67	.036	31	88	.001	47	79	.067	67	69	.480
39	66	.049	32	87	.001	48	78	.081	68	68	.520
40	65	.064	33	86	.002	49	77	.097		(8,9)	
41	64	.082	34	85	.003	50	76	.115	36	108	.000
42	63	.104	35	84	.004	51	75	.135	40	104	.000
43	62	.130	36	83	.006	52	74	.157	41	103	.001
44	61	.159	37	82	.008	53	73	.182	42	102	.001
45	60	.191	38	81	.011	54	72	.209	43	101	.002
46	59	.228	39	80	.016	55	71	.237	44	100	.003
47	58	.267	40	79	.021	56	70	.268	45	99	.004
48	57	.310	41	78	.027	57	69	.300	46	98	.006
49	56	.355	42	77	.036	58	68	.335	47	97	.008
50	55	.402	43	76	.045	59	67	.370	48	96	.010
51	54	.451	44	75	.057	60	66	.406	49	95	.014
52	53	.500	45	74	.071	61	65	.443	50	94	.018
	(7,8)		46	73	.087	62	64	.481	51	93	.023
28	84	.000	47	72	.105	63	63	.519	52	92	.030
29	83	.000	48	71	.126		(8,8)		53	91	.037
30	82	.001	49	70	.150	36	100	.000	54	90	.046
31	81	.001	50	69	.175	37	99	.000	55	89	.057
32	80	.002	51	68	.204	38	98	.000	56	88	.069
33	79	.003	52	67	.235	39	97	.001	57	87	.084
34	78	.005	53	66	.268	40	96	.001	58	86	.100
35	77	.007	54	65	.303	41	95	.001	59	85	.118
36	76	.010	55	64	.340	42	94	.002	60	84	.138
37	75	.014	56	63	.379	43	93	.003	61	83	.161
38	74	.020	57	62	.419	44	92	.005	62	82	.185
39	73	.027	58	61	.459	45	91	.007	63	81	.212
40	72	.036	59	60	.500	46	90	.010	64	80	.240
41	71	.047		(7,10)		47	89	.014	65	79	.271
42	70	.060	28	98	.000	48	88	.019	66	78	.303
43	69	.076	29	97	.000	49	87	.025	67	77	.336
44	68	.095	30	96	.000	50	86	.032	68	76	.371
45	67	.116	31	95	.000	51	85	.041	69	75	.407

TABLE A-20. DISTRIBUTION OF THE RANK SUM T' (*Continued*)

T'_{α}	$T'_{1-\alpha}$	α	T'_{α}	$T'_{1-\alpha}$	α	T'_{α}	$T'_{1-\alpha}$	α	T'_{α}	$T'_{1-\alpha}$	α
(8,9) (*Cont.*)			(9,9)			(9,10) (*Cont.*)			(10,10) (*Cont.*)		
70	74	.444	45	126	.000	54	126	.001	65	145	.001
71	73	.481	50	121	.000	55	125	.001	66	144	.001
72	72	.519	51	120	.001	56	124	.002	67	143	.001
(8,10)			52	119	.001	57	123	.003	68	142	.002
36	116	.000	53	118	.001	58	122	.004	69	141	.003
41	111	.000	54	117	.002	59	121	.005	70	140	.003
42	110	.001	55	116	.003	60	120	.007	71	139	.004
43	109	.001	56	115	.004	61	119	.009	72	138	.006
44	108	.002	57	114	.005	62	118	.011	73	137	.007
45	107	.002	58	113	.007	63	117	.014	74	136	.009
46	106	.003	59	112	.009	64	116	.017	75	135	.012
47	105	.004	60	111	.012	65	115	.022	76	134	.014
48	104	.006	61	110	.016	66	114	.027	77	133	.018
49	103	.008	62	109	.020	67	113	.033	78	132	.022
50	102	.010	63	108	.025	68	112	.039	79	131	.026
51	101	.013	64	107	.031	69	111	.047	80	130	.032
52	100	.017	65	106	.039	70	110	.056	81	129	.038
53	99	.022	66	105	.047	71	109	.067	82	128	.045
54	98	.027	67	104	.057	72	108	.078	83	127	.053
55	97	.034	68	103	.068	73	107	.091	84	126	.062
56	96	.042	69	102	.081	74	106	.106	85	125	.072
57	95	.051	70	101	.095	75	105	.121	86	124	.083
58	94	.061	71	100	.111	76	104	.139	87	123	.095
59	93	.073	72	99	.129	77	103	.158	88	122	.109
60	92	.086	73	98	.149	78	102	.178	89	121	.124
61	91	.102	74	97	.170	79	101	.200	90	120	.140
62	90	.118	75	96	.193	80	100	.223	91	119	.157
63	89	.137	76	95	.218	81	99	.248	92	118	.176
64	88	.158	77	94	.245	82	98	.274	93	117	.197
65	87	.180	78	93	.273	83	97	.302	94	116	.218
66	86	.204	79	92	.302	84	96	.330	95	115	.241
67	85	.230	80	91	.333	85	95	.360	96	114	.264
68	84	.257	81	90	.365	86	94	.390	97	113	.289
69	83	.286	82	89	.398	87	93	.421	98	112	.315
70	82	.317	83	88	.432	88	92	.452	99	111	.342
71	81	.348	84	87	.466	89	91	.484	100	110	.370
72	80	.381	85	86	.500	90	90	.516	101	109	.398
73	79	.414	(9,10)			(10,10)			102	108	.427
74	78	.448	45	135	.000	55	155	.000	103	107	.456
75	77	.483	52	128	.000	63	147	.000	104	106	.485
76	76	.517	53	127	.001	64	146	.001	105	105	.515

For sample sizes greater than 10 the chance that the statistic T' will be less than or equal to an integer k is given approximately by the area under the standard normal curve to the left of

$$z = \frac{k + \frac{1}{2} - N_1(N_1 + N_2 + 1)/2}{\sqrt{N_1 N_2 (N_1 + N_2 + 1)/12}}$$

TABLE A-21. PERCENTILES OF THE DISTRIBUTION OF d

N	$1-\alpha$				
	.80	.85	.90	.95	.99
5	.45	.47	.51	.56	.67
10	.32	.34	.37	.41	.49
20	.23	.25	.26	.29	.35
25	.21	.22	.24	.26	.32
30	.19	.20	.22	.24	.29
35	.18	.19	.20	.23	.27
40	.17	.18	.19	.21	.25
45	.16	.17	.18	.20	.24
50	.15	.16	.17	.19	.23
For larger values..	$\frac{1.07}{\sqrt{N}}$	$\frac{1.14}{\sqrt{N}}$	$\frac{1.22}{\sqrt{N}}$	$\frac{1.36}{\sqrt{N}}$	$\frac{1.63}{\sqrt{N}}$

α is the chance that the maximum deviation between the cumulative distributions of the population and of the sample exceeds the value d given in the table.

The maximum deviation is a discrete variable taking on values $0, 1/N, 2/N, \ldots, 1$. Exact chances that the maximum deviation exceeds most of these values for all N's ≤ 100 are given by Z. W. Birnbaum, "Numerical tabulation of the distribution of Kolmogorov's statistic for finite sample size," *Journal of the American Statistical Association*, vol. 47 (1952), p. 425.

For two samples of sizes N_1 and N_2, respectively, the sampling distribution of the maximum deviation between the two cumulative distribution curves has percentiles as follows: $P_{80} = 1.07\sqrt{\frac{1}{N_1}+\frac{1}{N_2}}$, $P_{85} = 1.14\sqrt{\frac{1}{N_1}+\frac{1}{N_2}}$, $P_{90} = 1.22\sqrt{\frac{1}{N_1}+\frac{1}{N_2}}$, $P_{95} = 1.36\sqrt{\frac{1}{N_1}+\frac{1}{N_2}}$, $P_{99} = 1.63\sqrt{\frac{1}{N_1}+\frac{1}{N_2}}$. These percentiles are approximate for large samples, say, N_1 and N_2 each greater than about 30. Some exact chances are given by F. J. Massey, in the *Annals of Mathematical Statistics*, vol. 22 (1951), p. 125, and vol. 23 (1952), p. 435.

Table A-22. Possible Populations* for Sampling Experiments

	Set number					
	1	2	3	4	5	6
Color of figures	Black	Red	Blue	Green	Black	Black
Mean	0	0	+2	0	+4	0
Standard deviation	1.715	1.715	1.715	3.470	1.715	6.055
Number on tag	Frequency					
10				1		10
9				1	1	10
8				1	3	10
7			1	3	10	10
6			3	5	23	10
5	1	1	10	8	39	10
4	3	3	23	12	48	10
3	10	10	39	16	39	10
2	23	23	48	20	23	10
1	39	39	39	22	10	10
0	48	48	23	23	3	10
−1	39	39	10	22	1	10
−2	23	23	3	20		10
−3	10	10	1	16		10
−4	3	3		12		10
−5	1	1		8		10
−6				5		10
−7				3		10
−8				1		10
−9				1		10
−10				1		10
	200	200	200	201	200	210

* E. G. Olds, L. A. Knowler, "Teaching statistical quality control for town and gown," *Journal of the American Statistical Association*, vol. 44 (1949), pp. 213–230.

TABLE A-23. RANDOM NORMAL NUMBERS, $\mu = 2$, $\sigma = 1$*

01	02	03	04	05	06	07	08	09	10
2.422	0.130	2.232	1.700	1.903	0.725	2.031	0.515	−0.684	2.788
0.694	2.556	1.868	1.263	2.115	1.516	1.972	3.627	1.482	3.263
1.875	2.273	0.655	2.299	0.055	1.955	−0.147	2.168	2.193	1.879
1.017	0.757	1.288	1.322	2.080	2.170	1.502	2.953	0.171	1.951
2.453	4.199	1.403	2.017	3.496	0.165	2.556	1.003	1.973	2.159
2.274	1.767	1.564	2.412	2.207	0.475	2.656	1.579	0.394	1.225
3.000	1.618	1.530	2.224	2.881	2.715	3.103	1.941	2.179	3.748
2.510	2.256	1.146	5.177	1.931	1.693	1.021	3.337	2.137	1.839
1.233	2.085	2.251	1.578	3.796	3.017	2.863	2.514	1.615	1.548
3.075	1.730	2.427	2.990	1.680	3.250	3.050	3.243	1.846	1.798
1.344	−0.095	2.166	4.116	2.500	1.939	1.567	3.047	1.385	−0.831
1.246	3.860	1.253	1.876	4.373	1.993	1.262	2.319	2.488	2.406
0.889	2.299	2.458	1.790	1.048	2.302	0.138	2.383	1.170	2.204
1.154	1.401	1.935	3.106	1.548	−0.096	2.153	2.333	1.761	3.728
3.031	1.048	0.719	1.474	2.779	0.292	2.341	2.707	1.741	2.353
0.534	1.155	1.705	1.662	0.457	0.602	1.365	2.663	3.755	1.900
2.230	3.096	0.045	3.639	0.680	0.970	1.593	2.117	2.395	1.935
2.355	1.761	1.816	1.822	1.434	2.259	3.788	3.280	1.317	2.940
1.461	0.947	0.717	2.923	2.133	2.526	2.687	2.144	1.692	1.469
3.034	1.778	2.122	2.025	3.008	1.447	−0.305	2.452	1.726	0.870
2.761	0.473	3.726	1.893	2.455	1.633	1.654	3.006	3.523	2.317
1.961	0.965	1.481	1.402	2.106	2.214	1.727	3.670	3.795	2.258
2.639	4.010	1.915	1.713	1.484	1.443	1.444	2.394	1.688	0.793
1.349	2.225	0.644	1.404	2.583	2.149	2.359	2.274	1.432	1.610
2.959	2.797	4.635	3.268	2.889	2.349	0.933	3.403	2.206	−0.214
2.440	2.919	1.455	0.695	1.466	1.124	1.257	1.265	0.096	3.412
3.078	3.279	0.352	2.583	1.690	0.729	2.072	1.332	1.158	1.827
1.736	1.968	0.011	2.418	1.026	1.342	2.103	1.792	2.175	1.646
3.275	3.147	2.800	2.172	0.004	1.763	3.801	2.510	2.517	−0.117
2.579	2.297	2.030	2.725	3.721	2.545	1.631	−0.346	−0.011	1.961
2.549	3.546	2.805	1.250	0.769	2.238	2.284	3.722	2.085	2.653
2.954	1.990	1.249	1.028	3.241	1.926	3.056	1.732	2.116	1.825
1.442	2.542	2.557	1.741	0.630	2.117	1.662	2.237	−0.046	3.132
4.039	2.030	2.859	3.538	2.424	2.169	3.643	3.290	2.742	1.336
2.127	0.288	2.921	0.175	1.670	3.151	1.443	0.935	1.125	2.872
1.102	2.536	1.476	2.980	0.416	1.784	2.521	1.867	1.709	1.558
2.938	2.112	1.350	2.115	1.164	1.761	1.350	1.798	3.160	2.593
2.975	2.681	0.721	1.291	2.276	2.131	2.187	2.752	1.380	0.676
1.386	1.712	1.692	2.844	1.559	0.418	3.020	0.785	1.962	3.184
2.834	1.485	0.632	0.872	0.735	1.934	1.221	2.544	1.797	1.410
3.346	1.147	1.766	1.862	2.595	1.524	3.499	2.652	2.139	2.533
2.243	3.881	2.846	2.670	3.377	1.380	4.183	0.883	1.373	1.992
2.705	2.661	1.521	1.290	2.280	1.638	0.884	2.636	2.077	1.012
2.760	1.182	1.152	3.074	1.073	2.917	2.150	2.866	1.688	1.684
2.086	1.250	1.577	2.871	2.985	2.585	2.897	2.398	0.999	1.764
0.802	1.421	4.793	0.268	2.838	2.227	3.331	2.395	2.064	2.916
4.165	2.014	0.616	1.929	0.641	2.304	1.263	2.125	0.908	1.768
2.291	2.549	0.851	1.856	2.452	3.282	0.978	2.255	1.683	1.926
1.428	4.194	2.262	2.957	1.991	2.759	1.553	3.538	1.272	3.417
2.051	2.455	2.759	2.267	2.794	4.106	2.373	1.401	2.562	2.502

* This table is reproduced with permission from tables of the RAND Corporation.

TABLE A-23. RANDOM NORMAL NUMBERS, $\mu = 2$, $\sigma = 1$ (*Continued*)

11	12	13	14	15	16	17	18	19	20
1.911	0.626	2.289	1.628	1.638	2.676	0.900	1.685	1.605	1.366
3.196	2.979	2.447	2.099	1.273	2.733	2.653	2.219	1.318	3.129
0.398	2.304	1.019	0.363	1.286	2.428	0.677	1.684	1.267	0.651
1.228	2.134	0.300	1.785	2.547	1.566	2.545	2.428	1.702	2.276
1.190	3.020	0.954	2.907	2.916	1.279	3.403	2.698	1.629	1.448
0.953	2.127	1.723	2.302	1.474	0.826	1.644	2.035	2.359	2.930
1.479	1.956	1.280	1.722	0.938	0.922	2.734	3.484	1.659	2.789
1.509	0.952	1.258	−0.864	1.620	1.789	2.931	2.616	1.622	1.566
0.627	2.404	0.571	2.940	2.705	1.709	2.404	1.456	2.486	2.869
1.923	2.765	2.422	1.725	1.009	2.372	1.925	1.083	3.314	1.961
2.760	2.633	3.011	2.277	1.539	0.873	2.379	2.610	1.635	−0.625
2.009	3.204	1.114	2.269	0.912	0.831	2.485	2.076	1.230	3.607
0.876	1.124	2.137	1.448	1.236	1.699	1.408	1.454	2.018	1.514
1.430	1.920	2.969	1.518	1.543	1.509	4.071	3.444	0.907	2.478
3.422	2.307	2.919	1.833	1.792	3.090	2.212	0.814	1.661	0.865
3.304	1.292	1.863	2.785	1.666	0.323	2.384	3.133	3.393	2.814
2.329	2.671	3.353	1.166	1.016	3.036	2.024	1.439	2.203	1.128
1.402	1.964	1.505	1.746	1.912	1.202	0.595	0.527	1.881	3.456
2.274	1.209	1.450	2.241	1.678	1.565	2.746	2.149	1.829	1.520
1.205	0.531	2.975	3.024	3.357	2.558	1.450	2.192	1.665	3.373
2.462	1.328	1.301	3.312	1.959	2.010	2.482	1.530	1.909	3.171
0.227	3.166	1.989	2.976	2.188	1.399	1.407	2.610	1.903	0.624
2.142	2.926	1.634	1.940	0.785	2.331	1.663	0.847	2.533	1.166
2.558	0.903	0.082	1.299	2.366	2.554	1.948	1.055	1.559	1.787
0.818	3.174	0.123	−1.149	1.606	2.118	−0.044	0.022	0.866	2.336
3.083	2.287	2.379	2.909	2.520	0.708	1.600	0.790	1.751	2.480
2.517	1.470	2.621	0.880	1.931	1.495	1.943	1.868	2.048	3.879
2.594	1.571	1.218	2.346	2.267	0.946	2.840	1.753	2.237	0.687
0.411	0.760	1.114	1.842	1.756	3.951	2.110	2.251	2.116	1.042
2.853	3.054	2.421	2.418	1.542	2.070	0.641	0.753	1.040	0.702
1.262	−0.591	1.320	2.049	2.705	3.826	3.272	1.054	2.494	2.050
0.540	1.678	2.534	1.944	1.939	2.544	1.582	1.333	1.895	1.746
2.381	2.968	1.656	3.152	1.730	3.927	3.183	3.211	3.765	2.035
2.225	1.420	1.334	1.923	1.664	1.939	0.680	2.785	1.569	1.701
1.953	2.779	2.584	2.228	0.221	1.378	1.381	2.209	2.979	2.906
3.413	2.229	2.976	2.535	3.589	0.615	3.425	1.187	2.748	0.906
1.610	2.376	2.086	0.610	2.532	3.083	1.332	1.776	0.407	0.721
0.984	2.243	2.939	1.704	2.277	1.026	1.879	0.405	1.003	0.755
1.808	2.362	1.717	0.831	2.160	0.546	2.686	1.924	1.756	1.829
−0.766	3.529	2.361	0.955	2.148	1.104	0.541	1.460	1.840	1.579
2.643	2.051	1.384	2.229	2.952	2.203	0.765	4.381	1.611	1.936
1.952	2.752	3.588	2.481	1.911	3.753	1.428	3.223	1.873	2.034
2.590	2.306	3.280	1.664	2.281	1.443	2.024	2.126	3.250	1.384
0.622	2.617	1.969	2.231	−0.079	0.768	2.547	1.365	1.163	1.280
0.433	−0.560	3.292	1.987	1.065	2.766	1.425	0.846	2.520	0.981
3.146	3.323	1.713	1.887	2.010	1.277	0.491	2.489	1.503	1.974
4.021	1.744	0.598	2.954	2.633	1.960	1.539	2.393	4.012	3.356
1.188	0.450	2.958	1.177	1.482	1.090	1.671	3.021	0.386	3.560
1.211	2.575	0.158	3.124	3.632	2.647	3.029	3.526	2.237	0.671
3.750	2.362	1.407	0.642	1.274	1.632	2.378	2.601	0.003	1.261

TABLE A-23. RANDOM NORMAL NUMBERS, $\mu = 2$, $\sigma = 1$ (*Continued*)

21	22	23	24	25	26	27	28	29	30
1.707	2.089	1.315	0.278	3.045	2.968	1.396	1.534	2.365	2.746
1.113	1.779	1.935	0.971	4.024	0.847	1.382	2.342	2.110	0.316
1.847	0.547	3.697	1.250	1.586	2.036	2.924	0.585	0.456	2.859
2.713	2.761	1.664	2.461	2.158	3.453	2.078	1.113	1.769	1.263
0.676	0.432	2.667	2.515	1.369	3.196	2.979	2.447	2.099	1.273
2.167	1.828	2.867	1.178	2.078	1.500	2.622	2.341	1.504	2.468
3.445	3.323	2.558	1.789	1.595	1.191	1.175	2.872	1.257	1.062
1.284	3.180	3.315	1.210	1.842	3.384	2.942	2.550	0.727	1.736
2.135	2.590	2.533	1.635	1.983	0.614	0.377	−0.663	0.427	2.445
2.944	2.043	2.220	1.987	2.859	3.029	2.091	1.052	1.532	1.956
3.654	2.333	1.468	3.126	1.241	2.936	1.557	2.020	1.423	2.701
0.821	1.542	2.365	2.199	3.479	3.111	−0.107	1.644	1.337	1.442
2.483	2.583	2.075	1.026	0.668	2.281	1.566	1.255	2.020	1.135
0.715	1.384	2.080	2.542	2.368	0.019	2.906	2.325	2.175	5.197
4.638	2.662	1.012	2.941	1.336	0.574	3.034	2.937	2.553	0.174
2.327	2.152	3.057	2.077	2.321	0.861	2.892	1.394	−0.556	1.459
−0.082	0.676	3.038	2.470	1.394	2.131	1.262	3.207	1.810	0.322
2.051	1.576	2.087	3.030	2.030	2.827	2.183	1.182	1.507	−0.042
2.438	0.924	1.699	0.477	2.449	2.540	1.620	2.509	2.347	3.022
2.284	2.159	2.975	3.268	0.484	1.862	1.676	1.449	2.475	2.556
0.872	0.474	2.213	3.602	3.244	3.078	1.376	2.612	2.421	1.014
2.236	1.963	1.839	1.598	2.195	2.680	2.228	1.107	−0.661	1.041
2.425	2.412	1.500	2.278	2.328	2.102	2.087	3.098	2.697	0.765
1.511	2.431	1.434	1.558	1.020	2.864	0.871	2.523	1.878	1.370
1.600	2.040	2.993	0.873	0.568	2.703	2.578	1.515	3.627	2.097
3.076	1.939	0.682	3.085	2.877	2.696	−0.771	2.560	1.954	0.999
2.593	1.610	2.800	2.456	0.226	3.575	1.435	2.170	1.165	3.506
1.362	2.727	2.145	2.023	0.509	0.336	2.045	0.375	1.010	2.316
1.603	2.783	0.682	2.108	2.031	0.854	2.028	2.357	0.722	1.562
1.908	1.635	2.009	1.203	1.775	2.868	1.949	1.391	1.151	1.352
3.486	0.507	2.322	1.204	2.434	1.720	1.804	2.235	2.439	1.492
2.029	1.352	3.629	2.076	1.587	0.891	3.029	1.242	0.014	4.019
2.894	1.688	0.657	1.800	2.943	1.373	1.269	3.411	1.316	2.405
0.965	−0.028	1.904	2.241	2.563	1.149	2.375	1.386	1.562	2.882
2.191	2.133	2.676	0.229	2.319	1.114	3.197	2.588	3.163	2.423
2.115	2.418	2.741	1.839	2.416	1.452	0.319	0.853	2.774	0.929
1.120	2.126	0.773	0.798	3.436	2.374	2.173	−0.333	2.004	1.765
3.524	0.008	3.260	1.109	4.111	2.474	2.482	2.416	0.832	4.059
0.103	2.774	2.056	2.463	0.383	−0.962	2.458	2.388	1.556	1.088
1.573	2.519	2.153	3.188	1.618	2.477	2.185	1.851	0.498	2.066
1.138	3.032	2.390	2.436	2.655	1.484	2.378	3.166	2.531	2.082
2.665	2.960	2.518	1.940	0.026	2.570	2.703	2.592	3.094	1.862
1.397	1.859	2.208	2.559	1.749	0.624	0.074	1.398	0.996	2.910
1.875	2.250	0.183	2.214	1.356	4.282	2.370	3.006	1.413	2.412
3.195	2.671	1.918	3.305	3.722	1.372	2.564	2.106	1.871	1.792
1.464	2.055	3.045	2.367	1.992	0.919	3.006	2.713	4.049	4.618
3.328	1.781	2.565	1.304	2.041	1.597	0.225	2.309	−0.558	2.504
2.804	3.606	1.858	3.028	2.456	1.730	1.430	3.405	0.474	2.222
2.590	1.641	3.857	2.582	2.594	1.933	3.341	1.002	2.704	1.341
2.980	0.601	1.595	2.248	2.381	1.911	0.626	2.289	1.628	1.638

TABLE A-23. RANDOM NORMAL NUMBERS, $\mu = 2$, $\sigma = 1$ (*Continued*)

31	32	33	34	35	36	37	38	39	40
3.355	0.073	3.139	2.472	1.825	0.296	1.685	3.401	1.820	1.428
1.086	1.955	2.529	2.503	1.687	1.754	4.138	2.394	0.303	3.776
2.367	1.525	2.625	1.789	0.991	4.127	0.915	3.023	1.377	3.435
0.248	0.749	3.697	4.166	2.544	1.620	3.217	1.083	1.907	2.951
1.694	0.258	1.836	1.953	1.853	3.590	3.604	1.907	1.995	2.468
1.546	1.255	2.856	3.221	2.397	−0.010	2.169	2.781	3.001	2.536
1.266	2.089	2.974	1.305	2.376	−0.475	1.792	1.546	0.583	1.214
0.713	2.473	1.381	1.750	1.064	3.744	2.470	1.004	2.155	2.332
−0.001	1.600	2.166	0.561	0.898	2.587	0.580	−0.461	0.954	1.364
3.406	2.207	2.110	1.522	3.923	1.379	3.613	3.379	2.716	2.796
1.432	1.651	1.584	3.649	2.485	2.820	2.948	2.626	1.763	3.329
1.541	1.154	4.311	2.354	2.257	1.262	2.304	2.178	1.657	2.126
2.216	3.505	−0.056	1.332	0.980	1.675	1.850	2.487	2.051	1.433
1.602	2.225	2.949	3.945	3.753	3.855	2.769	0.760	2.095	1.419
2.211	1.804	2.642	0.975	1.646	2.552	2.291	1.277	2.341	−0.219
3.006	2.279	1.097	3.473	0.919	2.535	2.459	3.934	1.826	1.587
2.520	2.468	2.156	2.438	1.625	1.604	1.628	1.139	2.608	2.643
2.666	4.058	2.805	3.069	0.945	2.533	2.761	1.140	2.604	1.627
2.852	0.570	3.920	1.572	2.924	2.135	1.558	2.604	2.191	2.529
2.014	2.825	3.502	2.006	1.879	3.304	1.538	0.906	3.125	1.009
1.540	0.444	1.541	1.850	1.793	2.284	1.890	3.091	2.293	2.491
1.190	2.087	2.159	1.157	2.314	1.753	0.722	2.447	2.124	2.927
0.741	3.411	1.689	1.945	0.286	3.288	1.390	0.240	1.448	2.768
2.169	1.937	2.261	0.766	2.075	0.457	2.031	0.831	−0.009	4.316
0.979	1.935	2.232	1.812	3.290	2.031	3.222	2.520	4.105	0.705
1.405	0.166	0.137	3.246	4.142	2.808	2.526	2.687	−0.627	2.023
0.923	2.287	1.164	0.732	0.736	0.892	2.633	2.107	1.260	0.615
1.529	3.188	2.153	3.828	3.610	1.654	2.596	0.957	1.479	1.497
0.781	3.562	3.633	0.889	0.832	2.068	2.103	3.360	1.686	1.538
2.153	2.125	1.930	3.161	2.931	1.941	3.108	1.732	4.296	1.830
3.204	3.945	0.682	4.165	2.419	0.565	1.637	1.931	1.092	2.482
2.154	1.889	1.391	1.690	1.356	2.560	1.784	1.041	2.808	0.576
3.391	2.602	2.496	2.177	1.564	1.781	0.302	2.499	1.501	1.410
3.266	2.051	1.958	0.979	2.454	1.438	2.098	3.208	2.374	2.710
1.842	0.513	1.736	2.878	1.893	1.614	2.775	1.060	1.508	1.197
2.799	0.757	0.625	3.336	2.268	1.418	1.616	2.363	0.751	2.138
0.104	3.564	0.681	1.231	2.527	0.172	1.331	0.991	3.570	1.382
2.232	3.514	−0.433	2.932	3.245	2.778	2.196	−0.326	1.034	1.889
4.201	3.351	1.761	1.957	1.342	3.575	3.216	1.335	1.527	0.812
1.046	1.646	1.363	1.051	4.600	3.209	3.041	3.234	2.034	0.682
2.874	1.663	2.591	1.396	1.052	1.068	2.226	3.048	1.906	2.755
1.389	2.966	2.846	2.410	1.663	3.620	2.151	2.036	3.733	1.462
−0.144	1.641	1.693	1.599	2.704	3.083	1.387	0.593	1.191	2.707
2.177	0.829	2.094	1.737	1.625	1.766	1.415	2.238	0.549	1.887
2.595	2.094	2.851	1.175	0.425	2.242	1.477	3.237	2.614	1.226
1.655	3.804	0.607	1.958	4.251	1.457	3.369	2.077	1.511	1.458
2.601	2.255	1.787	1.136	2.912	3.060	2.562	3.137	3.248	1.382
2.308	2.422	3.081	2.185	1.963	3.855	2.389	4.057	2.428	3.054
1.196	4.160	2.841	1.550	0.919	1.884	1.911	1.386	2.607	1.625
0.843	1.330	1.678	2.198	1.398	0.709	1.810	2.269	4.242	0.777

TABLE A-23. RANDOM NORMAL NUMBERS, $\mu = 2$, $\sigma = 1$ (*Continued*)

41	42	43	44	45	46	47	48	49	50
1.017	2.773	3.278	2.557	1.003	4.181	0.946	3.464	1.945	2.929
0.723	0.781	1.546	1.649	2.723	4.542	1.819	0.511	2.580	3.707
1.681	1.200	0.335	3.391	2.382	3.080	0.685	1.924	1.085	1.459
0.622	0.742	2.495	1.860	1.145	2.040	2.103	−0.256	0.976	2.414
1.815	2.061	2.092	2.089	2.281	2.377	1.821	1.760	2.515	1.898
4.334	1.662	0.044	1.363	0.681	2.111	2.443	1.603	1.803	2.149
0.863	2.642	5.436	0.332	2.847	1.466	3.031	1.571	3.024	1.988
2.414	1.988	2.666	0.867	1.589	2.192	3.027	2.257	1.868	1.927
1.505	2.364	0.762	1.955	1.888	1.845	3.180	2.618	1.730	1.603
3.048	2.037	2.759	2.609	−0.042	1.215	1.292	1.582	1.522	2.097
2.347	4.816	1.535	1.367	0.385	2.013	2.557	2.041	3.070	1.934
2.637	2.563	1.892	2.131	0.191	2.484	1.788	2.762	2.166	1.211
4.176	2.393	1.075	3.911	0.959	2.438	3.201	1.810	2.049	3.476
0.814	1.055	0.395	2.185	1.741	2.742	2.228	2.151	1.997	3.302
2.972	3.710	4.682	4.813	0.468	2.311	2.382	0.810	0.155	1.685
3.210	2.294	1.751	2.719	3.103	2.459	3.656	4.862	3.724	3.457
4.647	2.777	2.450	4.247	3.151	0.197	3.602	1.754	1.739	2.646
2.398	2.318	1.071	4.416	1.063	1.568	3.057	0.985	3.425	1.924
2.846	1.300	1.631	2.344	1.073	1.049	2.743	0.365	1.949	0.378
2.654	1.044	4.907	3.688	2.752	2.365	2.083	1.669	2.538	2.617
2.522	2.231	1.380	1.734	2.419	1.313	2.226	2.524	2.073	3.032
0.711	1.460	1.175	2.244	0.929	−0.091	1.096	2.061	3.099	2.186
3.372	3.769	0.942	3.646	2.481	1.554	3.715	1.193	1.956	1.735
2.854	1.464	3.607	2.428	1.384	1.977	1.504	0.492	2.102	2.624
1.851	0.855	2.913	2.684	3.043	2.595	1.803	1.303	0.233	−0.429
0.851	0.943	2.635	1.671	0.778	2.899	2.145	2.747	1.342	2.313
2.348	2.970	1.982	3.217	1.025	2.626	2.164	2.568	1.080	2.814
2.284	2.458	3.307	0.374	1.370	2.631	−0.649	1.111	1.296	2.403
0.983	2.360	1.880	4.331	3.672	−0.018	3.053	2.068	2.051	2.506
3.603	1.047	1.433	3.600	2.465	2.472	1.190	3.504	2.205	0.793
1.809	3.479	1.013	3.249	3.934	1.432	2.893	1.707	3.498	1.429
1.277	2.925	2.783	1.597	2.619	2.000	1.513	2.888	1.421	0.639
0.303	3.879	2.063	2.132	2.682	2.316	1.718	2.201	4.431	3.085
2.498	3.072	3.567	2.302	3.157	1.860	2.802	2.098	0.902	1.945
−0.542	0.666	3.987	2.668	2.360	2.762	1.351	2.835	2.972	1.796
1.640	2.193	0.976	1.777	1.383	3.100	1.663	1.609	2.503	1.596
2.248	1.911	0.620	2.295	1.884	3.421	1.086	2.085	1.861	−0.191
1.900	0.623	3.047	1.127	−0.199	3.653	0.976	−0.088	−0.966	2.626
1.536	0.718	−0.513	2.675	3.145	1.838	1.609	0.857	1.854	3.839
2.503	3.434	2.290	2.397	1.162	1.932	2.626	0.816	1.229	1.753
1.142	1.628	1.783	2.148	−0.105	3.072	2.312	3.666	2.784	2.102
1.877	3.107	0.960	1.363	1.139	1.135	2.370	4.245	3.284	0.188
3.632	2.586	1.531	1.613	1.645	0.963	4.596	1.979	2.649	1.435
4.072	0.554	1.319	2.224	1.879	1.806	1.606	3.049	0.099	2.996
1.564	1.624	1.014	1.414	1.796	1.244	1.712	2.319	2.166	2.727
2.876	0.772	−0.646	1.254	3.797	1.827	2.039	4.280	2.208	1.842
2.833	3.289	1.977	1.568	2.582	0.198	1.190	2.708	3.264	2.876
1.108	2.332	1.546	0.872	4.085	2.583	3.384	3.934	3.073	1.029
2.644	1.766	1.846	3.098	2.757	3.840	2.353	3.384	2.716	2.435
2.105	1.828	1.889	0.854	2.878	1.569	4.151	0.821	2.818	2.038

TABLE A-24. RANDOM NORMAL NUMBERS, $\mu = 0$, $\sigma = 2$*

01	02	03	04	05	06	07	08	09	10
−0.221	−0.540	−0.701	5.511	−2.404	−0.987	−0.158	−0.578	−1.893	0.854
−2.454	−2.816	0.580	−1.068	1.010	1.209	2.234	3.224	3.750	1.285
0.089	0.418	−0.421	2.448	−0.279	1.916	−3.166	−0.773	−0.818	−1.411
0.931	1.345	3.164	0.019	0.767	0.439	−3.412	−0.982	0.520	−0.473
0.361	0.794	0.120	−0.347	2.785	0.980	1.003	−1.796	−1.778	−0.783
−0.559	−2.111	−3.396	4.236	2.764	−1.990	−0.060	−2.488	−0.503	−4.406
−4.816	−1.369	1.856	0.383	0.016	−2.144	−0.187	−1.561	1.441	−2.246
0.784	0.607	0.663	−0.764	−1.395	1.738	−2.055	2.962	−1.616	1.326
2.576	−3.024	0.191	1.084	−3.698	−3.031	−0.517	−0.179	0.681	−0.719
−1.232	1.234	−0.046	1.338	1.726	1.448	2.216	−1.662	2.188	2.308
2.129	−1.936	3.381	1.319	−3.131	−1.037	1.191	1.449	0.690	−0.251
−2.753	1.049	1.616	1.232	2.910	0.389	−3.766	2.044	1.459	−0.002
0.071	1.869	−5.827	0.866	−1.191	2.508	1.552	−1.052	1.914	−0.274
0.507	0.595	−0.202	−0.775	−1.732	−2.771	0.049	5.221	3.059	0.015
0.384	−1.574	1.414	−0.789	−1.263	−0.470	0.020	1.489	0.497	1.316
1.688	4.311	2.305	−5.632	1.776	1.540	0.208	0.611	0.810	−1.241
−0.045	−1.563	3.687	−0.160	−0.101	1.838	1.590	1.222	0.377	2.069
2.516	−1.339	0.956	−1.285	0.301	3.739	−3.320	0.183	0.993	−4.678
0.536	1.965	−0.580	−0.307	1.564	0.163	−2.239	−2.460	−2.003	−1.609
0.775	1.427	−0.626	−1.134	−3.109	1.652	2.331	−0.188	2.137	−1.316
0.964	−3.740	1.995	−1.349	−1.068	−0.172	1.907	5.515	0.863	−1.018
2.597	2.328	−0.722	3.057	1.632	0.655	0.972	1.401	1.840	4.508
−1.343	−2.859	0.903	−0.631	−2.810	3.345	1.997	0.356	1.215	0.501
−1.097	0.798	−1.057	3.880	2.321	−1.677	−3.746	−1.125	−1.090	−1.972
−0.977	0.225	−0.004	−0.513	3.613	1.030	2.349	−1.278	−1.301	−5.159
2.421	−1.732	2.170	0.451	1.013	−0.912	0.615	−0.532	1.453	−2.155
0.921	−0.932	−2.511	−0.164	0.154	−0.004	0.516	2.240	−0.020	4.432
−1.854	−3.192	−3.633	0.067	3.709	0.560	−0.156	0.964	−2.618	−0.718
2.457	−0.566	−1.439	0.194	1.440	−1.568	−2.407	−1.356	0.849	0.801
1.143	0.212	4.088	−0.832	−0.361	0.303	−2.984	1.378	−0.649	−2.399
1.184	1.622	−1.896	0.026	−2.163	−1.683	3.778	3.585	−3.853	2.352
3.842	1.179	−0.987	0.498	2.348	3.263	1.924	−4.421	−0.680	2.129
1.930	0.114	−6.145	0.737	−0.353	2.478	−2.104	0.020	−2.250	−1.096
−0.174	−0.403	−1.539	1.740	−1.293	−1.922	1.228	1.433	−2.659	2.923
3.017	2.409	1.876	4.534	−0.539	−1.534	−0.847	−0.107	0.796	−1.257
2.632	−2.417	0.136	−1.155	4.277	−1.035	−0.968	−0.400	1.393	−0.858
−1.589	−2.199	0.776	0.821	3.237	4.810	1.012	−4.102	1.088	1.958
−1.308	0.561	−0.882	4.041	1.923	−0.717	0.599	1.705	0.241	2.677
−1.881	−1.808	−2.767	0.426	0.234	−4.060	1.036	−1.657	0.471	1.753
2.869	4.397	1.986	−2.123	−0.065	−0.705	−0.968	−2.265	−1.979	−1.114
0.252	−1.324	0.302	2.426	0.710	−1.454	−0.319	2.277	−0.971	−3.217
−0.833	1.653	−2.738	2.856	−0.789	−0.873	−0.809	−1.538	−1.334	2.289
0.276	0.020	−0.162	−1.720	0.048	0.401	−2.073	2.430	2.776	1.174
0.742	3.058	1.994	3.090	0.170	−0.789	−2.526	−0.980	−1.331	−1.834
0.770	1.419	4.391	1.502	−2.856	−3.648	−1.179	1.556	3.176	2.613
−2.208	1.766	−0.282	3.051	−1.734	−0.032	1.234	−0.626	1.052	−3.146
−1.161	−0.803	5.530	2.219	−0.371	1.372	−1.649	−2.059	1.456	0.677
−4.276	−0.196	−1.456	0.139	0.094	2.367	−1.902	1.123	−1.222	0.323
−1.615	−0.140	0.697	−0.647	1.289	1.416	0.811	0.523	1.406	−1.022
−3.831	−0.105	−2.271	−3.207	0.539	−1.010	2.646	−1.985	0.347	0.712

* This table is reproduced with permission from tables of the RAND Corporation.

Table A-24. Random Normal Numbers, $\mu = 0$, $\sigma = 2$ (*Continued*)

11	12	13	14	15	16	17	18	19	20
−0.686	0.678	−0.150	−0.334	5.096	0.708	0.403	1.538	1.217	−2.456
0.106	−0.018	2.558	−0.049	−1.061	−0.574	−0.510	−1.036	−0.168	2.516
−0.638	3.191	−4.587	−0.499	−0.510	−1.521	1.325	−1.355	−1.036	−3.305
−3.088	−0.998	0.883	2.230	0.603	0.906	−2.303	0.152	1.423	2.706
1.017	−2.496	−4.981	1.769	−0.252	3.018	2.764	1.105	−1.527	−1.187
0.132	−1.502	−1.748	−3.513	0.878	−0.483	−0.354	−1.103	−2.178	2.192
1.217	−2.380	−0.017	−0.072	−2.066	0.251	0.035	1.641	−1.298	2.070
0.540	−3.950	1.287	−0.771	−2.946	−1.181	−2.286	−1.561	0.420	−0.746
−0.395	−1.421	−2.163	0.270	−1.257	5.610	0.287	−1.138	−0.979	−2.224
−3.279	−2.813	1.125	−3.982	−0.102	0.576	−0.531	−0.695	−3.385	−1.045
3.510	3.235	2.623	−2.582	1.274	2.440	0.824	1.983	−0.770	2.489
−0.408	1.922	2.351	−0.146	−0.039	−0.648	−3.041	0.522	−1.659	−0.515
−2.434	1.297	2.813	−0.651	3.409	0.108	1.716	−1.801	0.344	0.923
0.541	0.820	−0.254	2.851	−3.027	1.553	2.218	1.758	1.003	−1.148
−0.813	1.562	2.116	−4.375	−2.289	1.593	0.163	−1.991	0.355	1.364
−0.238	−0.450	0.364	0.677	−0.711	−1.661	1.071	0.682	0.347	0.113
−1.214	−5.369	3.300	0.461	3.197	−0.368	−3.190	2.868	−0.943	0.931
3.521	1.655	2.373	1.993	−1.096	1.875	−1.143	−3.658	2.664	0.378
−1.075	−3.475	−2.069	−0.971	−0.909	−1.796	−0.760	−1.794	−1.576	3.863
−1.213	−1.760	0.397	−0.323	2.659	0.666	−4.368	2.704	1.160	−1.377
0.408	2.865	3.666	−0.433	−1.798	−1.434	−3.688	2.261	−1.084	0.722
−1.809	−2.890	−3.537	−2.701	0.656	0.684	0.905	1.953	2.720	−0.263
−1.633	0.283	−3.937	−0.224	−0.549	0.016	−1.265	−1.650	−1.506	0.504
−1.181	2.578	0.568	0.286	1.152	−0.929	−3.335	0.020	1.171	1.366
0.374	1.225	−0.213	−1.951	0.126	−1.551	−0.147	0.605	2.450	−1.514
−1.828	−3.459	2.624	2.605	0.698	−0.984	−2.289	−3.389	1.647	−2.592
−3.073	1.381	6.111	0.458	−0.792	−0.785	−1.254	2.784	−0.248	−0.965
−0.817	−1.048	−0.603	−0.647	−2.140	1.970	1.612	−2.050	1.926	−3.520
−0.778	−2.697	2.431	−2.011	2.810	0.010	1.830	−1.425	1.425	−2.506
1.866	0.259	−1.360	2.165	1.845	−0.326	2.054	−0.825	5.348	−0.384
0.715	−0.981	−0.126	0.263	−0.692	−3.790	−3.119	−0.547	−1.450	−0.791
0.802	−0.906	−0.726	0.071	3.693	−0.409	1.536	−0.907	3.216	−3.096
−0.363	0.030	−2.423	−0.517	−4.567	1.092	−1.194	0.253	−2.816	0.766
2.878	−2.689	0.797	0.820	0.764	0.366	−0.891	−0.122	0.196	1.052
−2.245	1.324	0.101	0.431	−2.152	0.779	−0.708	0.028	1.317	−1.259
−0.286	0.390	1.204	−4.414	−0.164	−3.724	0.207	1.835	0.334	0.660
−1.434	−0.736	−0.040	0.213	0.215	−0.565	0.915	−0.022	0.487	−0.487
0.004	−1.773	−0.480	0.768	−0.837	−0.513	0.828	4.563	1.298	2.837
1.299	−1.915	0.346	1.037	−2.953	−1.968	−1.704	1.639	2.802	−2.965
−1.694	1.993	1.021	−2.152	0.679	−0.763	0.577	2.860	0.329	−2.702
−0.506	0.328	−2.091	−0.238	2.582	−0.429	1.647	−1.048	−1.367	1.054
0.527	−3.033	−0.893	−0.776	−0.383	−0.708	−0.482	−2.686	1.369	1.040
3.815	−1.282	1.877	−1.177	0.000	−0.059	0.754	0.529	−0.522	2.073
1.838	−0.569	3.556	−0.956	−2.106	0.371	1.806	0.449	−0.867	2.664
0.810	3.394	1.224	−4.428	4.645	−0.644	−2.579	−2.198	2.683	1.338
4.048	−0.706	1.326	2.187	0.611	2.962	−2.137	−0.657	−3.539	−1.526
1.619	−1.214	−0.860	−0.625	−2.534	0.519	−2.539	0.737	−0.622	−0.146
1.732	−3.199	2.104	1.752	0.087	−0.333	3.943	0.037	0.135	1.756
−1.580	−3.456	2.934	0.580	1.665	2.331	−1.413	−1.558	2.144	1.876
1.176	−0.195	0.127	0.060	−3.145	−0.001	0.219	−1.803	−5.255	1.524

Table A-24. Random Normal Numbers, $\mu = 0$, $\sigma = 2$ (*Continued*)

21	22	23	24	25	26	27	28	29	30
−0.625	−1.119	0.772	−1.479	0.164	3.051	0.297	1.904	2.864	3.093
1.375	1.994	1.004	−3.128	−1.517	−2.916	2.196	3.544	−1.858	−1.021
−1.835	0.393	−1.426	−0.469	−0.009	−2.366	0.408	−0.669	−0.266	−0.907
0.764	−2.796	−1.932	−1.144	−4.177	−2.150	4.163	1.003	−1.088	−0.346
−0.913	−4.834	2.310	−0.154	−2.007	−1.741	−3.570	1.361	−0.219	−1.424
−4.228	0.846	−0.794	−1.756	2.621	0.128	−1.369	2.090	−4.471	0.440
−2.724	2.694	−0.585	1.094	2.116	−1.176	0.180	1.438	1.260	−1.730
4.168	−0.764	−0.791	−2.517	−2.103	0.901	0.141	1.796	−4.435	1.711
3.286	2.374	1.605	−0.951	−1.308	−0.903	1.562	3.537	3.340	−1.417
0.197	0.212	1.303	−0.289	1.441	−2.913	−0.606	−1.302	1.281	0.147
0.713	−1.532	−4.409	−2.502	−1.488	1.696	−2.390	0.517	−2.406	−0.457
0.925	−2.267	2.010	−1.381	−2.057	0.988	−0.024	−2.096	0.116	1.383
−3.312	1.604	0.955	−0.184	0.074	−0.714	2.059	−2.293	0.899	−0.837
0.320	−2.893	−1.005	1.527	−0.990	1.930	−1.512	1.333	3.188	−1.555
0.619	−1.545	1.543	−0.207	−0.586	2.409	−2.454	−0.738	−0.060	−1.533
0.119	−0.542	−2.461	−2.475	−1.265	−3.598	0.983	−1.702	−1.735	−4.773
1.814	−0.053	−0.063	−2.921	2.076	−0.535	2.585	−3.066	−0.771	1.553
−2.068	0.648	2.066	0.610	−0.681	0.845	1.349	0.515	−1.106	−3.860
−1.881	−2.033	1.704	1.161	0.316	1.623	−3.370	−0.261	−3.559	−0.647
−2.125	0.620	−0.838	2.278	0.230	2.962	1.925	−2.209	−0.676	0.859
2.054	−2.290	2.264	1.598	2.064	−1.129	−1.381	−1.149	−0.488	0.568
−2.516	−2.190	−0.629	2.361	1.734	0.607	0.935	1.275	3.125	−0.224
−0.143	−1.222	1.061	−2.668	−4.419	0.569	0.259	−0.027	1.989	4.602
−0.007	0.017	−0.811	−0.166	0.850	0.565	0.184	−2.887	1.101	0.192
−1.749	0.231	−2.380	−3.177	−1.077	4.460	0.494	1.941	−0.106	0.015
1.300	−0.289	−2.657	−0.160	−0.490	−0.329	1.602	−1.110	4.204	2.552
0.588	−1.072	0.935	−0.164	0.113	1.139	−0.923	−0.953	0.001	−0.033
1.719	−1.183	−1.051	−0.944	0.734	1.965	2.121	2.213	3.826	−2.004
0.726	1.867	0.624	2.066	−2.792	−2.507	−0.816	−0.569	0.002	−1.934
2.369	−0.361	2.216	−1.500	−0.350	−1.063	−3.979	−3.626	−1.326	−0.488
1.790	−0.290	2.601	6.261	−0.622	−0.534	0.477	0.075	0.167	−2.351
1.801	−2.408	0.408	−2.039	0.175	3.839	3.096	−0.001	2.912	−0.560
0.392	1.600	−0.940	−0.160	−0.885	−1.083	−3.503	1.814	−0.563	−2.682
−4.113	−3.018	0.523	−1.915	−0.722	−2.769	0.210	−0.381	−0.724	−2.013
−0.393	−0.828	−0.102	−2.457	1.702	2.257	−2.473	−1.459	−1.385	−3.669
0.688	−0.214	2.741	2.906	−0.778	1.158	0.713	0.815	−0.670	0.144
1.957	1.104	3.540	2.726	−0.028	−0.181	−1.477	−4.434	0.457	0.057
1.823	−1.371	−4.951	3.333	0.248	1.691	2.311	−2.996	1.573	2.319
−0.277	0.346	−1.354	3.170	0.268	0.773	1.242	3.542	0.940	−0.535
−0.484	1.447	−0.512	−1.379	−0.808	1.014	2.103	0.005	−2.122	0.843
3.209	−1.924	−0.833	1.158	3.203	−0.040	−0.880	−2.217	0.007	0.022
1.834	2.064	−0.319	2.672	1.281	4.921	0.819	0.634	−4.961	−0.739
−1.618	0.705	0.220	−0.177	−0.117	−4.699	2.210	0.035	2.403	−0.816
2.553	1.710	−2.844	−4.619	−4.328	0.459	−2.373	−1.069	2.792	1.942
−1.665	1.627	1.072	−0.902	1.336	3.850	−0.804	1.254	−2.493	−1.101
−0.468	2.177	1.703	1.897	1.139	−1.606	−1.139	−1.435	5.162	−0.146
−1.296	−0.646	0.193	0.534	−0.863	−3.178	2.461	−1.275	0.731	2.983
−3.086	−0.115	2.325	0.088	4.652	2.833	−0.054	−0.670	−2.313	−1.956
−1.324	0.102	0.665	0.878	−1.760	−1.038	0.685	−1.034	0.380	−0.463
1.936	2.264	0.379	4.480	−3.841	−3.992	−3.565	2.558	−0.906	−0.432

Table A-24. Random Normal Numbers, $\mu = 0$, $\sigma = 2$ (*Continued*)

31	32	33	34	35	36	37	38	39	40
−0.660	−0.996	−0.264	−1.823	0.818	−0.410	−1.786	2.399	1.986	0.242
1.785	−0.471	0.082	−3.006	−2.286	−0.222	0.388	−0.110	−0.358	−0.333
0.880	0.224	2.561	2.165	2.974	2.516	−4.148	−0.241	−1.318	−0.677
1.021	3.100	−1.783	−2.063	−2.176	1.959	0.248	0.597	1.394	0.612
−2.420	5.579	2.351	1.601	1.045	−2.857	1.400	3.411	−0.239	−2.323
−2.542	−3.145	−2.432	−0.444	−1.276	−3.342	3.479	2.630	−0.405	1.845
−2.437	0.104	1.110	0.008	−2.173	2.294	−0.529	1.723	−1.609	2.119
3.280	−1.213	−3.063	3.637	−0.038	0.217	−0.790	−1.412	−0.055	−0.612
0.502	−0.767	−1.569	0.386	−1.990	−0.062	3.319	−2.448	−0.445	0.059
−1.684	0.290	3.179	0.158	3.562	−1.929	−1.170	1.179	0.110	3.655
0.023	1.652	3.049	−1.410	−1.447	−0.638	−2.483	2.386	−0.331	1.215
−2.741	−2.313	−2.069	−1.305	−0.934	−7.769	2.654	−1.032	1.489	0.671
−0.746	2.099	−3.225	1.533	−1.741	−1.922	0.895	−2.974	−0.828	1.734
−0.934	−4.158	−3.297	−2.859	−4.026	2.722	−1.268	0.991	−1.196	−0.458
−1.574	0.097	2.122	−3.279	−0.820	0.483	2.196	0.642	−1.488	0.374
1.261	−0.663	0.616	−2.801	1.065	4.845	0.418	−0.226	1.897	3.554
2.030	1.692	0.265	0.511	−1.959	0.247	−1.381	−2.625	0.695	−2.248
−4.452	0.900	−1.646	0.573	0.973	−0.350	2.649	4.114	2.497	0.287
−0.075	−2.069	−0.574	0.001	−0.784	−1.235	−3.191	2.128	1.168	−0.742
0.369	0.919	−2.760	1.878	−5.001	−1.670	0.913	−2.853	0.002	1.885
1.360	−2.214	−2.175	0.193	3.298	−0.103	2.226	0.164	−2.429	−0.580
−3.271	2.845	−0.102	−0.822	−3.646	0.361	−3.188	−1.031	1.846	−1.622
−0.908	−3.907	1.407	0.078	1.324	0.276	−2.805	0.604	1.632	2.413
−1.323	2.717	−0.083	−1.645	1.103	−1.539	−0.173	2.429	−0.343	0.011
1.095	−0.871	1.636	2.345	−3.127	0.500	1.250	−0.072	−3.248	2.603
−1.907	−0.869	−4.388	−0.114	1.890	0.218	0.510	−0.768	−2.610	3.635
1.508	−0.333	−2.433	1.237	−1.733	−2.826	−3.761	−1.125	0.720	−0.832
2.937	1.887	−0.430	−5.194	4.716	−2.950	−0.393	−1.111	0.008	−0.186
−4.706	−1.302	−2.011	−0.124	−2.037	0.140	1.392	−1.869	−2.249	−0.075
5.019	−3.900	1.300	−0.034	−1.679	−0.621	0.285	1.197	−0.871	−1.240
−0.910	−0.495	0.074	3.144	−2.631	−3.152	0.192	−1.073	0.646	4.381
1.304	−1.010	−0.739	−1.028	2.886	−1.418	1.314	0.779	−2.139	0.173
0.371	−5.663	−0.017	−1.551	−3.508	1.305	−0.819	−0.199	−0.331	−0.358
−2.039	−3.961	0.679	2.451	−2.802	1.449	−0.964	−1.170	0.891	1.560
−0.911	1.904	0.062	−2.375	−1.548	−0.361	2.692	3.772	2.005	3.718
−1.720	0.871	3.594	0.889	0.162	0.112	−0.053	−2.597	−1.310	−2.234
−4.091	0.430	2.222	−0.141	0.506	2.751	−0.472	−1.141	1.671	−0.920
−1.797	−1.272	1.847	0.039	0.689	−0.080	1.457	−3.856	1.332	−2.898
−0.719	0.829	2.570	1.107	−0.314	−3.750	1.041	−1.657	−0.233	1.417
−1.890	3.240	1.877	2.552	3.389	0.215	1.979	−0.895	−1.996	0.611
−1.952	−1.276	−2.754	−0.049	−2.916	3.820	0.381	1.337	2.211	3.456
0.502	1.812	−0.577	0.551	−0.257	0.883	4.377	−4.180	−2.266	−0.100
1.971	2.333	−0.945	2.618	2.953	−1.997	1.491	−0.082	2.617	0.749
0.561	−1.506	4.127	0.933	−1.930	0.460	−0.008	0.352	−1.274	0.271
−1.409	−0.638	2.757	0.461	1.331	2.030	−0.846	−1.035	−1.580	−0.772
−2.066	0.218	0.070	−3.420	0.089	−0.084	4.944	−4.285	0.200	0.276
−2.734	3.622	−0.300	1.648	1.328	0.479	−0.498	1.997	2.203	2.792
−1.434	1.441	0.258	−1.893	−2.925	−1.753	0.272	0.747	−0.999	−0.155
−0.071	−4.344	−2.763	4.371	1.547	2.588	2.914	0.261	3.381	5.445
4.574	1.751	3.420	−1.383	0.966	−2.731	3.444	1.410	2.740	−2.011

TABLE A-24. RANDOM NORMAL NUMBERS, $\mu = 0$, $\sigma = 2$ (*Continued*)

41	42	43	44	45	46	47	48	49	50
−1.739	0.276	1.761	0.092	0.820	1.772	−3.258	0.707	−0.578	−1.611
−1.776	−1.482	1.399	1.031	−0.546	−0.204	2.591	2.129	1.615	0.919
−1.894	0.388	1.023	−1.493	1.513	1.003	2.547	−2.443	−1.855	2.898
−2.042	1.064	−2.399	−0.333	−2.141	−1.022	−2.976	−0.485	0.073	−0.891
0.287	0.120	−2.013	0.598	0.001	3.454	2.077	−1.966	−4.187	0.452
0.739	−4.324	0.088	1.124	0.610	0.368	0.953	−0.141	−0.441	3.163
0.749	0.597	2.194	−0.771	1.063	0.246	0.465	−3.122	−1.995	3.015
−1.111	−2.558	0.146	−0.590	−3.278	2.649	−1.299	−1.809	3.938	−1.766
−0.347	2.324	0.083	−0.152	−3.563	−1.062	0.901	0.882	0.865	0.581
−0.105	1.781	−0.775	−0.726	−3.211	−1.200	−2.688	1.639	−0.945	−1.022
1.968	2.056	−4.124	−1.126	−2.798	−1.150	−1.632	−3.405	1.182	1.985
1.614	−1.436	−4.649	−1.168	2.549	0.522	−0.616	2.009	−0.465	1.362
−1.671	−0.907	−0.459	2.880	2.640	−0.751	−2.414	−1.195	−2.334	−0.240
−1.328	0.335	−0.049	−1.903	0.225	−0.140	−1.121	0.820	0.282	0.635
−0.623	−0.823	1.655	1.997	−3.841	3.318	1.035	1.056	2.112	2.166
−2.292	−1.662	2.136	−0.223	1.372	−3.612	−0.276	−4.097	−0.419	−0.017
3.146	1.248	0.090	−1.069	−0.022	1.017	−1.157	1.803	−1.585	−1.526
1.553	−1.369	0.044	0.606	−1.734	−1.443	−3.016	−0.977	3.150	0.264
−3.179	3.510	−2.299	0.371	1.071	−1.044	−1.352	1.740	1.936	0.242
1.701	−0.455	2.119	−1.716	−2.857	−0.991	−1.621	2.934	3.487	0.754
−2.088	1.495	2.961	−2.029	−0.072	−0.664	0.992	1.659	0.834	−2.175
−3.757	0.316	0.763	−3.035	0.907	−3.804	−3.403	3.689	0.901	−2.386
−1.177	−1.422	−4.712	0.235	−1.048	−2.627	0.794	−1.473	2.598	−0.364
−1.380	−1.661	−1.714	−1.396	0.477	1.750	−2.458	−5.077	−0.194	1.093
−0.852	0.562	−0.199	0.802	0.494	−0.294	0.205	0.260	−2.616	4.117
2.591	1.323	0.458	4.020	−1.907	−0.065	−2.786	0.137	0.446	4.368
−2.240	2.744	0.551	−3.005	−2.677	4.492	2.928	0.061	−0.216	2.566
−1.488	−0.163	−0.187	2.081	−0.993	1.160	1.301	−2.236	1.586	0.011
0.622	−0.988	−0.956	−0.484	−0.648	−3.467	−3.778	1.181	1.740	0.092
−0.949	−2.527	−1.934	1.318	0.422	3.848	0.050	−1.448	0.278	3.041
−4.952	0.019	1.793	0.881	0.282	0.621	1.202	−0.373	3.665	3.386
−0.751	3.342	0.969	0.821	1.983	−0.533	−1.273	−2.214	−0.774	−1.210
0.618	−0.688	−2.960	−5.252	−0.543	0.104	−0.468	−3.139	0.594	−1.302
2.371	0.160	1.715	0.319	1.387	5.138	3.883	−1.869	−0.899	−1.019
−1.184	0.047	1.453	−0.889	−1.292	0.197	−0.302	−1.497	−1.838	−0.940
−0.287	2.329	2.028	−1.765	1.669	−1.024	1.600	0.454	3.098	2.275
1.764	−2.839	−1.942	0.008	4.001	0.083	−1.631	2.968	−0.146	−2.079
1.149	−1.571	1.296	1.510	−0.599	0.083	−0.688	6.017	0.012	−1.451
2.984	−1.432	−0.960	−2.124	1.353	0.934	0.666	3.096	2.905	−1.472
−1.701	−0.004	2.710	0.573	2.424	−0.119	−1.410	3.413	−3.588	0.047
−2.333	0.912	−0.773	−2.016	2.253	2.784	3.764	0.559	4.791	1.288
−0.214	2.787	0.095	−3.174	1.460	0.411	0.922	−0.474	3.113	−1.067
1.214	0.785	−2.686	1.909	−1.747	−4.551	0.589	−0.573	−1.364	−2.583
0.878	0.097	1.650	1.437	−1.643	−2.608	1.122	0.538	0.664	−0.323
−0.105	−0.297	3.821	2.105	2.021	−1.922	1.472	0.042	1.403	1.465
−0.593	0.136	0.910	−0.549	−1.472	3.214	−2.273	3.458	1.436	0.500
2.198	2.325	−1.229	−0.276	1.560	−0.482	−0.482	0.455	−0.181	1.417
1.160	0.139	0.997	−0.082	−0.689	0.995	−5.301	0.998	3.413	−1.797
3.024	−1.561	0.982	−1.244	1.407	−0.063	−1.176	2.355	2.006	−4.833
0.955	0.174	−0.401	2.472	0.584	3.811	1.115	0.951	−2.136	−2.324

TABLE A-25. CONFIDENCE INTERVALS FOR THE MEDIAN*

N	Largest k	$\alpha \leq .05$	Largest k	$\alpha \leq .01$	N	Largest k	$\alpha \leq .05$	Largest k	$\alpha \leq .01$
6	1	.031			36	12	.029	10	.004
7	1	.016			37	13	.047	11	.008
8	1	.008	1	.008	38	13	.034	11	.005
9	2	.039	1	.004	39	13	.024	12	.009
10	2	.021	1	.002	40	14	.038	12	.006
11	2	.012	1	.001	41	14	.028	12	.004
12	3	.039	2	.006	42	15	.044	13	.008
13	3	.022	2	.003	43	15	.032	13	.005
14	3	.013	2	.002	44	16	.049	14	.010
15	4	.035	3	.007	45	16	.036	14	.007
16	4	.021	3	.004	46	16	.026	14	.005
17	5	.049	3	.002	47	17	.040	15	.008
18	5	.031	4	.008	48	17	.029	15	.006
19	5	.019	4	.004	49	18	.044	16	.009
20	6	.041	4	.003	50	18	.033	16	.007
21	6	.027	5	.007	51	19	.049	16	.005
22	6	.017	5	.004	52	19	.036	17	.008
23	7	.035	5	.003	53	19	.027	17	.005
24	7	.023	6	.007	54	20	.040	18	.009
25	8	.043	6	.004	55	20	.030	18	.006
26	8	.029	7	.009	56	21	.044	18	.005
27	8	.019	7	.006	57	21	.033	19	.008
28	9	.036	7	.004	58	22	.048	19	.005
29	9	.024	8	.008	59	22	.036	20	.009
30	10	.043	8	.005	60	22	.027	20	.006
31	10	.029	8	.003	61	23	.040	21	.010
32	10	.020	9	.007	62	23	.030	21	.007
33	11	.035	9	.005	63	24	.043	21	.005
34	11	.024	10	.009	64	24	.033	22	.008
35	12	.041	10	.006	65	25	.046	22	.006

If the observations are arranged in order of size $X_1 < X_2 < X_3 < \cdots < X_N$, then we are $100(1 - \alpha)\%$ confident of the population median being between X_k and X_{N-k+1}, where k and α are given above.

* Reproduced by permission of S. K. Banerjee from K. R. Nair, "Table of confidence interval for the median in samples from any continuous population," *Sankhya*, vol. 4 (1940), pp. 551–558.

TABLE A-26. SOME ONE-SIDED AND SYMMETRICAL SIGNIFICANCE TESTS FOR $N \leq 10$*

Significance level of tests			Tests	
			Symmetrical: accept $\mu \neq \mu_0$ if either	
N	One-sided	Symmetrical	One-sided: accept $\mu < \mu_0$ if	One-sided: accept $\mu > \mu_0$ if
4	6.2%	12.5%	$X_4 < \mu_0$	$X_1 > \mu_0$
5	6.2%	12.5%	$\frac{1}{2}(X_4 + X_5) < \mu_0$	$\frac{1}{2}(X_1 + X_2) > \mu_0$
	3.1%	6.2%	$X_5 < \mu_0$	$X_1 > \mu_0$
6	4.7%	9.4%	$\max[X_5, \frac{1}{2}(X_4 + X_6)] < \mu_0$	$\min[X_2, \frac{1}{2}(X_1 + X_3)] > \mu_0$
	3.1%	6.2%	$\frac{1}{2}(X_5 + X_6) < \mu_0$	$\frac{1}{2}(X_1 + X_2) > \mu_0$
	1.6%	3.1%	$X_6 < \mu_0$	$X_1 > \mu_0$
7	5.5%	10.9%	$\max[X_5, \frac{1}{2}(X_4 + X_7)] < \mu_0$	$\min[X_3, \frac{1}{2}(X_1 + X_4)] > \mu_0$
	2.3%	4.7%	$\max[X_6, \frac{1}{2}(X_5 + X_7)] < \mu_0$	$\min[X_2, \frac{1}{2}(X_1 + X_3)] > \mu_0$
	1.6%	3.1%	$\frac{1}{2}(X_6 + X_7) < \mu_0$	$\frac{1}{2}(X_1 + X_2) > \mu_0$
	0.8%	1.6%	$X_7 < \mu_0$	$X_1 > \mu_0$
8	4.3%	8.6%	$\max[X_6, \frac{1}{2}(X_4 + X_8)] < \mu_0$	$\min[X_3, \frac{1}{2}(X_1 + X_5)] > \mu_0$
	2.7%	5.5%	$\max[X_6, \frac{1}{2}(X_5 + X_8)] < \mu_0$	$\min[X_3, \frac{1}{2}(X_1 + X_4)] > \mu_0$
	1.2%	2.3%	$\max[X_7, \frac{1}{2}(X_6 + X_8)] < \mu_0$	$\min[X_2, \frac{1}{2}(X_1 + X_3)] > \mu_0$
	0.8%	1.6%	$\frac{1}{2}(X_7 + X_8) < \mu_0$	$\frac{1}{2}(X_1 + X_2) > \mu_0$
	0.4%	0.8%	$X_8 < \mu_0$	$X_1 > \mu_0$
9	5.1%	10.2%	$\max[X_6, \frac{1}{2}(X_4 + X_9)] < \mu_0$	$\min[X_4, \frac{1}{2}(X_1 + X_6)] > \mu_0$
	2.2%	4.3%	$\max[X_7, \frac{1}{2}(X_5 + X_9)] < \mu_0$	$\min[X_3, \frac{1}{2}(X_1 + X_5)] > \mu_0$
	1.0%	2.0%	$\max[X_8, \frac{1}{2}(X_5 + X_9)] < \mu_0$	$\min[X_2, \frac{1}{2}(X_1 + X_5)] > \mu_0$
	0.6%	1.2%	$\max[X_8, \frac{1}{2}(X_7 + X_9)] < \mu_0$	$\min[X_2, \frac{1}{2}(X_1 + X_3)] > \mu_0$
	0.4%	0.8%	$\frac{1}{2}(X_8 + X_9) < \mu_0$	$\frac{1}{2}(X_1 + X_2) > \mu_0$
10	5.6%	11.1%	$\max[X_6, \frac{1}{2}(X_4 + X_{10})] < \mu_0$	$\min[X_5, \frac{1}{2}(X_1 + X_7)] > \mu_0$
	2.5%	5.1%	$\max[X_7, \frac{1}{2}(X_5 + X_{10})] < \mu_0$	$\min[X_4, \frac{1}{2}(X_1 + X_6)] > \mu_0$
	1.1%	2.1%	$\max[X_8, \frac{1}{2}(X_6 + X_{10})] < \mu_0$	$\min[X_3, \frac{1}{2}(X_1 + X_5)] > \mu_0$
	0.5%	1.0%	$\max[X_9, \frac{1}{2}(X_6 + X_{10})] < \mu_0$	$\min[X_2, \frac{1}{2}(X_1 + X_5)] > \mu_0$

* Reproduced with permission from J. E. Walsh, "Applications of some significance tests for the median which are valid under very general conditions," *Journal of the American Statistical Association*, vol. 44 (1949), p. 342.

TABLE A-27. CONFIDENCE BELTS FOR THE CORRELATION COEFFICIENT*
(Confidence coefficient .95)

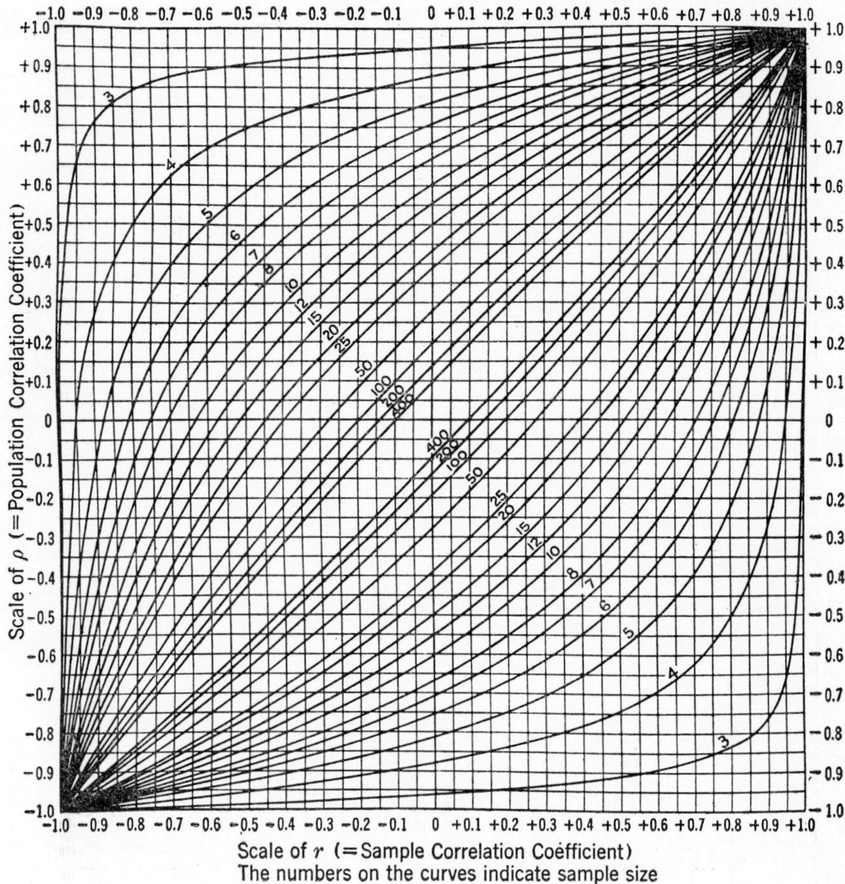

* This chart is reproduced with the permission of Professor E. S. Pearson from F. N. David, *Tables of the Ordinates and Probability Integral of the Distribution of the Correlation Coefficient in Small Samples.* The Biometrika Office, London.

TABLE A-28. VARIOUS FUNCTIONS OF A PROPORTION p

p	$1 - p$	$p(1 - p)$	$\sqrt{p(1 - p)}$	$1 - p^2$	$1 - (1 - p)^2$	$2 \arcsin \sqrt{p}$	$2 \arcsin \sqrt{1 - p}$
.01	.99	.0099	.09950	.9999	.0199	.2003	2.9413
.02	.98	.0196	.14000	.9996	.0396	.2838	2.8578
.03	.97	.0291	.17059	.9991	.0591	.3482	2.7934
.04	.96	.0384	.19596	.9984	.0784	.4027	2.7389
.05	.95	.0475	.21794	.9975	.0975	.4510	2.6906
.06	.94	.0564	.23749	.9964	.1164	.4949	2.6467
.07	.93	.0651	.25515	.9951	.1351	.5355	2.6062
.08	.92	.0736	.27129	.9936	.1536	.5735	2.5681
.09	.91	.0819	.28618	.9919	.1719	.6094	2.5319
.10	.90	.0900	.30000	.9900	.1900	.6435	2.4981
.11	.89	.0979	.31289	.9879	.2079	.6761	2.4655
.12	.88	.1056	.32496	.9856	.2256	.7075	2.4341
.13	.87	.1131	.33630	.9831	.2431	.7377	2.4037
.14	.86	.1204	.34699	.9804	.2604	.7670	2.3746
.15	.85	.1275	.35707	.9775	.2775	.7954	2.3462
.16	.84	.1344	.36661	.9744	.2944	.8230	2.3186
.17	.83	.1411	.37563	.9711	.3111	.8500	2.2916
.18	.82	.1476	.38419	.9676	.3276	.8763	2.2653
.19	.81	.1539	.39230	.9639	.3439	.9021	2.2395
.20	.80	.1600	.40000	.9600	.3600	.9273	2.2143
.21	.79	.1659	.40731	.9559	.3759	.9521	2.1895
.22	.78	.1716	.41425	.9516	.3916	.9764	2.1652
.23	.77	.1771	.42083	.9471	.4071	1.0004	2.1412
.24	.76	.1824	.42708	.9424	.4224	1.0239	2.1177
.25	.75	.1875	.43301	.9375	.4375	1.0472	2.0944
.26	.74	.1924	.43863	.9324	.4524	1.0701	2.0715
.27	.73	.1971	.44396	.9271	.4671	1.0928	2.0488
.28	.72	.2016	.44900	.9216	.4816	1.1152	2.0264
.29	.71	.2059	.45376	.9159	.4959	1.1374	2.0042
.30	.70	.2100	.45826	.9100	.5100	1.1593	1.9823
.31	.69	.2139	.46249	.9039	.5239	1.1810	1.9606
.32	.68	.2176	.46648	.8976	.5376	1.2025	1.9391
.33	.67	.2211	.47021	.8911	.5511	1.2239	1.9177
.34	.66	.2244	.47371	.8844	.5644	1.2451	1.8965
.35	.65	.2275	.47697	.8775	.5775	1.2661	1.8755
.36	.64	.2304	.48000	.8704	.5904	1.2870	1.8546
.37	.63	.2331	.48280	.8631	.6031	1.3078	1.8338
.38	.62	.2356	.48539	.8556	.6156	1.3284	1.8132
.39	.61	.2379	.48775	.8479	.6279	1.3490	1.7826
.40	.60	.2400	.48990	.8400	.6400	1.3694	1.7722
.41	.59	.2419	.49183	.8319	.6519	1.3898	1.7518
.42	.58	.2436	.49356	.8236	.6636	1.4101	1.7315
.43	.57	.2451	.49508	.8151	.6751	1.4303	1.7113
.44	.56	.2464	.49639	.8064	.6864	1.4505	1.6911
.45	.55	.2475	.49749	.7975	.6975	1.4706	1.6710
.46	.54	.2484	.49840	.7884	.7084	1.4907	1.6509
.47	.53	.2491	.49910	.7791	.7191	1.5108	1.6308
.48	.52	.2496	.49960	.7696	.7296	1.5308	1.6108
.49	.51	.2499	.49990	.7599	.7399	1.5508	1.5908
.50	.50	.2500	.50000	.7500	.7500	1.5708	1.5708

TABLE A-29a. BINOMIAL PROBABILITIES, $C(N,X)p^X(1-p)^{N-X}$ FOR $N \leq 10$ AND FOR VARIOUS VALUES OF p

N	X \ p	.01	.05	.10	.15	.20	.25	.30	$\frac{1}{3}$	.35	.40	.45	.50
2	0	.9801	.9025	.8100	.7225	.6400	.5625	.4900	.4444	.4225	.3600	.3025	.2500
	1	.0198	.0950	.1800	.2550	.3200	.3750	.4200	.4444	.4550	.4800	.4950	.5000
	2	.0001	.0025	.0100	.0225	.0400	.0625	.0900	.1111	.1225	.1600	.2025	.2500
3	0	.9703	.8574	.7290	.6141	.5120	.4219	.3430	.2963	.2746	.2160	.1664	.1250
	1	.0294	.1354	.2430	.3251	.3840	.4219	.4410	.4444	.4436	.4320	.4084	.3750
	2	.0003	.0071	.0270	.0574	.0960	.1406	.1890	.2222	.2389	.2880	.3341	.3750
	3	.0000	.0001	.0010	.0034	.0080	.0156	.0270	.0370	.0429	.0640	.0911	.1250
4	0	.9606	.8145	.6561	.5220	.4096	.3164	.2401	.1975	.1785	.1296	.0915	.0625
	1	.0388	.1715	.2916	.3685	.4096	.4219	.4116	.3951	.3845	.3456	.2995	.2500
	2	.0006	.0135	.0486	.0975	.1536	.2109	.2646	.2963	.3105	.3456	.3675	.3750
	3	.0000	.0005	.0036	.0115	.0256	.0469	.0756	.0988	.1115	.1536	.2005	.2500
	4	.0000	.0000	.0001	.0005	.0016	.0039	.0081	.0123	.0150	.0256	.0410	.0625
5	0	.9510	.7738	.5905	.4437	.3277	.2373	.1681	.1317	.1160	.0778	.0503	.0312
	1	.0480	.2036	.3280	.3915	.4096	.3955	.3602	.3292	.3124	.2592	.2059	.1562
	2	.0010	.0214	.0729	.1382	.2048	.2637	.3087	.3292	.3364	.3456	.3369	.3125
	3	.0000	.0011	.0081	.0244	.0512	.0879	.1323	.1646	.1811	.2304	.2757	.3125
	4	.0000	.0000	.0004	.0022	.0064	.0146	.0284	.0412	.0488	.0768	.1128	.1562
	5	.0000	.0000	.0000	.0001	.0003	.0010	.0024	.0041	.0053	.0102	.0185	.0312
6	0	.9415	.7351	.5314	.3771	.2621	.1780	.1176	.0878	.0754	.0467	.0277	.0156
	1	.0571	.2321	.3543	.3993	.3932	.3560	.3025	.2634	.2437	.1866	.1359	.0938
	2	.0014	.0305	.0984	.1762	.2458	.2966	.3241	.3292	.3280	.3110	.2780	.2344
	3	.0000	.0021	.0146	.0415	.0819	.1318	.1852	.2195	.2355	.2765	.3032	.3125
	4	.0000	.0001	.0012	.0055	.0154	.0330	.0595	.0823	.0951	.1382	.1861	.2344
	5	.0000	.0000	.0001	.0004	.0015	.0044	.0102	.0165	.0205	.0369	.0609	.0938
	6	.0000	.0000	.0000	.0000	.0001	.0002	.0007	.0014	.0018	.0041	.0083	.0156
7	0	.9321	.6983	.4783	.3206	.2097	.1335	.0824	.0585	.0490	.0280	.0152	.0078
	1	.0659	.2573	.3720	.3960	.3670	.3115	.2471	.2048	.1848	.1306	.0872	.0547
	2	.0020	.0406	.1240	.2097	.2753	.3115	.3177	.3073	.2985	.2613	.2140	.1641
	3	.0000	.0036	.0230	.0617	.1147	.1730	.2269	.2561	.2679	.2903	.2918	.2734
	4	.0000	.0002	.0026	.0109	.0287	.0577	.0972	.1280	.1442	.1935	.2388	.2734
	5	.0000	.0000	.0002	.0012	.0043	.0115	.0250	.0384	.0466	.0774	.1172	.1641
	6	.0000	.0000	.0000	.0001	.0004	.0013	.0036	.0064	.0084	.0172	.0320	.0547
	7	.0000	.0000	.0000	.0000	.0000	.0001	.0002	.0005	.0006	.0016	.0037	.0078
8	0	.9227	.6634	.4305	.2725	.1678	.1001	.0576	.0390	.0319	.0168	.0084	.0039
	1	.0746	.2793	.3826	.3847	.3355	.2670	.1977	.1561	.1373	.0896	.0548	.0312
	2	.0026	.0515	.1488	.2376	.2936	.3115	.2965	.2731	.2587	.2090	.1569	.1094
	3	.0001	.0054	.0331	.0839	.1468	.2076	.2541	.2731	.2786	.2787	.2568	.2188
	4	.0000	.0004	.0046	.0185	.0459	.0865	.1361	.1707	.1875	.2322	.2627	.2734
	5	.0000	.0000	.0004	.0026	.0092	.0231	.0467	.0683	.0808	.1239	.1719	.2188
	6	.0000	.0000	.0000	.0002	.0011	.0038	.0100	.0171	.0217	.0413	.0703	.1094
	7	.0000	.0000	.0000	.0000	.0001	.0004	.0012	.0024	.0033	.0079	.0164	.0312
	8	.0000	.0000	.0000	.0000	.0000	.0000	.0001	.0002	.0002	.0007	.0017	.0039
9	0	.9135	.6302	.3874	.2316	.1342	.0751	.0404	.0260	.0207	.0101	.0046	.0020
	1	.0830	.2985	.3874	.3679	.3020	.2253	.1556	.1171	.1004	.0605	.0339	.0176
	2	.0034	.0629	.1722	.2597	.3020	.3003	.2668	.2341	.2162	.1612	.1110	.0703
	3	.0001	.0077	.0446	.1069	.1762	.2336	.2668	.2731	.2716	.2508	.2119	.1641
	4	.0000	.0006	.0074	.0283	.0661	.1168	.1715	.2048	.2194	.2508	.2600	.2461
	5	.0000	.0000	.0008	.0050	.0165	.0389	.0735	.1024	.1181	.1672	.2128	.2461
	6	.0000	.0000	.0001	.0006	.0028	.0087	.0210	.0341	.0424	.0743	.1160	.1641
	7	.0000	.0000	.0000	.0000	.0003	.0012	.0039	.0073	.0098	.0212	.0407	.0703
	8	.0000	.0000	.0000	.0000	.0000	.0001	.0004	.0009	.0013	.0035	.0083	.0176
	9	.0000	.0000	.0000	.0000	.0000	.0000	.0000	.0001	.0001	.0003	.0008	.0020
10	0	.9044	.5987	.3487	.1969	.1074	.0563	.0282	.0173	.0135	.0060	.0025	.0010
	1	.0914	.3151	.3874	.3474	.2684	.1877	.1211	.0867	.0725	.0403	.0207	.0098
	2	.0042	.0746	.1937	.2759	.3020	.2816	.2335	.1951	.1757	.1209	.0763	.0439
	3	.0001	.0105	.0574	.1298	.2013	.2503	.2668	.2601	.2522	.2150	.1665	.1172
	4	.0000	.0010	.0112	.0401	.0881	.1460	.2001	.2276	.2377	.2508	.2384	.2051
	5	.0000	.0001	.0015	.0085	.0264	.0584	.1029	.1366	.1536	.2007	.2340	.2461
	6	.0000	.0000	.0001	.0012	.0055	.0162	.0368	.0569	.0689	.1115	.1596	.2051
	7	.0000	.0000	.0000	.0001	.0008	.0031	.0090	.0163	.0212	.0425	.0746	.1172
	8	.0000	.0000	.0000	.0000	.0001	.0004	.0014	.0030	.0043	.0106	.0229	.0439
	9	.0000	.0000	.0000	.0000	.0000	.0000	.0001	.0003	.0005	.0016	.0042	.0098
	10	.0000	.0000	.0000	.0000	.0000	.0000	.0000	.0000	.0000	.0001	.0003	.0010

Table A-29b. Binomial Coefficients

N	$C(N,0)$	$C(N,1)$	$C(N,2)$	$C(N,3)$	$C(N,4)$	$C(N,5)$	$C(N,6)$	$C(N,7)$	$C(N,8)$	$C(N,9)$	$C(N,10)$
0	1										
1	1	1									
2	1	2	1								
3	1	3	3	1							
4	1	4	6	4	1						
5	1	5	10	10	5	1					
6	1	6	15	20	15	6	1				
7	1	7	21	35	35	21	7	1			
8	1	8	28	56	70	56	28	8	1		
9	1	9	36	84	126	126	84	36	9	1	
10	1	10	45	120	210	252	210	120	45	10	1
11	1	11	55	165	330	462	462	330	165	55	11
12	1	12	66	220	495	792	924	792	495	220	66
13	1	13	78	286	715	1287	1716	1716	1287	715	286
14	1	14	91	364	1001	2002	3003	3432	3003	2002	1001
15	1	15	105	455	1365	3003	5005	6435	6435	5005	3003
16	1	16	120	560	1820	4368	8008	11440	12870	11440	8008
17	1	17	136	680	2380	6188	12376	19448	24310	24310	19448
18	1	18	153	816	3060	8568	18564	31824	43758	48620	43758
19	1	19	171	969	3876	11628	27132	50388	75582	92378	92378
20	1	20	190	1140	4845	15504	38760	77520	125970	167960	184756

Table A-29c. Factorials

N	$N!$	N	$N!$	N	$N!$	N	$N!$	N	$N!$
1	1.0000	21	5.1091(19)	41	3.3453(49)	61	5.0758(83)	81	5.7971(120)
2	2.0000	22	1.1240(21)	42	1.4050(51)	62	3.1470(85)	82	4.7536(122)
3	6.0000	23	2.5852(22)	43	6.0415(52)	63	1.9826(87)	83	3.9455(124)
4	2.4000(1)	24	6.2045(23)	44	2.6583(54)	64	1.2689(89)	84	3.3142(126)
5	1.2000(2)	25	1.5511(25)	45	1.1962(56)	65	8.2477(90)	85	2.8171(128)
6	7.2000(2)	26	4.0329(26)	46	5.5026(57)	66	5.4434(92)	86	2.4227(130)
7	5.0400(3)	27	1.0889(28)	47	2.5862(59)	67	3.6471(94)	87	2.1078(132)
8	4.0320(4)	28	3.0489(29)	48	1.2414(61)	68	2.4800(96)	88	1.8548(134)
9	3.6288(5)	29	8.8418(30)	49	6.0828(62)	69	1.7112(98)	89	1.6508(136)
10	3.6288(6)	30	2.6525(32)	50	3.0414(64)	70	1.1979(100)	90	1.4857(138)
11	3.9917(7)	31	8.2228(33)	51	1.5511(66)	71	8.5048(101)	91	1.3520(140)
12	4.7900(8)	32	2.6313(35)	52	8.0658(67)	72	6.1234(103)	92	1.2438(142)
13	6.2270(9)	33	8.6833(36)	53	4.2749(69)	73	4.4701(105)	93	1.1568(144)
14	8.7178(10)	34	2.9523(38)	54	2.3084(71)	74	3.3079(107)	94	1.0874(146)
15	1.3077(12)	35	1.0333(40)	55	1.2696(73)	75	2.4809(109)	95	1.0330(148)
16	2.0923(13)	36	3.7199(41)	56	7.1100(74)	76	1.8855(111)	96	9.9168(149)
17	3.5569(14)	37	1.3764(43)	57	4.0527(76)	77	1.4518(113)	97	9.6193(151)
18	6.4024(15)	38	5.2302(44)	58	2.3506(78)	78	1.1324(115)	98	9.4269(153)
19	1.2165(17)	39	2.0398(46)	59	1.3868(80)	79	8.9462(116)	99	9.3326(155)
20	2.4329(18)	40	8.1592(47)	60	8.3210(81)	80	7.1569(118)	100	9.3326(157)

The number in parentheses indicates the power of 10 by which the entry must be multiplied. For example, 8! = 40,320.

TABLE A-30a. PERCENTILES OF THE DISTRIBUTION OF r WHEN $\rho = 0$

N	$r_{.95}$	$r_{.975}$	$r_{.99}$	$r_{.995}$	$r_{.9995}$	N	$r_{.95}$	$r_{.975}$	$r_{.99}$	$r_{.995}$	$r_{.9995}$
5	.805	.878	.934	.959	.991	20	.378	.444	.516	.561	.679
6	.729	.811	.882	.917	.974	22	.360	.423	.492	.537	.652
7	.669	.754	.833	.875	.951	24	.344	.404	.472	.515	.629
8	.621	.707	.789	.834	.925	26	.330	.388	.453	.496	.607
9	.582	.666	.750	.798	.898	28	.317	.374	.437	.479	.588
10	.549	.632	.715	.765	.872	30	.306	.361	.423	.463	.570
11	.521	.602	.685	.735	.847	40	.264	.312	.366	.402	.501
12	.497	.576	.658	.708	.823	50	.235	.279	.328	.361	.451
13	.476	.553	.634	.684	.801	60	.214	.254	.300	.330	.414
14	.457	.532	.612	.661	.780	80	.185	.220	.260	.286	.361
15	.441	.514	.592	.641	.760	100	.165	.196	.232	.256	.324
16	.426	.497	.574	.623	.742	250	.104	.124	.147	.163	.207
17	.412	.482	.558	.606	.725	500	.074	.088	.104	.115	.147
18	.400	.468	.543	.590	.708	1000	.052	.062	.074	.081	.104
19	.389	.456	.529	.575	.693	∞	0	0	0	0	0
	$-r_{.05}$	$-r_{.025}$	$-r_{.01}$	$-r_{.005}$	$-r_{.0005}$		$-r_{.05}$	$-r_{.025}$	$-r_{.01}$	$-r_{.005}$	$-r_{.0005}$

Percentiles of r may be computed from percentiles of t by the relation

$$r = t/\sqrt{t^2 + N - 2}$$

where t is from Table A-5 for df $= N - 2$.

TABLE A-30b. VALUES OF $z = \frac{1}{2} \ln \frac{1 + r}{1 - r}$

For negative values of r put a minus sign in front of the tabled numbers.

r	.00	.01	.02	.03	.04	.05	.06	.07	.08	.09
.0	.00000	.01000	.02000	.03001	.04002	.05004	.06007	.07012	.08017	.09024
.1	.10034	.11045	.12058	.13074	.14093	.15114	.16139	.17167	.18198	.19234
.2	.20273	.21317	.22366	.23419	.24477	.25541	.26611	.27686	.28768	.29857
.3	.30952	.32055	.33165	.34283	.35409	.36544	.37689	.38842	.40006	.41180
.4	.42365	.43561	.44769	.45990	.47223	.48470	.49731	.51007	.52298	.53606
.5	.54931	.56273	.57634	.59014	.60415	.61838	.63283	.64752	.66246	.67767
.6	.69315	.70892	.72500	.74142	.75817	.77530	.79281	.81074	.82911	.84795
.7	.86730	.88718	.90764	.92873	.95048	.97295	.99621	1.02033	1.04537	1.07143
.8	1.09861	1.12703	1.15682	1.18813	1.22117	1.25615	1.29334	1.33308	1.37577	1.42192
.9	1.47222	1.52752	1.58902	1.65839	1.73805	1.83178	1.94591	2.09229	2.29756	2.64665

Table A-30c. Distribution of Σd_i^2 Used in the Rank-correlation Coefficient

The chance is α that Σd_i^2 equals or exceeds the value listed.

Σd_i^2	α	Σd_i^2	α	Σd_i^2	α
$N = 4$		$N = 7$		$N = 9$	
18	.167	82	.151	172	.125
20	.042	86	.118	180	.089
$N = 5$		90	.083	188	.060
32	.175	94	.055	196	.038
34	.117	98	.033	204	.022
36	.067	102	.017	212	.011
38	.042	106	.006	220	.004
40	.008	110	.001	228	.001
$N = 6$		$N = 8$		$N = 10$	
56	.121	120	.150	228	.139
58	.088	126	.108	238	.102
60	.068	132	.076	248	.072
62	.051	138	.048	258	.048
64	.029	144	.029	268	.030
66	.017	150	.014	278	.017
68	.008	156	.005	288	.009
70	.001	162	.001	298	.004

Table A-30d. Distribution of Quadrant Sum for Corner Test for Association for Samples of Size $2N$

The table gives α, the chance that the quadrant sum equals or exceeds S.

S \ $2N$	6	8	10	14	∞
8	.111	.126	.133	.132	.122
9	.100	.084	.093	.092	.081
10	.100	.055	.064	.063	.053
11	.100	.038	.044	.043	.034
12	.100	.030	.029	.030	.022
13	.000	.029	.019	.020	.013
14		.029	.013	.014	.008
15		.029	.010	.010	.005
16		.029	.008	.007	.003
17		.000	.008	.005	.002
18			.008	.003	.001
19			.008	.002	.001
20			.008	.001	.000
21			.000	.001	.000
22				.001	.000
23				.001	.000

TABLE A-31. TABLE OF RECIPROCALS

	0	1	2	3	4	5	6	7	8	9
1.00	1.00000	.99900	.99800	.99701	.99602	.99502	.99404	.99305	.99206	.99108
1.01	.99010	.98912	.98814	.98717	.98619	.98522	.98425	.98328	.98232	.98135
1.02	.98039	.97943	.97847	.97752	.97656	.97561	.97466	.97371	.97276	.97182
1.03	.97087	.96993	.96899	.96805	.96712	.96618	.96525	.96432	.96339	.96246
1.04	.96154	.96061	.95969	.95877	.95785	.95694	.95602	.95511	.95420	.95329
1.05	.95238	.95147	.95057	.94967	.94877	.94787	.94697	.94607	.94518	.94429
1.06	.94340	.94251	.94162	.94073	.93985	.93897	.93809	.93721	.93633	.93545
1.07	.93458	.93371	.93284	.93197	.93110	.93023	.92937	.92851	.92764	.92678
1.08	.92593	.92507	.92421	.92336	.92251	.92166	.92081	.91996	.91912	.91827
1.09	.91743	.91659	.91575	.91491	.91408	.91324	.91241	.91158	.91075	.90992
1.1	.90909	.90090	.89286	.88496	.87719	.86957	.86207	.85470	.84746	.84034
1.2	.83333	.82645	.81967	.81301	.80645	.80000	.79365	.78740	.78125	.77519
1.3	.76923	.76336	.75758	.75188	.74627	.74074	.73529	.72993	.72464	.71942
1.4	.71429	.70922	.70423	.69930	.69444	.68966	.68493	.68027	.67568	.67114
1.5	.66667	.66225	.65789	.65359	.64935	.64516	.64103	.63694	.63291	.62893
1.6	.62500	.62112	.61728	.61350	.60976	.60606	.60241	.59880	.59524	.59172
1.7	.58824	.58480	.58140	.57803	.57471	.57143	.56818	.56497	.56180	.55866
1.8	.55556	.55249	.54945	.54645	.54348	.54054	.53763	.53476	.53191	.52910
1.9	.52632	.52356	.52083	.51813	.51546	.51282	.51020	.50761	.50505	.50251
2.0	.50000	.49751	.49505	.49261	.49020	.48780	.48544	.48309	.48077	.47847
2.1	.47619	.47393	.47170	.46948	.46729	.46512	.46296	.46083	.45872	.45662
2.2	.45455	.45249	.45045	.44843	.44643	.44444	.44248	.44053	.43860	.43668
2.3	.43478	.43290	.43103	.42918	.42735	.42553	.42373	.42194	.42017	.41841
2.4	.41667	.41494	.41322	.41152	.40984	.40816	.40650	.40486	.40323	.40161
2.5	.40000	.39841	.39683	.39526	.39370	.39216	.39063	.38911	.38760	.38610
2.6	.38462	.38314	.38168	.38023	.37879	.37736	.37594	.37453	.37313	.37175
2.7	.37037	.36900	.36765	.36630	.36496	.36364	.36232	.36101	.35971	.35842
2.8	.35714	.35587	.35461	.35336	.35211	.35088	.34965	.34843	.34722	.34602
2.9	.34483	.34364	.34247	.34130	.34014	.33898	.33784	.33670	.33557	.33445
3.0	.33333	.33223	.33113	.33003	.32895	.32787	.32680	.32573	.32468	.32362
3.1	.32258	.32154	.32051	.31949	.31847	.31746	.31646	.31546	.31447	.31348
3.2	.31250	.31153	.31056	.30960	.30864	.30769	.30675	.30581	.30488	.30395
3.3	.30303	.30211	.30120	.30030	.29940	.29851	.29762	.29674	.29586	.29499
3.4	.29412	.29326	.29240	.29155	.29070	.28986	.28902	.28818	.28736	.28653
3.5	.28571	.28490	.28409	.28329	.28249	.28169	.28090	.28011	.27933	.27855
3.6	.27778	.27701	.27624	.27548	.27473	.27397	.27322	.27248	.27174	.27100
3.7	.27027	.26954	.26882	.26810	.26738	.26667	.26596	.26525	.26455	.26385
3.8	.26316	.26247	.26178	.26110	.26042	.25974	.25907	.25840	.25773	.25707
3.9	.25641	.25575	.25510	.25445	.25381	.25316	.25253	.25189	.25126	.25063
4.0	.25000	.24938	.24876	.24814	.24752	.24691	.24631	.24570	.24510	.24450
4.1	.24390	.24331	.24272	.24213	.24155	.24096	.24038	.23981	.23923	.23866
4.2	.23810	.23753	.23697	.23641	.23585	.23529	.23474	.23419	.23364	.23310
4.3	.23256	.23202	.23148	.23095	.23041	.22989	.22936	.22883	.22831	.22779
4.4	.22727	.22676	.22624	.22573	.22523	.22472	.22422	.22371	.22321	.22272
4.5	.22222	.22173	.22124	.22075	.22026	.21978	.21930	.21882	.21834	.21786
4.6	.21739	.21692	.21645	.21598	.21552	.21505	.21459	.21413	.21368	.21322
4.7	.21277	.21231	.21186	.21142	.21097	.21053	.21008	.20964	.20921	.20877
4.8	.20833	.20790	.20747	.20704	.20661	.20619	.20576	.20534	.20492	.20450
4.9	.20408	.20367	.20325	.20284	.20243	.20202	.20161	.20121	.20080	.20040

TABLE A-31. TABLE OF RECIPROCALS (*Continued*)

	0	1	2	3	4	5	6	7	8	9
5.0	.20000	.19960	.19920	.19881	.19841	.19802	.19763	.19724	.19685	.19646
5.1	.19608	.19569	.19531	.19493	.19455	.19417	.19380	.19342	.19305	.19268
5.2	.19231	.19194	.19157	.19120	.19084	.19048	.19011	.18975	.18939	.18904
5.3	.18868	.18832	.18797	.18762	.18727	.18692	.18657	.18622	.18587	.18553
5.4	.18519	.18484	.18450	.18416	.18382	.18349	.18315	.18282	.18248	.18215
5.5	.18182	.18149	.18116	.18083	.18051	.18018	.17986	.17953	.17921	.17889
5.6	.17857	.17825	.17794	.17762	.17731	.17699	.17668	.17637	.17606	.17575
5.7	.17544	.17513	.17483	.17452	.17422	.17391	.17361	.17331	.17301	.17271
5.8	.17241	.17212	.17182	.17153	.17123	.17094	.17065	.17036	.17007	.16978
5.9	.16949	.16920	.16892	.16863	.16835	.16807	.16779	.16750	.16722	.16694
6.0	.16667	.16639	.16611	.16584	.16556	.16529	.16502	.16474	.16447	.16420
6.1	.16393	.16367	.16340	.16313	.16287	.16260	.16234	.16207	.16181	.16155
6.2	.16129	.16103	.16077	.16051	.16026	.16000	.15974	.15949	.15924	.15898
6.3	.15873	.15848	.15823	.15798	.15773	.15748	.15723	.15699	.15674	.15649
6.4	.15625	.15601	.15576	.15552	.15528	.15504	.15480	.15456	.15432	.15408
6.5	.15385	.15361	.15337	.15314	.15291	.15267	.15244	.15221	.15198	.15175
6.6	.15152	.15129	.15106	.15083	.15060	.15038	.15015	.14993	.14970	.14948
6.7	.14925	.14903	.14881	.14859	.14837	.14815	.14793	.14771	.14749	.14728
6.8	.14706	.14684	.14663	.14641	.14620	.14599	.14577	.14556	.14535	.14514
6.9	.14493	.14472	.14451	.14430	.14409	.14388	.14368	.14347	.14327	.14306
7.0	.14286	.14265	.14245	.14225	.14205	.14184	.14164	.14144	.14124	.14104
7.1	.14085	.14065	.14045	.14025	.14006	.13986	.13966	.13947	.13928	.13908
7.2	.13889	.13870	.13850	.13831	.13812	.13793	.13774	.13755	.13736	.13717
7.3	.13699	.13680	.13661	.13643	.13624	.13605	.13587	.13569	.13550	.13532
7.4	.13514	.13495	.13477	.13459	.13441	.13423	.13405	.13387	.13369	.13351
7.5	.13333	.13316	.13298	.13280	.13263	.13245	.13228	.13210	.13193	.13175
7.6	.13158	.13141	.13123	.13106	.13089	.13072	.13055	.13038	.13021	.13004
7.7	.12987	.12970	.12953	.12937	.12920	.12903	.12887	.12870	.12853	.12837
7.8	.12821	.12804	.12788	.12771	.12755	.12739	.12723	.12706	.12690	.12674
7.9	.12658	.12642	.12626	.12610	.12594	.12579	.12563	.12547	.12531	.12516
8.0	.12500	.12484	.12469	.12453	.12438	.12422	.12407	.12392	.12376	.12361
8.1	.12346	.12330	.12315	.12300	.12285	.12270	.12255	.12240	.12225	.12210
8.2	.12195	.12180	.12165	.12151	.12136	.12121	.12107	.12092	.12077	.12063
8.3	.12048	.12034	.12019	.12005	.11990	.11976	.11962	.11947	.11933	.11919
8.4	.11905	.11891	.11876	.11862	.11848	.11834	.11820	.11806	.11792	.11779
8.5	.11765	.11751	.11737	.11723	.11710	.11696	.11682	.11669	.11655	.11641
8.6	.11628	.11614	.11601	.11587	.11574	.11561	.11547	.11534	.11521	.11507
8.7	.11494	.11481	.11468	.11455	.11442	.11429	.11416	.11403	.11390	.11377
8.8	.11364	.11351	.11338	.11325	.11312	.11299	.11287	.11274	.11261	.11249
8.9	.11236	.11223	.11211	.11198	.11186	.11173	.11161	.11148	.11136	.11123
9.0	.11111	.11099	.11086	.11074	.11062	.11050	.11038	.11025	.11013	.11001
9.1	.10989	.10977	.10965	.10953	.10941	.10929	.10917	.10905	.10893	.10881
9.2	.10870	.10858	.10846	.10834	.10823	.10811	.10799	.10787	.10776	.10764
9.3	.10753	.10741	.10730	.10718	.10707	.10695	.10684	.10672	.10661	.10650
9.4	.10638	.10627	.10616	.10604	.10593	.10582	.10571	.10560	.10549	.10537
9.5	.10526	.10515	.10504	.10493	.10482	.10471	.10460	.10449	.10438	.10428
9.6	.10417	.10406	.10395	.10384	.10373	.10363	.10352	.10341	.10331	.10320
9.7	.10309	.10299	.10288	.10277	.10267	.10256	.10246	.10235	.10225	.10215
9.8	.10204	.10194	.10183	.10173	.10163	.10152	.10142	.10132	.10121	.10111
9.9	.10101	.10091	.10081	.10070	.10060	.10050	.10040	.10030	.10020	.10010

TABLE A-32. FOUR-PLACE SQUARES OF NUMBERS

N	.00	.01	.02	.03	.04	.05	.06	.07	.08	.09
1.0	1.000	1.020	1.040	1.061	1.082	1.103	1.124	1.145	1.166	1.188
1.1	1.210	1.232	1.254	1.277	1.300	1.323	1.346	1.369	1.392	1.416
1.2	1.440	1.464	1.488	1.513	1.538	1.563	1.588	1.613	1.638	1.664
1.3	1.690	1.716	1.742	1.769	1.796	1.823	1.850	1.877	1.904	1.932
1.4	1.960	1.988	2.016	2.045	2.074	2.103	2.132	2.161	2.190	2.220
1.5	2.250	2.280	2.310	2.341	2.372	2.403	2.434	2.465	2.496	2.528
1.6	2.560	2.592	2.624	2.657	2.690	2.723	2.756	2.789	2.822	2.856
1.7	2.890	2.924	2.958	2.993	3.028	3.063	3.098	3.133	3.168	3.204
1.8	3.240	3.276	3.312	3.349	3.386	3.423	3.460	3.497	3.534	3.572
1.9	3.610	3.648	3.686	3.725	3.764	3.803	3.842	3.881	3.920	3.960
2.0	4.000	4.040	4.080	4.121	4.162	4.203	4.244	4.285	4.326	4.368
2.1	4.410	4.452	4.494	4.537	4.580	4.623	4.666	4.709	4.752	4.796
2.2	4.840	4.884	4.928	4.973	5.018	5.063	5.108	5.153	5.198	5.244
2.3	5.290	5.336	5.382	5.429	5.476	5.523	5.570	5.617	5.664	5.712
2.4	5.760	5.808	5.856	5.905	5.954	6.003	6.052	6.101	6.150	6.200
2.5	6.250	6.300	6.350	6.401	6.452	6.503	6.554	6.605	6.656	6.708
2.6	6.760	6.812	6.864	6.917	6.970	7.023	7.076	7.129	7.182	7.236
2.7	7.290	7.344	7.398	7.453	7.508	7.563	7.618	7.673	7.728	7.784
2.8	7.840	7.896	7.952	8.009	8.066	8.123	8.180	8.237	8.294	8.352
2.9	8.410	8.468	8.526	8.585	8.644	8.703	8.762	8.821	8.880	8.940
3.0	9.000	9.060	9.120	9.181	9.242	9.303	9.364	9.425	9.486	9.548
3.1	9.610	9.672	9.734	9.797	9.860	9.923	9.986	10.05	10.11	10.18
3.2	10.24	10.30	10.37	10.43	10.50	10.56	10.63	10.69	10.76	10.82
3.3	10.89	10.96	11.02	11.09	11.16	11.22	11.29	11.36	11.42	11.49
3.4	11.56	11.63	11.70	11.76	11.83	11.90	11.97	12.04	12.11	12.18
3.5	12.25	12.32	12.39	12.46	12.53	12.60	12.67	12.74	12.82	12.89
3.6	12.96	13.03	13.10	13.18	13.25	13.32	13.40	13.47	13.54	13.62
3.7	13.69	13.76	13.84	13.91	13.99	14.06	14.14	14.21	14.29	14.36
3.8	14.44	14.52	14.59	14.67	14.75	14.82	14.90	14.98	15.05	15.13
3.9	15.21	15.29	15.37	15.44	15.52	15.60	15.68	15.76	15.84	15.92
4.0	16.00	16.08	16.16	16.24	16.32	16.40	16.48	16.56	16.65	16.73
4.1	16.81	16.89	16.97	17.06	17.14	17.22	17.31	17.39	17.47	17.56
4.2	17.64	17.72	17.81	17.89	17.98	18.06	18.15	18.23	18.32	18.40
4.3	18.49	18.58	18.66	18.75	18.84	18.92	19.01	19.10	19.18	19.27
4.4	19.36	19.45	19.54	19.62	19.71	19.80	19.89	19.98	20.07	20.16
4.5	20.25	20.34	20.43	20.52	20.61	20.70	20.79	20.88	20.98	21.07
4.6	21.16	21.25	21.34	21.44	21.53	21.62	21.72	21.81	21.90	22.00
4.7	22.09	22.18	22.28	22.37	22.47	22.56	22.66	22.75	22.85	22.94
4.8	23.04	23.14	23.23	23.33	23.43	23.52	23.62	23.72	23.81	23.91
4.9	24.01	24.11	24.21	24.30	24.40	24.50	24.60	24.70	24.80	24.90
5.0	25.00	25.10	25.20	25.30	25.40	25.50	25.60	25.70	25.81	25.91
5.1	26.01	26.11	26.21	26.32	26.42	26.52	26.63	26.73	26.83	26.94
5.2	27.04	27.14	27.25	27.35	27.46	27.56	27.67	27.77	27.88	27.98
5.3	28.09	28.20	28.30	28.41	28.52	28.62	28.73	28.84	28.94	29.05
5.4	29.16	29.27	29.38	29.48	29.59	29.70	29.81	29.92	30.03	30.14
5.5	30.25	30.36	30.47	30.58	30.69	30.80	30.91	31.02	31.14	31.25
5.6	31.36	31.47	31.58	31.70	31.81	31.92	32.04	32.15	32.26	32.38
5.7	32.49	32.60	32.72	32.83	32.95	33.06	33.18	33.29	33.41	33.52
5.8	33.64	33.76	33.87	33.99	34.11	34.22	34.34	34.46	34.57	34.69
5.9	34.81	34.93	35.05	35.16	35.28	35.40	35.52	35.64	35.76	35.88

TABLE A-32. FOUR-PLACE SQUARES OF NUMBERS (*Continued*)

N	.00	.01	.02	.03	.04	.05	.06	.07	.08	.09
6.0	36.00	36.12	36.24	36.36	36.48	36.60	36.72	36.84	36.97	37.09
6.1	37.21	37.33	37.45	37.58	37.70	37.82	37.95	38.07	38.19	38.32
6.2	38.44	38.56	38.69	38.81	38.94	39.06	39.19	39.31	39.44	39.56
6.3	39.69	39.82	39.94	40.07	40.20	40.32	40.45	40.58	40.70	40.83
6.4	40.96	41.09	41.22	41.34	41.47	41.60	41.73	41.86	41.99	42.12
6.5	42.25	42.38	42.51	42.64	42.77	42.90	43.03	43.16	43.30	43.43
6.6	43.56	43.69	43.82	43.96	44.09	44.22	44.36	44.49	44.62	44.76
6.7	44.89	45.02	45.16	45.29	45.43	45.56	45.70	45.83	45.97	46.10
6.8	46.24	46.38	46.51	46.65	46.79	46.92	47.06	47.20	47.33	47.47
6.9	47.61	47.75	47.89	48.02	48.16	48.30	48.44	48.58	48.72	48.86
7.0	49.00	49.14	49.28	49.42	49.56	49.70	49.84	49.98	50.13	50.27
7.1	50.41	50.55	50.69	50.84	50.98	51.12	51.27	51.41	51.55	51.70
7.2	51.84	51.98	52.13	52.27	52.42	52.56	52.71	52.85	53.00	53.14
7.3	53.29	53.44	53.58	53.73	53.88	54.02	54.17	54.32	54.46	54.61
7.4	54.76	54.91	55.06	55.20	55.35	55.50	55.65	55.80	55.95	56.10
7.5	56.25	56.40	56.55	56.70	56.85	57.00	57.15	57.30	57.46	57.61
7.6	57.76	57.91	58.06	58.22	58.37	58.52	58.68	58.83	58.98	59.14
7.7	59.29	59.44	59.60	59.75	59.91	60.06	60.22	60.37	60.53	60.68
7.8	60.84	61.00	61.15	61.31	61.47	61.62	61.78	61.94	62.09	62.25
7.9	62.41	62.57	62.73	62.88	63.04	63.20	63.36	63.52	63.68	63.84
8.0	64.00	64.16	64.32	64.48	64.64	64.80	64.96	65.12	65.29	65.45
8.1	65.61	65.77	65.93	66.10	66.26	66.42	66.59	66.75	66.91	67.08
8.2	67.24	67.40	67.57	67.73	67.90	68.06	68.23	68.39	68.56	68.72
8.3	68.89	69.06	69.22	69.39	69.56	69.72	69.89	70.06	70.22	70.39
8.4	70.56	70.73	70.90	71.06	71.23	71.40	71.57	71.74	71.91	72.08
8.5	72.25	72.42	72.59	72.76	72.93	73.10	73.27	73.44	73.62	73.79
8.6	73.96	74.13	74.30	74.48	74.65	74.82	75.00	75.17	75.34	75.52
8.7	75.69	75.86	76.04	76.21	76.39	76.56	76.74	76.91	77.09	77.26
8.8	77.44	77.62	77.79	77.97	78.15	78.32	78.50	78.68	78.85	79.03
8.9	79.21	79.39	79.57	79.74	79.92	80.10	80.28	80.46	80.64	80.82
9.0	81.00	81.18	81.36	81.54	81.72	81.90	82.08	82.26	82.45	82.63
9.1	82.81	82.99	83.17	83.36	83.54	83.72	83.91	84.09	84.27	84.46
9.2	84.64	84.82	85.01	85.19	85.38	85.56	85.75	85.93	86.12	86.30
9.3	86.49	86.68	86.86	87.05	87.24	87.42	87.61	87.80	87.98	88.17
9.4	88.36	88.55	88.74	88.92	89.11	89.30	89.49	89.68	89.87	90.06
9.5	90.25	90.44	90.63	90.82	91.01	91.20	91.39	91.58	91.78	91.97
9.6	92.16	92.35	92.54	92.74	92.93	93.12	93.32	93.51	93.70	93.90
9.7	94.09	94.28	94.48	94.67	94.87	95.06	95.26	95.45	95.65	95.84
9.8	96.04	96.24	96.43	96.63	96.83	97.02	97.22	97.42	97.61	97.81
9.9	98.01	98.21	98.41	98.60	98.80	99.00	99.20	99.40	99.60	99.80

The square root of a number may be found by finding the first three places from this table, dividing the number by the three-place root and averaging the quotient and divisor. Repetition will give the square root to any desired accuracy. For example, $\sqrt{80.00}$ is just less than 8.95. First, 80.00/8.95 = 8.9385475. Second, (8.95 + 8.9385475)/2 = 8.9442738, which is close to the more precise value of 8.9442719.

Table A-33. Table of Square Roots

	0	1	2	3	4	5	6	7	8	9
1.0	1.0000	1.0050	1.0100	1.0149	1.0198	1.0247	1.0296	1.0344	1.0392	1.0440
10.	3.1623	3.1780	3.1937	3.2094	3.2249	3.2404	3.2558	3.2711	3.2863	3.3015
1.1	1.0488	1.0536	1.0583	1.0630	1.0677	1.0724	1.0770	1.0817	1.0863	1.0909
11.	3.3166	3.3317	3.3466	3.3615	3.3764	3.3912	3.4059	3.4205	3.4351	3.4496
1.2	1.0954	1.1000	1.1045	1.1091	1.1136	1.1180	1.1225	1.1269	1.1314	1.1358
12.	3.4641	3.4785	3.4928	3.5071	3.5214	3.5355	3.5496	3.5637	3.5777	3.5917
1.3	1.1402	1.1446	1.1489	1.1533	1.1576	1.1619	1.1662	1.1705	1.1747	1.1790
13.	3.6056	3.6194	3.6332	3.6469	3.6606	3.6742	3.6878	3.7014	3.7148	3.7283
1.4	1.1832	1.1874	1.1916	1.1958	1.2000	1.2042	1.2083	1.2124	1.2166	1.2207
14.	3.7417	3.7550	3.7683	3.7815	3.7947	3.8079	3.8210	3.8341	3.8471	3.8601
1.5	1.2247	1.2288	1.2329	1.2369	1.2410	1.2450	1.2490	1.2530	1.2570	1.2610
15.	3.8730	3.8859	3.8987	3.9115	3.9243	3.9370	3.9497	3.9623	3.9749	3.9875
1.6	1.2649	1.2689	1.2728	1.2767	1.2806	1.2845	1.2884	1.2923	1.2961	1.3000
16.	4.0000	4.0125	4.0249	4.0373	4.0497	4.0620	4.0743	4.0866	4.0988	4.1110
1.7	1.3038	1.3077	1.3115	1.3153	1.3191	1.3229	1.3266	1.3304	1.3342	1.3379
17.	4.1231	4.1352	4.1473	4.1593	4.1713	4.1833	4.1952	4.2071	4.2190	4.2308
1.8	1.3416	1.3454	1.3491	1.3528	1.3565	1.3601	1.3638	1.3675	1.3711	1.3748
18.	4.2426	4.2544	4.2661	4.2778	4.2895	4.3012	4.3128	4.3243	4.3359	4.3474
1.9	1.3784	1.3820	1.3856	1.3892	1.3928	1.3964	1.4000	1.4036	1.4071	1.4107
19.	4.3589	4.3704	4.3818	4.3932	4.4045	4.4159	4.4272	4.4385	4.4497	4.4609
2.0	1.4142	1.4177	1.4213	1.4248	1.4283	1.4318	1.4353	1.4387	1.4422	1.4457
20.	4.4721	4.4833	4.4944	4.5056	4.5166	4.5277	4.5387	4.5497	4.5607	4.5717
2.1	1.4491	1.4526	1.4560	1.4595	1.4629	1.4663	1.4697	1.4731	1.4765	1.4799
21.	4.5826	4.5935	4.6043	4.6152	4.6260	4.6368	4.6476	4.6583	4.6690	4.6797
2.2	1.4832	1.4866	1.4900	1.4933	1.4967	1.5000	1.5033	1.5067	1.5100	1.5133
22.	4.6904	4.7011	4.7117	4.7223	4.7329	4.7434	4.7539	4.7645	4.7749	4.7854
2.3	1.5166	1.5199	1.5232	1.5264	1.5297	1.5330	1.5362	1.5395	1.5427	1.5460
23.	4.7958	4.8062	4.8166	4.8270	4.8374	4.8477	4.8580	4.8683	4.8785	4.8888
2.4	1.5492	1.5524	1.5556	1.5588	1.5620	1.5652	1.5684	1.5716	1.5748	1.5780
24.	4.8990	4.9092	4.9193	4.9295	4.9396	4.9497	4.9598	4.9699	4.9800	4.9900

TABLE A-33. TABLE OF SQUARE ROOTS (*Continued*)

	0	1	2	3	4	5	6	7	8	9
2.5	1.5811	1.5843	1.5875	1.5906	1.5937	1.5969	1.6000	1.6031	1.6062	1.6093
25.	5.0000	5.0100	5.0200	5.0299	5.0398	5.0498	5.0596	5.0695	5.0794	5.0892
2.6	1.6125	1.6155	1.6186	1.6217	1.6248	1.6279	1.6310	1.6340	1.6371	1.6401
26.	5.0990	5.1088	5.1186	5.1284	5.1381	5.1478	5.1575	5.1672	5.1769	5.1865
2.7	1.6432	1.6462	1.6492	1.6523	1.6553	1.6583	1.6613	1.6643	1.6673	1.6703
27.	5.1962	5.2058	5.2154	5.2249	5.2345	5.2440	5.2536	5.2631	5.2726	5.2820
2.8	1.6733	1.6763	1.6793	1.6823	1.6852	1.6882	1.6912	1.6941	1.6971	1.7000
28.	5.2915	5.3009	5.3104	5.3198	5.3292	5.3385	5.3479	5.3572	5.3666	5.3759
2.9	1.7029	1.7059	1.7088	1.7117	1.7146	1.7176	1.7205	1.7234	1.7263	1.7292
29.	5.3852	5.3944	5.4037	5.4129	5.4222	5.4314	5.4406	5.4498	5.4589	5.4681
3.0	1.7321	1.7349	1.7378	1.7407	1.7436	1.7464	1.7493	1.7521	1.7550	1.7578
30.	5.4772	5.4863	5.4955	5.5045	5.5136	5.5227	5.5317	5.5408	5.5498	5.5588
3.1	1.7607	1.7635	1.7664	1.7692	1.7720	1.7748	1.7776	1.7804	1.7833	1.7861
31.	5.5678	5.5767	5.5857	5.5946	5.6036	5.6125	5.6214	5.6303	5.6391	5.6480
3.2	1.7889	1.7916	1.7944	1.7972	1.8000	1.8028	1.8055	1.8083	1.8111	1.8138
32.	5.6569	5.6657	5.6745	5.6833	5.6921	5.7009	5.7096	5.7184	5.7271	5.7359
3.3	1.8166	1.8193	1.9221	1.8248	1.8276	1.8303	1.8330	1.8358	1.8385	1.8412
33.	5.7446	5.7533	5.7619	5.7706	5.7793	5.7879	5.7966	5.8052	5.8138	5.8224
3.4	1.8439	1.8466	1.8493	1.8520	1.8547	1.8574	1.8601	1.8628	1.8655	1.8682
34.	5.8310	5.8395	5.8481	5.8566	5.8652	5.8737	5.8822	5.8907	5.8992	5.9076
3.5	1.8708	1.8735	1.8762	1.8788	1.8815	1.8841	1.8868	1.8894	1.8921	1.8947
35.	5.9161	5.9245	5.9330	5.9414	5.9498	5.9582	5.9666	5.9749	5.9833	5.9917
3.6	1.8974	1.9000	1.9026	1.9053	1.9079	1.9105	1.9131	1.9157	1.9183	1.9209
36.	6.0000	6.0083	6.0166	6.0249	6.0332	6.0415	6.0498	6.0581	6.0663	6.0745
3.7	1.9235	1.9261	1.9287	1.9313	1.9339	1.9365	1.9391	1.9416	1.9442	1.9468
37.	6.0828	6.0910	6.0992	6.1074	6.1156	6.1237	6.1319	6.1400	6.1482	6.1563
3.8	1.9494	1.9519	1.9545	1.9570	1.9596	1.9621	1.9647	1.9672	1.9698	1.9723
38.	6.1644	6.1725	6.1806	6.1887	6.1968	6.2048	6.2129	6.2209	6.2290	6.2370
3.9	1.9748	1.9774	1.9799	1.9824	1.9849	1.9875	1.9900	1.9925	1.9950	1.9975
39.	6.2450	6.2530	6.2610	6.2690	6.2769	6.2849	6.2929	6.3008	6.3087	6.3166

TABLE A-33. TABLE OF SQUARE ROOTS (*Continued*)

	0	1	2	3	4	5	6	7	8	9
4.0	2.0000	2.0025	2.0050	2.0075	2 0100	2.0125	2.0149	2.0174	2.0199	2.0224
40.	6.3246	6.3325	6.3403	6.3482	6.3561	6.3640	6.3718	6.3797	6.3875	6.3953
4.1	2.0248	2.0273	2.0298	2.0322	2.0347	2.0372	2.0396	2.0421	2.0445	2.0469
41.	6.4031	6.4109	6.4187	6.4265	6.4343	6.4420	6.4498	6.4576	6.4653	6.4730
4.2	2.0494	2.0518	2.0543	2.0567	2.0591	2.0616	2.0640	2.0664	2.0688	2.0712
42.	6.4807	6.4885	6.4962	6.5038	6.5115	6.5192	6.5269	6.5345	6.5422	6.5498
4.3	2.0736	2.0761	2.0785	2.0809	2.0833	2.0857	2.0881	2.0905	2.0928	2.0952
43.	6.5574	6.5651	6.5727	6.5803	6.5879	6.5955	6.6030	6.6106	6.6182	6.6257
4.4	2.0976	2.1000	2.1024	2.1048	2.1071	2.1095	2.1119	2.1142	2.1166	2.1190
44.	6.6332	6.6408	6 6483	6.6558	6.6633	6.6708	6.6783	6.6858	6.6933	6.7007
4.5	2.1213	2.1237	2.1260	2.1284	2.1307	2.1331	2.1354	2.1378	2.1401	2.1424
45.	6.7082	6.7157	6.7231	6.7305	6.7380	6.7454	6.7528	6.7602	6.7676	6.7750
4.6	2.1448	2.1471	2.1494	2.1517	2.1541	2.1564	2.1587	2.1610	2.1633	2.1656
46.	6.7823	6.7897	6.7971	6.8044	6.8118	6.8191	6.8264	6.8337	6.8411	6.8484
4.7	2.1679	2.1703	2.1726	2.1749	2.1772	2.1794	2.1817	2.1840	2.1863	2.1886
47.	6.8557	6.8629	6.8702	6.8775	6.8848	6.8920	6.8993	6.9065	6.9138	6.9210
4.8	2.1909	2.1932	2.1954	2.1977	2.2000	2.2023	2.2045	2.2068	2.2091	2.2113
48.	6.9282	6.9354	6.9426	6.9498	6.9570	6.9642	6.9714	6.9785	6.9857	6.9929
4.9	2.2136	2.2159	2.2181	2.2204	2.2226	2.2249	2.2271	2.2293	2.2316	2.2338
49.	7.0000	7.0071	7.0143	7.0214	7.0285	7.0356	7.0427	7.0498	7.0569	7.0640
5.0	2.2361	2.2383	2.2405	2.2428	2.2450	2.2472	2.2494	2.2517	2.2539	2.2561
50.	7.0711	7.0781	7.0852	7.0922	7.0993	7.1063	7.1134	7.1204	7.1274	7.1344
5.1	2.2583	2.2605	2.2627	2.2650	2.2672	2.2694	2.2716	2.2738	2.2760	2.2782
51.	7.1414	7.1484	7.1554	7.1624	7.1694	7.1764	7.1833	7.1903	7.1972	7.2042
5.2	2.2804	2.2825	2.2847	2.2869	2.2891	2.2913	2.2935	2.2956	2.2978	2.3000
52.	7.2111	7.2180	7.2250	7.2319	7.2388	7.2457	7.2526	7.2595	7.2664	7.2732
5.3	2.3022	2.3043	2.3065	2.3087	2.3108	2.3130	2.3152	2.3173	2.3195	2.3216
53.	7.2801	7.2870	7.2938	7.3007	7.3075	7.3144	7.3212	7.3280	7.3348	7.3417
5.4	2.3238	2.3259	2.3281	2.3302	2.3324	2.3345	2.3367	2.3388	2.3409	2.3431
54.	7.3485	7.3553	7.3621	7.3689	7.3756	7.3824	7.3892	7.3959	7.4027	7.4095

TABLE A-33. TABLE OF SQUARE ROOTS (*Continued*)

	0	1	2	3	4	5	6	7	8	9
5.5	2.3452	2.3473	2.3495	2.3516	2.3537	2.3558	2.3580	2.3601	2.3622	2.3643
55.	7.4162	7.4229	7.4297	7.4364	7.4431	7.4498	7.4565	7.4632	7.4699	7.4766
5.6	2.3664	2.3685	2.3707	2.3728	2.3749	2.3770	2.3791	2.3812	2.3833	2.3854
56.	7.4833	7.4900	7.4967	7.5033	7.5100	7.5166	7.5233	7.5299	7.5366	7.5432
5.7	2.3875	2.3896	2.3917	2.3937	2.3958	2.3979	2.4000	2.4021	2.4042	2.4062
57.	7.5498	7.5565	7.5631	7.5697	7.5763	7.5829	7.5895	7.5961	7.6026	7.6092
5.8	2.4083	2.4104	2.4125	2.4145	2.4166	2.4187	2.4207	2.4228	2.4249	2.4269
58.	7.6158	7.6223	7.6289	7.6354	7.6420	7.6485	7.6551	7.6616	7.6681	7.6746
5.9	2.4290	2.4310	2.4331	2.4352	2.4372	2.4393	2.4413	2.4434	2.4454	2.4474
59.	7.6811	7.6877	7.6942	7.7006	7.7071	7.7136	7.7201	7.7266	7.7330	7.7395
6.0	2.4495	2.4515	2.4536	2.4556	2.4576	2.4597	2.4617	2.4637	2.4658	2.4678
60.	7.7460	7.7524	7.7589	7.7653	7.7717	7.7782	7.7846	7.7910	7.7974	7.8038
6.1	2.4698	2.4718	2.4739	2.4759	2.4779	2.4799	2.4819	2.4839	2.4860	2.4880
61.	7.8102	7.8166	7.8230	7.8294	7.8358	7.8422	7.8486	7.8549	7.8613	7.8677
6.2	2.4900	2.4920	2.4940	2.4960	2.4980	2.5000	2.5020	2.5040	2.5060	2.5080
62.	7.8740	7.8804	7.8867	7.8930	7.8994	7.9057	7.9120	7.9183	7.9246	7.9310
6.3	2.5100	2.5120	2.5140	2.5159	2.5179	2.5199	2.5219	2.5239	2.5259	2.5278
63.	7.9373	7.9436	7.9498	7.9561	7.9624	7.9687	7.9750	7.9812	7.9875	7.9937
6.4	2.5298	2.5318	2.5338	2.5357	2.5377	2.5397	2.5417	2.5436	2.5456	2.5475
64.	8.0000	8.0062	8.0125	8.0187	8.0250	8.0312	8.0374	8.0436	8.0498	8.0561
6.5	2.5495	2.5515	2.5534	2.5554	2.5573	2.5593	2.5612	2.5632	2.5652	2.5671
65.	8.0623	8.0685	8.0747	8.0808	8.0870	8.0932	8.0994	8.1056	8.1117	8.1179
6.6	2.5690	2.5710	2.5729	2.5749	2.5768	2.5788	2.5807	2.5826	2.5846	2.5865
66.	8.1240	8.1302	8.1363	8.1425	8.1486	8.1548	8.1609	8.1670	8.1731	8.1792
6.7	2.5884	2.5904	2.5923	2.5942	2.5962	2.5981	2.6000	2.6019	2.6038	2.6058
67.	8.1854	8.1915	8.1976	8.2037	8.2098	8.2158	8.2219	8.2280	8.2341	8.2401
6.8	2.6077	2.6096	2.6115	2.6134	2.6153	2.6173	2.6192	2.6211	2.6230	2.6249
68.	8.2462	8.2523	8.2583	8.2644	8.2704	8.2765	8.2825	8.2885	8.2946	8.3006
6.9	2.6268	2.6287	2.6306	2.6325	2.6344	2.6363	2.6382	2.6401	2.6420	2.6439
69.	8.3066	8.3126	8.3187	8.3247	8.3307	8.3367	8.3427	8.3487	8.3546	8.3606

TABLE A-33. TABLE OF SQUARE ROOTS (*Continued*)

	0	1	2	3	4	5	6	7	8	9
7.0	2.6458	2.6476	2.6495	2.6514	2.6533	2.6552	2.6571	2.6589	2.6608	2.6627
70.	8.3666	8.3726	8.3785	8.3845	8.3905	8.3964	8.4024	8.4083	8.4143	8.4202
7.1	2.6646	2.6665	2.6683	2.6702	2.6721	2.6739	2.6758	2.6777	2.6796	2.6814
71.	8.4261	8.4321	8.4380	8.4439	8.4499	8.4558	8.4617	8.4676	8.4735	8.4794
7.2	2.6833	2.6851	2.6870	2.6889	2.6907	2.6926	2.6944	2.6963	2.6981	2.7000
72.	8.4853	8.4912	8.4971	8.5029	8.5088	8.5147	8.5206	8.5264	8.5323	8.5381
7.3	2.7019	2.7037	2.7055	2.7074	2.7092	2.7111	2.7129	2.7148	2.7166	2.7185
73.	8.5440	8.5499	8.5557	8.5615	8.5674	8.5732	8.5790	8.5849	8.5907	8.5965
7.4	2.7203	2.7221	2.7240	2.7258	2.7276	2.7295	2.7313	2.7331	2.7350	2.7368
74.	8.6023	8.6081	8.6139	8.6197	8.6255	8.6313	8.6371	8.6429	8.6487	8.6545
7.5	2.7386	2.7404	2.7423	2.7441	2.7459	2.7477	2.7495	2.7514	2.7532	2.7550
75.	8.6603	8.6660	8.6718	8.6776	8.6833	8.6891	8.6948	8.7006	8.7063	8.7121
7.6	2.7568	2.7586	2.7604	2.7622	2.7641	2.7659	2.7677	2.7695	2.7713	2.7731
76.	8.7178	8.7235	8.7293	8.7350	8.7407	8.7464	8.7521	8.7579	8.7636	8.7693
7.7	2.7749	2.7767	2.7785	2.7803	2.7821	2.7839	2.7857	2.7875	2.7893	2.7911
77.	8.7750	8.7807	8.7864	8.7920	8.7977	8.8034	8.8091	8.8148	8.8204	8.8261
7.8	2.7928	2.7946	2.7964	2.7982	2.8000	2.8018	2.8036	2.8054	2.8071	2.8089
78.	8.8318	8.8374	8.8431	8.8487	8.8544	8.8600	8.8657	8.8713	8.8769	8.8826
7.9	2.8107	2.8125	2.8142	2.8160	2.8178	2.8196	2.8213	2.8231	2.8249	2.8267
79.	8.8882	8.8938	8.8994	8.9051	8.9107	8.9163	8.9219	8.9275	8.9331	8.9387
8.0	2.8284	2.8302	2.8320	2.8337	2.8355	2.8373	2.8390	2.8408	2.8425	2.8443
80.	8.9443	8.9499	8.9554	8.9610	8.9666	8.9722	8.9778	8.9833	8.9889	8.9944
8.1	2.8460	2.8478	2.8496	2.8513	2.8531	2.8548	2.8566	2.8583	2.8601	2.8618
81.	9.0000	9.0056	9.0111	9.0167	9.0222	9.0277	9.0333	9.0388	9.0443	9.0499
8.2	2.8636	2.8653	2.8671	2.8688	2.8705	2.8723	2.8740	2.8758	2.8775	2.8792
82.	9.0554	9.0609	9.0664	9.0719	9.0774	9.0830	9.0885	9.0940	9.0995	9.1049
8.3	2.8810	2.8827	2.8844	2.8862	2.8879	2.8896	2.8914	2.8931	2.8948	2.8965
83.	9.1104	9.1159	9.1214	9.1269	9.1324	9.1378	9.1433	9.1488	9.1542	9.1597
8.4	2.8983	2.9000	2.9017	2.9034	2.9052	2.9069	2.9086	2.9103	2.9120	2.9138
84.	9.1652	9.1706	9.1761	9.1815	9.1869	9.1924	9.1978	9.2033	9.2087	9.2141

TABLE A-33. TABLE OF SQUARE ROOTS (*Continued*)

	0	1	2	3	4	5	6	7	8	9
8.5	2.9155	2.9172	2.9189	2.9206	2.9223	2.9240	2.9257	2.9275	2.9292	2.9309
85.	9.2195	9.2250	9.2304	9.2358	9.2412	9.2466	9.2520	9.2574	9.2628	9.2682
8.6	2.9326	2.9343	2.9360	2.9377	2.9394	2.9411	2.9428	2.9445	2.9462	2.9479
86.	9.2736	9.2790	9.2844	9.2898	9.2952	9.3005	9.3059	9.3113	9.3167	9.3220
8.7	2.9496	2.9513	2.9530	2.9547	2.9563	2.9580	2.9597	2.9614	2.9631	2.9648
87.	9.3274	9.3327	9.3381	9.3434	9.3488	9.3541	9.3595	9.3648	9.3702	9.3755
8.8	2.9665	2.9682	2.9698	2.9715	2.9732	2.9749	2.9766	2.9783	2.9799	2.9816
88.	9.3808	9.3862	9.3915	9.3968	9.4021	9.4074	9.4128	9.4181	9.4234	9.4287
8.9	2.9833	2.9850	2.9866	2.9883	2.9900	2.9917	2.9933	2.9950	2.9967	2.9983
89.	9.4340	9.4393	9.4446	9.4499	9.4552	9.4604	9.4657	9.4710	9.4763	9.4816
9.0	3.0000	3.0017	3.0033	3.0050	3.0067	3.0083	3.0100	3.0116	3.0133	3.0150
90.	9.4868	9.4921	9.4974	9.5026	9.5079	9.5131	9.5184	9.5237	9.5289	9.5341
9.1	3.0166	3.0183	3.0199	3.0216	3.0232	3.0249	3.0265	3.0282	3.0299	3.0315
91.	9.5394	9.5446	9.5499	9.5551	9.5603	9.5656	9.5708	9.5760	9.5812	9.5864
9.2	3.0332	3.0348	3.0364	3.0381	3.0397	3.0414	3.0430	3.0447	3.0463	3.0480
92.	9.5917	9.5969	9.6021	9.6073	9.6125	9.6177	9.6229	9.6281	9.6333	9.6385
9.3	3.0496	3.0512	3.0529	3.0545	3.0561	3.0578	3.0594	3.0610	3.0627	3.0643
93.	9.6437	9.6488	9.6540	9.6592	9.6644	9.6695	9.6747	9.6799	9.6850	9.6902
9.4	3.0659	3.0676	3.0692	3.0708	3.0725	3.0741	3.0757	3.0773	3.0790	3.0806
94.	9.6954	9.7005	9.7057	9.7108	9.7160	9.7211	9.7263	9.7314	9.7365	9.7417
9.5	3.0822	3.0838	3.0854	3.0871	3.0887	3.0903	3.0919	3.0935	3.0952	3.0968
95.	9.7468	9.7519	9.7570	9.7622	9.7673	9.7724	9.7775	9.7826	9.7877	9.7929
9.6	3.0984	3.1000	3.1016	3.1032	3.1048	3.1064	3.1081	3.1097	3.1113	3.1129
96.	9.7980	9.8031	9.8082	9.8133	9.8184	9.8234	9.8285	9.8336	9.8387	9.8438
9.7	3.1145	3.1161	3.1177	3.1193	3.1209	3.1225	3.1241	3.1257	3.1273	3.1289
97.	9.8489	9.8539	9.8590	9.8641	9.8691	9.8742	9.8793	9.8843	9.8894	9.8944
9.8	3.1305	3.1321	3.1337	3.1353	3.1369	3.1385	3.1401	3.1417	3.1432	3.1448
98.	9.8995	9.9045	9.9096	9.9146	9.9197	9.9247	9.9298	9.9348	9.9398	9.9448
9.9	3.1464	3.1480	3.1496	3.1512	3.1528	3.1544	3.1559	3.1575	3.1591	3.1607
99.	9.9499	9.9549	9.9599	9.9649	9.9700	9.9750	9.9800	9.9850	9.9900	9.9950

INDEX *

* Author references will be found on pages 357–364.